CHEMISTRY

Cambridge
Pre U

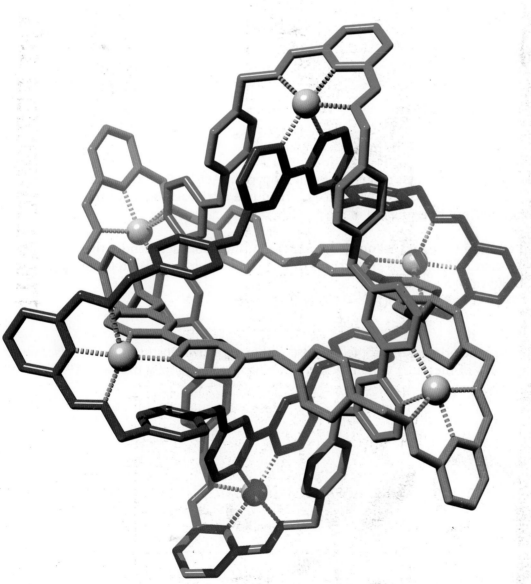

Dr. Michael A. Thompson

First published in 2009 by keytomes, Victoria, Australia.

Library Catalogue:

1. Chemistry

2. Pre-U

3. Dr. Michael A. Thompson

ISBN: 978-0-9807110-0-4

The answers on the website may be printed and copied for use within your own institution. Likewise, we have provided some enlarged versions of the more detailed diagrams which teachers may use as OHP slides or as computer projections.

Cover design by Kaia Anderson.

Published by keytomes, a division of Key-Strokes Pty. Ltd. (ABN: 60 007 232 055), PO Box 9, Camberwell, Australia.

Printed by Printer Trento, Italy.

Associated website: www.keytomes.com/chem

Introduction

To the student:

This book has been written for the Cambridge Pre-U syllabus Chemistry 9791, developed by Cambridge International Examinations (CIE). There are thirty chapters written in the same order as the syllabus. Each chapter is divided into sections that match the individual syllabus statements. The chapters start with a short introduction that sets the topic in an interesting historical or modern context. There are questions throughout the book for each section with answers given on the book's website (www.keytomes/chem). It is important that you work through the questions after reading each section to test and check your understanding. The styles of question in the book match the four synoptic examination papers that you will face at the end of your two year course. There are multiple choice questions with four options A, B, C or D in the style of Paper 1, plus short and long answer questions in the style of Papers 2, 3 and 4. The course places an emphasis on three dimensions and symmetry as well as unifying concepts such as the van Arkel triangle for bonding and functional group levels for organic transformations. I was part of the team that wrote the syllabus for CIE along with Professor Peter Wothers (Cambridge), Dr Simon Cotton (Uppingham School) and Dr Charles McCaw (Winchester College). I continue to write multiple choice questions for Paper 1 as well as the International A-level.

Good luck and enjoy your chemistry!

To the teacher:

Since the Pre-U chemistry course provides greater breadth and depth than the revised A-levels and IB chemistry courses, this book will be of great help, not only to students studying for Pre-U, but also for those who want a greater and deeper understanding of chemistry as a subject. It is anticipated that the book will provide an additional boost for students taking chemistry or chemistry modules at university. It is an ideal book to bridge the gap that has always existed between school chemistry and university chemistry. The course is supported by an online forum for teachers / lecturers which I have been moderating for CIE at *http://cambridgepreu.cie.org.uk.* This forum is a place where we can share ideas for teaching topics and for posting resources.

Good luck and enjoy your teaching!

Dr Michael A. Thompson

(Winchester College August 2009)

Dedicated to my immediate family

Arthur Thompson, Sylvia Thompson, Janet Wells (Thompson),

Margaret Clark (Thompson), Peter W. Thompson, Catherine C. Thompson (Gower),

Daniel J. Thompson, Isobel S. A. Thompson and Charles O. M. Thompson

and to Dr Simon Cotton, Uppingham School, UK (friend and chemistry guru)

Acknowledgements: Whilst this is an extraordinarily long list many people have helped me with answers to questions in person and via email and some have been kind enough to provide me with some of the pictures for use in this book. I apologise unreservedly if I have missed anyone off the list. Roger Burrage, Chief Examiner, Pre-U Chemistry, UK (CIE), Tony Tooth, Paper 3 Examiner, Pre-U Chemistry, UK (CIE), Chas McCaw, Paper 3 Examiner, Pre-U chemistry, UK (CIE), Rob Ritchie, Chief examiner OCR A-level Chemistry, UK, Lois Hopkins (CIE), Elkie Wootton (CIE), Gillian Whitehouse (CIE), Ian Thomas (CIE), Caroline Gavine (CIE), Irana Morrish (CIE), Clare Wilkes (CIE), Josie Warren (CIE), Victoria Grebe (CIE), Peter Simmons (CIE), Barry Marsh at the School of Ocean and Earth Science, University of Southampton, UK (photo of galena), Suzanne Church, USA (photo of the gecko), Robert Mays, USA (photo of fluorite), Professor Sir Fraser Stoddart at the Northwestern University, USA (borromean ring), Dave Waters, Department of Earth Sciences, University of Oxford, UK (advice on minerals), Chris Evans, chemistry diagrams website (QEGS Blackburn), Trevor White (Rugby School), Sean Stayte, USA (white phosphorus photo), Hussam Khatib, USA (borromean ring), Professor Peter Wothers, Chemistry Department, University of Cambridge, UK (advice on functional group levels), Professor Peter Atkins, Department of Chemistry, University of Oxford, UK (inspirational entropy talk held at Winchester College), Jonathan Lord, Jewish Virtual Library, USA, Margaret Schott at the Northwestern University, USA (letter to RSC), Nicholas Barker, RSC Teacher Fellow, Warwick University, UK, Adam Clarke (Warwick University) (photos of analytical machines and numerous nmr spectra), Stuart Cantrill, Editor, Nature Chemistry, UK (Pre-U chemistry article), NASA, USA (information on hydrogen fuel cells), Andy Jonson (Charterhouse School), Ed How (Charterhouse School), Stephen Shuttleworth (Charterhouse School), Rod Beavon (Westminster School), Rob King (Radley College), Dan Evans (Oundle School), James Bessent (Oundle School), Robin Hammond (Oundle School), Ian Sturton (Winchester College), Patrick Maclure (Winchester College), Suzanne Foster (Winchester College), Jon Falconer (Winchester College), Julian Spencer (Winchester College), Stephen Anderson (Winchester College), Andrew Leigh (Winchester College), Jonathan Hunt (Winchester College), Scott Camazine, USA (photo of honeycomb), Professor Paul May, Department of Chemistry, Bristol University, UK (advice on diamonds), Roger Weller, Cochise College, USA (photo of graphite), Doug Friedman, USA (borromean ring), Jeff Hynam, Bursar, Winchester College (photo of Mount Kilimanjaro), Peter Stubbs, Scotland, UK (photo of roadworks), Alastair Land (Winchester College), Michael Thain (Winchester College), Jamie McManus (Winchester College), Menbere Watson (Winchester College), David Belcher (Winchester College), Giles Munn (Winchester College), Hugh Hill (Winchester College), John Cullerne (Winchester College), Richard Shorter (Winchester College), Adrian McManus, Munich, Germany, Allan Soares, School of Education, Birmingham University, UK (PGCE tutor), Professor Robert Pettit, Cancer Research Institute, Arizona State University, USA (Postdoctoral supervisor), and Simon Cotton, Uppingham School, UK (friend, chemistry champion, advisor and extraordinary A-level chemistry teacher).

A few colleagues at Winchester College deserve a particular mention for their special brand of support during the writing of this book. A book which essentially meant sacrificing two summer holidays, evenings and weekends for the last 13 months for which I hope my wife and children will soon forgive me. The Headmaster Ralph Townsend for giving me some space and time away from the sports field to spend most afternoons writing in between walking my dog Jim. Secondly I must thank my dear friend Dr Andrew Wolters who truly is an exceptional chemistry teacher with an encyclopaedic knowledge of the subject who really enjoys and understands his subject and is also very funny. I also owe an enormous debt of gratitude to Dr Charles McCaw for bringing me to Winchester to teach in his department and for encouraging me in my recent running of the chemistry department. I have had the pleasure of working with the legendary Chas in the writing of the Pre-U chemistry syllabus from the very beginning and there is no one out there who loves the subject more than him. I cannot thank him enough for answering an unbelievably high volume of emails at ridiculous times of the day and night. Many thanks must also go to the chemistry technicians David Belcher and Menbere Watson for providing me with chemicals for the majority of the photographs, often at a moment's notice. Finally and most importantly I must thank my friend Dr David Follows for his time and his patience and take this opportunity to congratulate him on his high level skills at proof reading the book and his first class knowledge of chemistry.

I must of course thank the hundreds of A-level and Pre-U students that I have taught at the following schools since 1995; Highbury Fields School (Islington), King Solomon High School (Redbridge), Greensward College (Essex), Stonyhurst College (Lancashire), Uppingham School (Rutland), Radley College (Oxfordshire) and Winchester College (Hampshire).

The final thank must of course go to my publisher Rory McAuliffe for believing in my as an untried author and for believing in the Pre-U chemistry course which was also untried when we first met back in 2008. Together we made a very good team and I need to acknowledge his greater skills in the art of mathematics and his excellent chemistry and for never rushing me in the writing. He worked hard with the word documents that I sent him and his skills as an editor have produced a book that I hope students and teachers alike will enjoy. And finally at last we have a book that matches in order the whole syllabus. Isn't this exactly what students have always wanted! It is a cliché but any mistakes that are still to be found in the book are my own. Any suggestions for the second edition will be gratefully received.

Dr Mike Thompson, Winchester, August 2009

Topic teaching order for Pre-U Chemistry CIE 9791

The Pre-U course will be taught to sixth formers over two years which in many UK schools would be six terms. It is for this reason that the suggested teaching order is designed for five terms. This leaves the last term for revision before the examinations which are all taken at the end of the course. Any topic with an asterisk * is partly taught in the lower sixth (Year 12) and finished in the upper sixth (Year 13). 20% of the teaching time should be given over to practicals which include the Qualitative tests and Quantitative analysis (A4.1) and other practicals which are suggested throughout the book.

Term 1	
Topic	Syllabus Code
Atomic Structure	A 1.1
Electronic spectroscopy	A 4.3
Chemical Forces	A 1.2
Chemical models & evidence	B 1.7
Energy Changes	A 1.3
Equilibrium (LCP, acid models, pH)*	B 1.5 a-f
Gases & Kinetics*	B 1.6 a-c

Term 2	
Topic	Syllabus Code
Periodic Table* (periodicity)	A2.1 a-e
Main group chemistry	A2.2
Qualitative & quantitative analysis	A4.1
Organic preliminaries	A3.1
Functional Group Levels (FGL)	A3.2
Periodic Table* (periodicity)	A2.1 a-e
Main group chemistry	A2.2
Qualitative & quantitative analysis	A4.1
Organic preliminaries	A3.1
Functional Group Levels (FGL)	A3.2

Term 3	
Topic	Syllabus Code
Mass spectrometry	A4.2
Infra-red	A4.4
Alcohol level	A3.3
Carbonyl level	A3.4
Addition & elimination reactions	A3.5
Mechanisms*	B3.9 a-e
Green Chemistry	A3.6

Term 4	
Topic	Syllabus Code
Carboxylic acid levels	B3.7
Carbon dioxide level	B3.8
Mechanisms*	B3.9 f-i
Aromatic chemistry	B3.10
Stereochemistry	B3.12
Carbon-13 nmr	A4.5
NMR of other spin ½ nuclei	B4.6
Transition elements	B2.4

Term 5	
Topic	Syllabus Code
Gases & Kinetics*	B 1.6 d-j
Equilibrium*	B 1.5 g-q
Acidity & basicity	B3.11
Free Energy & Entropy	B1.4
Periodic Table*	A2.1 f-i
Group 14	B2.3
Crystal structures	B4.6

Term 6			
Revision	Syllabus	Paper	Weighting (%)
Multiple choice	Part A	1	15
Written questions	Part A	2	35
Written questions	Part B	3	35
Practical	Qualitative & Quantitative analysis	4	15

Publisher's Note

This book was planned by the miracle of email. However, it was face to face over a 'pie and a pint in a pub' that the determination to actually write it was forged. Amongst the oak beams, one thing above all others became obvious:

The Pre-U chemistry syllabus required a completely original book if it was to fully serve the course's content and objectives.

This book has been written from the ground up and contains no material from existing texts massaged to fit the purpose. This, of course, presented us with a major quality control challenge. We are grateful to both the author and proofreader for their careful work in removing errors ranging from irritating typos to deep questions of scientific truth. Every publisher hopes that their books are perfect. A first printing such as this is seldom so. We are, after all, human. As a senior aviation examiner once said to me: "We understand that pilots make errors. What we don't like is pilots who don't notice them or do nothing about them". So it is with publishing!

We would be very grateful to hear of errors from anyone who finds them so that subsequent printings can be refined.

A feedback form and errata list can be found at this book's website:

www.keytomes.com/chem

Rory McAuliffe

Table of Contents

1

Atomic Structure

Contents

A1.1 (a)
Shell number and number of subshells

The familiar Bohr circular orbits model of an atom is shown with its small central nucleus containing the nucleons (neutrons and protons) and its electrons in shells. Each shell of electrons can only hold a given number of electrons. The first shell, which is the shell nearest the nucleus, can hold a maximum of two electrons. The second shell can hold up to eight electrons and the third shell holds eight electrons. It is convenient to show electrons in the second and third shells in pairs, as this assists in the drawing of bonds for covalent molecules. Once you get to the transition elements of Period 4 you may already know that the third shell has reserve space for a further ten electrons, bringing its maximum number to eighteen.

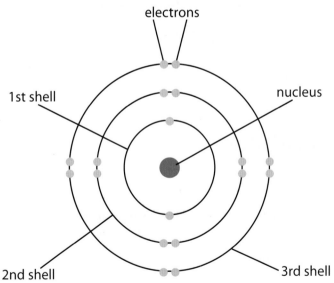

In the simple Bohr model, atoms are represented as flat circles. We now develop this model further by considering the atom and the orbits in three dimensions. Electron microscopes have confirmed this theory. It is helpful to remember that the shell number is the same as the Period number. For example the metal sodium (atomic number 11) has an electron arrangement of 2,8,1. There are three shells containing electrons and sodium is in Period 3. Sodium is in Group 1 and this matches the number of electrons in its outermost shell, *i.e.* the one furthest from the nucleus.

Evidence for electrons in shells is twofold and comes from successive ionisation energies (A1.1j) and from lines in emission spectra (A4.3a). It is often helpful to think of a shell as an energy level. Electron shells having greater radii (further from the nucleus) are at a higher potential energy. Quantum Theory, which is covered in depth at university shows that electrons are arranged in shells, rather like the layers in a Spanish red onion.

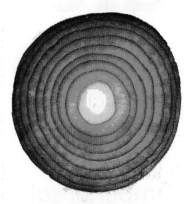

Except the first shell, each shell contains a number of subshells which are given letters s, p, d or f. Letter s stands for sharp. The letter p stands for passion. The letter d stands for diffuse and the letter f stands for fundamental. The number of subshells exactly matches the shell number. The more refined model does not negate earlier models. It is best to think of it as increasing the magnification to look at finer detail.

Shell	Number of Subshells	Subshells
1	1	1s
2	2	2s 2p
3	3	3s 3p 3d
4	4	4s 4p 4d 4f

A1.1 (b) Orbitals

Bohr's circular orbit for the electron has now been superseded by the idea of an orbital. An orbital is a negative charge cloud with a particular shape and volume where there is about a 95% chance of an electron being found. The different orbitals have a unique set of quantum numbers (n, l, m and s), the details of which are not needed until university. The shapes of the orbitals (s, p, d or f) come from the Schrodinger wave equation. An individual orbital can only contain no electrons (empty), one electron (half full) or two electrons (full). The maximum number of electrons in an orbital is two and this is known as **Pauli's exclusion principle**. Examples of orbitals from different shells are; 1s, 2s, $2p_x$, $3d_{xy}$.

A1.1 (c)
Orbital shapes (s, p & d)

The different types of orbitals have different shapes. They are also to be found at different distances from the nucleus. The s orbitals are spherical in shape and are symmetrical around the nucleus. There is one type of s orbital in each shell (energy level). Electrons behave as if they are spread evenly around the nucleus. The shape of the orbital reveals the electron (probability) density in the cloud. The s orbital is the one closest to the nucleus. The 2s orbital is slighter larger than the 1s orbital as shown.

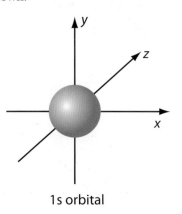

1s orbital

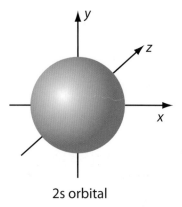

2s orbital

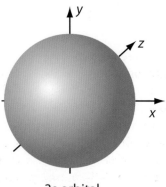

3s orbital

There are three types of p orbitals in each shell, after the first shell, which can reasonably be described as dumbbell, hour glass or figure of eight shaped. The three p orbitals of a subshell are at 90° to each other, and aligned along either the x, y or z axes. For clarity they have been shown separately.

There is no electron density at the centre of the atom so each p orbital has what is described as a node at the nucleus. As with the s orbitals, the p orbitals also increase in size as the shell number (**Principal Quantum number**) increases. The three different types of 2p orbitals can each hold up to two electrons. Therefore the 2p subshell can hold up to six electrons.

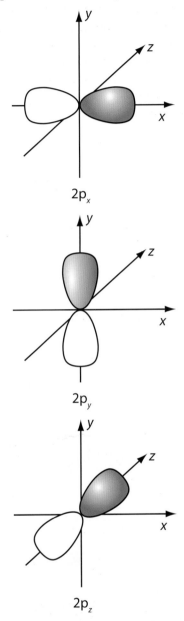

$2p_x$

$2p_y$

$2p_z$

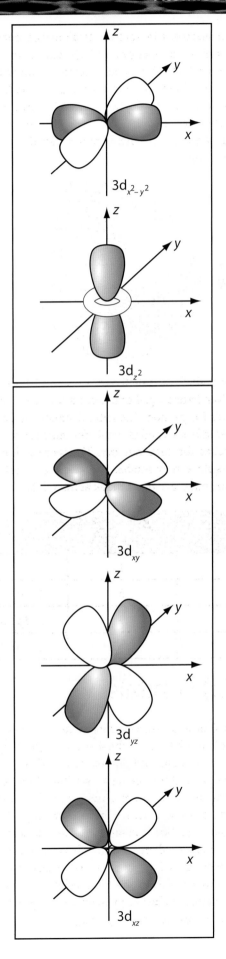

$3d_{x^2-y^2}$

$3d_{z^2}$

$3d_{xy}$

$3d_{yz}$

$3d_{xz}$

There are five types of d orbital in each shell after the second shell, four of which can reasonably be described as propeller or windmill shaped. The fifth d orbital ($3d_{z^2}$) is similar in shape to a p orbital but with a doughnut shaped ring in the middle. Care is needed when drawing these d orbitals. Pay particular attention to the axis labels as the z and y axes have swapped places when compared with the drawings of the s and p orbital shapes. The five d orbitals all have the same energy and are described as being **degenerate**. They have been deliberately drawn as a pair and a three as this has relevance with transition element complexes (B2.4f). The five different types of 3d orbitals can each hold up to two electrons. Therefore the 3d subshell can hold up to ten electrons.

The table summarises the maximum number of electrons in each shell. All you need to do is remember there are two electrons in the first shell and then the maximum number of electrons fits the formula $2n^2$ where n is the shell number.

Shell	Subshells in each shell	Maximum number of electrons
1st	1s	2 = **2**
2nd	2s 2p	2 + 6 = **8**
3rd	3s 3p 3d	2 + 6 + 10 = **18**
4th	4s 4p 4d 4f	2 + 6 + 10 + 14 = **32**

A1.1 (d) Relative energies of s,p,d,f sub-shells

The diagram shows the relative energies of the subshells and is sometimes referred to as an energy level diagram. There are rules for adding electrons in orbitals to achieve the correct electronic configuration for atoms and ions (A1.1g). The 1st energy level (shell) consists entirely of the 1s orbital which is the closest to the nucleus and has the lowest (potential) energy. The second shell consists of the 2s and the 2p subshells. The 2s subshell is lower in energy than the 2p subshell. The three different 2p orbitals of the 2p subshell are all at the same energy level. The third shell is where many students generally come unstuck and it is worth noting that the 4s subshell is slightly lower in energy than the 3d subshell. Yet again the different orbitals in a subshell, e.g. the 3d, are at the same energy level. As the different subshells are filled with electrons, the inner electrons shield the outer electrons from the amount of positive nuclear pull. **Shielding** is a concept that only applies to multi-electron atoms, which includes all elements from lithium (atomic number 3) onwards. In the case of lithium, its 1s electrons act as a shield for the 2s electron.

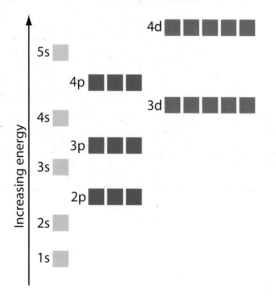

A 1.1 (e) Electron spin and spin pairing

One property that electrons possess is **spin**. All electrons spin about their own axis as shown in the diagram. A pair of electrons in the same orbital must spin in opposite directions. Electrons spinning in a clockwise direction are indicated by an arrow up ($\uparrow$), and electrons spinning in an anti-clockwise (counter clockwise) direction are indicated by an arrow down ($\downarrow$).

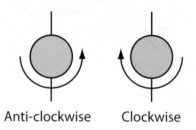

Anti-clockwise   Clockwise

A 1.1 (f) Aufbau principle

Aufbau is a German word which means 'building up'. The **Aufbau** principle states that; 'ground state electrons go into the available orbital with the lowest energy'. The diagram shows the order in which electrons fill the orbitals. The first electron goes into the 1s orbital which is the orbital with lowest energy. The order of filling for electron orbitals, according to the *Aufbau* principle is: 1s 2s 2p 3s 3p 4s 3d 4p 5s 4d 5p.

Aufbau Principle

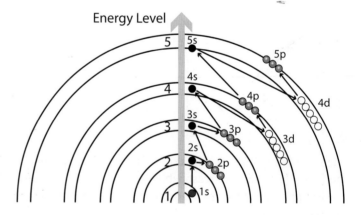

The *Aufbau* principle explains why electrons are added to orbitals in a particular order as the Periodic Table is built up. Hydrogen and helium and all the elements in Groups 1 and 2 are known as the s block. Groups 3-12 are the d block, and Groups 13-18 are the p block. The f block is the two sets of metals called the lanthanides and actinides and these are revealed at university level chemistry.

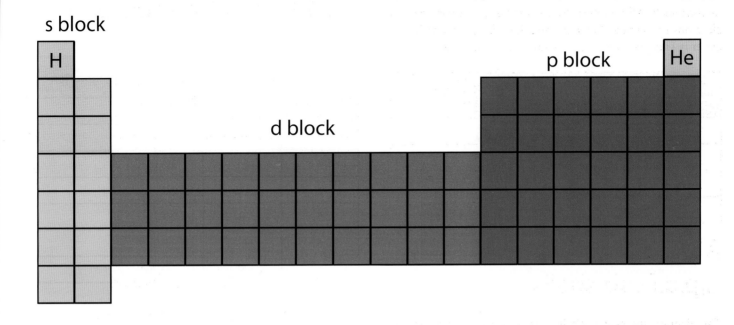

s block

H

p block

He

d block

A1.1 (g) Ground state electron configurations

An electron in its lowest energy level is said to be in the **ground state**. This is where electrons are generally found under standard conditions. An electron in higher energy levels is described as being in an **excited state**. Transitions of electrons from ground state to excited state are discussed when explaining the colours of transition element compounds (B2.4g). The Periodic Table below shows the outer electron configuration for the different

Groups of the Periodic Table. It is useful to know that alkali metals (Group 1) will have their outer electron (valence) in an s orbital. This is written as s^1, where the superscript gives you the number of electrons in the orbital. All the halogens (Group 17) have seven electrons in their outer shell, s^2p^5, two electrons in an s orbital and five electrons in the p subshell.

1	s^1																s^2
2	s^1	s^2											s^2p^1	s^2p^2	s^2p^3	s^2p^4	s^2p^5	s^2p^6
3	s^1	s^2											s^2p^1	s^2p^2	s^2p^3	s^2p^4	s^2p^5	s^2p^6
4	s^1	s^2											s^2p^1	s^2p^2	s^2p^3	s^2p^4	s^2p^5	s^2p^6
5	s^1	s^2											s^2p^1	s^2p^2	s^2p^3	s^2p^4	s^2p^5	s^2p^6
6	s^1	s^2											s^2p^1	s^2p^2	s^2p^3	s^2p^4	s^2p^5	s^2p^6
7	s^1	s^2																

A strategy is needed to work out the order of the orbitals starting at 1s. One approach is to write out the following list of orbitals and then to link them up using diagonal lines. The order is 1s 2s 2p 3s 3p 4s 3d 4p 5s *etc*.

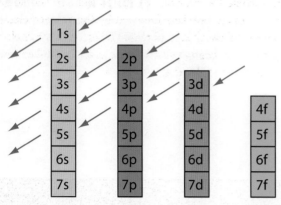

A second approach is to write out the following list of orbitals fitting them into a triangle and then connecting them up using a zigzag approach. Others might find it easy to remember the order with the answers written as a list. It is important to practise getting the correct order for the first 36 elements (hydrogen to krypton) as it is quite easy to forget in the early stages of a chemistry course.

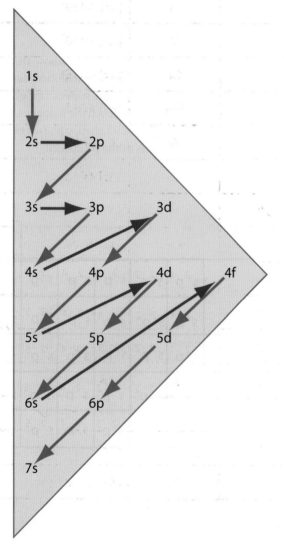

The ground state electronic structures, also known as electronic configurations for elements having atomic number 1-36 are shown in the tables.

Proton number	Symbol	Electron configuration
1	H	$1s^1$
2	He	$1s^2$
3	Li	$1s^2\,2s^1$
4	Be	$1s^2\,2s^2$
5	B	$1s^2\,2s^2\,2p^1$
6	C	$1s^2\,2s^2\,2p^2$
7	N	$1s^2\,2s^2\,2p^3$
8	O	$1s^2\,2s^2\,2p^4$
9	F	$1s^2\,2s^2\,2p^5$
10	Ne	$1s^2\,2s^2\,2p^6$
11	Na	$1s^2\,2s^2\,2p^6\,3s^1$
12	Mg	$1s^2\,2s^2\,2p^6\,3s^2$
13	Al	$1s^2\,2s^2\,2p^6\,3s^2\,3p^1$
14	Si	$1s^2\,2s^2\,2p^6\,3s^2\,3p^2$
15	P	$1s^2\,2s^2\,2p^6\,3s^2\,3p^3$
16	S	$1s^2\,2s^2\,2p^6\,3s^2\,3p^4$
17	Cl	$1s^2\,2s^2\,2p^6\,3s^2\,3p^5$
18	Ar	$1s^2\,2s^2\,2p^6\,3s^2\,3p^6$
19	K	$1s^2\,2s^2\,2p^6\,3s^2\,3p^6\,4s^1$
20	Ca	$1s^2\,2s^2\,2p^6\,3s^2\,3p^6\,4s^2$
21	Sc	$1s^2\,2s^2\,2p^6\,3s^2\,3p^6\,4s^2\,3d^1$
22	Ti	$1s^2\,2s^2\,2p^6\,3s^2\,3p^6\,4s^2\,3d^2$
23	V	$1s^2\,2s^2\,2p^6\,3s^2\,3p^6\,4s^2\,3d^3$
24	**Cr**	$1s^2\,2s^2\,2p^6\,3s^2\,3p^6\,4s^1\,3d^5$
25	Mn	$1s^2\,2s^2\,2p^6\,3s^2\,3p^6\,4s^2\,3d^5$
26	Fe	$1s^2\,2s^2\,2p^6\,3s^2\,3p^6\,4s^2\,3d^6$
27	Co	$1s^2\,2s^2\,2p^6\,3s^2\,3p^6\,4s^2\,3d^7$
28	Ni	$1s^2\,2s^2\,2p^6\,3s^2\,3p^6\,4s^2\,3d^8$
29	**Cu**	$1s^2\,2s^2\,2p^6\,3s^2\,3p^6\,4s^1\,3d^{10}$
30	Zn	$1s^2\,2s^2\,2p^6\,3s^2\,3p^6\,4s^2\,3d^{10}$
31	Ga	$1s^2\,2s^2\,2p^6\,3s^2\,3p^6\,4s^2\,3d^{10}\,4p^1$
32	Ge	$1s^2\,2s^2\,2p^6\,3s^2\,3p^6\,4s^2\,3d^{10}\,4p^2$

Proton number	Symbol	Electron configuration
33	As	$1s^2\ 2s^2\ 2p^6\ 3s^2\ 3p^6\ 4s^2\ 3d^{10}\ 4p^3$
34	Se	$1s^2\ 2s^2\ 2p^6\ 3s^2\ 3p^6\ 4s^2\ 3d^{10}\ 4p^4$
35	Br	$1s^2\ 2s^2\ 2p^6\ 3s^2\ 3p^6\ 4s^2\ 3d^{10}\ 4p^5$
36	Kr	$1s^2\ 2s^2\ 2p^6\ 3s^2\ 3p^6\ 4s^2\ 3d^{10}\ 4p^6$

Chromium and copper have rather surprising electron arrangements as, in both cases, one electron is promoted from the 4s to the 3d. This results in the more stable half-filled or filled 3d subshell. There is also a convenient shorthand notation where the previous Group 18 element (noble gas) is written in square brackets followed by the valence electrons. Another useful check is to note that when the correct electron arrangement has been attained, the outer shell number matches the Period that the element is found in.

Careful attention is needed when writing out the 4s (filled first) and the 3d orbitals.

Proton number	Symbol	Electron configuration	Proton number	Symbol	Electron configuration
1	H	$1s^1$	19	K	$[Ar]\ 4s^1$
2	He	$1s^2$	20	Ca	$[Ar]\ 4s^2$
3	Li	$[He]\ 2s^1$	21	Sc	$[Ar]\ 4s^2\ 3d^1$
4	Be	$[He]\ 2s^2$	22	Ti	$[Ar]\ 4s^2\ 3d^2$
5	B	$[He]\ 2s^2\ 2p^1$	23	V	$[Ar]\ 4s^2\ 3d^3$
6	C	$[He]\ 2s^2\ 2p^2$	24	**Cr**	$[Ar]\ 4s^1\ 3d^5$
7	N	$[He]\ 2s^2\ 2p^3$	25	Mn	$[Ar]\ 4s^2\ 3d^5$
8	O	$[He]\ 2s^2\ 2p^4$	26	Fe	$[Ar]\ 4s^2\ 3d^6$
9	F	$[He]\ 2s^2\ 2p^5$	27	Co	$[Ar]\ 4s^2\ 3d^7$
10	Ne	$[He]\ 2s^2\ 2p^6$	28	Ni	$[Ar]\ 4s^2\ 3d^8$
11	Na	$[Ne]\ 3s^1$	29	**Cu**	$[Ar]\ 4s^1\ 3d^{10}$
12	Mg	$[Ne]\ 3s^2$	30	Zn	$[Ar]\ 4s^2\ 3d^{10}$
13	Al	$[Ne]\ 3s^2\ 3p^1$	31	Ga	$[Ar]\ 4s^2\ 3d^{10}\ 4p^1$
14	Si	$[Ne]\ 3s^2\ 3p^2$	32	Ge	$[Ar]\ 4s^2\ 3d^{10}\ 4p^2$
15	P	$[Ne]\ 3s^2\ 3p^3$	33	As	$[Ar]\ 4s^2\ 3d^{10}\ 4p^3$
16	S	$[Ne]\ 3s^2\ 3p^4$	34	Se	$[Ar]\ 4s^2\ 3d^{10}\ 4p^4$
17	Cl	$[Ne]\ 3s^2\ 3p^5$	35	Br	$[Ar]\ 4s^2\ 3d^{10}\ 4p^5$
18	Ar	$[Ne]\ 3s^2\ 3p^6$	36	Kr	$[Ar]\ 4s^2\ 3d^{10}\ 4p^6$

Metal ions are isoelectronic with the previous noble gas in the Periodic Table. Non-metal ions are isoelectronic with the next noble gas in the Periodic Table. Remember to remove the 4s electrons before the 3d when writing electron configuration for the first row transition element ions.

Ion	Electron configuration	Isoelectronic noble gas
H^{1+}	$1s^0$	
Li^{1+}	$1s^2 (2s^0)$	Helium
Be^{2+}	$1s^2 (2s^0)$	Helium
N^{3-}	$1s^2 2s^2 2p^6$	Neon
O^{2-}	$1s^2 2s^2 2p^6$	Neon
F^{1-}	$1s^2 2s^2 2p^6$	Neon
Na^{1+}	$1s^2 2s^2 2p^6$	Neon
Mg^{2+}	$1s^2 2s^2 2p^6$	Neon
Al^{3+}	$1s^2 2s^2 2p^6$	Neon
P^{3-}	$1s^2 2s^2 2p^6 3s^2 3p^6$	Argon
S^{2-}	$1s^2 2s^2 2p^6 3s^2 3p^6$	Argon
Cl^{1-}	$1s^2 2s^2 2p^6 3s^2 3p^6$	Argon
K^{1+}	$1s^2 2s^2 2p^6 3s^2 3p^6$	Argon
Ca^{2+}	$1s^2 2s^2 2p^6 3s^2 3p^6$	Argon
Fe^{2+}	$1s^2 2s^2 2p^6 3s^2 3p^6 (4s^0) 3d^6$	
Co^{2+}	$1s^2 2s^2 2p^6 3s^2 3p^6 (4s^0) 3d^7$	
Cu^{1+}	$1s^2 2s^2 2p^6 3s^2 3p^6 (4s^0) 3d^{10}$	

A1.1 (h) Electrons-in-a-box

Another way to describe the ground state configuration of electrons in a subshell is by using the **electron-in-a-box** notation. Each box represents an orbital which is identified by writing above the box. Electrons are indicated by upwards or downward arrows (A1.1e).

When filling the boxes you need to remember to apply **Hund's Rule**, which states, 'orbitals in subshells having the same energy are occupied singly before being paired'. This is a result of electrons repelling each other leading to a slightly higher energy. The elements nitrogen, oxygen and fluorine illustrate how the orbitals are filled. In the case of nitrogen the 2p orbitals are filled singly. When the eighth electron of oxygen is added it goes into the $2p_x$ orbital with opposite spin to the other electron present. When the ninth electron of fluorine is added it goes into the $2p_y$ orbital with opposite spin to the other electron present.

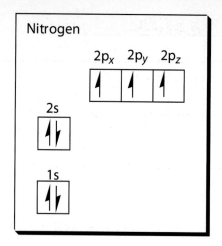

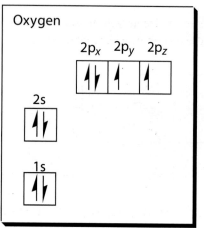

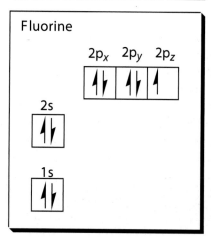

Electrons in boxes can be shown in terms of their relative energies (diagram above) or written horizontally in order with the lowest energy orbitals written first, *e.g.* nitrogen:

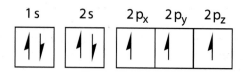

A1.1 (i) Period 3 trends

Period 3 elements are perhaps some of the most familiar elements of the periodic table.

They all have interesting uses; sodium (coolant in nuclear reactors), magnesium (bicycle frames), aluminium (cooking foil), silicon (computer chips), phosphorus (matches), sulfur (gunpowder), chlorine (water sterilisation), argon (light bulbs).

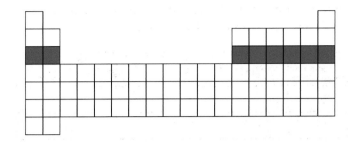

Variation of atomic radii across Period 3

Atoms decrease in size as you go across Period 3 because they all have the 'same' shielding but their effective nuclear charge increases as the proton number increases. This is the reason why the atoms of Period 3 elements get smaller across the Period.

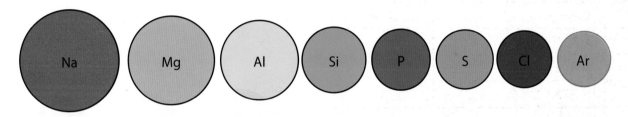

Variation of ionic radii across Period 3

X-ray diffraction allows the distance between nuclei to be accurately measured, but not the actual radii of ions. The reason is that electron transfer is not 100% complete and there will be some sharing of electron density between the ions. The difficulty for x-ray crystallographers comes in where to draw the boundary for one ion in order to calculate the radius of an oppositely charged ion. As is often the case in science, a standard is chosen to allow comparison and measurement.

Ionic radii are based on oxides where oxide O^{2-} has an ionic radius of 0.140 nm = 140 pm. [nm = nanometre = 10^{-9} m and pm = picometre = 10^{-12} m]. The values for ionic radii vary for different coordination numbers and, to make the data comparable, values are set for coordination numbers of six. Elements with variable oxidation states have their ionic radii shown for the ions in different oxidation states.

Period 3 elements	Element's symbol	Proton number	Ions/symbols			Ionic radii /pm (10^{-12} m)		
Sodium	Na	11	Na^+			102		
Magnesium	Mg	12	Mg^{2+}			72		
Aluminium	Al	13	Al^{3+}			54		
Silicon	Si	14	Si^{4+}			40		
Phosphorus	P	15	P^{5+}	P^{3-}	P^{3+}	38	190	44
Sulfur	S	16	S^{6+}	S^{2-}	S^{4+}	29	184	37
Chlorine	Cl	17	Cl^{7+}	Cl^{1-}	Cl^{5+}	22	167	26
Argon	Ar	18						

The trend is not quite so straightforward with the ions of Period 3 elements. Metals form positive ions by losing their valence electrons, whereas non-metals gain electrons to fill their outer shells and complete their octet.

The table shows the relative size of the commonest ions of Period 3 elements. The atomic and ionic radii diagrams have been drawn to the same scale to allow comparison.

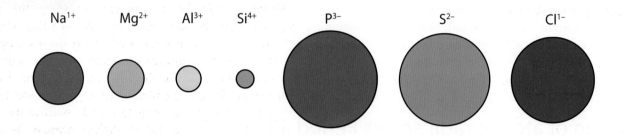

For each element, half an atom (right-hand side) and half an ion (left-hand side) with the same colour are shown together. It is clear from this diagram that metal ions (cations) are considerably smaller than their atoms. It is also evident that non-metal ions (anions) are larger than their atoms.

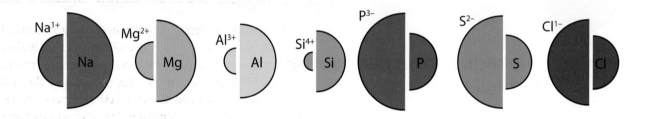

Explanations of trends

Metal ions are smaller than their atoms. This is because they have lost their valence electrons and effectively a shell of electrons. The effective nuclear charge increases with loss of outer electrons. With fewer electrons to attract in a cation, those remaining electrons are pulled closer to the nucleus. So the period 3 ions decrease in size as their charges increase from $1+$ to $4+$. In other words the cation sizes are inversely proportional to their charges. The more electrons lost, the smaller the ion will be as there will be less electronic repulsions in addition to the increasing nuclear charge due to additional protons in the nucleus. The Si^{4+} ion is only 23% the radius of a silicon atom. The trend is that cations get smaller with increasing positive charge.

Non-metal ions are larger than their atoms. This is due to an increase in electronic repulsions. All the anions are similar in size as there are two forces acting in opposite directions having similar effects: the increasing nuclear charge *versus* the additional electronic repulsions. There is a slight reduction in size of anions from phosphide ion to chloride. The trend is that anions get larger with increasing negative charge.

Questions 1.1

1. Which of the following options is in the correct order of **decreasing** ionic radii?

   A $Na^+ > Mg^{2+} > Al^{3+} > Si^{4+}$

   B $Si^{4+} > Al^{3+} > Mg^{2+} > Na^+$

   C $Na^+ < Mg^{2+} < Al^{3+} < Si^{4+}$

   D $Na^+ > Mg^{2+} < Al^{3+} > Si^{4+}$

2. Which of these Period 3 ions has the **largest** ionic radius?

   A Cl^-

   B P^{3-}

   C P^{5+}

   D S^{2-}

3. Which of the following is a Period 3 element that does not form ions?

   A   S

   B   Na

   C   Ar

   D   Ne

4. Which of the following Period 3 elements does not form ions with variable oxidation states?

   A   S

   B   Cl

   C   P

   D   Si

Variation of electronegativities across Period 3

Electronegativity is the 'pulling power' of an atom for the electrons within the bond(s) of a molecule. The larger the numerical value for electronegativity (E_{neg}) the greater the attraction by the atom for the bonding electrons. Electronegativity values given are using the **Pauling scale**, where the most electronegative element fluorine is given the arbitrary value of 4.0. The size of E_{neg} for the elements has great importance for the chemical reactivity of substances with reagents which are attracted to slightly positive δ+ centres (nucleophiles) or attracted to slightly negative δ– centres (electrophiles).

The table shows the electronegativity values of Period 3 elements.

Element	Na	Mg	Al	Si	P	S	Cl
E_{neg}	0.9	1.2	1.5	1.8	2.1	2.5	3.0

All the elements in Period 3 experience similar shielding from the nuclear force because they have outer electrons in the third shell. The trend (pattern) for electronegativity across Period 3 is that it steadily increases. This happens as the number of protons increases and so the effective nuclear charge also increases. It is worth remembering that electronegativity always increases as you move towards fluorine in the Periodic Table from all directions (across Periods and up Groups).

When the differences in electronegativity are calculated for the subsequent elements in any period, there are steady increases in electronegativity. The electronegativity difference (ΔE_{neg}) between sodium and magnesium is 0.3 and ΔE_{neg} and between magnesium and aluminium is 0.3. The next ΔE_{neg} have the following numbers; 0.3, 0.3, 0.4 & 0.5. The chart clearly shows the trend in electronegativity when plotted against atomic number for the Period 3 elements. The proton number (atomic number) has the greatest effect on the value when comparing elements in the same Period, such as Period 3.

Proton number vs. electronegativity

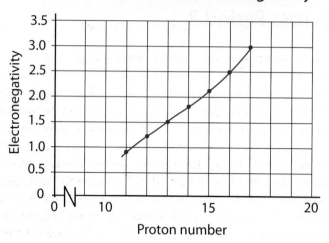

As argon rarely forms compounds, it has not been assigned an electronegativity value as it is stable, because of its full outer shell.

Questions 1.2

1. Which Period 3 compounds would have the greatest difference in electronegativity (ΔE_{neg})? [Na = 0.9, Mg = 1.2, Cl = 3.5, S = 2.5]

    A SCl_2

    B   MgS

    C Na_2S

    D S_2Cl_2

2. Which Period 3 element is the **least** electronegative?

    A   Cl

    B   Si

    C   P

    D   S

3. Which Period 3 element is the **most** electronegative?

    A   Al

    B   Na

    C   Mg

    D   Si

Variation of first ionisation energies across Period 3

First ionisation energy is the energy needed to remove one mole of electrons from one mole of atoms of a gaseous element. It has the symbol $\Delta H_{i1}^{\ominus}$. The units are kilojoules per mole (kJ mol^{-1}). The larger the numerical value for $\Delta H_{i1}^{\ominus}$ the harder it is to remove the electron. Factors which affect ionisation energies are shell number (distance), nuclear charge and shielding. All first ionisation energies are endothermic, having a positive value, as energy is required to strip away the first electron from the atom. Ionisation energies can be measured using mass spectrometry (A4.2a) and calculated from the convergence limit in the emission spectra (A4.3c). The equation for the first ionisation for sodium is shown along with its value.

$$Na\ (g) \rightarrow \quad Na^+\ (g) \quad + e^- \qquad\qquad \Delta H_{i1}^{\ominus} = +496\ kJ\ mol^{-1}$$

1 mole   *1 mole*   *1 mole*

The table shows the first ionisation energies for all the elements of Period 3. Elements (except hydrogen) can have several ionisation energies. The number of ionisation energies matches their atomic number which is identical to the number of electrons.

Element	ΔH_{i1} / kJ mol^{-1}
Na	496
Mg	738
Al	578
Si	789
P	1012
S	1000
Cl	1251
Ar	1521

The general trend is that first ionisation energies from sodium to argon increase as you go across Period 3. The alkali metals have the lowest first ionisation energies in any period because they have the same shielding as the other elements but have fewer protons and so a 'weaker' attractive force pulling on the outermost electron by the nucleus. Magnesium has a higher first ionisation energy than sodium because it has the same shielding but there is a larger attractive force from the nucleus because of the additional proton. There are two decreases (dips) in first ionisation energies as you go across the third Period. The first decrease in ionisation energy is when you change from the s block of magnesium to the p block of aluminium. This decrease in ionisation energy is because of the shielding by the $3s^2$ electrons, which are closer to the nucleus than the $3p^1$ electron. From aluminium to silicon and then silicon to phosphorus there are increases in the size of the first ionisation energies with increasing proton number. There is no additional shielding for these elements as electrons are being added singly to the 3p orbitals (**Hund's rule**), which are all the same distance from the nucleus. The second decrease in ionisation energy is when you move from phosphorus to sulfur. This small decrease in ionisation energy is because of the spin pair repulsion experienced when the second electron enters the $3p_x$ orbital. Chlorine has a higher first ionisation energy than sulfur because of the additional proton and the same can be said for argon which has the highest first ionisation energy of the Period 3 elements. A graph of first ionisation energies *vs.* proton number shows the general trend and the dips in ΔH_{i1}.

$$Li\ (g) \rightarrow Li^+\ (g) + e^- \qquad \Delta H_{i1}^{\ominus} = 520\ kJ\ mol^{-1}$$

$$Li^+\ (g) \rightarrow Li^{2+}\ (g) + e^- \qquad \Delta H_{i2}^{\ominus} = 7298\ kJ\ mol^{-1}$$

$$Li^{2+}\ (g) \rightarrow Li^{3+}\ (g) + e^- \qquad \Delta H_{i3}^{\ominus} = 11815\ kJ\ mol^{-1}$$

Evidence for the existence of electrons in shells comes from the study of the ionisation energies of atoms. The 2nd ionisation of lithium is greater than the 1st ionisation energy because the second electron is being removed from an increasingly positive ion with a greater effective nuclear charge, and it is being removed from an inner shell (1s) closer to the nucleus with less shielding. This means that the attractive force is much greater for the removal of lithium's second electron. The same argument applies for the removal of the third electron. There are large jumps in ionisation energies when an electron is being removed from another energy level much closer to the nucleus.

First ionisation energy vs. proton number

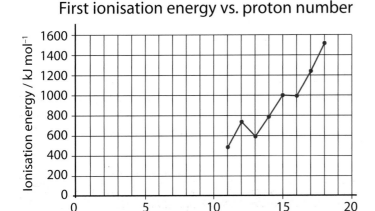

A1.1 (j)
Relationship between Group number and successive ionisation energies

Lithium has three electrons and can be ionised by removing one electron at a time. Each successive ionisation energy will be much larger than the previous one because of the ever increasing effective nuclear charge. The size of successive ionisation energies provides clues to the electron arrangement for the elements. There are large jumps in ionisation energies when electrons are being removed from inner shells. The values and the equations for the successive ionisation energies for lithium follow. Note that the subscript for the ionisation symbol matches the final charge on the gaseous ion in the equation. All equations for first, second and third ionisation energies are for molar quantities.

"Neon signs" owe their colours to light emitted when electrons 'jump' from one level to another in various elements, including neon. (GNU licensed photographs)

This is because of the large increase in attraction for the electron being removed. This is clear to see when you plot a graph of ionisation energy *vs.* number of electrons removed for any element. The table following gives the successive ionisation energies for the first eleven elements. Use the data to see how large jumps in successive ionisation energies relate to Group number.

Successive ionisation energies / kJ mol^{-1}

Element	$\Delta H_{i1}^{\ominus}$	$\Delta H_{i2}^{\ominus}$	$\Delta H_{i3}^{\ominus}$	$\Delta H_{i4}^{\ominus}$	$\Delta H_{i5}^{\ominus}$	$\Delta H_{i6}^{\ominus}$	$\Delta H_{i7}^{\ominus}$	$\Delta H_{i8}^{\ominus}$	$\Delta H_{i9}^{\ominus}$	$\Delta H_{i10}^{\ominus}$	$\Delta H_{i11}^{\ominus}$
H	1312										
He	2372	5251									
Li	520	7298	11815								
Be	900	1757	14849	21007							
B	801	2427	3660	25026	32828						
C	1086	2353	4621	6223	37832	47278					
N	1402	2856	4578	7475	9445	53268	64362				
O	1314	3388	5301	7469	10989	13327	71337	84080			
F	1681	3374	6051	8408	11022	15164	17868	92040	106437		
Ne	2081	3952	6122	9370	12177	15239	19999	23069	115382	131435	
Na	496	4563	6913	9544	13352	16611	20115	25491	28934	141367	159079

Lithium and sodium are both in Group 1 and both have a large increase in ionisation energy from their first ionisation energies to their second ionisation energies. It is even easier to see where the jumps occur when the logarithms (base 10) are taken for the successive ionisation energies.

Questions 1.3

1. Which type of subshell does **every** shell have?

   A   f

   B   p

   C   s

   D   d

2. Which shell does **not** have a p subshell?

   A   3rd shell.

   B   2nd shell.

   C   4th shell.

   D   1st shell.

3. Which shells do **not** have a d subshell?

   A   2nd and 3rd.

   B   2nd only.

   C   1st only.

   D   1st and 2nd.

4. Complete the table for the first four shells of electrons by filling in the blanks.

Electron shells										
Shell number	1st	2nd		3rd			4th			
Subshells	s	s	p	s	p	d	s	p	d	f
Orbitals										
Maximum number of electrons										
Total electrons										

5. Which option shows the correct number of orbitals for the different subshells?

Number of orbitals				
	s	p	d	f
A	1	3	5	7
B	2	8	8	18
C	1	3	6	9
D	2	6	10	14

6. Which is the correct electron configuration for nitrogen using the electron-in-a-box notation?

A

B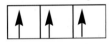

C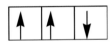

D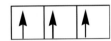

7. The first ionisation energies of five successive elements in the periodic table are;

1402, 1314, 1681, 2081, 496 kJ mol⁻¹. These elements could be:

A the first five elements of a period.

B the last five elements of a period.

C the last four elements of one period and the first element of the next period.

D the last element of one period and the first four elements of the next period.

8. The first ionisation energy of an element can be found using which method?

A From measuring the frequencies of x-rays produced when it is bombarded with electrons.

B From the electrical conductivity of its vapour as it is bombarded with electrons.

C From the diffraction pattern produced when its vapour is bombarded with electrons.

D From the frequencies of the lines in the most energetic part of its emission spectrum.

9. Which equation correctly represents the second ionisation energy of magnesium ?

A $Mg^+ (s) \rightarrow Mg^{2+} (g) + e^-$

B $Mg^+ (g) \rightarrow Mg^{2+} (g) + e^-$

C $Mg (s) \rightarrow Mg^{2+} (s) + 2 e^-$

D $Mg (g) \rightarrow Mg^{2+} (g) + 2 e^-$

10. The successive ionisation energies in kJ mole⁻¹ of an element X are: 738, 1451, 7733, 10541, 13629, 17995, 21704. Which ion is the most likely to be formed when X reacts with chlorine ?

A X^{2-}

B X^-

C X^+

D X^{2+}

11. Consider the following changes:

I $M (s) \rightarrow M (g)$

II $M (s) \rightarrow M^{2+} (g) + 2 e^-$

III $M (g) \rightarrow M^+ (g) + e^-$

IV $M^+ (g) \rightarrow M^{2+} (g) + e^-$

V $M (g) \rightarrow M^{2+} (g) + 2 e^-$

The 2nd ionisation energy of M could be calculated from the energy values associated with:

A III + IV

B V - III

C I + IV

D II – I – III

12. Plot a graph of $\log_{10}$ ionisation energies *versus* number of electrons removed for sodium.

Describe the shape of the graph in terms of sodium's electron arrangement.

Ionisation energy	/ kJmol^{-1}
1st	496
2nd	4563
3rd	6913
4th	9544
5th	13352
6th	16611
7th	20115
8th	25491
9th	28934
10th	141367
11th	159079

13. The first five ionisation energies of an element are: 578, 1817, 2745, 11578, 14831 kJ mol^{-1}.

In which Group of the Periodic Table would you expect it to be? Explain your answer.

2 Chemical Forces

Contents

A1.2 (a) Dot and cross diagrams

In chemical reactions, the compounds formed from elements are either ionic or covalent. These compounds are energetically more stable (lower in energy) than the separate elements. In ionic bonding, valence electrons are transferred from metal to non-metal. In covalent bonding, valence electrons are shared in pairs, usually between non-metals. Ionic and covalent substances generally give rise to more stable electronic configurations, which are isoelectronic with the noble gases of Group 18. Both types of bonding can be represented using dot and cross diagrams, where electrons from different atoms are distinguished by either a dot or a cross. In reality all electrons are identical and indistinguishable.

Ionic bonding

An **ionic bond** is an electrostatic force of attraction between oppositely charged ions. Positive ions (cations) are formed when metals lose electron(s). Cations form most easily when the charge is small and the atomic radius is large. Negative ions (anions) are formed when non-metals gain electron(s). Anions form most easily when the charge is small and the atomic radius is also small. When metals react with non-metals it is not too surprising that electrons transfer from the least electronegative (A1.2i) to the most electronegative element. Group 1 and 2 metals react readily with Groups 16 and 17 to produce ionic compounds. In the dot and cross diagrams for ionic compounds, only the outer (valence) electrons are shown. Electrons for metals are shown as dots and the electrons for non-metals are shown as crosses. In the formation of sodium chloride from its elements, the valence electron is transferred from sodium to chlorine. How the ions are held together is dealt with in the chapter on crystallography (B2.5).

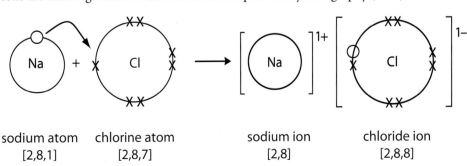

| sodium atom [2,8,1] | chlorine atom [2,8,7] | sodium ion [2,8] | chloride ion [2,8,8] |

Electrons carry a negative charge so this transfer results in the sodium ion having a positive charge and the chloride ion a negative charge. The sodium ion has an identical electronic arrangement to neon and the chloride ion an identical electronic arrangement to argon.

Another example is the formation of magnesium oxide from its elements.

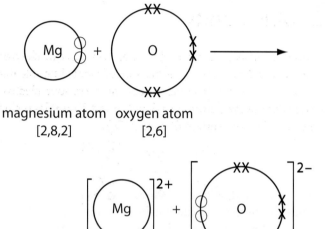

magnesium atom   oxygen atom
    [2,8,2]   [2,6]

Dot and cross diagrams only give relative numbers of ions present in ionic compounds and this information can also be gleaned from the unit cell of a crystal structure (B2.5b). The size of the charges on the cations and anions depends on the number of transferred electrons. The size of metals' positive charges on their ions matches their Group number. For non-metals, the size of the anion charge is equal to the Group number minus eighteen. As noble gases do not form ions they have been omitted from the Group number vs. ion table.

Group	Charge on ion	Example
1	1+	Li^{1+}
2	2+	Mg^{2+}
13	3+	Al^{3+}
14	4+	Sn^{4+}
15	3−	N^{3-}
16	2−	O^{2-}
17	1−	F^{1-}

Examples 2.1

Some ionic compounds are: sodium chloride (NaCl), potassium bromide (KBr), lithium fluoride (LiF), magnesium oxide (MgO), magnesium chloride ($MgCl_2$), magnesium nitride (Mg_3N_2), magnesium sulfide (MgS), lead(II) oxide (PbO), aluminium oxide (Al_2O_3) and calcium bromide ($CaBr_2$). The electron from the metal is shown as a red dot. Note that when

the formula requires more than one metal or non-metal ion, a subscript is used outside the square brackets in the dot and cross diagrams.

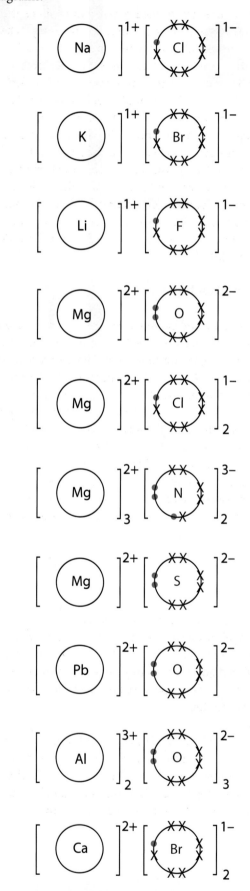

Covalent bonding

Covalent bonds are formed when atoms share their outer electrons between atoms. Covalent bonding takes place between non-metallic elements (p block) and is used to explain the structures of non-metallic elements (halogens, nitrogen, hydrogen, oxygen, phosphorus, and sulfur) and also compounds formed between different non-metallic elements (*e.g.* methane, carbon dioxide). More often than not a noble gas configuration is attained. The dot and cross diagrams only show the outer (valence) electrons, with dots and crosses being used to distinguish the different electrons from atoms involved in covalent bonding. One should realise that whilst dot and cross diagrams do accurately show the numbers of electrons present, they do not show their positions. This is discussed under the Valence Shell Electron Pair Repulsion Theory (A1.2g).

Single bonds

In the formation of hydrogen chloride from its elements, a pair of valence electrons (dot and cross) is shared and this constitutes a single covalent bond. Shared pairs of electrons make strong bonds. A single covalent bond is shown as a pair of electrons (dot and cross) between the hydrogen and chlorine atoms either side of a single line. Electron density maps of crystals determined by x-ray diffraction studies confirm the high electron density shared between atoms of covalent molecules. It is important that models of bonding account for the correct formula of a substance as well as the correct number of valence electrons. A common mistake is to forget to add all the non-bonding valence electrons for halogens.

In the formation of covalent molecules there has been no transfer of electrons so the molecules are electrically neutral. They can, however, be polar (A1.2j) and this is discussed later in this chapter. Covalently bonded atoms are held by the attractive force of their positive nuclei for the negative electron cloud between them.

Another example is the formation of boron trifluoride from its elements. This illustrates the point that not all atoms in covalent compounds achieve a full outer shell. The boron atom is electron deficient and this means it is capable of accepting a pair of electrons to form a dative covalent bond.

Double bonds

A **double covalent bond** is shown as two pairs of electrons (two dots and two crosses) either side of parallel double lines between the atoms. In other words there are four electrons shared between two atoms in a double bond. Examples include ethene (C_2H_4) and carbon dioxide (CO_2).

Triple bonds

A **triple covalent bond** is shown as three pairs of electrons (three dots and three crosses) between the atoms either side of parallel triple lines. In a triple bond there are six electrons shared between two atoms. Examples include ethyne (C_2H_2) and nitrogen (N_2).

Dative covalent bonds

A **dative covalent bond** is indistinguishable from a single covalent bond except in the way it is drawn as a pair of electrons (two dots) with a single line ending in an arrow head pointing to an electron deficient atom/ion. The difference is that in a dative covalent bond both electrons in the bond are provided by one atom in the bonding pair. Examples include the hydroxonium ion (H_3O^+) and the ammonium ion (NH_4^+).

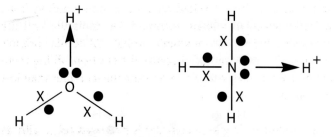

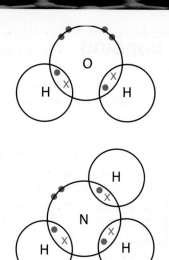

Examples 2.2

Covalent compounds can exist as simple molecules, *e.g.* chlorine (Cl_2), hydrogen (H_2), hydrogen chloride (HCl), boron trifluoride (BF_3), hydrogen oxide (H_2O), ammonia (NH_3), or giant molecules, *e.g.* graphite (B2.3a). The electrons in the covalent bond are placed in overlapping circles and are shown as dots and crosses.

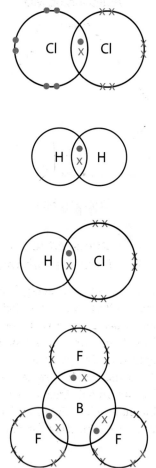

Questions 2.1

1. Draw dot and cross diagrams for the following covalent molecules/ions; NH_3, H_2SO_4, H_2S, NO_2, SO_3, O_2, CH_4, N_2H_4, SF_6, $S_2O_3^{2-}$, $S_4O_6^{2-}$, PO_4^{3-}, and NO_3^-.

2. Draw dot and cross diagrams for the following molecules; CO, O_3, $BF_3.NH_3$, B_2H_6, Al_2Cl_6 and N_2O. All contain at least one dative covalent bond. Interestingly the reducing agent diborane (B_2H_6) had its structure solved by Christopher Longuet Higgins whilst still a pupil at Winchester College (England). The allotrope of oxygen (A2.2e) has several solutions.

3. Draw dot and cross diagrams to show the equations for the formation of lithium bromide, sodium oxide, calcium oxide and potassium fluoride, by adding dots, crosses and charges to all reactants and ionic products. [Hint: Check that your equations balance].

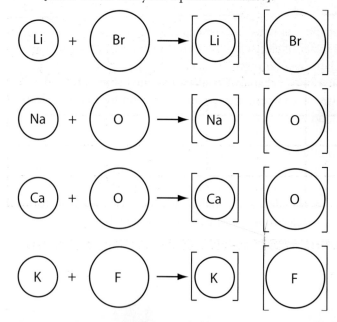

4. What are the formulae of the following ionic compounds: barium sulfide, calcium phosphide, caesium iodide and gallium nitride?

5. Complete the table by filling the gaps for the ionic compounds.

Binary Ionic Compounds	Formula	Electronic configuration of the metal's cation	Electronic configuration of the non-metal's anion
	Li_2S	$1s^2$ or [He]	
Potassium arsenide			
	AlN		
Sodium selenide			
Barium chloride			$1s^2 2s^2 2p^6 3s^2 3p^6$ or [Ar]

6. Explain the difference between a single covalent bond and a dative covalent bond. What are dative covalent bonds often called when found in transition element complexes?

7. Name and draw dot and cross diagrams for molecules with the formulae; HCN, SO_2, and H_2CO_3. What is unusual about sulfur in its compound?

8. Which option correctly describes single, double and dative covalent bonds?

	Number of electrons in a single covalent bond	Number of electrons in a double covalent bond	Number of electrons in a dative covalent bond
A	2	4	4
B	2	8	8
C	2	4	2
D	1	2	3

A1.2 (b) Molecular orbitals

Covalent bonding can be considered in terms of orbitals rather than electrons. An orbital is a volume of space where electrons are mostly found (A1.1b). It should come as no surprise to discover that electrons also occupy orbitals in covalent molecules called **molecular orbitals** (MO). Molecular orbitals hold up to two electrons with opposing (anti-parallel) spins. The three types of molecular orbitals are: bonding (**ground state**), antibonding ('**excited state**') and non-bonding (**lone pairs**). Molecular orbitals surround the molecule and are formed by the overlap of atomic orbitals. Molecular orbitals differ from atomic orbitals because the electrons filling them are under the influence of two or more nuclei rather than just one nucleus.

The simplest molecule to consider is hydrogen (H_2), with its two protons (**nucleons**) and two electrons. The two kinds of orbital in hydrogen are the bonding molecular orbital (sigma σ) and antibonding molecular orbital (sigma star σ*). The bonding orbital is where the electrons are found in the ground state for hydrogen molecules. The bonding orbitals lead to the nuclei being held together. Quantum mechanics would say that bonding molecular orbitals are constructed by the addition of the 1s wave function for one hydrogen atom to the other.

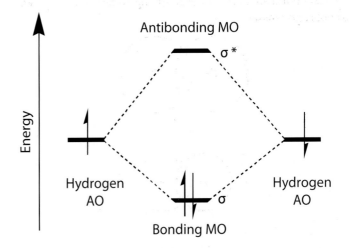

AO: Atomic orbital
MO: Molecular orbital

The antibonding orbital (higher energy) is not normally occupied as electrons in these types of orbitals pull the nuclei, and hence the molecule, apart. Irradiation of a hydrogen molecule by UV light may lead to homolytic bond fission and the atoms separating. This is because of the promotion of one electron from the bonding molecular orbital to the antibonding molecular orbital. Quantum mechanics would say that antibonding molecular orbitals are constructed by the subtraction of the 1s wave function for one hydrogen atom from the other.

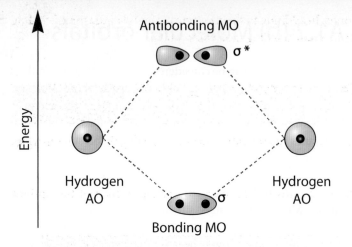

Antibonding MO

σ*

Energy

Hydrogen AO

Hydrogen AO

σ

Bonding MO

There is a decrease in electron density between the nuclei in the antibonding MO which serves to increase the electrostatic repulsion between the two nuclei, which are indicated with a black dot. There is an increase in electron density between the two nuclei in the bonding MO which serves to reduce the electrostatic repulsion between the two nuclei. This means that in a hydrogen molecule the effective nuclear charge for each electron is greater than the value of 1 for an atom. The two electrons in the bonding orbital are equivalent to a shared pair of electrons in a dot and cross diagram (A1.2b). The shape of the hydrogen bonding orbital (σ) has rotational symmetry about the inter-nuclear axis.

A1.2 (c)
Covalent bond strength

The strength of a covalent bond is a measure of how much lower in energy the bonding molecular orbital is compared with the atomic orbitals. The stability of the covalent bond formed when the atomic orbitals of hydrogen overlap is indicated by the highly endothermic bond enthalpy for hydrogen, which has a value of 436 kJ mol^{-1}. This suggests that one of the molecular orbitals (bonding) is of lower energy and therefore more stable than the atomic orbitals of the hydrogen atoms. The greater the energy drop from atomic orbitals to molecular bonding orbitals, the stronger the covalent bond.

A1.2 (d) Sigma and pi bonds

Sigma (σ) and pi (π) bonds result from the overlap of atomic orbitals. In the case of hydrogen the sigma bond is formed by overlap of two s orbitals. It is easy to remember sigma as it is both symmetrical and a single bond.

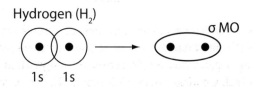

Hydrogen (H_2)

σ MO

1s   1s

Sigma bonds can also be formed by the overlap of other orbitals. The sigma bond in hydrogen chloride is formed by the overlap of the 1s atomic orbital in hydrogen with the $3p_x$ orbital in chlorine.

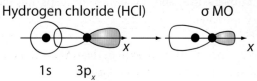

Hydrogen chloride (HCl)   σ MO

1s $3p_x$

Sigma bonds can also form by the 'head on' overlap of $3p_x$ orbitals from each of the chlorine atoms. This overlap occurs when the two $3p_x$ orbitals are linearly oriented.

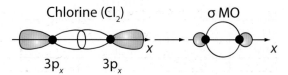

Chlorine (Cl_2)   σ MO

$3p_x$ $3p_x$

The weaker pi bonds are formed by 'sideways on' overlap of p orbitals. The pi bond in oxygen is formed by the overlap between the two $2p_z$ orbitals which are laterally oriented, *i.e.* 'sideways on'. This double overlap leads to a molecular orbital with electron density above and below the sigma bond. There is no negative charge along the molecular axis from the pi bond as shown in the diagram showing the nodal plane.

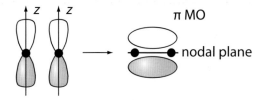

z   z   π MO

nodal plane

A1.2 (e)
Strengths of σ and π bonds

Sigma bonds are relatively stronger than pi bonds. This is because pi orbitals are less effective at holding atoms together than sigma orbitals. You can have sigma orbitals without pi orbitals, but pi orbitals only form where there is already a sigma bond. The double bonds of alkenes consist of a sigma and a pi bond. When they react by electrophilic addition (B3.9) it is the weaker pi bond that breaks during reaction. It has been found that the combination of a sigma and a pi bond is less than twice as strong as a single sigma bond.

This is illustrated by the bond enthalpy (A1.3d) values for the single and double bonds in ozone O_3 an allotrope of oxygen.

Ozone	
Bond	Bond energy / kJ mol^{-1}
O-O	302
O=O	498

The triple bond in nitrogen (N≡N) consists of a sigma and two pi bonds. In addition to the six electrons found in the three bonding molecular orbitals, each nitrogen atom has a lone pair, which exists in a non-bonding molecular orbital.

Questions 2.2

1. Why does helium not exist as diatomic (He$_2$) molecules? Illustrate your answer with a diagram showing the relative energies of atomic and molecular orbitals.

2. Hydrogen molecules are formed when the atomic orbitals (1s) of two hydrogen atoms overlap. Which of the options correctly describes a hydrogen molecule?

	Symbol for the bonding orbital	Energy of the bonding orbital relative to the atomic orbital	Electron density in the bonding orbital	Antibonding orbital
A	σ*	lower	not between nuclei	empty
B	σ	higher	between nuclei	full
C	σ*	lower	not between nuclei	full
D	σ	lower	between nuclei	empty

3. Overlap of which atomic orbitals does **not** lead to the formation of a sigma bond?

A   1s & 1s

B   1s & 2p$_x$

C   2p$_x$ & 2p$_x$

D   2p$_z$ & 2p$_z$

A1.2 (f) Bond order

Bond order (BO) tells you whether a molecule has a single bond, a double bond or a triple bond. Single bonds (C-C, C-O) have BO = 1, double bonds (C=C, O=O) have BO = 2, and triple bonds (C≡C, N≡N) have BO = 3.

For interest's sake only, bond order can be calculated from the number of electrons in bonding orbitals (N_b) and the number of electrons in antibonding orbitals (N_a),

$$BO = \frac{1}{2}(N_b - N_a).$$

Bond length is the distance between the nuclei of two covalently bonded atoms. Half the bond length is the covalent radius as shown in the diagram. It is worth trying to visualise molecules to improve your understanding. To imagine more closely 'reality', you need to realise two things. Firstly, that bonds are not static but are vibrating, and secondly, that as molecules rotate their bonds will stretch.

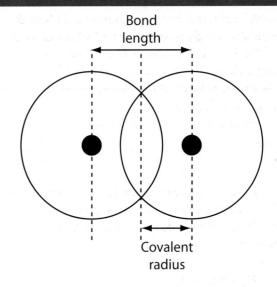

There is a qualitative relationship between bond order and bond length. The table shows that as bond order increases the bond length decreases. Single bonds are longer than double bonds, which are longer than triple bonds. The order for bond lengths is single > double > triple.

Example	Bond order	Bond length / nm
C-C	1	0.154
C=C	2	0.134
C≡C	3	0.120
C-O	1	0.143
C=O	2	0.122
C≡O *	3	0.113

* taken from carbon monoxide

The shorter bond lengths are a reflection of the greater attraction of both nuclei by the increased electron density between them. It is important to compare examples using the same bonded atoms, but which differ only in their **multiplicity** (number of joining bonds). Molecules with resonance structures can have fractional bond orders, *e.g.* benzene (B3.1a), with its carbon-carbon bond length of 0.140 nm, is intermediate between C-C and C=C. It has been shown that all the C-O bonds in the carbonate ion are of equal length (0.131 nm), which is between the tabulated values for C-O and C=O. Carbonate has three plausible resonance structures. Bond lengths can be determined using x-ray crystallographic data and from microwave spectra with an accuracy of ±0.001 nm.

There is also a qualitative relationship between bond order and bond strength (energy). The tabulated data show that, as the bond order increases, so does the bond energy (A2.2j/k). Bond energy is the energy needed to split a covalent bond.

Example	Bonds	Bond order	Bond energy / kJ mol⁻¹
alcohols	C-O	1	336
ketones	C=O	2	749
carbon monoxide	C≡O *	3	1077

In doubling the bond order from alcohols to ketones, the bond energy more than doubles. In other words, bond energies of double bonds are not simple multiples of single bonds. Otherwise a value of 672 kJ mol⁻¹ would have been obtained. The reason is that it is more than twice as difficult to break a C=O double bond than a C-O single bond is because the increased electron density between the carbon and oxygen atoms leads to a greater force of attraction between their nuclei. In stronger covalent bonds there has been more overlap of atomic orbitals (A1.2d).

Bond energies need to be used with caution as they are average values for many different types of molecules possessing the same bond. When there are differences in oxidation numbers (A2.1e) the bond enthalpies can be quite different. The P-Cl bond energy is 319 kJ mol⁻¹ in PCl_3 and 264 kJ mol⁻¹ in PCl_5. Bond energies can be determined using enthalpy cycles (A1.3d). Differences in bond strength lead to differences in the wavenumber of absorptions in infra-red spectroscopy (A4.4).

Questions 2.3

1. The diatomic molecules nitrogen, oxygen and fluorine are in the p block of the Periodic Table and in Period 2. For each of them give their bond orders. Arrange them in order of increasing bond strength. Arrange them in order of increasing bond length.

2. How does the energy of a molecule with bond order zero compare with its separated atoms?

    A   Significantly lower.

    B   Identical.

    C   Slightly lower.

    D   Higher.

A1.2 (g) VSEPR theory
Valence electrons

Valence electrons are the ones shown in dot and cross diagrams. They are the outermost electrons and the electrons that take part in bonding. For elements in Groups 1, 2 & 13-18, the number of valence electrons is equal to the last number in the group number. The only exception to this rule is helium, which is in Group 18 and has two outermost electrons.

Group number	Period 3 element	Number of valence electrons
1	Na	1
2	Mg	2
13	Al	3
14	Si	4
15	P	5
16	S	6
17	Cl	7
18	Ar	8

Valence shell electron pair repulsion theory

The valence shell electron pair repulsion theory (VSEPR) is a general theory that was developed by Sidgwick and Powell and which allows the prediction of the shapes of simple covalent molecules and ions. The theory states that electron pairs around a central atom will repel each other and will position themselves as far apart as possible in three dimensions. When the electron pairs get as far apart as possible they minimise electron-electron repulsion to end up in the lowest possible energy state. It is also possible to suggest bond angles within molecules and ions with reasonable accuracy.

Types of electron pairs

The two types of electron pairs in covalent molecules are bonding pairs and lone pairs (non-bonding pairs). Valence electrons in covalent bonds are referred to as bonding pairs. Lone pairs are pairs of valence electrons not used in bonding. It is important to remember that covalent bonds are directional, so it is not surprising to learn that molecules also have definite and predictable shapes. Chlorine is a linear molecule and it is shown with the bonding pairs of electrons in red and the lone pairs in blue. It is worth pointing out that, in terms of the VSEPR theory, there is no distinction between a covalent bond where each electron in the bond has come from a different atom, and a dative covalent bond where both electrons are donated by the same atom (Lewis base).

When faced with a formula for a molecule, the central atom will be the one fewest in number. So for carbon dioxide (CO_2) the central atom will be carbon and for water (H_2O) the central atom will be oxygen.

Shapes of molecules

There are eight shapes that can be encountered with simple covalent molecules. The first step is to be able to draw, recognise and name these shapes. They all need drawing in three dimensions except the two simplest shapes: linear and trigonal planar. The central atom is shown in black and the adjoining atoms in green. Lone pairs are shown as red lobes with yellow electron pairs.

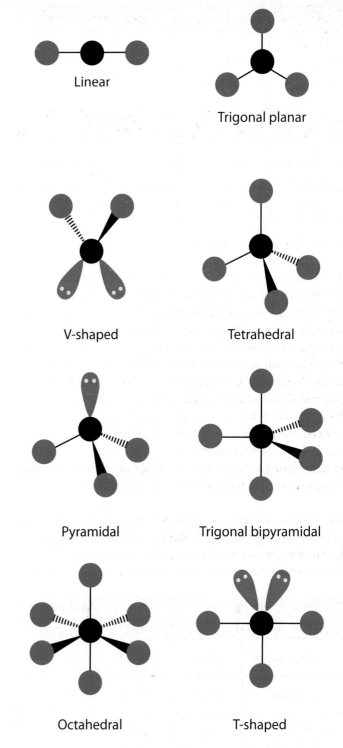

Linear

Trigonal planar

V-shaped

Tetrahedral

Pyramidal

Trigonal bipyramidal

Octahedral

T-shaped

Working out the shapes of molecules

- Identify the central atom in the formula (the one with the smallest number).

- Count the number of bonding pairs of electrons to the central atom.

- Count the number of lone pairs on the central atom.

25

- Arrange the atoms so the electrons are as far apart as possible.

- Lone pairs squash bond angles by about 2.5° each.

- Treat multiple bonds as single covalent bonds.

- Note that there are differences in size of the different electron pair repulsions.

Each shape will be discussed in turn. To make the diagram easier to understand, electrons from each atom will be coloured differently, rather than using dots and crosses.

Linear molecules

Hydrogen chloride gas has the formula HCl. This is not to be confused with the acid which forms when this gas reacts with water to produce aqueous hydrochloric acid, HCl (aq). It is a binary compound with only two atoms so there is no central atom. There is a single covalent bond and therefore only one bonding pair of electrons. The molecule is linear with the electrons as far apart as possible.

Carbon dioxide gas has the formula CO_2. The central atom is carbon because there is only one carbon. There are four bonding pairs of electrons to the central atom and two double bonds from the carbon to the oxygens (C=O). There are no lone pairs on the central carbon atom as all its valence electrons are tied up with the sigma and pi bonds of the carbon-oxygen double bonds.

These multiple bonds are treated as single bonds in terms of repulsion. The carbon dioxide molecule is linear with a bond angle of 180° to get the electrons as far apart as possible.

Trigonal planar molecules

Boron trifluoride (BF_3) is an interesting example because the central boron atom is electron deficient. There are three single covalent bonds and no lone pairs on the central boron atom. The boron trifluoride molecule is trigonal planar with a bond angle of 120°, again to get the electrons as far apart as possible. The angle is essentially 360°/3 = 120°. This shape is also described as **triangular planar**.

Tetrahedral molecules

Methane gas has the formula CH_4. The central atom is carbon because there is only one carbon. There are four bonding pairs (single bonds) of electrons to the central atom. There are no lone pairs on the central carbon atom as all its valence electrons are tied up with the sigma bonds of the carbon-hydrogen single bonds (C-H). The methane molecule is tetrahedral with a bond angle of 109.5°, to get the electrons as far apart as possible. Methane is shown in three dimensions on the left and shown fitting into the tetrahedron shape on the right.

The ammonium ion has the formula NH_4^+. The central atom is nitrogen because there is only one nitrogen atom. There are four bonding pairs (single bonds) of electrons to the central atom. There are no lone pairs on the central nitrogen atom as all its valence electrons are tied up with the sigma bonds of the nitrogen-hydrogen single bonds (N-H). One of the electron pairs is dative covalent and is indistinguishable from the other three bonds. It has no bearing on the geometry of the molecule. The ammonium ion is also tetrahedral with a bond angle of 109.5°, again to get the electrons as far apart as possible.

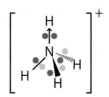

Pyramidal shaped molecules

Ammonia gas has the formula NH_3. The central atom is nitrogen because there is only one atom. There are three bonding pairs (single bonds) of electrons to the central atom. There is one lone pair of electrons on the central nitrogen atom. The ammonia molecule is also pyramidal with a bond angle of 107° to get the electrons as far apart as possible. Lone pairs of electrons are closer to the nucleus than bonding pairs so they take up more 'bonding space' and consequently they need more room. This makes lone pairs more repulsive than bonding pairs and generally they squash the bond angle by 2.5°. Distortion of the regular tetrahedron by the lone pair can be calculated as follows; 109.5° - 2.5° = 107°.

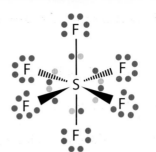

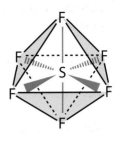

V-shaped molecules

Hydrogen oxide (water) has the formula H_2O. The central atom is oxygen because there is only one atom of it. There are two bonding pairs (single bonds) of electrons to the central atom. There are two lone pairs of electrons on the central oxygen atom. The water molecule is V-shaped (bent) with a bond angle of 104.5° to maximise the distance between the electrons. Lone pairs find each other more repulsive than any other pair of electrons because of their increased electron density. Distortion of the regular tetrahedron by the lone pairs can be calculated as follows; 109.5° – (2 × 2.5°) = 104.5°.

Trigonal bipyramidal shaped molecules

Phosphorus pentachloride has the formula PCl_5. The central atom is phosphorus because there is only one atom. There are five bonding pairs (single bonds) of electrons to the central atom. There are no lone pairs of electrons on the central phosphorus atom. The phosphorus pentachloride molecule is trigonal pyramidal with bond angles of 120° and 90° to get the electrons as far apart as possible. Phosphorus has vacant 3d orbitals, so it can expand the number of its valency electrons to ten.

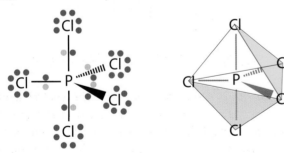

Octahedral shaped molecules

Sulfur hexafluoride (SF_6) is an interesting example because the central sulfur atom has expanded its octet to accommodate twelve electrons. The central atom is sulfur because there is only one atom. There are six bonding pairs (single bonds) of electrons to the central atom. There are no lone pairs of electrons on the central sulfur atom. The sulfur hexafluoride molecule is octahedral with bond angles of 90°, once again to get the electrons as far apart as possible. Sulfur has vacant 3d orbitals so it can expand the number of its valency electrons to twelve.

Order of repulsion

It is understood that two electrons of the same spin cannot occupy the same space. So the electrons in bonding pairs must have opposite spins. Also the electrons in a lone pair must have opposite spins. When two pairs of electrons come close they will repel each other as there will inevitably be electrons with the same spin in close proximity. The physical force behind the repulsion of pairs of electrons is called the **Pauli force**.

The lone pairs are also closer to the nucleus as they are not involved in a bond and are only attracted to one nucleus. Thus lone pairs of electrons occupy a greater angular volume than bonding electrons. Bonding pairs of electrons are slightly further from the nucleus than lone pairs and are attracted to two nuclei. With two types of electron pairs (lone pair and bonding pair) there are essentially three possible types of electron pair repulsions. They are shown in order of repulsive strength. The greatest repulsion is between two lone pairs of electrons and the least repulsion is between two bonding pairs of electrons.

Electron pairs	🥚🥚	>	🥚⚫	>	⚫⚫
Repulsion	Lone pair-lone pair	>	Lone pair-bonding pair	>	Bonding pair-bonding pair

Bonds and shape

The number of bonds around a central atom determines the shape as well as the various electron pair repulsions. The table shows the number of bonds and the shapes of molecules.

Number of bonds to a central atom (coordination number)	Shape (ideal geometry)
2	Linear
3	Trigonal planar
4	Tetrahedral (or square planar)
5	Trigonal bipyramidal
6	Octahedral

Examples of each shape

It is always useful to be able to recall a few examples from each of the possible shapes of molecules. But it is more important to be able to work out the shapes from first principles by considering electron pairs present around a central atom and the order of electron pair repulsions.

Shapes of molecules				
Planar molecules		3D molecules		
Linear	Trigonal planar	Tetrahedral	Pyramidal	V-shaped
HCl	BCl_3	CH_4	NH_3	H_2O
CO_2	SO_3	CCl_4	H_3O^+	F_2O
HCN	BBr_3	NH_4^+	SO_3^{2-}	SO_2
$BeCl_2$	H_2CO	CrO_4^{2-}	PCl_3	$[ClO_2]^-$
C_2H_2	C_2H_4	AlH_4^-	ClO_3^-	H_2S
N_2	CO_3^{2-}	PO_4^{3-}	XeO_3	Cl_2O
I_3^-	NO_3^-	$Si(CH_3)_4$	$BiCl_3$	NO_2

Shapes of molecules			
3D molecules			
Trigonal bipyramidal	Octahedral	Square planar	Pentagonal bipyramidal
PCl_5	SF_6	XeF_4	IF_7
IF_5	PF_6^-	$[Pt(NH_3)_2(Cl)_2]$	
PF_5	$[Cu(H_2O)_6]^{2+}$	ICl_4^-	
AsF_5	UF_6	$Ni(CN)_4^{2-}$	
$SbCl_5$	XeF_6		

Questions 2.4

1. Which of the following is **not** a planar shaped molecule?

   A $H_2C=O$

   B NH_3

   C NO_3^-

   D CO_3^{2-}

2. Which structure has an unpaired electron ?

   A   N=O

   B   N≡N

   C   H-O-H

   D   H-C≡N

3. By ticking box(es), indicate which of the following oxides of chlorine and nitrogen are odd electron molecules?

Oxide	Unpaired electrons
NO_2	
N_2O_4	
Cl_2O	
ClO_2	

Inter-halogen molecules

Inter-halogens are binary compounds that contain two different halogens. It is possible to make the red liquid and inter-halogen compound iodine chloride (ICl) by passing a stream of chlorine gas over solid iodine.

Example 2.3

What shape would you expect for the ion ICl_2^-? The central atom is iodine because there is only one iodine atom. There are two bonding pairs (single bonds) of electrons to the central atom. There are three lone pairs of electrons on the central iodine atom. The molecule adopts a linear shape with the three lone pairs adopting equatorial positions. This arrangement minimises repulsion of the two bonding pairs and three lone pairs of electrons.

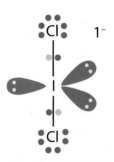

Example 2.4

What shape would you expect for the ion ICl_4^-? The central atom is iodine because there is only one iodine atom. There are four bonding pairs (single bonds) of electrons to the central atom. There are two lone pairs of electrons on the central iodine atom. The molecule adopts a square planar shape with the two lone pairs adopting axial positions. This arrangement minimises repulsion of the two lone pairs of electrons.

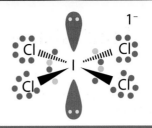

Noble gas molecules

Up until now you might have thought that noble gases (Group 18) are inert (unreactive) monatomic gases which do not form molecules. The first scientist to get a noble gas to react in a laboratory was Neil Bartlett in 1962. He synthesized xenon platinum hexafluoride. Since then various fluorides of xenon have been prepared, *e.g.* XeF_4.

Example 2.5

What shape would you expect for the molecule XeO_4? The central atom is xenon and there are four bonding pairs (single bonds) of electrons to the central atom. All four sigma bonds are dative covalent bonds with the electrons being donated by the xenon atom. The molecule adopts a perfect tetrahedron shape.

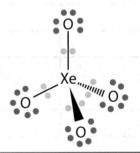

Questions 2.5

1. An inexperienced student incorrectly applied the VSEPR theory when trying to solve the structure of the following molecules. Correct the student's wrong answers by writing in the correct shape, taking into account any lone pairs when making the prediction.

Formula	Incorrect shape	Correct shape
BrF_3	trigonal planar	
ICl_4^-	octahedral	
SF_4	tetrahedral	

2. Explain using 3D diagrams what you understand by the following shapes of covalent molecules:

a) tetrahedral

b) octahedral

c) pyramidal

3. Why is boron trichloride (BCl_3) triangular planar but ammonia (NH_3), which also contains four atoms, has a very different shape?

4. Why does sulfur dioxide have a dipole moment but carbon dioxide does not?

A1.2 (h) Changes in geometry and bond angles

During the course of a chemical reaction there may also be changes in geometries and bond angles in addition to producing new substances (products). Changes to bond angles and shapes (geometries) can be worked out by application of the VSEPR theory.

Example 2.6

Protonation of the base ammonia (NH_3) results in the formation of the ammonium ion (NH_4^+). Ammonia is pyramidal (107°) and the ammonium ion is tetrahedral (109.5°).

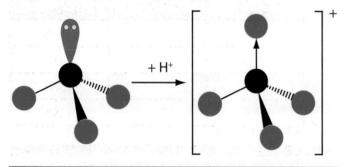

Example 2.7

Addition across carbon-carbon double bonds (C=C) by hydrogen (H_2), hydrogen chloride (HCl) and halogens (*e.g.* Cl_2) will give similar changes in geometry and bond angles. The addition of hydrogen chloride to ethene yields chloroethane.

Ethene has a trigonal planar (120°) geometry around each carbon atom, which changes to a tetrahedral (109.5°) geometry in chloroethane.

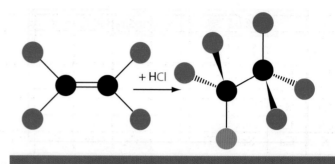

Questions 2.6

1. Phosphorus(V) chloride can be prepared by heating phosphorus(III) chloride in the presence of excess chlorine. Give a balanced equation for this reaction and describe any accompanying geometry changes and bond angles.

2. Sulfur trioxide can be prepared in a reversible reaction by heating sulfur dioxide and oxygen in the presence of the catalyst vanadium pentoxide (V_2O_5). Give a balanced equation for this reaction and describe any accompanying geometry changes and bond angles.

A1.2 (i) Electronegativity and bond polarity

Electronegativity

Electronegativity is the ability of an atom to attract electrons to itself in a covalent bond. This means that when two different types of atoms are covalently bonded they do not have an equal share of the electrons in the molecular orbital. The double Nobel laureate Linus Pauling used bond energies to determine electronegativity values for the elements. His concept of electronegativity (E_{neg}) is valuable in determining whether a compound will be ionic or covalent (A2.1d). Using the **Pauling scale**, the most electronegative element fluorine is given a value of 4.0. The least electronegative element that chemists can realistically use in reactions is caesium with a value of 0.7. More electronegative elements, which get a greater share of bonding electrons, have larger electronegativity values. The most ionic compound is caesium fluoride (CsF) as, the greater the electronegativity difference (ΔE_{neg}) between atoms, the more likely that they will have an ionic bond 'between' them.

The following table shows the electronegativity values for all the elements except the f-block. Take a close look at the table and see if you can spot any patterns (trends).

1	2	3	4	5	6	7	8	9	10	11	12	13	14	15	16	17	18
H 2.1																	He
Li 1.0	Be 1.5											B 2.0	C 2.5	N 3.0	O 3.5	F 4.0	Ne
Na 0.9	Mg 1.2											Al 1.5	Si 1.8	P 2.1	S 2.5	Cl 3.0	Ar
K 0.8	Ca 1.0	Sc 1.3	Ti 1.5	V 1.6	Cr 1.6	Mn 1.5	Fe 1.8	Co 1.9	Ni 1.9	Cu 1.9	Zn 1.6	Ga 1.6	Ge 1.8	As 2.0	Se 2.4	Br 2.8	Kr 3.0
Rb 0.8	Sr 1.0	Y 1.2	Zr 1.4	Nb 1.6	Mo 1.8	Tc 1.9	Ru 2.2	Rh 2.2	Pd 2.2	Ag 1.9	Cd 1.7	In 1.7	Sn 1.8	Sb 1.9	Te 2.1	I 2.5	Xe 2.6
Cs 0.7	Ba 0.9	La 1.1	Hf 1.3	Ta 1.5	W 1.7	Re 1.9	Os 2.2	Ir 2.2	Pt 2.2	Au 2.4	Hg 1.9	Tl 1.8	Pb 1.9	Bi 1.9	Po 2.0	At 2.2	Rn 2.4
Fr 0.7	Ra 0.9	Ac 1.1	Rf	Ha	Sg	Ns	Hs	Mt									

Trends in electronegativity values which can be explained in terms of effective nuclear charge are;

- Most electronegative atoms are found in the top right-hand corner of the Periodic Table.

- E_{neg} increases across Periods.

- E_{neg} decreases down Groups.

The bar chart helps to illustrate how E_{neg} diminishes down Group 17 (halogens) as additional shielding electrons (A1.1d) reduce the effective nuclear charge experienced by the valence electrons.

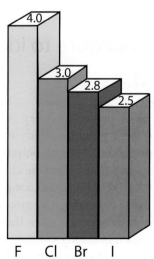

Others have devised their own electronegativity scales. Mulliken came up with $\frac{IE + EA}{2}$.

Where IE is ionisation energy (B2.4a) and EA is electron affinity (A1.3e). Allred and Rochow based their figures on the ratio of effective nuclear charge to r^2, where r is the atomic radius.

Question 2.7

1. Calculate the electronegativity differences (ΔE_{neg}) for the hydrogen halides. Is there a relationship between these differences and bond energies?

Hydrogen halide	ΔE_{neg}	Bond energies / kJ mol⁻¹
H-F		+ 565
H-Cl		+431
H-Br		+364
H-I		+297

Bond polarity

Covalent compounds will have unequal sharing of the bonding electrons. The atom with the greatest E_{neg} will pull the bonding electrons in its direction. This displacement of the charge within the molecular orbital will give the bond some ionic character, causing it to be polar. To indicate bond polarization, the more electronegative atom is assigned delta negative (δ^-) and the more electropositive element assigned delta positive (δ^+). Understanding polarity in molecules is very important as it affects their physical and chemical properties and the mechanisms by which they react (B3.9). Polarised molecules have a separation of charge by a small distance and this is described as a **dipole**. Hydrogen chloride is used to illustrate these ideas. The dot and cross diagram for hydrogen chloride shows how the electrons in the bonding pair are closer to the chlorine atom. The middle diagram shows the dipoles and the bottom diagram shows how the electron density is shifted towards the chlorine atom. Molecules like hydrogen chloride, which have dipoles and are asymmetric, have dipole moments. These are discussed in section A3.2a.

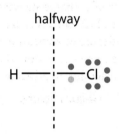

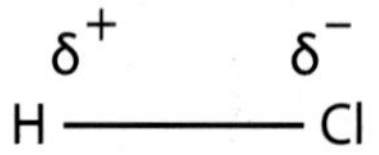

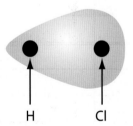

Polarity affects bond lengths by shortening them. Polarity also affects bond angles. The angle in water (104.5°) is greater than it is in hydrogen sulphide (92.2°) because the H-O bond is more polar than the H-S bond.

Questions 2.8

1. Why are the following diatomic gaseous molecules H_2, N_2, O_2, F_2, Cl_2 non-polar?

2. Label the following covalent bonds with the correct dipoles. [Hint: Refer to the Periodic Table with elemental electronegativity values].

Al —— Cl	O —— H
H —— S	C —— S
C —— O	S —— H
N —— H	B —— F
N —— F	P —— Cl
Cl —— Br	N —— O
B —— H	Cl —— O
Cl —— Cl	F —— F

3. Arrange the following σ bonds (C-F, C-Cl, C-H, C-O) in order of polarity, starting with the most polar bond.

4. Place a tick in the appropriate box to indicate which of the following molecules are polar.

Molecule's name	Formula	Polar	Non-polar
Propanone	$(CH_3)_2C=O$		
Carbon tetrachloride	CCl_4		
Hydrogen chloride	HCl		
Chloromethane	CH_3Cl		
1,1-dichloroethane	$CHCl_2CH_3$		

Practical procedure to identify polar liquids

Fill a burette with a polar liquid, *e.g.* water, ethanol, or propanone. Open the tap until a steady stream is achieved. Charge an insulating rod (polythene, polystyrene) by rubbing it vigorously with a dry cloth. Place the charged rod close to the stream of liquid. Deflected liquids are polar because they contain a small highly electronegative atom such as F, O, Cl, or N. This experiment works best when the humidity level in the air is low and when the cloth and rod come directly from a warm oven (70°C) prior to carrying out the experiment. The molecules in the stream orient themselves so that their dipoles are facing towards the oppositely charged rod. The result is a deflection of the stream because of the electrostatic poles on the molecule. It is just as easy to do this experiment with a plastic comb and a water tap.

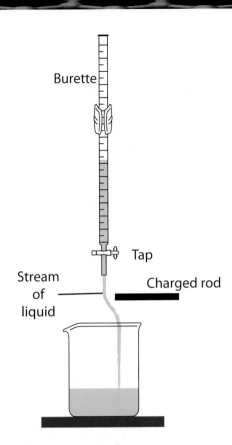

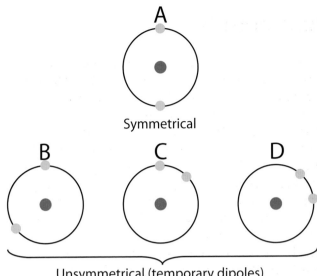

Symmetrical

Unsymmetrical (temporary dipoles)

A1.2 (j) Van der Waals forces

Van der Waals forces exist between all atoms and molecules in all types of matter. Without this very weak intermolecular force everything (non-polar) would exist as a gas. It is a force which is fleeting, existing for only brief periods of time, and which acts over very short distances - roughly twice the distance of a covalent bond. So think of Van der Waals forces as the force holding all substances together. Van der Waals forces are strongest in solids, then liquids, and, weakest of all in gases. Van der Waals forces are roughly twenty times weaker than covalent bonds in solids. This generalisation is non-examinable but gives chemists a feel for its relative size.

Instantaneous dipoles

Helium, like the other noble gases, is monatomic with the atoms going around as single atoms. Atoms of helium (like other atoms) are electrically neutral because they contain two positive protons and two negative electrons and two neutral neutrons. Yet it is possible to liquefy helium at temperatures below −269°C (4 K). The two electrons (yellow) orbit the nucleus (red). Any of the three arrangements; **B**, **C** or **D**, where the electrons are more to one side of the atom than the other will result in the atom having an instantaneous dipole. This instantaneous dipole is temporary as the electrons are still moving incredibly fast within the 1s orbital.

The temporary dipole of the helium atom can be thought of in terms of an electron cloud wobble. The temporary dipole is indicated by δ^+ and δ^- symbols. This instantaneous dipole induces dipoles in nearby atoms. The Van der Waals force is the attractive force that occurs between the two helium atoms. The sequence of events is shown visually below. These instantaneous-induced-dipole forces are continuously coming and going as molecules are moving around. When drawing the third diagram in the sequence, ensure that alternating dipoles are shown next to each other in adjacent atoms.

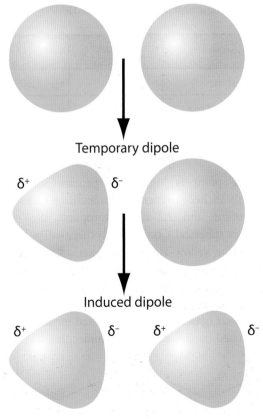

Helium atoms

Temporary dipole

Induced dipole

Van der Waals force

Polarisability

The more easily the electron clouds distort (**polarisability**), the greater the size of the Van der Waals force. For the noble gases (Group 18) and other substances, the size of the Van der Waals forces increases with the number of electrons present. Analysis of the melting and boiling point data for the noble gases shows a clear trend in Van der Waals forces.

	He	Ne	Ar	Kr	Xe	Rn
mp / K	1 *	25	84	116	161	202
bp / K	4	27	87	121	166	211
number of electrons	2	10	18	36	54	86

* datum obtained at 26 atmospheres.

As polarisability increases, it is much easier for a dipole to be induced. This is why molecules with more electrons have stronger Van der Waals forces of attraction between them.

Shapes of molecules

Another factor, apart from the number of electrons, that affects the size of Van der Waals forces is the shape of molecules. This can be illustrated by the differences in boiling point for the non-polar pentane and its isomers (A3.1d).

Isomer	Molecular formula	Boiling point / K
pentane	C_5H_{12}	309.2
2-methylbutane	C_5H_{12}	301.0
2,2-dimethylpropane	C_5H_{12}	282.6

The boiling point is highest in pentane, which is the longest unbranched isomer. As branching increases with 2-methylbutane and 2,2-dimethylpropane, the molecules become more spherical. Consequently there will be less contact (shown by the yellow zigzag) between adjacent molecules of 2-methylbutane compared with pentane. Therefore, there will be weaker Van der Waals forces of attraction to overcome (on heating) to separate the molecules, allowing them to pass into the vapour (gaseous) state. Elongated molecules are more easily polarised than more compact molecules.

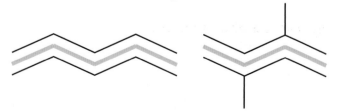

Van der Waals forces in solids

Solid carbon dioxide (CO_2) is commonly known as dry ice. It is an unusual solid in that it **sublimes**. It goes from the solid state to the gaseous state without passing through the liquid phase. Iodine is a crystalline substance which also sublimes. Comparison of their 'melting points' with other higher melting crystals illustrates just how low these values are. Iodine and carbon dioxide both have very weak Van der Waals forces holding their molecules together in the solid state. It is clear that substances which are only held together by weak forces of attraction (Van der Waals) have very low melting points compared with substances with similar molar masses.

Substance	Type of crystals	Molar mass	Melting point /K
SiO_2 (quartz)	Giant covalent	60.1	1883
NaCl	Giant ionic	58.5	1074
I_2	Molecular covalent	254	387
CO_2	Molecular covalent	44	217 *

* 5.2 atmospheres

Permanent dipoles

Another type of intermolecular force is found between polar molecules which have permanent dipoles. Polar molecules also have dipole-dipole interactions between their molecules. Hydrogen bonding is a special case of dipole-dipole interaction and is dealt with in section A1.2 (k). Polar molecules will contain one of the more highly electronegative elements such as nitrogen, oxygen or chlorine.

Example 2.8

Propanone ($(CH_3)_2C=O$) is the simplest member of the ketones (A3.2g). Propanone has the same molar mass as butane (58 g mol⁻¹) and yet its boiling point is 329 K compared with butane's boiling point, which is much lower at 273 K. The dipole-dipole intermolecular forces shown in the diagram (light blue) make it more difficult to separate propanone molecules than butane molecules, as additional energy needs to be supplied. Dipole-dipole interactions are stronger than Van der Waals forces (instantaneous-induced dipoles).

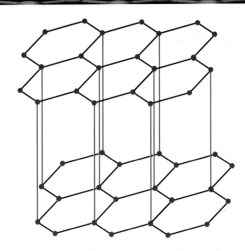

Example 2.9

Terylene is a condensation polymer (B3.7). It is a polyester made from a dicarboxylic acid (B3.7a) and a diol (A3.2). Esters have a dipole on their carbonyl (C=O) group which leads to dipole-dipole interactions. These forces account for the strong forces holding the chains of polymer together, allowing it to find use as a fibre for clothing.

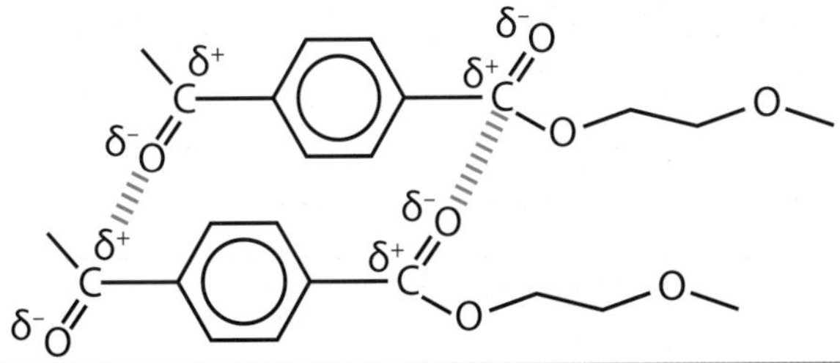

Questions 2.9

1. Explain the pattern of the boiling points of the hydrogen halides.

	HF	HCl	HBr	HI
bp / K	293	188	206	238

2. Explain how it is possible for non-polar molecules to have forces of attraction between them.

Van der Waals forces in nature

Geckos are believed to use Van der Waals forces to climb walls. They can even climb smooth surfaces such as glass. They achieve this remarkable feat by using microscopic hairs on the undersides of their feet. Van der Waals forces between the foot hairs and surfaces allow these small lizards seemingly to defy gravity.

Van der Waals equation

The ideal gas equation (B1.6b) was modified by J. Van der Waals to take into account the deviations of real gases from ideal behaviour. Real gases have forces of attraction between molecules (Van der Waals) and their volumes are taken into account and not assumed to be negligible.

The Van der Waals equation is:

$$\left(p + \frac{a}{v^2}\right)(V - b) = nRT$$

where $\frac{a}{v^2}$ is the Van der Waals forces correction

and $(V - b)$ is the volume of gas correction.

This equation is left until university.

Van der Waals forces in graphite

Graphite is an allotrope of carbon (B2.3a). It is composed of hexagonal layers held together by weak Van der Waals forces, shown in red in the diagram. This structure gives graphite the property of being slippery, which has been exploited in its uses as a lubricant and a writing material (pencil). The structure was solved by J. D. Bernal, who showed early promise as a young scientist at Stonyhurst College.

Question 2.10

1. Explain the trend in boiling point for the following diatomic Group 17 elements.

Halogen	Number of electrons	Boiling point / K
Fluorine (F$_2$)	18	85
Chlorine (Cl$_2$)	34	238
Bromine (Br$_2$)	70	332
Iodine (I$_2$)	106	457

A1.2 (k) Hydrogen bonding

Hydrogen bonding is a special case of dipole-dipole interaction. It is the strongest of the intermolecular forces and is crucial to life on earth. Water would not exist as a liquid at temperatures found on earth without it being able to form hydrogen bonds. Hydrogen bonds occur between molecules that contain small highly electronegative atoms (F, N, O) covalently bonded to a hydrogen atom. Hydrogen bonds are about 10% as strong as covalent bonds, typically about 30 kJ mol^{-1}. The strongest recorded hydrogen bond is 150 kJ mol^{-1} in the ion, [F–H–F]$^-$. Hydrogen bonds are quite a bit longer than covalent bonds. In diagrams, hydrogen bonds are shown as dashes or dots. When drawing them, don't forget to include the lone pair from the highly electronegative atom and draw all relevant dipoles. Many covalent compounds are soluble in water because they can form hydrogen bonds.

Example 2.10

Hydrogen fluoride (HF) has a boiling point of 293 K compared with a boiling point of 188 K for hydrogen chloride (HCl). This anomalously high boiling point for hydrogen fluoride can be explained because the liquid contains zigzag chains with hydrogen bonds between molecules.

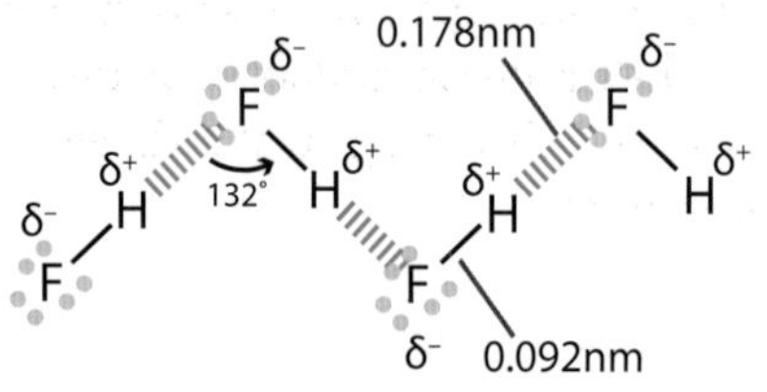

Example 2.11

Ethanol (CH$_3$CH$_2$OH) dissolves in water in all proportions because of its ability to form hydrogen bonds with water. The 'space lost' on mixing ethanol and water can be demonstrated in the laboratory by mixing ethanol (50 cm^3) and distilled water (50 cm^3). The decrease in total volume can be explained in terms of hydrogen bonding. The diagram shows three of the potential intermolecular hydrogen bonding possibilities for an ethanol / water mixture. Note how there is a 180° angle along the hydrogen bond, so there are effectively four atoms in a straight line.

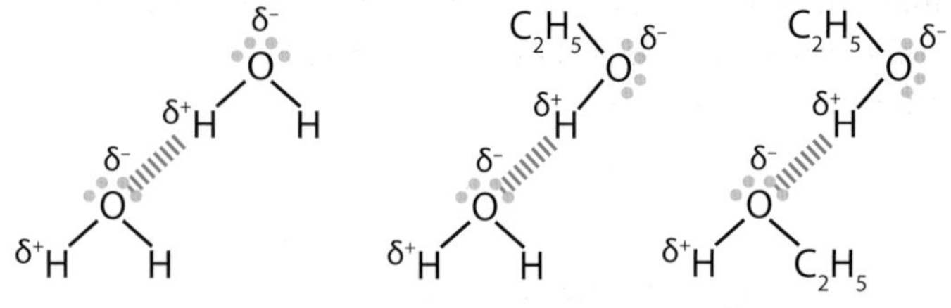

water-water   water-ethanol   ethanol-ethanol

Hydrogen bonding in ice

One interesting property of water is that it is less dense as a solid (ice) than as a liquid. This is why ice floats on water and fish can survive the winter in lakes even in the Arctic Circle. The diagram showing the structure of ice shows how water molecules are arranged. Molecules are held together by hydrogen bonds and the structure adopts a low density open structure similar to diamond (B2.3a). Each oxygen atom is at the centre of a tetrahedron of four oxygen atoms each 0.273 nm apart. The hydrogen bonds shown with dashed lines are 0.177 nm long and the O-H bond lengths are 0.096 nm. Note how each water molecule has four hydrogen bonds, two from the O-H and two from the lone pairs.

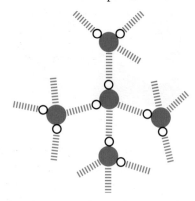

Hydrogen bonding in base pairs

Deoxyribonucleic acid (DNA) is a very important biological molecule. It contains the necessary instructions for making all the proteins needed for the cells, tissues and organs for all known organisms. One very important feature of this 'molecule of life' is that it has a double helix that is held together by hydrogen bonds. The hydrogen bonds can be thought to be the teeth on a zip which can be unzipped during replication. The hydrogen bonds are *via* the nitrogen and oxygen atoms in the purine-pyrimidine base pairs, as shown in the diagram. There is no need to learn this diagram by rote. It is more important to understand where and why hydrogen bonding occurs in DNA and to realise that some base pairs (A=T) have two hydrogen bonds and others (G≡C) have three hydrogen bonds.

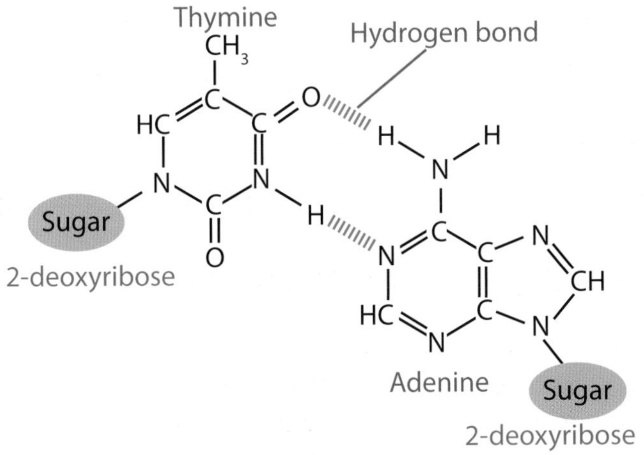

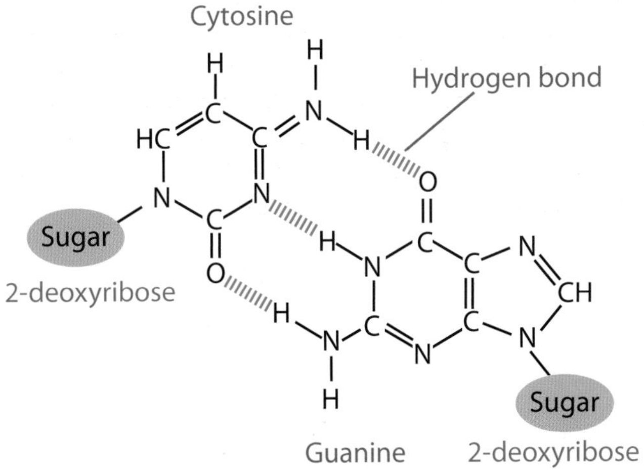

Thymine — Hydrogen bond — Adenine
Sugar 2-deoxyribose / Sugar 2-deoxyribose

Cytosine — Hydrogen bond — Guanine
Sugar 2-deoxyribose / Guanine 2-deoxyribose

The DNA bases hydrogen bond to one other in preference to water because it is energetically favourable. It also means that their non-polar sections are hidden from the aqueous environment by the water-soluble phosphate and sugar groups.

A1.2 (l) Protein structure

Hydrogen bonding is also important in stabilising the folded structures of proteins. Hydrogen bonds are the major intermolecular forces holding giant (**macromolecular**) biologically important molecules in their three dimensional shapes (**conformations**). Two of the most important protein shapes are the alpha helix and the beta pleated sheets.

Alpha helix

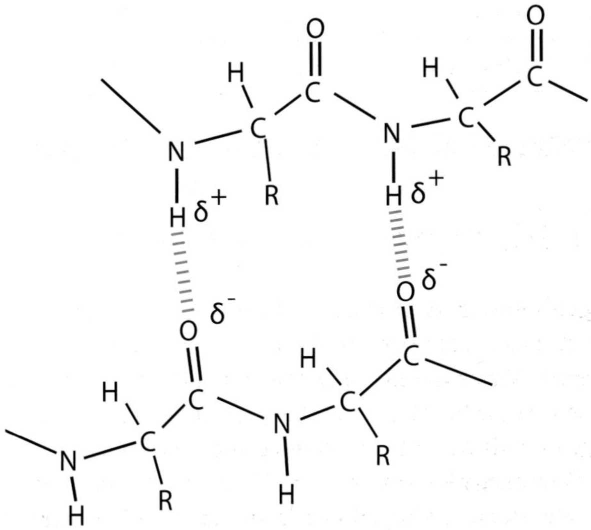

Hair and wool consist of the protein α-keratin which is a right-handed helix made up of several amino acids (B3.7c). Wool can be spun because its helical structure can be unwound when strong forces are applied. In the alpha helix, N-H groups of one amide hydrogen bond to C=O (carbonyl) groups from another amide (A3.2g). These structures, which were first described by Linus Pauling, have been confirmed by crystallographic studies. It is important to realise that the portion of the molecule with the hydrogen bonds is planar. Interestingly, one of the huge scientific advances coming from the NASA space program has been the realisation that it is easier to grow crystals of proteins such as enzymes in the absence of gravity.

Beta pleated sheet

Silk is a protein (β-keratin) which forms β-pleated sheets. It is extruded from spinnerets found at the end of web spiders' abdomens. Silk is the material of spiders' webs. In some sections, about half a dozen amino acids line up in parallel arrangements. One such arrangement is shown with hydrogen bonds as dashed lines.

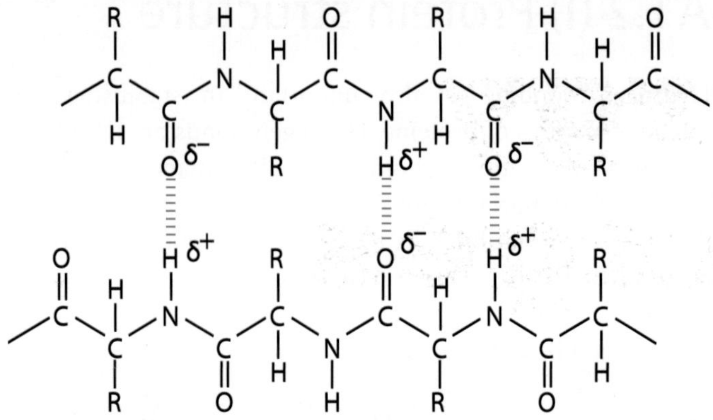

Questions 2.11

1. Explain why you think scientists thought for a long time that ethanoic acid (CH_3COOH) had twice its actual molar mass.

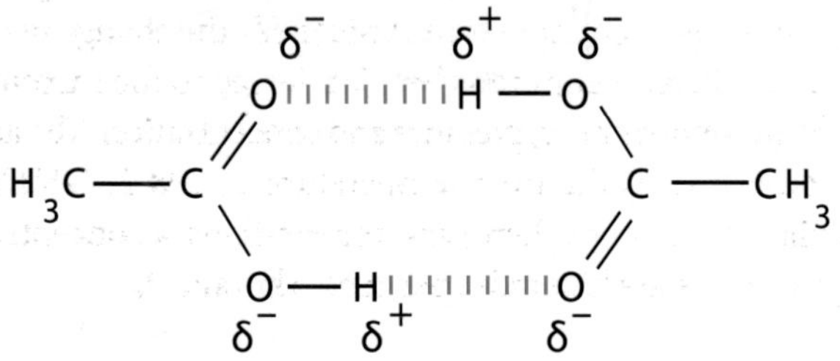

2. Which option is the correct order for the relative bond strengths and intermolecular forces?

   A   ionic > covalent > hydrogen bonding > Van der Waals

   B   covalent > ionic > hydrogen bonding > Van der Waals

   C   ionic > covalent > Van der Waals > hydrogen bonding

   D   covalent > ionic > Van der Waals > hydrogen bonding

3

Energy Changes

Contents

A1.3 (a) Energy changes

Matter contains potential chemical energy stored in bonds. During chemical reactions, reactant bonds are broken (endothermic processes) and product bonds are formed (exothermic processes). Nearly all chemical changes involve an overall change in energy. Most reactions are exothermic (ΔH - the change in energy - is negative) involving an increase in temperature as heat is released to the surroundings. Enthalpy changes are affected by: temperature, pressure and concentration. The accepted standard conditions ($\div$) around the world are a temperature of 298 K (25°C) and a pressure of 100 kPa (approximately 1 atmosphere) and for solutions, a concentration of 1 mol dm^{-3}. Units of energy changes are kilojoules per mole (kJ mol^{-1}).

Managing the energy changes in large reaction vessels such as these is a crucial part of the chemical industry.

What are the different energy changes?

There a number of different types of energy (enthalpy) changes and it is important to be able to distinguish between them. They are identified by different subscripts, *e.g.* $\Delta_r H^\ominus$, where 'r' stands for reaction.

Enthalpy change	Symbol	Definition
Enthalpy of reaction.	$\Delta_r H^\ominus$	Enthalpy change when the molar quantities of reactants (equation) react together under standard conditions.
Enthalpy of formation.	$\Delta_f H^\ominus$	Enthalpy change when one mole of compound is formed from its constituent elements in their reference states under standard conditions.
Enthalpy of combustion.	$\Delta_c H^\ominus$	Enthalpy change when one mole of substance is completely burnt in oxygen under standard conditions.
Enthalpy of hydration.	$\Delta_{hydr} H^\ominus$	Enthalpy change when one mole of gaseous ions forms a 1 mol dm^{-3} solution (hydrated ions) under standard conditions.
Enthalpy of solution.	$\Delta_{soln} H^\ominus$	Enthalpy change when one mole of ionic solid (solute) dissolves to form a 1 mol dm^{-3} solution under standard conditions.
Enthalpy of neutralisation.	$\Delta_{neut} H^\ominus$	Enthalpy change when one mole of water (or salt) forms from an acid-base reaction under standard conditions.
Enthalpy of atomisation (*applies to elements*).	$\Delta_{atom} H^\ominus$	Enthalpy change when one mole of gaseous (single) atoms is formed from its element under standard conditions.
Enthalpy of vaporisation.	$\Delta_{vap} H^\ominus$	Enthalpy change when one mole of a liquid is converted to one mole of gas at its boiling point at standard pressure.

Enthalpy of reaction

$2 \, Mg \, (s) + O_2 \, (g) \rightarrow 2 \, MgO \, (s)$ $\Delta_r H^\ominus = -1204 \text{ kJ mol}^{-1}$

$2 \, H_2 \, (g) + O_2 \, (g) \rightarrow 2 \, H_2O \, (l)$ $\Delta_r H^\ominus = -571.6 \text{ kJ mol}^{-1}$

Enthalpies of combustion and formation are often simple multiples of enthalpies of reaction.

Enthalpy of formation

$C_{(graphite)} + 2 \, H_2 \, (g) \rightarrow CH_4 \, (g)$ $\Delta_f H^\ominus = -74.8 \text{ kJ mol}^{-1}$

$2C_{(graphite)} + H_2 \, (g) \rightarrow C_2H_2 \, (g)$ $\Delta_f H^\ominus = +228 \text{ kJ mol}^{-1}$

$Mg \, (s) + \frac{1}{2} \, O_2 \, (g) \rightarrow MgO \, (s)$ $\Delta_f H^\ominus = -602 \text{ kJ mol}^{-1}$

$Na \, (s) + \frac{1}{2} \, Cl_2 \, (g) \rightarrow NaCl \, (s)$ $\Delta_f H^\ominus = -411.2 \text{ kJ mol}^{-1}$

$Na \, (s) \rightarrow Na \, (s)$ $\Delta_f H^\ominus = 0 \text{ kJ mol}^{-1}$

Enthalpies of formation can be measured experimentally using bomb calorimeters. Enthalpies of formation for all elements are zero as they are already in their standard states. Enthalpies of formation can be either exothermic or endothermic.

Enthalpy of combustion

$C_{(graphite)} + O_2 \, (g) \rightarrow CO_2 \, (g)$ $\Delta_c H^\ominus = -393.5 \text{ kJ mol}^{-1}$

$H_2 \, (g) + \frac{1}{2} \, O_2 \, (g) \rightarrow H_2O \, (l)$ $\Delta_c H^\ominus = -285.8 \text{ kJ mol}^{-1}$

$CH_4 \, (g) + 2 \, O_2 \, (g) \rightarrow CO_2 \, (g) + 2 \, H_2O \, (l)$

$\Delta_c H^\ominus = -890.3 \text{ kJ mol}^{-1}$

$C_2H_5OH \, (l) + 3 \, O_2 \, (g) \rightarrow 2 \, CO_2 \, (g) + 3 \, H_2O \, (l)$

$\Delta_c H^\ominus = -1367.3 \text{ kJ mol}^{-1}$

Enthalpies of combustion can be measured experimentally (A1.3b) using (bomb) calorimeters. Enthalpies of combustion are always exothermic.

Enthalpy of neutralisation

$HCl \, (aq) + NaOH \, (aq) \rightarrow NaCl \, (aq) + H_2O \, (l)$

$\Delta_{neut} H^\ominus = -57.9 \text{ kJ mol}^{-1}$

$HCl \ (aq) + NH_3 \ (aq) \rightarrow NH_4Cl \ (aq) \quad \Delta_{neut}H^\ominus = -53.4 \text{ kJ mol}^{-1}$

$CH_3CO_2H \ (aq) + NaOH \ (aq) \rightarrow CH_3CO_2Na \ (aq) + H_2O \ (l)$

$$\Delta_{neut}H^\ominus = -53.4 \text{ kJ mol}^{-1}$$

Enthalpies of neutralisation are nearly always exothermic. An example of a notable endothermic neutralisation is the reaction between a sodium hydrogen carbonate and a mineral acid such as hydrochloric acid.

Enthalpy of atomisation

$C_{(graphite)} \rightarrow C \ (g)$ $\qquad \Delta_{atm}H^\ominus = +717 \text{ kJ mol}^{-1}$

$\frac{1}{2}H_2 \ (g) \rightarrow H \ (g)$ $\qquad \Delta_{atm}H^\ominus = +218 \text{ kJ mol}^{-1}$

$\frac{1}{2}N_2 \ (g) \rightarrow N \ (g)$ $\qquad \Delta_{atm}H^\ominus = +473 \text{ kJ mol}^{-1}$

$\frac{1}{2}O_2 \ (g) \rightarrow O \ (g)$ $\qquad \Delta_{atm}H^\ominus = +250 \text{ kJ mol}^{-1}$

The relationship $E = hf$ (A4.3b) can be used to calculate atomisation enthalpies by finding the minimum frequency to dissociate gaseous molecules into atoms. Enthalpies of atomisation are always endothermic.

Enthalpy of vaporisation

$H_2O \ (l) \rightarrow H_2O \ (g)$ $\qquad \Delta_{vap}H^\ominus = +44.0 \text{ kJ mol}^{-1}$

$C_2H_5OH \ (l) \rightarrow C_2H_5OH \ (g)$ $\qquad \Delta_{vap}H^\ominus = +38.6 \text{ kJ mol}^{-1}$

$C_6H_{14} \ (l) \rightarrow C_6H_{14} \ (g)$ $\qquad \Delta_{vap}H^\ominus = +30.7 \text{ kJ mol}^{-1}$

This energy required to turn 1 mole (18 g) of liquid water into gaseous water (steam) at its boiling point (100°C) is +44.0 kJ mol^{-1}. Enthalpy of vaporisation is the difference in enthalpy between the vapour (gaseous) and liquid states.

$$\Delta_{vap}H^\ominus = H^\ominus_{(vapour)} - H^\ominus_{(liquid)}$$

Enthalpies of vaporisation are always endothermic.

Enthalpy of hydration

$Na^+ \ (g) \rightarrow Na^+ \ (aq)$ $\qquad \Delta_{hydr}H^\ominus = -406 \text{ kJ mol}^{-1}$

$Cl^- \ (g) \rightarrow Cl^- \ (aq)$ $\qquad \Delta_{hydr}H^\ominus = -364 \text{ kJ mol}^{-1}$

Enthalpies of hydration cannot be measured directly, but they can be obtained from enthalpy cycles (A1.3d) using experimentally determined enthalpies of solution and lattice enthalpies calculated from Born-Haber energy cycles (A1.3e).

Enthalpy of solution

$NaCl \ (s) + \text{excess water} \rightarrow NaCl \ (aq) \quad \Delta_{soln}H^\ominus = +10 \text{ kJ mol}^{-1}$

$NaI \ (s) + \text{excess water} \rightarrow NaI \ (aq) \qquad \Delta_{soln}H^\ominus = -8 \text{ kJ mol}^{-1}$

Enthalpies of solution can be measured experimentally (A1.3b) and from enthalpy cycles (A1.3d). Enthalpies of solution are the differences between lattice and hydration enthalpies.

Enthalpies of solution can be either exothermic or endothermic.

The figure below shows how solution, hydration and lattice enthalpies are related using an energy profile diagram (A1.3g).

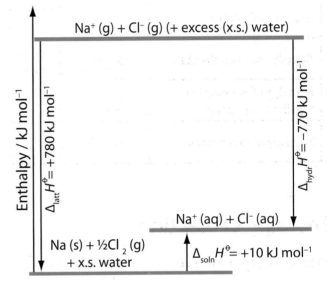

Enthalpy changes of reaction can be calculated from enthalpies of formation.

$$\Delta_r H^\ominus = \Delta_f H^\ominus \ (\text{products}) - \Delta_f H^\ominus \ (\text{reactants})$$

Don't forget that elements have a $\Delta_f H^\ominus$ value of zero, which is why they are not given. Remember to take into account the stoichiometry in any calculations.

Example 3.1

Calculate $\Delta_r H^\ominus$ for the following reaction:

$SO_2 \ (g) + 2 \ H_2S \ (g) \rightarrow 3 \ S \ (s) + 2 \ H_2O \ (l)$

Solution:

$$SO_2 \text{ (g)} + 2\,H_2S \text{ (g)} \to 3\,S \text{ (s)} + 2\,H_2O \text{ (l)}$$

| $\Delta_f H^\ominus$ (kJ mol⁻¹) | -296.8 | -20.6 | 0 | -285.8 |

Stoichiometry accounted for

| | -296.8 | -41.2 | 0 | -571.6 |

$\Delta_r H^\ominus = \Delta_f H^\ominus \text{ (products)} - \Delta_f H^\ominus \text{ (reactants)}$

$\Delta_r H^\ominus = -571.6 - -296.8 - -41.2$

$\Delta_r H^\ominus = -571.6 + 296.8 + 41.2$

$\Delta_r H^\ominus = -233.6$ kJ mol⁻¹

Example 3.2

Calculate $\Delta_r H^\ominus$ for the following reaction:

$$3\,PbO \text{ (s)} + \tfrac{1}{2}O_2 \text{ (g)} \to Pb_3O_4 \text{ (s)}$$

Solution:

$$3\,PbO \text{ (s)} + \tfrac{1}{2}O_2 \text{ (g)} \to Pb_3O_4 \text{ (s)}$$

| $\Delta_f H^\ominus$ (kJ mol⁻¹) | -217.3 | 0 | -718.4 |

Stoichiometry accounted for

| | -651.9 | 0 | -718.4 |

$\Delta_r H^\ominus = \Delta_f H^\ominus \text{ (products)} - \Delta_f H^\ominus \text{ (reactants)}$

$\Delta_r H^\ominus = -718.4 - -651.9$

$\Delta_r H^\ominus = -718.4 + 651.9$

$\Delta_r H^\ominus = -66.5$ kJ mol⁻¹

Questions 3.1

1. Calculate $\Delta_r H^\ominus$ for the following reaction:

$$2\,N_2H_4 \text{ (l)} + N_2O_4 \text{ (g)} \to 3\,N_2 \text{ (g)} + 4\,H_2O \text{ (l)}$$

$\Delta_f H^\ominus (N_2H_4) = +50.6$ kJ mol⁻¹

$\Delta_f H^\ominus (N_2O_4) = +9.2$ kJ mol⁻¹

$\Delta_f H^\ominus (H_2O) = -285.8$ kJ mol⁻¹

2. Calculate $\Delta_r H$ for the following reaction:

$$4\,NH_3 \text{ (g)} + 5\,O_2 \text{ (g)} \to 4\,NO \text{ (g)} + 6\,H_2O \text{ (l)}$$

$\Delta_f H^\ominus (NH_3) = -46.1$ kJ mol⁻¹

$\Delta_f H^\ominus (NO) = +90.2$ kJ mol⁻¹

$\Delta_f H^\ominus (H_2O) = -285.8$ kJ mol⁻¹

3. Using the table of hydration enthalpies ($\Delta_{hydr} H^\ominus$) for some simple cations, suggest what might affect their values and give a plausible explanation.

Cation	$\Delta_{hydr} H^\ominus$ / kJ mol⁻¹
H⁺	-1091
Li⁺	-519
Na⁺	-406
K⁺	-322
Mg²⁺	-1920
Al³⁺	-4690

4. Which enthalpy change does not describe the following reaction?

$$H_2 \text{ (g)} + \tfrac{1}{2}O_2 \text{ (g)} \to H_2O \text{ (l)}$$

A $\quad \Delta_f H^\ominus$

B $\quad \Delta_c H^\ominus$

C $\quad \Delta_{hyd} H^\ominus$

D $\quad \Delta_r H^\ominus$

5. Explain why all three neutralisations have almost identical enthalpies of neutralisation.

$HCl \text{ (aq)} + NaOH \text{ (aq)} \to NaCl \text{ (aq)} + H_2O \text{ (l)}$
$\Delta_{neut} H^\ominus = -57.9$ kJ mol⁻¹

$HBr \text{ (aq)} + NaOH \text{ (aq)} \to NaBr \text{ (aq)} + H_2O \text{ (l)}$
$\Delta_{neut} H^\ominus = -57.6$ kJ mol⁻¹

$HNO_3 \text{ (aq)} + NaOH \text{ (aq)} \to NaNO_3 \text{ (aq)} + H_2O \text{ (l)}$
$\Delta_{neut} H^\ominus = -57.6$ kJ mol⁻¹

6. Explain the difference between the following enthalpies of neutralisation with sodium hydroxide reacting with different acids.

HCl (aq) + NaOH (aq) → NaCl (aq) + H$_2$O (l)
$\Delta_{neut}H^{\ominus}$ = −57.9 kJ mol^{-1}

CH$_3$CO$_2$H(aq)+NaOH(aq) → CH$_3$CO$_2$Na(aq)+H$_2$O(l)
$\Delta_{neut}H^{\ominus}$ = −53.4 kJ mol^{-1}

7. Which enthalpy change is never endothermic?

A $\Delta_r H^{\ominus}$

B $\Delta_{soln} H^{\ominus}$

C $\Delta_f H^{\ominus}$

D $\Delta_c H^{\ominus}$

8. Which neutralisation will give the least exothermic energy change?

A   CH$_3$CO$_2$H + KOH

B   HCl + NaOH

C   H$_2$SO$_4$ + NaOH

D   H$_2$SO$_4$ + KOH

A1.3 (b) Equation 1

Thermochemistry is the study of heat as the energy change. In times of high oil prices this is a particularly important branch of chemistry. Heat changes in a reaction can be determined experimentally using a simple calorimeter, or theoretically from bond energy values (A1.3 d). It is important to realise that heat always flows from high to low temperature.

Historically, chemists measured energy in calories. 1 calorie is the amount of heat energy needed to increase the temperature of 1 g of water by 1°C. Today the unit of energy is the **joule**. In physics, 1 joule is the energy needed to move a force of 1 N (~100 g on Earth) through a distance of 1 m. 1 calorie = 4.2 J, a useful conversion if you have the time to work out how much food you consume daily.

When measuring heat, three things need to be considered:

- Temperature.

- Mass of substance.

- Type of substance (specific heat capacity).

There is no instrument to measure heat directly, which has the symbol q. Heat can be calculated by transferring heat to a known mass of water and measuring the change in temperature in a piece of apparatus called a **calorimeter**. Experimentally this can be achieved by:

- combusting a fuel which then heats a known mass of water.

- or mixing two reactants of known volume.

In both examples the start temperature (initial) and finish temperature (final) need recording. All calorimetry experiments make use of **Equation 1** which states that, $q = m\,c\,\Delta T$ where q = heat, m = mass of water (g), c = specific heat capacity and ΔT is the change in temperature. ΔT = final temperature − initial temperature. Specific heat capacity (c) is a property of a substance and is the amount of heat needed to increase the temperature of 1 g of the substance by 1 K. For water c = 4.2 Jg^{-1}K^{-1} and for ethanol c = 2.4 Jg^{-1}K^{-1}.

The enthalpy of combustion of alcohols (fuels) can be determined using a spirit burner with the fuel (alcohol) heating a beaker of water containing a thermometer.

The mass of the spirit burner plus fuel is recorded. The fuel is ignited and it heats a known volume (mass) of water in the beaker. After the experiment, the burner's mass is recorded and the amount of fuel combusted calculated.

Example 3.3

Ethanol was ignited in a spirit burner and the tabulated results were obtained.

[A_r of carbon = 12, oxygen = 16 and hydrogen =1] and where c = 4.2 Jg^{-1}K^{-1}

Calculate the enthalpy of combustion of ethanol.

Results

Combustion of ethanol	
START mass of burner + ethanol	256.80 g
FINISH mass of burner + ethanol	256.26 g
START temperature of water	298 K
FINISH temperature of water	308 K
Volume of water	100 cm³

Calculations

$T = 308 - 298 = 10$ K

Mass of fuel used $= 256.80 - 256.26 = 0.54$ g

Molar mass of ethanol $= (12 \times 2 + 1 \times 6 + 16 \times 1) = 46$ g mol⁻¹

$q = m\,c\,\Delta T$

$q = 100 \times 4.2 \times 10$

[as the density of water is 1 g cm⁻³, 100 cm³ = 100 g]

$q = 4200$ J

Amount of ethanol $= \dfrac{0.54}{46} = 0.0117$ mol

$\Delta_c H = \dfrac{4200}{0.0117} = -358974$ J mol⁻¹

[negative as the reaction is exothermic]

$\Delta_c H = -359$ kJ mol⁻¹ $\left[\dfrac{\text{Joules}}{1000} \text{ gives kJ} \right]$

The enthalpies of neutralisation ($\Delta_{neut} H^{\ominus}$) and the enthalpies of solution ($\Delta_{soln} H^{\ominus}$) can be determined using a polystyrene cup and a thermometer.

The simple calorimeter is a polystyrene cup. The reactants are mixed with the thermometer and the temperature rise (or fall) is recorded. Polystyrene is a good insulating material and is a reliable vessel for a quick and simple way to measure the quantity of energy released or absorbed during physical or chemical changes. Care is needed not to poke a hole through the polystyrene with

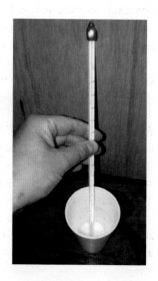

the thermometer. In the process, energy is transferred to the water or reaction mixture. The assumption made for aqueous solutions is that $c = 4.2$ Jg⁻¹K⁻¹. To make calculations more straightforward, the heat capacity of the container is assumed to be negligible. Once again, the energy evolved as heat can be calculated using equation 1 [$q = mc\Delta T$].

Example 3.4

Hydrochloric acid (40 cm³, 1 mol dm⁻³) was placed in a polystyrene cup. A thermometer was placed into the acid and left to equilibrate. The initial temperature was recorded. Sodium hydroxide (40 cm³, 1 mol dm⁻³) was added quickly to the acid and stirred rapidly with the thermometer. The temperature was recorded every 15 seconds until there was no further temperature rise. Calculate the enthalpy of neutralisation for this reaction [$c = 4.2$ Jg⁻¹K⁻¹].

Results

Neutralisation: $HCl + NaOH \rightarrow NaCl + H_2O$	
START temperature of water	293 K
FINISH temperature of water	300 K
Volume of solution	80 cm³

Calculations

$\Delta T = 300 - 293 = 7$K

$q = m\,c\,\Delta T$

$q = 80 \times 4.2 \times 7$

[as the density of water is 1 g cm⁻³, 80 cm³ = 80 g]

$q = 2352$ J

Amount of water produced $= 1 \times \dfrac{40}{1000} = 0.04$ mol

$\Delta_{neut} H = \dfrac{2352}{0.04} = -58800$ J mol⁻¹   [negative as heat given out]

$= -58.8$ kJ mol⁻¹ $\left[\dfrac{\text{Joules}}{1000} \text{ gives kJ} \right]$

During these experiments there will be some heat loss due to cooling of the reaction mixture. This can be corrected for by drawing a graph of temperature (y-axis) versus time of reaction/dissolution (x-axis) and extrapolating back to the time of mixing. This gives a better estimate of ΔT. When performing the experiment, results will have to be collected after the reaction has finished.

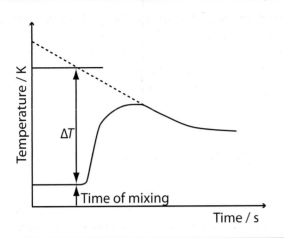

1. Explain why all neutralisations involving a strong acid and a strong base give almost identical temperature rises when using the same volumes and concentrations.

2. What are the sources of error when calculating enthalpies of combustion of an alcohol using a spirit burner under a beaker of water? What observations might suggest partial combustion? What improvements could be made to the apparatus?

3. An excess of zinc powder was added, a spatula at a time, to an aqueous solution of copper(II) sulfate (50 cm^3, 0.1 mol dm^{-3}). Calculate the increase in temperature given that the enthalpy of reaction was calculated to be -217 kJ mol^{-1}. Take the specific heat capacity of water as 4.2 Jg^{-1}K^{-1} in the equation $q = m\,c\,\Delta T$.

4. Explain why the enthalpies of neutralisation are lower for weak acids (-56 kJ mol^{-1}) compared with strong acids (-58 kJ mol^{-1}). Give equations for weak and strong acids reacting with potassium hydroxide.

5. The correct symbol and unit for specific heat capacity are:

	Symbol	Unit
A	c	J^{-1} g K^{-1}
B	c	J g^{-1} K^{-1}
C	H	J g^{-1} K
D	q	J g^{-1} K^{-1}

6. How much heat would be needed to raise 100 g of water by 2.0 K?

7. The enthalpy of combustion of ethanol in a data book is listed as -1368 kJ mol^{-1}. Calculate the experimental value for the combustion of ethanol from the data following and explain why it is smaller than the listed value. The mass of ethanol burned was 1.50 g, the mass of water heated was 500 g and the rise in temperature was 19.6°C; $c = 4.18$ Jg^{-1}K^{-1}.

8. What information can be deduced from knowing that an enthalpy change is negative?

A1.3 (c) Hess's Law and the First Law of Thermodynamics

Thermodynamics is the study of systems involving energy in the form of heat (chemistry) and work (physics). One useful way to view a chemical reaction is to think of it as rearranging atoms to make new substances (products) from starting materials (reactants). In this chapter we will look at changes in heat energy (enthalpy), which has the symbol H.

The First Law of Thermodynamics

There are three main laws of thermodynamics. The first law states that in any process (*e.g.* a chemical reaction), energy can be changed from one form to another, but it is neither created nor destroyed. So energy can never be made or lost. The First Law of Thermodynamics is sometimes known as the **Law of Conservation of Energy**. The law is based on experimental observations. Some substances, such as fuels, are highly prized because their energy can be released through combustion reactions. The energy released can do useful work, such as turning the wheels of a motor vehicle. Chemical energy is a form of **potential energy**.

When there is a change in heat content (enthalpy) in a chemical reaction, this is shown by a change in temperature which is measurable. Changes in temperature (ΔT), recorded during chemical reactions, provide evidence that a chemical change has happened. If the temperature rises, the reaction is described as **exothermic**. Most reactions are exothermic. If the temperature falls, the reaction is described as **endothermic**.

Before energy changes (ΔH) for different reactions can be compared, they must be measured using the same temperature (298K = 25°C), same pressure (100 kPa ≈ 1 atmosphere) and, where appropriate, the same concentration (1 mol dm^{-3}). These conditions are called **standard conditions** and when writing chemical equations for standard enthalpy changes, all substances need to be in their correct states for this temperature and pressure.

The enthalpy change (ΔH) in a reaction is the difference in enthalpy between the products (H_p) and reactants (H_r). ΔH refers only to the enthalpy change with respect to the reactants. It is a comparison of the final enthalpy compared with the starting point. This is important as the chemical potential is different for different reactants.

$$\text{Reactants} \rightarrow \text{Products}$$

$$\Delta H = H_p - H_r$$

For endothermic reactions $H_p > H_r$ and for exothermic reactions $H_p < H_r$.

Hess's Law

Hess's Law has also been known as the **law of constant heat summation**. Hess's Law states that, "the enthalpy change accompanying a chemical reaction is independent of the route (pathway) taken between the initial and final states". Hess's Law is a consequence of the first law of thermodynamics. Since energy cannot be created or destroyed, the energy change must be identical for two routes in a cyclic process. Hess's Law is particularly useful for calculating enthalpy changes ($\Delta_f H^\ominus$ and $\Delta_r H^\ominus$) that cannot be determined experimentally, e.g. the formation of a hydrocarbon.

Example 3.5

Route 1: One mole of hydrogen can be combusted in the presence of one mole of oxygen to produce one mole of water and leave half a mole of oxygen unreacted. The enthalpy change for this reaction is –286 kJ mol^{-1}.

Route 2: Is a two step reaction with the same initial and final states as Route 1. In the first step, one mole of hydrogen can react with one mole of oxygen to make one mole of hydrogen peroxide. The enthalpy change for this reaction is –188 kJmol^{-1}. The second step is the decomposition of hydrogen peroxide to produce one mole of water and half a mole of oxygen. The enthalpy change for this reaction is –98 kJmol^{-1} According to Hess's Law: enthalpy change of route 1 = enthalpy change of route 2.

$$H_2\,(g) + O_2\,(g) \xrightarrow{-286 \text{ kJ mol}^{-1}} H_2O\,(l) + \tfrac{1}{2}O_2\,(g)$$

–188 kJ mol^{-1} –98 kJ mol^{-1}

$$H_2O_2\,(l)$$

Route 1 = –286 kJmol^{-1} & route 2 = –188 kJmol^{-1} + –98 kJmol^{-1} = –286 kJmol^{-1}.

Example 3.6

What is the enthalpy of reaction $\Delta_r H^\ominus$ when one mole of ethyne reacts with hydrogen to form the saturated ethane?

$$C_2H_2\,(g) + 2H_2\,(g) \xrightarrow{\Delta_r H^\ominus ?} C_2H_6\,(g)$$

–176 kJ mol^{-1} –137 kJ mol^{-1}

$$C_2H_4\,(g)$$

According to Hess's Law, the enthalpy of this reaction will equal the sum of the stepwise hydrogenations *via* the intermediate ethene. Therefore, $\Delta_r H^\ominus = -176 + -137 = -313$ kJ mol^{-1}.

This works because the initial state (ethyne) and final state (ethane) are identical.

What happens when the route in a Hess cycle encounters an arrow in the wrong direction? It is a straightforward matter of reversing the sign of the enthalpy change in the calculation. This is obvious when it is realised that if a forward reaction is exothermic then the reverse reaction is endothermic, e.g.

$$C_2H_4\,(g) + HCl\,(g) \underset{+96.7 \text{ kJ mol}^{-1}}{\overset{-96.7 \text{ kJ mol}^{-1}}{\rightleftharpoons}} C_2H_5Cl\,(g)$$

To illustrate the idea that a reverse reaction has the negative ΔH value of the forward reaction and that it is simple algebra that is needed, the following four diagrams show all the possibilities that could be encountered with Route 1 being from A to B, and Route 2 being A to B *via* C.

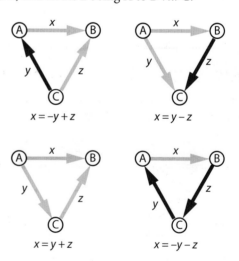

A useful thing to remember when doing these calculations is that the sum of the clockwise arrows = the sum of the anticlockwise arrows. This is true for the Hess triangles and also the Born-Haber cycles.

Example 3.7

Calculate the enthalpy of formation $\Delta_f H^\ominus$ of carbon monoxide using the following enthalpy data:

$$C\ (s) + O_2\ (g) \rightarrow CO_2\ (g) \qquad \Delta_f H^\ominus = -393\ kJ\ mol^{-1}$$

$$2\ CO\ (g) + O_2\ (g) \rightarrow 2\ CO_2\ (g) \qquad \Delta_r H^\ominus = -566 kJ\ mol^{-1}$$

Construct a triangle with the reaction to be calculated $\Delta_r H^\ominus$ across the top.

Make sure to balance the equations. Don't forget the $\Delta_f H^\ominus$ of elements = zero so they do not affect the calculation.

Solution:

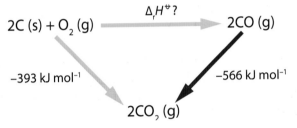

According to Hess's Law: route 1 = route 2.

Route 1 $(\Delta_r H^\ominus) = -393 \times 2 - -566 = -220\ kJ\ mol^{-1}$

$\Delta_f H^\ominus$ of carbon monoxide $= \dfrac{\Delta_r H^\ominus}{2}$ so that one mole of CO is formed.

$$= \frac{-220}{2} = -110\ kJ\ mol^{-1}$$

Questions 3.3

1. Calculate the enthalpy of reaction $\Delta_r H^\ominus$ for the isomerisation (A3.1 d) of methoxymethane into ethanol.

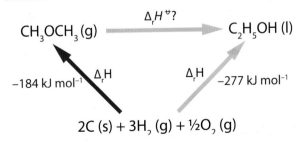

2. Calculate the enthalpy of reaction for:

$$NH_3\ (g) + HBr\ (g) \rightarrow NH_4Br\ (s)$$

from the enthalpies of formation; $\Delta_f H^\ominus$ (NH_3) = $-46\ kJ\ mol^{-1}$, $\Delta_f H^\ominus$ (HBr) = $-36\ kJ\ mol^{-1}$, $\Delta_f H^\ominus$ (NH_4Br) = $-271\ kJ\ mol^{-1}$.

3. Give the correct symbols for each of the enthalpy changes in the following diagram.

Calculate $\Delta_r H^\ominus$ for the reaction shown and calculate the mean bond dissociation energy. The form of carbon used is graphite.

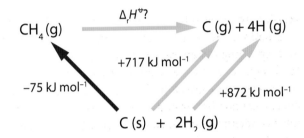

4. Calculate the enthalpy of reaction $\Delta_r H^\ominus$ for:

$$CO\ (g) + H_2\ (g) \rightarrow HCHO\ (g)$$

from the enthalpies of formation;

$$\Delta_f H^\ominus\ (CO) = -110.5\ kJ\ mol^{-1},$$

$$\Delta_f H^\ominus\ (HCHO) = -108.7\ kJ\ mol^{-1}.$$

5. What happens to the total energy for a highly exothermic reaction?

   A   Small decrease.

   B   Large decrease.

   C   Large increase.

   D   Stays the same.

6. What happens to the total energy for a slightly endothermic reaction?

   A   Small decrease.

   B   Stays the same.

   C   Small increase.

   D   Small increase.

7. What is the First Law of Thermodynamics?

A Energy is conserved in reactions.

B Energy is lost in reactions.

C Energy is gained in reactions.

D Entropy is conserved in reactions.

8. Which of the following cannot be used to calculate a reaction's enthalpy change ($\Delta_r H^\ominus$)?

A Hess's Law.

B Bond enthalpies.

C Bond entropies.

D Born-Haber cycle.

9. The H-F bond in hydrogen fluoride is 0.14 nm in length. Which graph gives the correct shape for the potential energy (P.E.) on the y-axis *versus* distance on the x-axis?

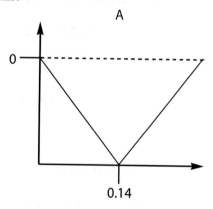

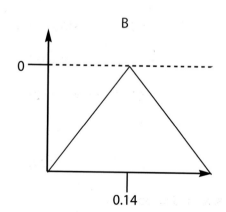

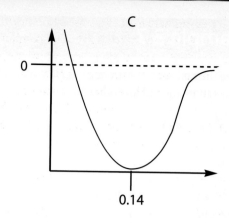

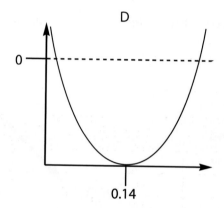

A1.3 (d) Calculating Enthalpy Changes 1

Bond energies

Each bond in a covalent molecule has a certain amount of energy that has to be put into the bond to break it (**endothermic**). An equal and opposite amount of energy is released when the bonds in the same covalent molecule are formed (**exothermic**).

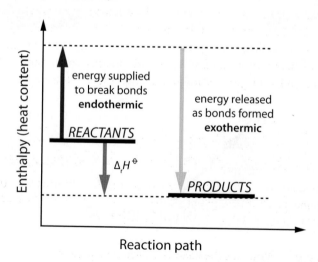

Bond energies (enthalpies) can be used to estimate enthalpies of formation $\Delta_f H^\ominus$, reaction $\Delta_r H^\ominus$ and combustion $\Delta_c H^\ominus$. Bond energies used in calculations are average gas phase values calculated from many different molecules containing a particular bond, e.g. C-H. Methane contains four C-H bonds which have very different energies and their average is close to the tabulated value for the C-H bond. Note how all the bond dissociation energies are endothermic.

$$CH_4 (g) \rightarrow CH_3 (g) + H (g) \qquad \Delta H^\ominus = +425 \text{ kJ mol}^{-1}$$

$$CH_3 (g) \rightarrow CH_2 (g) + H (g) \qquad \Delta H^\ominus = +480 \text{ kJ mol}^{-1}$$

$$CH_2 (g) \rightarrow CH (g) + H (g) \qquad \Delta H^\ominus = +425 \text{ kJ mol}^{-1}$$

$$CH (g) \rightarrow C (g) + H (g) \qquad \Delta H^\ominus = +335 \text{ kJ mol}^{-1}$$

Average = +416 kJ mol^{-1}

Bond	Energy / kJ mol^{-1}	Bond	Energy / kJ mol^{-1}
C–H	413	O–O	146
C–C	346	O=O	497
C=C	610	N–N	163
C≡C	835	N≡N	945
C–F	495	N–H	390
C–Cl	339	O–H	463
C–Br	280	H–F	565
C–I	230	H–Cl	431
F–F	158	H–Br	365
Cl–Cl	242	C–O	360
Br–Br	193	C=O	740
I–I	151	H–H	435

Bond energies can be determined by electron impact methods (A4.2a) and spectroscopic methods (A4.3). Bond energies decrease as electronegativity differences decrease (A1.2i) between the two bonded atoms. Bond energies increase as bond order (A1.2f) increases and bond lengths (A1.2f) decrease.

Example 3.8

Calculate the enthalpy of reaction for the chlorination of ethane, given the bond enthalpies (kJ mol^{-1}); C–H (413), C–C (346), Cl–Cl (242), C–Cl (339) & Cl–H (431).

Step 1:   Write out the balanced formula equation.

Step 2:   Draw the displayed formulae to make it easier to count bonds.

Step 3:   Calculate bonds broken in reactants (endothermic).

Step 4:   Calculate bonds formed in products (exothermic).

Step 5:   Calculate $\Delta_r H^\ominus$ (difference between the answers in steps 4 & 5).

Step 6:   The sign of the answer is the same as the largest numerically in steps 3 & 4.

Step 1: $C_2H_6 (g) + Cl_2 (g) \rightarrow C_2H_5Cl (g) + HCl (g)$

Step 2:

Step 3:

BENDO (breaking bonds is **endo**thermic)

$$1 \times C–C = 1 \times 346 = 346$$

$$6 \times C–H = 6 \times 413 = 2478$$

$$1 \times Cl\text{-}Cl = 1 \times 242 = 242$$

$$\text{-------}$$

$$+3066$$

Step 4:

MEX (making bonds is **ex**othermic)

$$5 \times C–H = 5 \times 413 = 2065$$

$$1 \times C–C = 1 \times 346 = 346$$

$$1 \times C–Cl = 1 \times 339 = 339$$

$$1 \times Cl–H = 1 \times 431 = 431$$

$$\text{-------}$$

$$-3181$$

Steps 5 & 6: –115 kJ mol^{-1}

Example 3.9

Calculate the enthalpy of reaction for the hydrogenation of ethyne to produce ethene, given the bond enthalpies (kJ mol⁻¹); C–H (413), C≡C (835), C=C (610) & H–H (435).

Step 1: C_2H_2 (g) + H_2 (g) → C_2H_4 (g)

Step 2:

H–C≡C–H + H–H ⟶

Step 3:

BENDO (breaking bonds in **endo**thermic)

$$2 \times C–H = 2 \times 413 = 826$$

$$1 \times C≡C = 1 \times 835 = 835$$

$$1 \times H–H = 1 \times 435 = 435$$

$$+2096$$

Step 4:

MEX (**m**aking bonds in **ex**othermic)

$$4 \times C–H = 4 \times 413 = 1652$$

$$1 \times C=C = 1 \times 610 = 610$$

$$-2262$$

Step 5 & 6 : –166 kJ mol⁻¹

Questions 3.4

1. Use the bond enthalpy data to calculate $\Delta_r H^\ominus$ for the hydrogenation of ethene; C=C (610), H–H (435), C–H (413) & C–C (346).

2. Use the bond enthalpy data to calculate $\Delta_r H^\ominus$ for the addition of hydrogen cyanide to propanone; C=O (740), C–H (413), C–O (360), C–C (346) & H–O (463).

3. Use the bond enthalpy data to calculate $\Delta_r H^\ominus$ for the oxidation of hydrogen; H–H (435), O=O (497) & H–O (463). What is the $\Delta_f H^\ominus$ for steam?

$$2 \ H_2 \ (g) + O_2 \ (g) → 2 \ H_2O \ (g)$$

4. Use the bond enthalpy data to calculate $\Delta_f H^\ominus$ for hydrogen chloride; H–H (435), Cl–Cl (242) & H–Cl (431).

5. Use the bond enthalpy data to calculate $\Delta_c H^\ominus$ for methane; C–H (413), O=O (497) & C=O (740) & H–O (463).

6. Use the bond enthalpy data to calculate $\Delta_c H^\ominus$ for ethyne; O=O (497), C–H (413) C≡C (835) & C=O (740) & H–O (463)

7. Explain why hydrazine (N_2H_4) has been used as a rocket fuel using the bond enthalpy data to calculate $\Delta_c H^\ominus$ for hydrazine N–H (390), N–N (163), O=O (497), N≡N (945), H–O (463).

$$N_2H_4 \ (g) + O_2 \ (g) → N_2 \ (g) + 2 \ H_2O \ (g)$$

8. Explain the small differences between theoretical and experimental values for $\Delta_r H^\ominus$.

9. A molecule of dinitrogen tetroxide decomposes to give two molecules of nitrogen dioxide. Give an equation for this reaction and explain why $\Delta_r H^\ominus$ = +57.2 kJ mol⁻¹.

A1.3 (e) Calculating lattice enthalpies

Lattice enthalpy ($\Delta_{latt} H^\ominus$) is the energy released when one mole of an ionic compound is formed from its gaseous ions. The lattice enthalpy for sodium chloride, like all $\Delta_{latt} H^\ominus$, is exothermic and can be shown by the equation:

$$Na^+ \ (g) + Cl^- \ (g) → NaCl \ (s) \qquad \Delta_{latt} H^\ominus = -755 \ kJ \ mol^{-1}$$

Lattice enthalpies cannot be measured directly but can be calculated from **Born-Haber cycles**. Born-Haber cycles are essentially Hess's Law (A1.3c) applied to enthalpy changes for the formation of ionic compounds. Route 1 makes the ionic compound directly from it elements ($\Delta_f H$).

Route 1:

$$Na\ (s) + \tfrac{1}{2}Cl_2\ (g) \rightarrow NaCl\ (s) \qquad \Delta_f H^\ominus = -411\ \text{kJ mol}^{-1}$$

The overall energy for route 2 = route 1. Route 2 atomises and ionises each element in turn and then brings the ions together to make the ionic solid. The new enthalpy changes not met before (A1.3a) are **electron affinity** ($\Delta_{EA} H^\ominus$) and **ionisation energy** ($\Delta_i H^\ominus$). **First electron affinity** ($\Delta_{EA1} H^\ominus$) is the enthalpy released when one mole of gaseous atoms all gain an electron to form one mole of gaseous anions with a one minus (1−) charge. All $\Delta_{EA1} H^\ominus$ are exothermic, but second electron affinities and beyond are endothermic, due to repulsion when adding a negative electron to an already negatively charged species. **First ionisation energy** ($\Delta_{i1} H^\ominus$) is the energy required to remove a mole of electrons from a mole of gaseous element.

Route 2:

$$Na\ (s) \rightarrow Na\ (g) \qquad \Delta_{atm} H^\ominus = +109\ \text{kJ mol}^{-1}$$

$$Na\ (g) \rightarrow Na^+\ (g) + e^- \qquad \Delta_{i1} H^\ominus = +494\ \text{kJ mol}^{-1}$$

$$\tfrac{1}{2}Cl_2\ (g) \rightarrow Cl\ (g) \qquad \Delta_{atm} H^\ominus = +121\ \text{kJ mol}^{-1}$$

$$Cl\ (g) + e^- \rightarrow Cl^-\ (g) \qquad \Delta_{EA1} H^\ominus = -380\ \text{kJ mol}^{-1}$$

$$Na^+\ (g) + Cl^-\ (g) \rightarrow NaCl\ (s) \qquad \Delta_{latt} H^\ominus = -755\ \text{kJ mol}^{-1}$$

Born-Haber cycles are often shown as energy level diagrams (not drawn to scale), with endothermic processes shown as upwards arrows and exothermic processes shown as downward arrows.

In the Born-Haber cycle for sodium chloride:

Route 1 = Route 2 (from Hess's Law).

$$\Delta_f H^\ominus = \Delta_{atm} H^\ominus\ (Na) + \Delta_{atm} H^\ominus\ (Cl) + \Delta_{i1} H^\ominus\ (Na) + \Delta_{EA1} H^\ominus\ (Cl) + \Delta_{latt} H^\ominus\ (NaCl).$$

If all but one of the values is given, it is straightforward to calculate the unknown enthalpy change.

The lattice enthalpy for magnesium oxide (MgO) is −3791 kJ mol^{-1}. This large $\Delta_{latt} H^\ominus$ (MgO) is a measure of the ionic bond strength, which is much stronger in MgO than in NaCl. This is one reason magnesium oxide has found use as a heatproof (refractory) lining in furnaces. When drawing the Born-Haber cycle for magnesium oxide, remember the second ionisation energy for magnesium and the second electron affinity for oxygen.

$$Mg\ (g) \rightarrow Mg^+\ (g) + e^- \qquad \Delta_{i1} H^\ominus\ (Mg)$$

$$Mg^+\ (g) \rightarrow Mg^{2+}\ (g) + e^- \qquad \Delta_{i2} H^\ominus\ (Mg)$$

$$O\ (g) + e^- \rightarrow O^-\ (g) \qquad \Delta_{EA1} H^\ominus\ (O) \qquad \textit{exothermic}$$

$$O^-\ (g) + e^- \rightarrow O^{2-}\ (g) \qquad \Delta_{EA2} H^\ominus\ (O) \qquad \textit{endothermic}$$

Born-Haber cycle for magnesium oxide

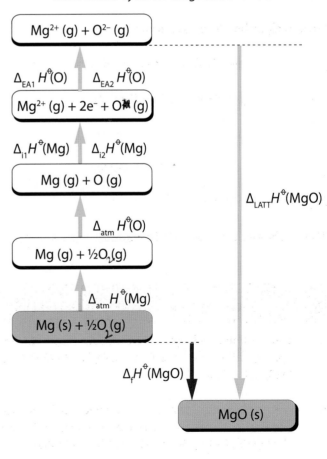

Born-Haber cycle for sodium chloride

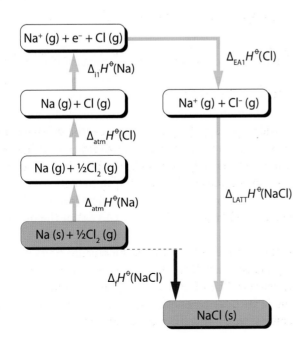

Size of lattice enthalpies

Two factors affect the size of $\Delta_{latt}H^{\ominus}$; the charges on the ions and the radii of the ions. Smaller ions can approach more closely and this leads to a stronger force of attraction between the ions. Consequently, NaCl has a larger $\Delta_{latt}H^{\ominus}$ than KCl and NaF has a larger $\Delta_{latt}H^{\ominus}$ than NaCl. A generality is that lattice enthalpy is proportional to the product of ion charges / sum of ionic radii.

$$\Delta_{latt}H^{\ominus} \; \alpha \; \frac{\text{cation charge} \times \text{anion charge}}{\text{cation radius} + \text{anion radius}}$$

Questions 3.5

1. Explain which of the Group II oxides will have the largest lattice enthalpy.

2. Explain which will have the largest lattice enthalpy; sodium chloride or magnesium oxide. [Ionic radii: Na⁺ 0.102 nm, Mg²⁺ 0.072 nm, Cl 0.180 nm, O²⁻ 0.140 nm].

3. Give equations for the following changes. Using Hess's Law, how do all the energy changes relate to each other?

    I = First ionisation energy of sodium.

    II = Atomisation enthalpy of fluorine.

    III = Lattice enthalpy of sodium fluoride.

    IV = Enthalpy of formation of sodium fluoride.

    V = First electron affinity of fluorine.

    VI = Atomisation enthalpy of sodium.

4. Calculate the lattice enthalpy for calcium oxide, given the following enthalpy values:

    $\Delta_{atm}H^{\ominus}$ (Ca) +177 kJ mol⁻¹, $\Delta_{i1}H^{\ominus}$ (Ca) +590 kJ mol⁻¹, $\Delta_{i2}H^{\ominus}$ (Ca) +1100 kJ mol⁻¹, $\Delta_{atm}H^{\ominus}$ (O) = +249 kJ mol⁻¹, $\Delta_{f}H^{\ominus}$ (CaO) = −636 kJ mol⁻¹, $\Delta_{EA1}H^{\ominus}$ (O) = −141 kJ mol⁻¹ & $\Delta_{EA2}H^{\ominus}$ (O) = +790 kJ mol⁻¹.

5. The Born-Haber cycle for potassium chloride is shown. Give the names of the standard enthalpy changes represented by the letters **A**-**F**.

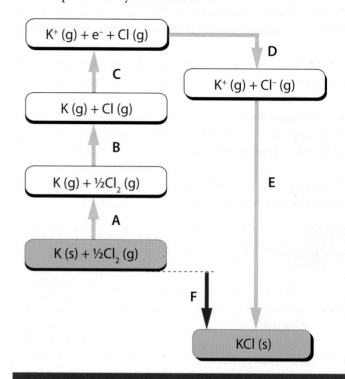

A1.3 (f)
Understanding catalysts

The world market for **catalysts** is very lucrative and is in excess of $US10 billion per annum. Without the use of catalysts many industrial processes would be uneconomic due to the increased energy costs. More importantly, life processes without biological catalysts (enzymes) would be impossible. Catalysts are of interest to chemists because they increase the rate of reaction (B1.6) without a permanent change to the catalyst.

Catalysts speed up reactions because they provide an alternative reaction route (path) which has significantly lower activation energy (E_a). Activation energy may be defined as the minimum energy (barrier) that reactants must overcome in order to react. Activation energy is the difference in energy between the reactants and the activated complex as shown in energy profile diagrams (A1.3g) and like other energy changes it has the units kJ mol⁻¹. When catalysts are used to speed up reactions, there is no change in the **yield** (proportion of product formed) or the **atom economy** (A3.6a) or the **position of an equilibrium** (B1.5a). A catalyst may be thought of as lowering the bar for the height required for qualification in the Olympic high jump final.

There are three types of catalyst: homogeneous, heterogeneous and enzymes (which are in the same phase as the reactants).

Homogeneous catalysts: Catalysts and reactants are all in the same phase (*e.g.* solution).

Heterogeneous catalysts: Catalysts and reactants are in different phases, usually solid catalyst with gaseous reactants.

Enzymes are biological catalysts. They are proteins which operate at their optimum pH (B1.5f) and temperature.

All types of catalysts achieve a greater rate of reaction by increasing the frequency of successful atomic/molecular collisions leading to reaction.

There are plenty of good examples of heterogeneous catalysts, some of which should be familiar.

Heterogeneous catalyst	Type of reaction	Example / Process
Ni	Hydrogenation	Alkene → alkane (margarine)
Fe	Reduction	Haber Process (making NH_3)
Pt	Oxidation	Ostwald Process (NH_3 → NO)
MnO_2	Decomposition	H_2O_2 → H_2O + $\frac{1}{2}O_2$
Pt	Oxidation	Catalytic converter
V_2O_5	Oxidation	Contact Process (SO_2 → SO_3)
Al_2O_3	Dehydration	Ethanol → ethene
$Al(C_2H_5)_3$/$TiCl_4$ *Ziegler-Natta* catalysts	Polymerisation	Stereoregular polymers

Sulfuric acid is the homogeneous catalyst of choice when making esters (A3.1g) from carboxylic acids and alcohols. It is important to realise it also catalyses the reverse reaction (**acid hydrolysis**).

CH_3COOH (aq) + CH_3OH (aq)
   acid   *alcohol*

$$\xrightarrow{\text{H}^+ \text{(aq)}} CH_3COOCH_3 \text{ (aq)} + H_2O \text{ (l)}$$
                    ester   *water*

Catalysts lower activation energies

The decomposition of 2 mol dm^{-3} hydrogen peroxide (A2.2f) can be affected by a number of catalysts: manganese(IV) oxide (MnO_2), zinc oxide (ZnO), copper(I) oxide (Cu_2O), platinum (Pt) and the enzyme catalase.

$$H_2O_2 \rightarrow H_2O + \frac{1}{2}O_2$$

For the uncatalysed reaction $E_a = 75$ kJ mol^{-1}. For the catalysed reaction with platinum $E_a = 50$ kJ mol^{-1} and with catalase $E_a = 21$ kJ mol^{-1}. **Catalase**, like other enzymes, is highly efficient and shape specific. It prevents the accumulation of harmful peroxide in the blood stream. Activation energies can be found experimentally using the **Arrhenius equation** (B1.6d).

Catalysts provide alternative pathways

Evidence for the **intermediate compound theory** for catalysis is supported by the isolation of intermediates in reactions. Direct combination of chlorine (Cl_2) with nitrogen monoxide (NO) produces the yellow gas, nitrosyl chloride (NOCl).

$$2\text{ NO (g)} + Cl_2 \text{ (g)} \rightarrow 2\text{ NOCl (g)}$$

Joke: When chemists say NO they generally mean nitrogen monoxide

The reaction has been found to go much faster in the presence of bromine. One possible explanation for bromine's role as a catalyst is given in the following equations. The overall equation is the same as the uncatalysed reaction and the catalyst is regenerated.

$$2NO + Br_2 \rightarrow 2\text{ NOBr}$$

$$2\text{ NOBr} + Cl_2 \rightarrow 2\text{ NOCl} + Br_2$$

Surface of catalysts

Transition metals (B2.4) are very good catalysts because they have electrons in d- and s- subshells which can be utilised in bonding. Bonds form between reactant molecules and the atoms at the surface of the catalyst and this process of **chemisorption** is often described as **adsorption**. This 'sticking' to the surface of the catalyst serves to increase the concentration of reactants and to the lowering of the activation energy by weakening the covalent bonds. The catalytic hydrogenation of ethene with a nickel catalyst at 400K will illustrate the processes involved in the catalysis. The equation for the reaction is:

$$H_2C{=}CH_2 + H_2 \rightarrow CH_3{-}CH_3$$

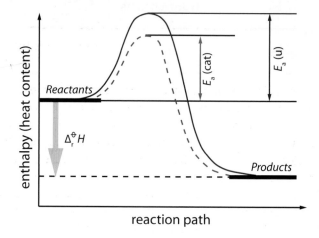

The sequence of events is: diffusion of reactants to the surface of the catalyst, adsorption, bond weakening in reactants, reaction to form products, desorption and diffusion away of product. This leaves the catalyst chemically unchanged at the end of the reaction.

Questions 3.6

1. The enthalpy change associated with a particular chemical reaction:

   A   depends on whether the change is exothermic.

   B   depends on the time for the reaction to go to completion.

   C   depends on the atom economy.

   D   is independent of the number of changes involved in the reaction.

2. A reaction may be described as exothermic when:

   A   there is no enthalpy change.

   B   enthalpy of reactants > enthalpy of products.

   C   enthalpy of products > enthalpy of reactants.

   D   heat is taken into the system.

3. A chemist was investigating the effect of adding a small amount of manganese(IV) oxide on the decomposition of potassium chlorate ($KClO_3$) which was heated to just below its decomposition temperature (673K). As a precaution the flask was quickly plunged into iced water on adding the powdered MnO_2. The evolved gas was collected at a fast rate. The gas was greenish in appearance but still ignited a glowing splint. A purple colour was noticed in the reaction mixture which disappeared once the reaction had finished. Suggest equations to explain the observed colour changes and explain the role of MnO_2 in the reaction.

A1.3 (g)
Enthalpy profile diagrams

Enthalpy changes for chemical changes (reactions) are often shown as **enthalpy profile diagrams**. Enthalpy is plotted on the y-axis and the reaction path(way) on the x-axis. When drawing these diagrams you need to be able to label: reactants, products, activation energies and enthalpies of reaction. The enthalpy of reaction $\Delta_r H^{\ominus}$ is the difference between the enthalpy of the reactants (left side of x-axis) and products (right side of x-axis). Activation energy is the 'hump' in the energy profile diagram. The activation energy for the uncatalysed reaction $E_a(u)$ is larger than the activation energy for the catalysed reaction $E_a(cat)$. Activation energy can be calculated experimentally using the **Arrhenius equation** (B1.6d). Catalysts speed up reactions because they provide an alternative route for the reaction with lower activation energy.

In reversible reactions (B1.5), a catalyst will reduce the activation energies of both the forward and the reverse reactions.

A1.3 (h)
Boltzmann distribution

In any mixture of molecules there will be a large spread of energies. This spread of energies can be illustrated graphically using a **Boltzmann distribution**. On the y-axis is the number of molecules (particles) and on the x-axis is the (kinetic) energy. For molecules with the same mass, their kinetic energy ($\frac{1}{2}mv^2$) is only dependent on the speed of the particles. The Boltzmann distribution shows that there are very few molecules with low energy and also very few molecules with high energy values. Most of the particles, however, will be moving at a speed close to the average (mean). Note also, the shape of the Boltzmann distribution, which is asymmetric (not symmetrical) and which is not to be confused with a normal distribution curve. In a Boltzmann distribution, the area under the curve is equal to the total number of molecules.

There are no particles with zero energy as it is not possible to reach a temperature of absolute zero. Also, note how the tail of the curve never quite reaches zero on the x-axis. Temperature increases the average energy of the molecules and results in a Boltzmann distribution shifting to the right with a lower maximum. We are concerned here with how a catalyst affects a Boltzmann distribution.

Boltzmann distribution

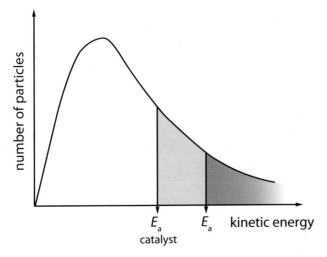

For a collision to lead to a reaction, the particles need a minimum amount of energy called the **activation energy** (E_a). For the uncatalysed reactions, particles in the blue shaded area can react as they have energies equal to or exceeding the activation energy. The activation energy is lowered when a catalyst is used and additional particles (yellow shaded area) will have sufficient energy to react. If a particle is not in a shaded area then it will have insufficient kinetic energy and its collision will not have enough energy to break bonds.

Question 3.7

1.   Glycerine (propane-1,2,3-triol) has been found to inhibit the decomposition of hydrogen peroxide. What effect does glycerine have on the activation energy for the following reaction?

$$H_2O_2 \text{ (l)} \rightarrow H_2O \text{ (l)} + \tfrac{1}{2}O_2 \text{ (g)}$$

A   Lowers the activation energy.

B   Raises the activation energy.

C   Lowers and then raises the activation energy.

D   No effect on the activation energy.

4 Free Energy and Entropy

Contents

The concept of energy, which is fundamental to our understanding of the physical world, was developed by Nicolas Carnot in the nineteenth century in his work on the **Carnot Heat Engine**. Energy is one of the ten big ideas of science which is covered admirably in Peter Atkins' book *Galileo's Finger*. Also in this book is the concept of entropy. This was unravelled by some of the great historical figures of science such as Paul Clapeyron, Rudolf Clausius and Ludwig Boltzmann. The word entropy comes from the Greek words *en* meaning 'in' and *trope* meaning 'change'. **Entropy** is a measure of the randomness or disorder of the system.

The **First Law of Thermodynamics** (A1.3c) and the **Second Law of Thermodynamics** (B1.4e) were written and sung about in the 1960s by Michael Flanders and Donald Swann, both of whom attended Westminster School.

[CON BRIO]
> ... heat can't pass from the cooler to the hotter,
> you can try it if you like but you'd far better notter ...

More recently the word entropy was included by the popular Scottish band *Travis* in their song *Colder*.

B1.4 (a) What is entropy?

Entropy has the symbol S. Entropy is a property of matter and its units are J K^{-1} mol^{-1}. In calculations it is important to keep units consistent. When using entropy in a calculation with enthalpy (kJ mol^{-1}), the entropy value is divided by 1000 to convert it to kJ mol^{-1} K^{-1}. Entropy is associated with randomness and order. An entrée into entropy is by considering the three states of matter. The solid is the state where there is most order and this is revealed to us beautifully in those solids that crystallize (B2.5). A substance will have lower entropy when it is in the solid state. A perfect crystal at the (impossible to reach) absolute zero (0 Kelvin) has an entropy value of zero J K^{-1} mol^{-1}. A liquid has more entropy than a solid as its particles are more randomly arranged. They can and do slide past each other, which are why liquids take the shape of their containers. Of the three states of matter, a substance will have its highest entropy when it is a gas since its molecules are in rapid and random motion. Since entropy is clearly temperature dependent, values are given for 298 K (standard conditions).

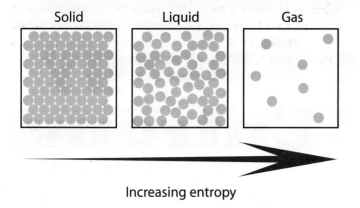

Increasing entropy

Entropy can be thought of as the degree of randomness of the dispersal of molecules in space. For our purposes we can consider a closed container to be the space of the reaction. This is often called 'the **system**'. In the same way that particles of a gas are randomly arranged in a container, so is the kinetic energy of each particle. The random dispersal of quanta of energy amongst the molecules can be shown graphically by the Boltzmann distribution (B1.6c).

Reactions can lead to an increase in entropy, *i.e.* $\Delta S > 0$ (positive) or a decrease in entropy, *i.e.* $\Delta S < 0$ (negative). When there is an increase in entropy there is more disorder in the products than the reactants. This can be determined qualitatively by looking at the reaction stoichiometry and the state symbols of both reactants and products.

The Second Law of Thermodynamics states that all spontaneous processes increase the entropy of the universe until they reach equilibrium. The physical process of crystallisation illustrates this. If a hot, concentrated solution of a salt (cupric sulfate is often used) is prepared and allowed to cool, it becomes 'super-saturated'. If the solution is then 'seeded' by introducing a small crystal of the salt, the seed crystal will grow quite rapidly. It appears that an ordered solid has spontaneously grown from a disordered liquid and that the entropy of the system has decreased. However, the solution gets hot again as the lattice forms, the molecules and ions in the solution move more rapidly and their entropy increases. Thus, the total entropy of the system (and the universe) is increased.

A more prosaic example is the *Adolescent Bedroom Effect*. As everyone knows, the rooms of some young people become spontaneously more messy as time passes. Their entropy increases. Then, when everybody has had enough, the system is sealed and large amounts of energy (which increases entropy again) are expended to restore order.

The Second Law of Thermodynamics is considered in more detail later in this chapter in section B1.4(e). However, it will help you understand what follows if you bear in mind that entropy has a natural tendency to increase.

Examples where $\Delta S > 0$

Decomposition of copper(II) nitrate gives a positive entropy change ($\Delta S > 0$) because 2 moles of an ordered ionic lattice are decomposed to form 2 moles of another ionic solid and 5 moles of gas:

$$2\,Cu(NO_3)_2\,(s) \rightarrow 2\,CuO\,(s) + 4\,NO_2\,(g) + O_2\,(g)$$

This process has a favourable entropy change.

In the stratosphere the allotrope of oxygen called ozone (A2.2e), is being formed from diatomic oxygen and the reverse reaction is also happening. There is a positive entropy change ($\Delta S > 0$) when 2 moles of ozone are converted into 3 moles of oxygen:

$$2\,O_3\,(g) \rightleftharpoons 3\,O_2\,(g)$$

Examples where $\Delta S < 0$

The formation of lithium chloride by reaction of its constituent elements gives a negative entropy change ($\Delta S < 0$). This is because an ordered ionic lattice is formed by reaction of a metallic lattice with a diatomic gas:

$$2\,Li\,(s) + Cl_2\,(g) \rightarrow 2\,LiCl\,(s).$$

This unfavourable entropy change is more than compensated for by the highly exothermic formation enthalpy (A1.3a).

The complete combustion of pentane in the presence of excess oxygen gives a negative entropy change ($\Delta S < 0$) since only 5 moles of gas are formed from 8 moles of gas:

$$C_5H_{12}\,(l) + 8\,O_2\,(g) \rightarrow 5\,CO_2\,(g) + 6\,H_2O\,(l)$$

This unfavourable entropy change is more than compensated for by the energy released in the formation of C=O bonds in carbon dioxide and O–H bonds in water (A1.3d).

Looking at the entropy values of water, the lowest value is for ice and the highest value is for steam. The increase in entropy is going from solid to liquid and then to gas is because the water molecules become more randomly dispersed. The entropy value for water as a liquid is fairly low because of the order that hydrogen bonding brings to this phase.

Entropy values for water in its three states

Compound	State	S (J K⁻¹ mol⁻¹)
Water	(s)	45.0
Water	(l)	69.9
Water	(g)	188.8

The entropy of a liquid is generally greater than the entropy of a solid. One interesting exception to this rule is the entropy of solid iodine ($116.8 \text{ J K}^{-1} \text{ mol}^{-1}$) which is higher than the value for liquid water ($69.9 \text{ J K}^{-1} \text{ mol}^{-1}$) at room temperature. Liquid water forms a network of hydrogen bonds (A1.2k) so there is order in the liquid state and hence a lower entropy than found in solid iodine. This is another example of an anomalous property of water due to its intermolecular hydrogen bonding.

Allotropes will also have different entropy values as their atoms are arranged differently. The two main allotropes of carbon (B2.3a) graphite and diamond have entropy values of $5.7 \text{ J K}^{-1} \text{ mol}^{-1}$ and $2.4 \text{ J K}^{-1} \text{ mol}^{-1}$ respectively. Diamond is denser than graphite because its atoms are closer together in the tetrahedral arrangement, so it should come as no surprise that it has a lower entropy value than that reported for graphite. At university, the standard molar entropy of a substance is calculated from its heat capacity.

Entropy values for some elements (298 K)

Element	State	S (J K⁻¹ mol⁻¹)
Iron	(s)	27.3
Copper	(s)	33.2
Mercury	(l)	76.0
Oxygen	(g)	102.5*
Argon	(g)	154.7

*Per mole of atoms.

When an element can form more than one compound with another element the more complex product has the higher entropy. Carbon dioxide has a slightly higher entropy value than carbon monoxide. The lower entropy value for silicon(IV) oxide (B2.3d) compared to lead(II) oxide is due to its highly ordered 'diamond' like structure.

Entropy values for some compounds (298 K)

Compound	State	S (J K⁻¹ mol⁻¹)
Carbon monoxide	(g)	197.6
Carbon dioxide	(g)	213.6
Silicon(IV) oxide	(s)	41.8
Sodium chloride	(s)	72.1
Calcium fluoride	(s)	68.9

When given entropy values for reactants and products, it is straightforward to work out the entropy change for the reaction (ΔS_{system}) by taking the sum of the entropies of the reactants from the sum of the entropies of the products (A1.3c).

Questions 4.1

1. Which option shows the correct units of entropy?

   A kJ mol^{-1}

   B J K mol^{-1}

   C J mol^{-1}

   D $\text{J K}^{-1} \text{mol}^{-1}$

2. Which option shows the correct order of magnitude for the entropy of water in its three states?

   A (s) < (l) > (g)

   B (g) > (l) > (s)

   C (s) > (l) > (g)

   D (g) < (l) < (s)

3. Write balanced symbol equations for the formation of sodium chloride and water from their constituent elements and explain why there is a change in entropy.

4. Plot a graph of entropy (y–axis) versus temperature (x–axis) to show how entropy varies with temperature. Show how the melting point and boiling point might be identified.

B1.4 (b)
Total entropy change (ΔS_{total})

The total entropy change (ΔS_{total}) is the sum of the entropy change of the system (ΔS_{system}) and the entropy change of the surroundings ($\Delta S_{surroundings}$). The entropy change of the system (ΔS_{system}) is of course referring to the entropy change of the reaction that is being investigated. The total entropy change (ΔS_{total}) is the entropy change of the universe. The entropy change of the surroundings ($\Delta S_{surroundings}$) is the entropy change of everything except the reaction.

$$\Delta S_{total} = \Delta S_{system} + \Delta S_{surroundings}$$

In an exothermic process the heat energy given out increases the entropy of the surroundings. This is because the additional heat energy will lead to surrounding molecules moving faster and more randomly as this additional heat lost from a system (reaction) is absorbed. The opposite is true for endothermic reactions which absorb heat energy from the surroundings.

Type of process	$\Delta S_{surroundings}$
exothermic	increases
endothermic	decreases

A classic experiment to show visually the relative rates of diffusion of gases is placing cotton wool soaked in concentrated ammonia at one end of a diffusion tube and cotton wool soaked in concentrated hydrochloric acid at the other end of a diffusion tube. About 15 minutes after the start of the experiment, a white ring of ammonium chloride is visible in the diffusion tube. Since ammonia diffuses faster than hydrogen chloride, the white ring of ammonium chloride forms closest to the concentrated hydrochloric acid end.

Diffusion tube

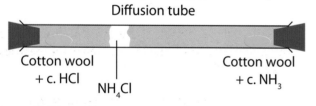

Cotton wool + c. HCl NH_4Cl Cotton wool + c. NH_3

The balanced formula equation for this reaction is:

$$NH_3\,(g) + HCl\,(g) \rightarrow NH_4Cl\,(s)$$

There is a decrease in the entropy of the system (ΔS_{system}) as one mole of ionic solid is made from two moles of gas in this acid–base reaction. The entropy of the surroundings ($\Delta S_{surroundings}$) will increase as this reaction is exothermic. For a reaction to be feasible, the total entropy change (ΔS_{total}) has to increase, therefore $\Delta S_{surroundings} > \Delta S_{system}$ for the reaction between ammonia and hydrogen chloride.

Questions 4.2

1. Find the total entropy change (ΔS_{total}) when the entropy change of the system (ΔS_{system}) is +336 J K^{-1} mol^{-1} and the entropy change of the surroundings ($\Delta S_{surroundings}$) was calculated as –302 J K^{-1} mol^{-1}.

2. What is the entropy change of the system (ΔS_{system}) when the total entropy change (ΔS_{total}) is +86 J K^{-1} mol^{-1} and the entropy change of the surroundings ($\Delta S_{surroundings}$) is –96 J K^{-1} mol^{-1}?

3. Which option shows a total entropy change (ΔS_{total}) which is not feasible for a highly exothermic reaction?

   A   +2 J K^{-1} mol^{-1}

   B   +200 J K^{-1} mol^{-1}

   C   –200 J K^{-1} mol^{-1}

   D   +20 J K^{-1} mol^{-1}

B1.4 (c) Calculating ΔS

Given the standard entropies of reactants ($S_{reactants}$) and the standard entropies of products ($S_{products}$) it is possible to calculate the entropy change for a given reaction (ΔS_{system}). When doing these calculations to find the entropy change of the system (reaction), it is the difference between the sum of the entropies for the products minus the sum of the entropies for the reactants. When writing the values of ΔS, also include the sign, even if it is positive, *e.g.* + 122 J K^{-1} mol^{-1}. In calculations, it is important to account for the stoichiometry as it was in enthalpy change calculations (A1.3c).

$$\Delta S_{system} = S_{products} - S_{reactants}$$

$$\Delta S_{reaction} = S_{products} - S_{reactants}$$

Since $\Delta S_{system} = \Delta S_{reaction}$

Example 4.1

Calculate ΔS_{system} for the following reaction:

$$2\,NO_2\,(g) \rightarrow 2\,NO\,(g) + O_2\,(g)$$

Solution:

	$2\,NO_2\,(g)$	$\rightarrow$	$2\,NO\,(g)$	$+$	$O_2\,(g)$
$S\,(J\,K^{-1}\,mol^{-1})$	240		211		205
Stoichiometry accounted for	480		422		205

$\Delta S_{system} = S_{products} - S_{reactants}$

$\Delta S_{system} = (422 + 205) - 480$

$\qquad = +147\,J\,K^{-1}\,mol^{-1}$

Example 4.2

Calculate ΔS_{system} for the following reaction.

$$2\,NO_2\,(g) \rightarrow N_2\,(g) + 2\,O_2\,(g)$$

Solution:

	$2\,NO_2\,(g)$	$\rightarrow$	$N_2\,(g)$	$+$	$2\,O_2\,(g)$
$S\,(J\,K^{-1}\,mol^{-1})$	240		192		205
Stoichiometry accounted for	480		192		410

$\Delta S_{system} = S_{products} - S_{reactants}$

$\Delta S_{system} = (192 + 410) - 480$

$\qquad = +122\,J\,K^{-1}\,mol^{-1}$

Questions 4.3

1. Calculate ΔS_{system} for the following reaction (S values given in $J\,K^{-1}\,mol^{-1}$).

   $$2\,NaHCO_3\,(s) \rightarrow Na_2CO_3\,(s) + CO_2\,(g) + H_2O\,(l)$$
   $S:\quad 101.7 \qquad\quad 135.0 \qquad 213.6 \qquad 69.9$

2. Calculate ΔS_{system} for the following reaction (S values given in $J\,K^{-1}\,mol^{-1}$).

   $$H_2O_2\,(l) \rightarrow H_2O\,(l) + \tfrac{1}{2}O_2\,(g)$$
   $S:\quad 109.6 \qquad 69.9 \qquad 205$

3. Calculate the entropy for ammonia ($J\,K^{-1}\,mol^{-1}$) from the following data.

   $$N_2\,(g) + 3\,H_2\,(g) \rightleftharpoons 2\,NH_3\,(g)$$
   $S:\quad 191.6 \qquad 130.6$

   $\Delta S_{system} = -198.8\,J\,K^{-1}\,mol^{-1}$

4. Use the following data to calculate the entropy ($J\,K^{-1}\,mol^{-1}$) for calcium carbonate:

   $$CaCO_3\,(s) \rightarrow CaO\,(s) + CO_2\,(g)$$
   $\qquad\qquad\qquad\quad 39.7 \qquad 213.6$

   $\Delta S_{system} = +160\,J\,K^{-1}\,mol^{-1}$

5. Calculate the entropy change for the formation of strontium hydroxide from the reaction of the metal and water at 298K.

   $$Sr\,(s) + 2\,H_2O\,(l) \rightarrow Sr(OH)_2\,(aq) + H_2\,(g)$$
   $S:\quad 52.3 \qquad 69.9 \qquad\quad 88.0 \qquad\quad 130.6$

6. Calculate the entropy change for the formation of copper(II) oxide from its elements (S values given in $J\,K^{-1}\,mol^{-1}$).

   $$Cu\,(s) + \tfrac{1}{2}O_2\,(g) \rightarrow CuO\,(s)$$
   $S:\quad 33.2 \qquad 205 \qquad\quad 42.6$

B1.4 (d) Entropy change of the surroundings

So far we have met the following equations involving entropy changes:

$$\Delta S_{system} = S_{products} - S_{reactants} \text{ and } \Delta S_{total} = \Delta S_{system} + \Delta S_{surroundings}$$

It is possible to experimentally determine the entropy change of the surroundings.

The entropy change of the surroundings is given as:

$$\Delta S_{surroundings} = -\frac{\Delta_r H}{T}$$

where T = temperature (K) and $\Delta_r H$ is the enthalpy change of reaction (A1.3a).

If temperature is given in degrees celsius (°C) it is a simple matter of adding 273 to the temperature in °C to convert into kelvin, *i.e.* °C + 273 = K.

Example 4.3

Calculate the entropy change of the surroundings ($\Delta S_{surroundings}$) when copper is reacted with oxygen to form cupric oxide.

$2\,Cu\,(s) + O_2\,(g) \rightarrow 2\,CuO\,(s)$ where $\Delta_r H = -157.3$ kJ mol^{-1} at 298K.

To ensure the units are consistent $\Delta_r H$ needs to be converted into J mol^{-1} by multiplying the given $\Delta_r H$ value by 1000. For the reaction $\Delta_r H = -157300$ J mol^{-1}.

$$\Delta S_{surroundings} = -\frac{\Delta_r H}{T}$$

$$= -\frac{-157300}{298}$$

$$= +527.9 \text{ J K}^{-1} \text{ mol}^{-1}.$$

Example 4.4

Calculate the entropy change of the surroundings ($\Delta S_{surroundings}$) when magnesium is reacted with oxygen to form magnesium oxide.

$2\,Mg\,(s) + O_2\,(g) \rightarrow 2\,MgO\,(s)$ where $\Delta_r H = -1203$ kJ mol^{-1} at 25°C.

To ensure the units are consistent $\Delta_r H$ needs to be converted into J mol^{-1} by multiplying the given $\Delta_r H$ value by 1000. For the reaction $\Delta_r H = -1203000$ J mol^{-1}. To calculate the temperature in Kelvin = 25°C + 273 = 298 K.

$$\Delta S_{surroundings} = -\frac{\Delta_r H}{T}$$

$$= -\frac{-1203000}{298}$$

$$= +4036.9 \text{ J K}^{-1} \text{ mol}^{-1}.$$

Questions 4.4

1. Explain why $\Delta S_{surroundings}$ always has a positive value for exothermic reactions.

2. Calculate the entropy change of the surroundings ($\Delta S_{surroundings}$) for the hydrogenation of benzene at 333 K.

   $C_6H_6\,(l) + 3H_2\,(g) \rightarrow C_6H_{12}\,(l)$

   where $\Delta_r H = -214$ kJ mol^{-1} at 333 K.

3. Calculate the entropy change of the surroundings ($\Delta S_{surroundings}$) for the reduction of zinc oxide by carbon monoxide at 1000 K. Could this reaction be carried out in the laboratory?

   $ZnO\,(s) + CO\,(g) \rightarrow Zn\,(s) + CO_2\,(g)$

   where $\Delta_r H = +66$ kJ mol^{-1} at 1000 K

4. Calculate the entropy change of the surroundings ($\Delta S_{surroundings}$) for the decomposition of calcium carbonate at;

   a. 298K,

   b. 832°C

   c. 1400K.

What information can be gained from these calculations knowing that the decomposition temperature is 832°C?

$$CaCO_3 \text{ (s)} \rightarrow CaO \text{ (s)} + CO_2 \text{ (g)}$$

$$\Delta_r H = +178 \text{ kJ mol}^{-1} \, \Delta S_{system} = +160.4 \text{ J K}^{-1} \text{ mol}^{-1}$$

	T / °C	T / K	$\Delta S_{surroundings}$ J K^{-1} mol^{-1}	ΔS_{total} J K^{-1} mol^{-1}
a.	25	298		
b.	832			
c.		1400		

B1.4 (e) Second Law of Thermodynamics

The **Second Law of Thermodynamics** is an expression of the universal law of increasing entropy. It states that the entropy of an isolated system which is not in equilibrium will tend to increase over time, approaching a maximum value at equilibrium. The second law of thermodynamics is useful in predicting whether a particular reaction is possible. When a reaction is possible, chemists tend to use the word **feasible**. The second law does not give an indication of the rate of reaction, which is determined experimentally (B1.6f).

Total entropy (ΔS_{total}) is the sum of the entropy of the system (ΔS_{system}) and the entropy of the surroundings ($\Delta S_{surroundings}$).

$$\Delta S_{total} = \Delta S_{system} + \Delta S_{surroundings}$$

The second law of thermodynamics effectively says that ΔS_{total} increases in every chemical reaction so $\Delta S_{total} > 0$. The second law of thermodynamics can account for endothermic phenomena (A1.0i). For an endothermic process, $\Delta S_{surroundings}$ will always have a negative value because $\Delta_r H$ is positive and also $\Delta S_{surroundings} = -\Delta_r H/T$. In endothermic reactions, entropy is considered to be the driving force because ΔS_{system} must be more positive than $\Delta S_{surroundings}$ (which is negative), to give an overall positive ΔS_{total}.

Most chemical reactions are exothermic so particular care is needed when learning examples of endothermic chemical processes. An easy physical process to remember is sweating which is endothermic as the evaporation of sweat from the skin is how the body temperature is regulated. Examples of endothermic phenomena:

Endothermic Phenomena	
Physical process	Chemical process
Evaporation of sweat	Decomposition of Group 2 carbonates $CaCO_3 \rightarrow CaO + CO_2$
Melting of ice	Barium hydroxide $Ba(OH)_2.8H_2O$ crystals reacting with ammonium chloride NH_4Cl
Dissolving of ammonium nitrate in water (chemical cold pack)	Thionyl chloride $SOCl_2$ reacting with cobalt(II) sulfate heptahydrate $CoSO_4.7H_2O$
Dissolving ammonium chloride in water	Ethanoic acid CH_3CO_2H reacting with sodium carbonate Na_2CO_3

Questions 4.5

1. Which option shows a plausible value for ΔS_{system} if $\Delta S_{surroundings}$ was −86 J K^{-1} mol^{-1}?

    A   −87 J K^{-1} mol^{-1}

    B   +86 J K^{-1} mol^{-1}

    C   −86 J K^{-1} mol^{-1}

    D   +87 J K^{-1} mol^{-1}

2. Calculate ΔS_{system} for a reaction where ΔS_{total} = 57 J K^{-1} mol^{-1} and $\Delta S_{surroundings}$ = 118 J K^{-1} mol^{-1}.

3. Explain how endothermic reactions are possible despite the fact that, in their reactions, $\Delta S_{surroundings}$ will always have a negative value.

4. Explain, in terms of entropy, why liquid water spontaneously freezes at −20°C.

5. Which option shows two processes where ΔS_{system} decreases and $\Delta S_{surroundings}$ increases?

A   freezing and evaporation

B   freezing and condensation

C   melting and condensation

D   melting and evaporation

B1.4 (f)
Gibbs free energy and the Gibbs energy equation

The **Gibbs equation** is the final piece in the entropy jigsaw and brings together enthalpy change (ΔH), entropy change (ΔS) and temperature (T). The Gibbs free energy change is ΔG. In calculations, multiply ΔH by 1000 if given in kJ mol^{-1} to ensure consistency of units with ΔS.

$$\Delta G = \Delta H - T\Delta S$$

There are two parts to Gibbs energy:

• an enthalpy term and

• an entropy term.

Another way of looking at these components is to rearrange the equation to give $\Delta H = \Delta G + T\Delta S$. In other words, the enthalpy change (ΔH) can be split into two parts, the free energy part (ΔG) that is available for useful work, and $T\Delta S$ which is energy that is not available for work. The sign of ΔG is negative for spontaneous processes, such as the formation of compounds like CuF_2, but not N_2O. It is the work that must be done to make a compound from its elements in their reference states.

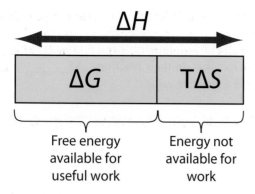

A spontaneous process is one in which the Gibbs energy decreases, *i.e.* ΔG is negative, which is allowed by the second law of thermodynamics (B1.4e). For a reaction to be feasible at a particular temperature ΔG needs to be negative. This equation goes part of the way to explain why many compounds dissolve in water despite the enthalpy change being endothermic (positive).

If the entropy change (ΔS) is positive enough, it will outweigh a positive ΔH according to the equation $\Delta G = \Delta H - T\Delta S$ and will lead to a negative ΔG.

The derivation of $\Delta G = \Delta H - T\Delta S$ is a case of remembering the two equations and some maths.

$\Delta S_{total} = \Delta S_{system} + \Delta S_{surroundings}$ which is the same as writing $\Delta S_{total} = \Delta S_{surroundings} + \Delta S_{system}$

$$\Delta S_{surroundings} = -\frac{\Delta_r H}{T}$$

so substituting it into the ΔS_{total} equation gives:

$$\Delta S_{total} = -\frac{\Delta_r H}{T} + \Delta S_{system}$$

and multiplying by $-T$ gives:

$$-T\Delta S_{total} = \Delta_r H - T\Delta S_{system}$$

Since ΔG is equal to $-T\Delta S_{total}$ it follows that:

$$\Delta G = \Delta H - T\Delta S.$$

ΔG varies with temperature and since $\Delta G = \Delta H - T\Delta S$, it is possible to determine both ΔH and ΔS from a graph of ΔG (x–axis) *versus* T (y–axis). ΔH is equal to the value of ΔG when temperature = zero Kelvin. The graph has to be extrapolated back to absolute zero (0 K), which is a temperature that is yet to be achieved practically. The entropy change, ΔS, is found from the gradient of a ΔG *vs.* T graph. Idealised graphs are shown (following) for reactions where there is an increase or a decrease in entropy. When there is a decrease in entropy ($-\Delta S$), it is found that ΔG increases as the temperature increases, which is shown by the positive gradient. When there is an increase in entropy ($+\Delta S$) it is found that ΔG decreases as the temperature increases, which is shown by the negative gradient.

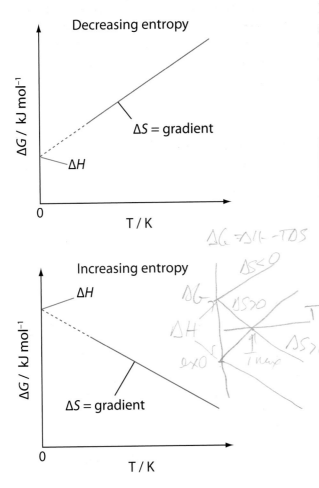

Decreasing entropy

ΔS = gradient

ΔH

ΔG / kJ mol^{-1}

0

T / K

Increasing entropy

ΔH

ΔS = gradient

ΔG / kJ mol^{-1}

0

T / K

Graphs of changes of ΔG with Temperature

If ΔG is calculated as being positive, then a reaction is not going to happen under these conditions. Once again, the decomposition of calcium carbonate is considered at different temperatures to show that, when ΔG becomes negative, this endothermic decomposition takes place, *e.g.* 1300 K.

Data for the decomposition of CaCO$_3$						
Temp / K	298	500	700	900	1100	1300
ΔG/ kJ mol^{-1}	130.1	97.5	65.3	33.9	2.1	−29.0
ΔH/ kJ mol^{-1}	177.8	177.4	177.0	177.0	176.6	176.1
$T\Delta S$/ kJ mol^{-1}	47.7	79.9	111.7	143.1	174.5	205.1

Example 4.6

Calculate the Gibbs free energy change ΔG (kJ mol^{-1}) for the following reaction at 293 K, where ΔH = −67 kJ mol^{-1} and ΔS = +122 J K^{-1} mol^{-1}. Comment on the size of ΔS, ΔH and the feasibility of the forward reaction.

$$2\,NO_2\,(g) \rightarrow N_2\,(g) + 2\,O_2\,(g)$$

$\Delta G \; = \Delta H - T\Delta S$

$\quad = -67000 - (293 \times 122)$

$\quad = -67000 - 35746$

$\quad = -102746$ J mol^{-1}

$\quad = -102.8$ kJ mol^{-1}

The forward reaction is feasible at this temperature since ΔG is negative. There is a large entropy change (ΔS) for this reaction as three moles of gas are made from two moles of gas. There is quite an exothermic enthalpy change (ΔH) as the reaction forms nitrogen with its very strong N≡N bond.

Example 4.5

Calculate the Gibbs free energy change ΔG (kJ mol^{-1}) for the following reaction at 300 K where ΔH = +114 kJ mol^{-1} and ΔS = 147 J K^{-1} mol^{-1}. Comment on the feasibility of the forward reaction.

$$2\,NO_2\,(g) \rightarrow 2\,NO\,(g) + O_2\,(g)$$

$\Delta G \; = \Delta H - T\Delta S$

$\quad = 114000 - (300 \times 147)$

$\quad = 114000 - 44100$

$\quad = 69900$ J mol^{-1}

$\quad = 69.9$ kJ mol^{-1}

The forward reaction is not feasible at this temperature since ΔG is positive.

Questions 4.6

1. Calculate the Gibbs free energy change ΔG (kJ mol^{-1}) for the following reaction at 373 K where $\Delta H = -360$ kJ mol^{-1} and $\Delta S = -63.9$ J K^{-1} mol^{-1}.

$$Mg\ (s) + H_2O\ (g) \rightarrow MgO\ (s) + H_2\ (g)$$

2. Calculate the Gibbs free energy change ΔG (kJ mol^{-1}) for the following reaction at 400 K, given that $\Delta H = -36$ kJ mol^{-1} and $\Delta S = +446$ J K^{-1} mol^{-1}.

$$NH_4NO_3\ (s) \rightarrow N_2O\ (g) + 2\ H_2O\ (g)$$

3. Calculate the enthalpy change ΔH (kJ mol^{-1}) for a reaction at 500 K, where $\Delta G = -101.5$ kJ mol^{-1} and $\Delta S = -189$ J K^{-1} mol^{-1}.

$$NH_4NO_3\ (s) \rightarrow N_2O\ (g) + 2\ H_2O\ (g)$$

4. Write an equation for the complete oxidation of glucose. Given that the ΔG for this reaction is -2880 kJ mol^{-1}, why doesn't glucose spontaneously combust in air?

5. Write a balanced formula equation for the decomposition of lead(II) nitrate and use the data to find ΔH and ΔS. At what temperature does this reaction become feasible?

ΔG / kJ mol^{-1}	600	430	260	80	-95
Temperature / K	0	200	400	600	800

B1.4 (g) Gibbs Energy and the Equilibrium constant (K)

An equilibrium is reached in a reversible reaction when the rate of the forward reaction equals the rate of the reverse reaction. It can be shown that the position of any equilibrium depends upon the temperature (B1.5a). The formation of ammonia (**Haber Process**) is an example of an important industrial reaction where an equilibrium can be reached.

$$N_2\ (g) + 3\ H_2\ (g) \rightleftharpoons 2\ NH_3\ (g)$$

Equilibrium constants (K) for reactions in the gas phase can be calculated from values of Gibbs free energy changes (ΔG) according to the equation; $\Delta G = -RT \ln K$, where R is the universal gas constant 8.3 J K^{-1} mol^{-1} and T is the temperature in Kelvin. Natural logarithm has the symbol ln and is also known as log to the base e (log$_e$). To succeed in these calculations it is important not to become confused with log to the base ten (log$_{10}$) used in pH calculations (B1.5f). It is worth spending time learning how to use the logarithmic functions on your calculator by trying out the worked examples. As in other calculations, it is necessary to ensure consistency of units. ΔG values are usually given in kJ mol^{-1} and need to be multiplied by 1000 to convert them into J mol^{-1}. It is also worth remembering in calculations; that a negative × a negative = a positive, *i.e.* ($- \times - = +$).

Example 4.7

Calculate the Gibbs free energy change ΔG (kJ mol^{-1}) for the following reaction at 298 K where the equilibrium constant $K = 794$.

$$H_2\ (g) + I_2\ (g) \rightleftharpoons 2\ HI\ (g)$$

Solution:

$\Delta G = -RT \ln K$

$= -8.3 \times 298 \times \ln 794$

$= -8.3 \times 298 \times 6.677$

$= -16515.1$ J mol^{-1}

$= -16.52$ kJ mol^{-1}

It is possible to rearrange the equation $\Delta G = -RT \ln K$ in terms of the equilibrium constant (K).

This gives a new equation $K = \exp(-\Delta G/RT) = e^{\left(\frac{-\Delta G}{RT}\right)}$

which shows that there is an exponential relationship between the standard Gibbs free energy change (ΔG) and the equilibrium constant (K).

Example 4.8

Calculate the equilibrium constant (K) for the following reaction at 298 K where the Gibbs free energy change $\Delta G = -71$ kJ mol^{-1}.

$$SO_2\,(g) + \tfrac{1}{2}O_2\,(g) \rightleftharpoons SO_3\,(g)$$

Solution:

$\Delta G = -71$ kJ mol^{-1} = -71000 J mol^{-1} where

$$\Delta G = -RT \ln K$$

$$K = \exp\left(-\frac{\Delta G}{RT}\right)$$

$$= \exp\left(-\frac{-71000}{8.3 \times 298}\right)$$

$$= \exp\left(\frac{71000}{2473.4}\right)$$

$$= \exp 28.705$$

$$= 2.93 \times 10^{12}$$

The very large value for the equilibrium constant shows that the equilibrium very much favours the product and this is confirmed industrially where the yield is >98%.

The equation $\Delta G = -RT \ln K$ tells us that the position of an equilibrium is affected by the Gibbs free energies of the reactant and the product since $\Delta G = G_{product} - G_{reactant}$. The value of K for an equilibrium is therefore dependent upon the value of ΔG. The relationship between ΔG and the proportions of reactant and products in a reaction mixture can be shown graphically. Gibbs free energy (G) is on the y–axis and the proportion of reactant and product (expressed as a percentage) is on the x–axis. An equilibrium is reached at the point at which the minimum is reached on these graphs. The position of an equilibrium lies towards the substance, either reactant or product, with the lowest Gibbs free energy.

In terms of the relative energies of the Gibbs free energies of the reactant ($G_{reactant}$) and the Gibbs free energy of the product ($G_{product}$), there are three possibilities.

	$G_{reactant}$	$G_{product}$	ΔG
$K < 1$	lower	higher	positive
$K = 1$	same	same	zero
$K > 1$	higher	lower	negative

In reactions where $K < 1$, the equilibrium lies towards the reactants. When $K = 1$ there will be equimolar amounts of reactants and products at equilibrium and when $K > 1$ the equilibrium lies towards the products. ΔG for the reaction is the difference in energy between the reactants and products. The equilibrium composition is found from the minimum points of these curves. When $K < 1$ there is a greater proportion of reactants at equilibrium and ΔG is positive. When $K > 1$ there is a greater proportion of products at equilibrium and ΔG is negative. When $K = 1$ there are equimolar amounts of reactants and products at equilibrium and ΔG is zero. It is a common misconception to think that there will always be a 1:1 ratio of reactants to products at equilibrium. If ΔG is positive and does not exceed +40 kJ mol^{-1}, reaction can still occur but the equilibrium will favour the reactants. If ΔG is negative and less than -40 kJ mol^{-1} the reaction will give nearly 100% products.

Graphs of Gibbs energy (G) for different sized equilibrium constants (K):

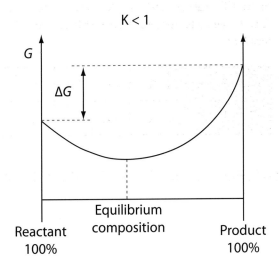

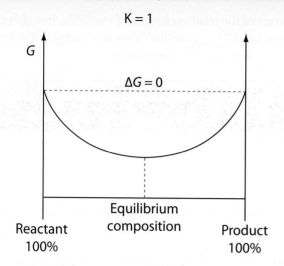

K = 1

G

ΔG = 0

Reactant 100%　Equilibrium composition　Product 100%

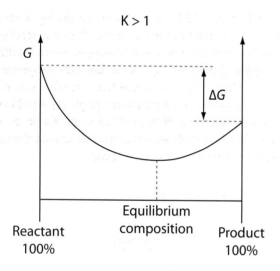

K > 1

G

ΔG

Reactant 100%　Equilibrium composition　Product 100%

Using the equation K = exp (−ΔG/RT) it is worth looking at graphs of K versus ΔG. When the equilibrium constant K is greater than 1 formation of products is favoured. When the equilibrium constant K is less than 1 formation of reactants is favoured.

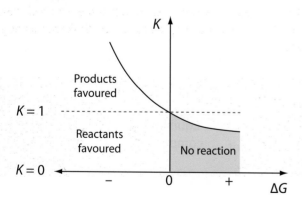

K

Products favoured

K = 1

Reactants favoured

No reaction

K = 0

−　0　+　ΔG

Graph of changes of ΔG with K and $\log_e K$

Questions 4.7

1. Which option shows a typical ΔG value for a highly endothermic reaction in dynamic equilibrium?

    A　−200

    B　+2000

    C　+200

    D　0

2. How large is ΔG when an equilibrium mixture results in equimolar amounts of A and B? Give reasons.

    $$A \rightleftharpoons B$$

3. Calculate the equilibrium constant (K) for the following reaction at 298 K where:

    the entropy change $\Delta S = -176$ J K^{-1} mol^{-1} and

    the Gibbs free energy change $\Delta G = -4.6$ kJ mol^{-1}.

    $$2\,NO_2\,(g) \rightleftharpoons N_2O_4\,(g)$$

4. The graph of Gibbs free energy (G) vs. composition is shown for the following reversible gas phase reaction; $2\,NO_2\,(g) \rightleftharpoons N_2O_4\,(g)$. Label ΔG, show the equilibrium composition and explain the relative size of the equilibrium constant (K) compared with 1.

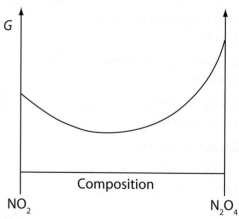

G

Composition

NO₂　　N₂O₄

5

Equilibrium

Contents

A n **equilibrium** is a steady state which can be achieved during a reversible reaction. It is reached when the rates of the forward and reverse reactions are equal. This does not mean that the reaction has stopped when equilibrium is reached. There are still changes at the microscopic level, but bulk properties such as colour and pH do not change. It is for this reason that they are often described as **dynamic equilibria** (A1.0j). In a concentration *versus* time graph the equilibrium is reached at the point where the concentrations of the reactants and products remain constant. This is because the rate of formation of product in the forward reaction exactly matches the rate of formation of reactant in the reverse reaction.

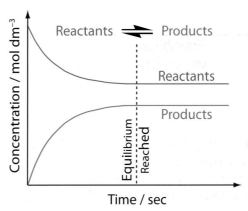

For an equilibrium to occur, there needs to be closed system so that there is no exchange of matter. A closed system in the laboratory is as simple as a conical flask with a bung in it or a syringe with a sealed end.

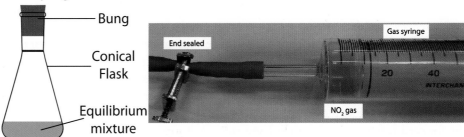

The symbol for an equilibrium ($\rightleftharpoons$) is essentially two arrows with half arrow head pointing in opposite directions. It is conventional to show the top arrow pointing to the right and the lower arrow pointing to the left. Despite the symbol representing an equilibrium, do not fall into the trap of thinking that every equilibrium mixture contains

50% reactant and 50% product. This is certainly not the case and we will return to this point again in terms of equilibrium constants (B1.5c).

One area of chemistry which is seemingly understood well by students is the pH scale. But does everyone know that the pH of the blood is 7.4 and that if it should vary by more than ± 0.5 from its usual equilibrium value, then the organism will be in trouble? Climbing to high altitudes can lead to an increase in the pH of blood which is one of the hazards climbers face on top of mountains such as Mount Kilimanjaro in Tanzania.

Climbers on top of Mount Kilimanjaro, the highest point in Africa

B1.5 (a)
Le Chatelier's principle

Le Chatelier's Principle states: "if a chemical system at equilibrium undergoes changes to the established conditions, then the chemical system will alter in such a way as to tend to restore the original conditions and therefore responds by minimising the effects of the changes."

Le Chatelier's Principle was first published in 1888 and it is very important because it allows chemists to deduce qualitatively the effects of a system in equilibrium when subjected to changes in temperature, pressure and concentration. When an equilibrium is disturbed, it can do one of three things. It can remain as it was before the disturbance or it can shift towards the forward reaction (RHS = right hand side) or it can shift towards the reverse reaction (LHS = left hand side).

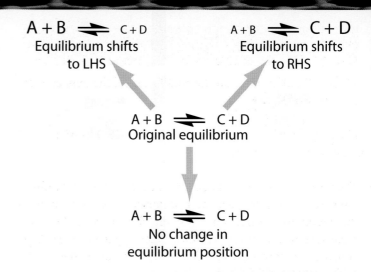

Le Chatelier's principle says that an equilibrium has a tendency to oppose every change that you make to it. A useful analogy is to view an equilibrium in much the same way that a parent views a stubborn child who does the exact opposite of what the parent asks them to do.

The three factors which do affect an equilibrium's position (temperature, pressure and concentration) will be looked at it in turn. Pressure is the only factor which is exclusive to gaseous equilibria and catalysts do not affect the equilibrium position but they do allow the equilibrium to be achieved in a quicker time.

Knowledge of Le Chatelier's Principle can help to increase the yield in an equilibrium reaction, *e.g.* esterification (B3.7b). Molecular sieves can be added to reaction mixtures to greatly increase the yield of ester as these zeolites (cavity-containing aluminosilicates) absorb the product, water.

Effect of changes in temperature

This section takes a look at the qualitative effect that changes in temperature will have on the equilibrium positions of some examples. When considering how changes in temperature affect an equilibrium, you need to establish whether the reaction is exothermic or endothermic. This is done by looking at the sign of the enthalpy change given for the reaction (A1.3a). If the forward reaction is exothermic (negative ΔH) then the reverse reaction will be endothermic (positive ΔH). The opposite is also true so if the forward reaction is endothermic (positive ΔH) then the reverse reaction will be exothermic (negative ΔH). According to Le Chatelier's principle, an increase in temperature results in the equilibrium shifting in the cooler, endothermic direction. According to Le Chatelier's principle a decrease in temperature results in the equilibrium shifting in the warmer, exothermic direction.

Example 5.1

What will be the effect on the equilibrium if the temperature is increased?

$$N_2O_4 (g) \rightleftharpoons 2\,NO_2 (g) \qquad \Delta_r H = +\,58.0\ kJ\ mol^{-1}$$
colourless   *brown*

The forward reaction is endothermic as $\Delta_r H$ is positive. If the temperature is increased, the equilibrium will shift towards the endothermic direction, *i.e.* it will shift towards the right hand side in an attempt to minimise the applied change. As a consequence of this change in equilibrium position, the colour of the mixture will darken.

Example 5.2

What will be the effect on the equilibrium if the temperature is decreased?

$$CO (g) + H_2O (g) \rightleftharpoons CO_2 (g) + H_2 (g)$$
$$\Delta_r H = -\,41.2\ kJ\ mol^{-1}$$

The forward reaction is exothermic as $\Delta_r H$ is negative. If the temperature is decreased, the equilibrium will shift towards the exothermic direction, *i.e.* it will shift towards the right hand side in an attempt to minimise the applied change.

Effect of changes in pressure

This section takes a look at the qualitative effect that changes in pressure will have on the equilibrium positions of some examples. When considering how changes in pressure affect an equilibrium, you need to count the total number of moles on each side of the equilibrium. This is done by adding the numbers (coefficients) in front of the formulae in the balanced equation. An increase in pressure will result in the equilibrium shifting to the side with the fewest moles of gas in an attempt to minimise the applied change. A decrease in pressure will result in the equilibrium shifting to the side with the most moles in an attempt, again, to minimise the applied change. If there are equal numbers of moles on the left hand side and right hand side of the equilibrium, the pressure has no effect on the equilibrium position.

Example 5.3

What will be the effect on the following equilibrium if the pressure is increased?

$$N_2O_4 (g) \rightleftharpoons 2\,NO_2 (g)$$
colourless   *brown*

There is 1 mole on the left hand side and 2 moles on the right hand side. If the pressure is increased, the equilibrium will shift towards the side with the fewest moles, *i.e.* it will shift towards the left hand side in an attempt to minimise the applied change. As a consequence of this change in equilibrium position, the colour of the mixture will lighten.

Example 5.4

What will be the effect on the equilibrium if the pressure is decreased?

$$CO_2 (g) + H_2 (g) \rightleftharpoons CO (g) + H_2O (g)$$

There are 2 moles on the left hand side and 2 moles on the right hand side. If the pressure is decreased, the equilibrium will not shift as there are an equal number of moles on both sides of the equilibrium.

Example 5.5

What will be the effect on the equilibrium if the pressure is decreased?

$$N_2 (g) + 3\,H_2 (g) \rightleftharpoons 2\,NH_3 (g)$$

There are 4 moles on the left hand side and 2 moles on the right hand side. If the pressure is decreased, the equilibrium will shift towards the side with the most moles, *i.e.* it will shift towards the left hand side in an attempt to minimise the applied change.

Effect of changes in concentration

This section takes a look at the qualitative effect that changes in concentration will have on the equilibrium positions of some examples. Once an equilibrium has been reached, a change in concentration can be achieved by adding more reactant or more product to the system. Another way to change the concentration of a substance is to add an additional chemical that it reacts with, *e.g.* OH$^-$ (aq) which will react with H$^+$ (aq) to form water. An increase in concentration of a reactant will result in the equilibrium shifting to the right hand side in an attempt to minimise the applied change. An increase in concentration of a product will result in the equilibrium shifting to the left hand side, again in an attempt to minimise the applied change.

Example 5.6

What will be the effect on the following equilibrium if acid (H$^+$) is added to the equilibrium mixture?

$$2 \, CrO_4^{\,2-} \, (aq) + 2 \, H^+ \, (aq) \rightleftharpoons Cr_2O_7^{\,2-} \, (aq) + H_2O \, (l)$$
yellow   *orange*

Aqueous solutions of sodium chromate(VI) and sodium dichromate(VI)

Addition of acid will increase the concentration of H$^+$ ions. The equilibrium will shift away from the side containing H$^+$ ions, *i.e.* it will shift towards the right hand side in an attempt to minimise the applied change by mopping up the additional H$^+$ ions. As a consequence of this change in equilibrium position, the colour of the mixture will become more orange.

Example 5.7

What will be the effect on the equilibrium if alkali (OH$^-$) is added to this equilibrium mixture?

$$2 \, CrO_4^{\,2-} \, (aq) + 2 \, H^+ \, (aq) \rightleftharpoons Cr_2O_7^{\,2-} \, (aq) + H_2O \, (l)$$
yellow   *orange*

Addition of alkali will decrease the concentration of H$^+$ ions because of this reaction taking place:

$$OH^- \, (aq) + H^+ \, (aq) \rightarrow H_2O \, (l)$$

The equilibrium will shift towards the side containing H$^+$ ions, *i.e.* it will shift towards the left hand side in an attempt to minimise the applied change by replacing the H$^+$ ions removed in the neutralization reaction. As a consequence of this change in equilibrium position, the colour of the mixture will become more yellow.

Example 5.8

What will be the effect on the equilibrium if nitrogen monoxide (NO) is added to this equilibrium mixture?

$$2 \, NO \, (g) + Br_2 \, (g) \rightleftharpoons 2 \, NOBr \, (g)$$

Addition of NO will increase its concentration. The equilibrium will shift away from the side containing NO (g), *i.e.* it will shift towards the right hand side in an attempt to minimise the applied change by removing the additional NO (g).

Questions 5.1

1. Which option shows a factor that does not affect the position of a dynamic equilibrium?

    A   Pressure

    B   Concentration

    C   Temperature

    D   Catalyst

2. How does Le Chatelier's principle help chemists?

3. What will be the effect on the following equilibrium if the temperature is increased?

$$PCl_5 (g) \rightleftharpoons PCl_3 (g) + Cl_2 (g)$$
$$\Delta_r H = + 90.0 \text{ kJ mol}^{-1}$$

4. What will be the effect on the following equilibrium if the temperature is decreased?

$$N_2 (g) + O_2 (g) \rightleftharpoons 2 NO (g)$$
$$\Delta_r H = + 180 \text{ kJ mol}^{-1}$$

5. What will be the effect on the following equilibrium if the temperature is decreased?

$$2 SO_2 (g) + O_2 (g) \rightleftharpoons 2 SO_3 (g)$$
$$\Delta_r H = - 197 \text{ kJ mol}^{-1}$$

6. What will be the effect on the following equilibrium if the pressure is increased?

$$SO_2Cl_2 (g) \rightleftharpoons SO_2 (g) + Cl_2 (g)$$

7. What will be the effect on the following equilibrium if the pressure is increased?

$$2 NO_2 (g) + 7 H_2 (g) \rightleftharpoons 2 NH_3 (g) + 4 H_2O (g)$$

8. What will be the effect on the following equilibrium if the pressure is increased?

$$H_2 (g) + I_2 (g) \rightleftharpoons 2 HI (g)$$

9. An equilibrium can be approached from opposite directions. Describe, practically, how the equilibrium between the two chromium(VI) species might be approached from the two opposite directions.

$$2 CrO_4^{2-} (aq) + 2 H^+ (aq)$$
$$\rightleftharpoons Cr_2O_7^{2-} (aq) + H_2O (l)$$

10. What will be the effect on the following equilibrium if some chlorine is removed from the equilibrium mixture?

$$PCl_3 (g) + Cl_2 (g) \rightleftharpoons PCl_5 (g)$$

11. What will be the effect on the following equilibrium if some hydrogen is added to this equilibrium mixture?

$$CO (g) + 2 H_2 (g) \rightleftharpoons CH_3OH (g)$$

12. Complete the table by placing a tick in the correct box to say which direction, if any, the equilibrium will shift if the equilibrium is then subjected to an increase in pressure.

Equilibria	Shift left hand side	No shift	Shift right hand side
$COCl_2 (g) \rightleftharpoons CO (g)$ $+ Cl_2 (g)$			
$2 CO (g) + 2 NO (g)$ $\rightleftharpoons 2 CO_2 (g) + N_2 (g)$			
$CH_4 (g) + 2 H_2S (g)$ $\rightleftharpoons CS_2 (g) + 4H_2 (g)$			

Equilibria	Shift left hand side	No shift	Shift right hand side
$CO\ (g) + H_2O\ (g) \rightleftharpoons$ $CO_2\ (g) + H_2\ (g)$			
$N_2O_4\ (g) \rightleftharpoons 2\ NO_2\ (g)$			
$2\ N_2O\ (g) + 3\ O_2\ (g)$ $\rightleftharpoons 2\ N_2O_4\ (g)$			

13. Complete the table by placing a tick in the correct box to say which direction, if any, the equilibrium will shift if the equilibrium is then subjected to an increase in temperature.

Equilibria	$\Delta_r H$ / kJ mol^{-1}	Shift left hand side	Shift right hand side
$CO\ (g) + 2\ H_2\ (g) \rightleftharpoons$ $CH_3OH\ (g)$	-18		
$N_2\ (g) + 3\ H_2\ (g) \rightleftharpoons$ $2\ NH_3\ (g)$	-92		
$N_2O\ (g) + NO_2\ (g) \rightleftharpoons$ $3\ NO\ (g)$	$+156$		
$CO_2\ (g) + H_2\ (g) \rightleftharpoons$ $CO\ (g) + H_2O\ (g)$	$+41.2$		
$4\ NH_3\ (g) + 5\ O_2\ (g) \rightleftharpoons$ $4\ NO\ (g) + 6\ H_2O\ (g)$	-909		

B1.5 (b)
Weak acids and weak alkalis

To understand what is meant by a weak acid, it is helpful to first understand what is meant by a strong acid. Strong acids **fully** ionise in solution, *e.g.* the mineral acids sulfuric acid (H_2SO_4), nitric acid (HNO_3) and hydrochloric acid (HCl).

$$H_2SO_4 \rightarrow 2\ H^+ + SO_4^{2-}$$
$$HNO_3 \rightarrow H^+ + NO_3^-$$
$$HCl \rightarrow H^+ + Cl^-$$

Sulfuric acid is described as **diprotic** because it releases two protons (H^+) for every sulfuric acid molecule. Nitric acid and hydrochloric acid are **monoprotic** because they both release one proton for every acid molecule. Strong acids fully ionize and do not form equilibria.

Acid		Alkali	
Strong	Weak	Strong	Weak
HCl	HCOOH	LiOH	NH_4OH
HNO_3	CH_3COOH	NaOH	NH_2OH
H_2SO_4	H_3PO_4	KOH	CH_3NH_2

Weak acids **partially** ionise in solution and an equilibrium is set up between the acid molecule and the two ions formed when it loses a proton. Weak acids include carboxylic acids (A3.2g) and, perhaps surprisingly, hydrofluoric acid (A2.2k). Ethanoic acid partially ionises to form the ethanoate ion ($CH_3CO_2^-$) and a proton (H^+).

$$CH_3CO_2H \rightleftharpoons CH_3CO_2^- + H^+$$

To distinguish between strong and weak acids is a case of having the same volume and same concentration for the two types of acid and adding a ribbon of the fairly reactive metal, magnesium. The strongest acid will produce the greatest number of bubbles of hydrogen immediately because of the greater concentration of hydrogen ions. The ionic equation for the reaction between magnesium and an acid is shown.

$$Mg\ (s) + 2\ H^+\ (aq) \rightarrow Mg^{2+}\ (aq) + H_2\ (g)$$

Weak alkalis partly ionise. For example, a solution of ammonia, which will contain a small proportion of ammonium and hydroxide ions according to this equilibrium:

$$NH_3\ (aq) + H_2O\ (l) \rightleftharpoons NH_4^+\ (aq) + OH^-\ (aq)$$

This equilibrium is why ammonia solutions are used to precipitate hydroxides in qualitative tests (A4.1a)

Brønsted-Lowry theory of acids and bases

There have been many definitions of acids over the centuries and a very useful one, developed by Johannes Brønsted and Thomas Lowry, deals with the definition of acids in terms of proton transfer. Equilibria also exist for weak acids and weak alkalis and the acid and base can be identified by looking at which species donates the proton (acid) and which species accepts the proton (base).

The Brønsted-Lowry theory states that an acid is a proton donor and a base is a proton acceptor. Ethanoic acid molecules react with water to form ethanoate and hydroxonium ions with the equilibrium towards the left hand side as ethanoic acid is a weak acid.

$$CH_3COOH\ (aq) + H_2O\ (l) \rightleftharpoons CH_3COO^-(aq) + H_3O^+\ (aq)$$
$acid$ $\qquad\qquad$ $base$

In the equilibrium, ethanoic acid becomes the ethanoate ion because it has behaved as a Brønsted-Lowry acid and donated a proton. The water molecule has behaved as a Brønsted-Lowry base and accepted a proton to become the hydroxonium ion.

Ammonia molecules react with water to form ammonium and hydroxide ions, with the equilibrium towards the left hand side, as ammonia is a weak base.

$$NH_3\ (aq) + H_2O\ (l) \rightleftharpoons NH_4^+(aq) + OH^-\ (aq)$$
$base$ $\qquad$ $acid$

In the equilibrium, ammonia becomes the ammonium ion because it has behaved as a Brønsted-Lowry base and accepted a proton. The water molecule has behaved as a Brønsted-Lowry acid and donated a proton to become a hydroxide ion.

Water can behave as an acid and a base in its reactions and it is termed **amphiprotic**. This word is specific to water and is based on the more familiar word **amphoteric**.

Conjugate pairs

In an equilibrium reaction, there is both a forward reaction and a reverse reaction. If we look at the equilibrium between ethanoic acid and water in terms of its reverse reactions, then we soon realise that there is also an acid and a base in the reverse reaction. The proton donor (acid) in the reverse reaction is known as the **conjugate acid** and the proton acceptor (base) in the reverse reaction is known as the **conjugate base**.

$$CH_3COOH\ (aq) + H_2O\ (l) \rightleftharpoons CH_3COO^-\ (aq) + H_3O^+\ (aq)$$

Conjugate base: $CH_3COO^-\ (aq)$

Conjugate acid: $H_3O^+\ (aq)$

Using the same logic, the conjugate acid and conjugate base are identified in the ammonia and water equilibrium.

$$NH_3\ (aq) + H_2O\ (l) \rightleftharpoons NH_4^+\ (aq) + OH^-\ (aq)$$

Conjugate base: $OH^-\ (aq)$

Conjugate acid: $NH_4^+\ (aq)$

In a reaction between an acid and a base, there will be two sets of conjugate pairs. In each conjugate pair, the acid and the base will differ from each other by a proton. In other words, the conjugate base is the acid with loss of a proton, and the conjugate acid is the base with the addition of a proton. Conjugate base pairs are shown for the two previous equilibria and it is good practice to clearly show which species are conjugate pairs by connecting them with lines.

Conjugate pair

$$CH_3COOH\ (aq) + H_2O\ (l) \rightleftharpoons CH_3COO^-\ (aq) + H_3O^+\ (aq)$$

Conjugate pair

Conjugate pair

$$NH_3\ (aq) + H_2O\ (l) \rightleftharpoons NH_4^+\ (aq) + OH^-\ (aq)$$

Conjugate pair

Example 5.9

Using the Brønsted-Lowry theory, identify the acids and bases and conjugate pairs in the following equilibrium.

$$HCl\ (aq) + H_2O\ (l) \rightleftharpoons H_3O^+\ (aq) + Cl^-\ (aq)$$

An acid is a proton donor and a base is a proton acceptor in the forwards reaction. A conjugate acid is a proton in the reverse reaction and a conjugate base is a proton acceptor in the reverse reaction. A conjugate pair differs by a proton.

Acid	Base	Conjugate acid	Conjugate base
HCl	H_2O	H_3O^+	Cl^-

Conjugate pairs: HCl & Cl^- and H_2O & H_3O^+

Example 5.10

Using the Brønsted-Lowry theory, identify the acids and bases and conjugate pairs in the following equilibrium.

$$HSO_4^- \text{ (aq)} + H_2O \text{ (l)} \rightleftharpoons SO_4^{2-} \text{ (aq)} + H_3O^+ \text{ (aq)}$$

An acid is a proton donor and a base is a proton acceptor in the forwards reaction. A conjugate acid is a proton donor in the reverse reaction and a conjugate base is a proton acceptor in the reverse reaction. A conjugate pair differs by a proton.

Acid	Base	Conjugate acid	Conjugate base
HSO_4^-	H_2O	H_3O^+	SO_4^{2-}

Conjugate pairs: HSO_4^- & SO_4^{2-} and H_2O & H_3O^+

There are limitations with the Brønsted-Lowry theory of acids. As a theory it does not explain all reactions, *e.g.* the reaction between ammonia and boron trichloride.

$$NH_3 + BCl_3 \rightarrow NH_3.BCl_3$$

What type of reaction is this and which reactant is the acid?

Knowing that ammonia is a weak alkali, a good student might deduce that boron trichloride is an acid and that it is an acid-base reaction. BCl_3 has no hydrogen so it cannot be considered an acid using the Brønsted-Lowry theory.

Lewis acids and bases

Another theory of acids and bases is the **Lewis theory**. In 1938, building on the work of others, Gilbert Lewis developed a definition that allows a greater understanding of which substances are acids than previous definitions. A **Lewis acid** is an **electron pair acceptor**. By definition a Lewis acid is a substance that is electron deficient or is capable of accommodating another pair of electrons (lone pair) into a vacant orbital. A **Lewis base** is a substance that is electron rich and can donate a lone pair of electrons into a vacant orbital.

The reaction between ammonia and boron trichloride is an acid base reaction because NH_3 is an electron pair donor (Lewis base) and BCl_3 is an electron pair acceptor (Lewis acid). The boron in BCl_3 is electron deficient as it only has six valence electrons until it forms a dative covalent (coordinate) bond with NH_3.

Metal ions as Lewis acids: Transition metal complexes form when metal ions are surrounded by ligands. Ligands have lone pairs of electrons which can form coordinate bonds to the metal ion. Therefore, a new way to look at these complexes is by thinking of the ligands (electron pair donors) as Lewis bases and the central metal ions (electron pair acceptors) as Lewis acids. It is important to remember that ligands can be neutral, *e.g.* CO, NH_3, H_2O or anions, *e.g.* Cl^-, SCN^-, OH^-. The requirement is for them to have at least one lone pair donating a pair of electrons to the transition element's vacant d-orbitals. A solution of copper(II) ions provides a simple example, $[Cu(H_2O)_6]^{2+}$ (aq).

Aluminium halides as Lewis acids: Boron and aluminium halides are Lewis acids because they are all electron deficient. Aluminium chloride ($AlCl_3$) has six valence electrons rather than eight. This deficiency allows it to react as an electron pair acceptor (Lewis acid) and also to dimerise and form Al_2Cl_6.

In reactions where aluminium chloride is a Lewis acid, it gains two additional electrons to complete the octet (6 → 8 valence electrons). Examples of it reacting as a Lewis acid are the Friedel Craft reactions; halogenation, alkylation or acylation. Lewis acids which have been used in these reactions are $FeCl_3$, $FeBr_3$ and $AlBr_3$. Lewis acids react with the halogen or organic halide to produce the electrophile for the electrophilic substitution.

$$AlCl_3 + Cl_2 \rightleftharpoons Cl^+ + AlCl_4^-$$

Boron halides are Lewis acids: Boron trifluoride is a Lewis acid because it is also an electron pair acceptor. It reacts with the solvent ethoxyethane (diethyl ether) *via* one of the lone pairs on the central oxygen atom. Therefore, the ether can be thought of as a Lewis base because it is donating a pair of electrons to the electron deficient boron atom.

$$BF_3 + (C_2H_5)_2O \rightarrow (C_2H_5)_2O \rightarrow BF_3$$

Tollens' reagent
(Lewis acid + Lewis base)

Tollens' reagent (ammoniacal silver nitrate) is formed by reaction between ammonia, a strong electron pair donor (Lewis base) and silver(I) ions as electron pair acceptors (Lewis acid).

The resulting complex diammine silver(I):

$$[H_3N{:}\rightarrow Ag \leftarrow{:}NH_3]^+$$

is reduced to elemental silver by the reducing sugar glucose (aldehyde).

Ammonia and amines are Lewis bases

The familiar blue solution of copper(II) sulfate forms a deep blue complex in the presence of excess ammonia. Four ammonia molecules undergo a ligand exchange with four water molecules. Ammonia uses its lone pair of electrons to form a coordinate bond to the copper(II) ion. Ammonia is a Lewis base precisely because it is a lone pair donor.

$$[Cu(H_2O)_6]^{2+} + 4\,NH_3 \rightleftharpoons [Cu(NH_3)_4(H_2O)_2]^{2+} + 4\,H_2O$$
Light blue   *Deep blue*

The bidentate ligand ethylenediamine (1,2-diaminoethane - $NH_2CH_2CH_2NH_2$) has two lone pairs available for coordination with metal ions. This ligand readily forms complexes with transition metal ions such as nickel(II). Ethylenediamine, which is an example of a primary amine (RNH_2), is a Lewis base precisely because it is an electron lone pair donor when it forms complexes.

$$3\,NH_2CH_2CH_2NH_2\,(aq) + [Ni(H_2O)_6]^{2+}\,(aq) \rightarrow$$
$$[Ni(NH_2CH_2CH_2NH_2)_3]^{2+}\,(aq) + 6\,H_2O\,(l)$$

Sulfur trioxide is a Lewis acid

It is a good generalisation to think of non-metal oxides as acids and metal oxides as bases. So it is no surprise that sulfur trioxide reacts with calcium oxide to form the salt calcium sulphate. Sulfur trioxide is a Lewis acid in this reaction as it accepts a pair of electrons from the oxide. The reverse argument is that the oxide is a Lewis base because it is an electron pair donor.

Summary of Lewis acids and bases

Lewis acids	Lewis bases
Electron pair acceptors	Electron pair donors
Electron deficient atoms (BF_3, $AlCl_3$) Catalysts in Friedel Crafts reactions	Has an unshared pair of electrons
Metal ions (cations)	Non-metal ions (anions)
Electrophiles (H^+, Br^+, NO_2^+)	Nucleophiles (NH_3, H_2O, RNH_2, Cl^-, O^{2-}, OH^-, CN^-)
Orbital vacancy available for electron pair acceptance	Orbital filled available for electron pair donation
Opposite of Lewis base	Opposite of Lewis acid
Low energy LUMO (Lowest Unoccupied Molecular Orbital)	High energy HOMO (Highest Occupied Molecular Orbital)

Questions 5.2

1. Using the Brønsted-Lowry theory identify the acids and bases and conjugate pairs in the following equilibria.

    a. $NH_3\,(l) + NH_3\,(l)$
        $$\rightleftharpoons NH_2^- + NH_4^+$$

    b. $HCO_3^-\,(aq) + H_2O\,(l)$
        $$\rightleftharpoons CO_3^{2-}\,(aq) + H_3O^+\,(aq)$$

    c. $NH_3\,(aq) + HCl\,(aq)$
        $$\rightleftharpoons Cl^-\,(aq) + NH_4^+\,(aq)$$

    d. $NH_2^-\,(aq) + H_2O\,(l)$
        $$\rightleftharpoons NH_3\,(aq) + OH^-\,(aq)$$

e. $H_2SO_4 + HNO_3 \rightleftharpoons H_2NO_3^+ + HSO_4^-$

f. $[Fe(H_2O)_6]^{3+}$ (aq) $+ H_2O$ (l)
    $\rightleftharpoons [Fe(H_2O)_5OH]^{2+}$ (aq) $+ H_3O^+$ (aq)

g. C_6H_5OH (aq) $+ H_2O$ (l)
    $\rightleftharpoons H_3O^+$ (aq) $+ C_6H_5O^-$ (aq)

h. $C_6H_5CO_2H$ (aq) $+ H_2O$ (l)
    $\rightleftharpoons C_6H_5CO_2^-$ (aq) $+ H_3O^+$ (aq)

2. Which of the following substances does not act as a Lewis acid?

    A $AlCl_3$

    B H^+

    C Cl^-

    D Cu^{2+}

3. What is the best description of AlH_3 in its reaction with a hydride (H^-) ion?

    $AlH_3 + H^- \rightarrow AlH_4^-$

    A   Lewis acid

    B   Brønsted-Lowry acid

    C   Lewis base

    D   Brønsted-Lowry base

4. In the following Friedel Crafts alkylation, an ethyl (C_2H_5) group can swap for an H atom on benzene (C_6H_6).

    $$CH_3CH_2Cl + C_6H_6 \xrightarrow{AlCl_3} C_6H_5CH_2CH_3 + HCl$$

    Explain why it is correct to describe aluminium chloride as a Lewis acid catalyst in this reaction. Why does the reaction have to be carried out under anhydrous conditions?

5. What type of substance is ammonia in its reaction to form ammonium?

    $NH_3 + H^+ \rightarrow NH_4^+$

    A   Brønsted-Lowry acid

    B   Lewis acid

    C   Conjugate base

    D   Lewis base

6. Boric(III) acid has the formula $B(OH)_3$. Its reaction with water releases a proton. Explain why $B(OH)_3$ is a Lewis acid and water is a Lewis base. Suggest a possible mechanism for this reaction.

    $$B(OH)_3 + H_2O \rightarrow [B(OH)_4]^- + H^+$$

7. For each of the following reactions identify the Lewis acid and Lewis base by placing ticks ($\sqrt{}$) in the appropriate boxes. Suggest a possible mechanism for both reactions 1 & 2.

    Reaction 1: H_3O^+ (aq) $+ OH^-$ (aq) $\rightarrow 2\,H_2O$ (l)

    Reaction 2: NH_3 (aq) $+ HCl$ (aq) $\rightarrow NH_4Cl$ (s)

Reaction 1	H_3O^+ (aq)	OH^- (aq)
Lewis acid		
Lewis base		

Reaction 2	NH_3 (aq)	HCl (aq)
Lewis acid		
Lewis base		

B1.5 (c) Equilibrium constant expressions (K_c)

The equilibrium law is the relationship between the concentration of reactants and products for an equilibrium at a particular temperature. Take the generalised equilibrium between reactants A and B and products C and D. The number of moles of each substance is indicated by the small letter (coefficient) before the capitalised letter, *e.g.* there are b moles of B.

$$a\,A + b\,B \rightleftharpoons c\,C + d\,D$$

The equilibrium constant K_c is expressed in terms of concentrations, which are indicated by square brackets with the units mol dm^{-3}. The subscript *eq* is written after the concentration of each species to indicate that we are dealing with an equilibrium concentration.

$$K_c = \frac{[C]^c_{eq}\,[D]^d_{eq}}{[A]^a_{eq}\,[B]^b_{eq}}$$

In words, K_c is the product of the concentration of the products raised to the power of their coefficients divided by the product of the concentration of the reactants raised to the power of their coefficients. The only factor that affects the size of K_c is temperature, which is why it is always quoted with values of K_c. It is unlikely that $K_c = 1$ (equimolar reactants and products). Values of $K_c > 1$ indicates that the equilibrium mixture contains mainly products and $K_c < 1$ indicates that the equilibrium mixture contains mainly reactants.

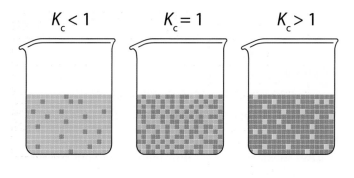

$K_c < 1$ $K_c = 1$ $K_c > 1$

Reactant ■

Product ■

At first it might seem unlikely, but K_c is **not** altered by the addition of more reactants or products to an equilibrium mixture. The equilibrium will shift in the appropriate direction according to Le Chatelier's principle (B1.5a) and the equilibrium constant K_c will be maintained.

The unit of a specific K_c depends upon the number of moles present in the balanced equation. If there is an equimolar number of reactants and products in the equilibrium equation then K_c will have no units (**dimensionless**). To work out units for K_c you substitute mol dm^{-3} into the K_c expression.

For the equilibrium:

$$K_c = \frac{[N_2O_4]}{[NO_2]^2}$$

the units are calculated as follows:

$$K_c = \frac{[\text{mol dm}^{-3}]}{[\text{mol dm}^{-3}]\,[\text{mol dm}^{-3}]}$$

The top concentration cancels out with one of the bottom concentrations to leave:

$$K_c = \frac{1}{[\text{mol dm}^{-3}]} = \text{mol}^{-1}\,\text{dm}^3.$$

Example 5.11

What is the equilibrium constant K_c for this equilibrium?

$$CH_3CH_2OH\,(l) + CH_3CO_2H\,(l) \rightleftharpoons CH_3CO_2CH_2CH_3\,(l) + H_2O\,(l)$$

$$K_c = \frac{[CH_3CO_2CH_2CH_3\,(l)]_{eq}\,[H_2O\,(l)]_{eq}}{[CH_3CH_2OH\,(l)]_{eq}\,[CH_3CO_2H\,(l)]_{eq}}$$

Example 5.12

What is the equilibrium constant K_c for this equilibrium?

$$N_2\,(g) + 3\,H_2\,(g) \rightleftharpoons 2\,NH_3\,(g)$$

$$K_c = \frac{[NH_3\,(g)]^2_{eq}}{[N_2\,(g)]_{eq}\,[H_2\,(g)]^3_{eq}}$$

Example 5.13

What is the equilibrium constant K_c for this equilibrium? Solids do not appear in equilibrium constants.

$$Ag^+ (aq) + Fe^{2+} (aq) \rightleftharpoons Ag (s) + Fe^{3+} (aq)$$

$$K_c = \frac{[Fe^{3+} (aq)]_{eq}}{[Ag^+ (aq)]_{eq} [Fe^{2+} (aq)]_{eq}}$$

Questions 5.3

1. Which option changes the value of K_c?

   A   Decreasing the temperature

   B   Increasing the [reactants]

   C   Addition of a catalyst

   D   Decreasing the [products]

2. What information is provided by a high value for K_c?

3. When is K_c fixed?

4. For the following equilibria write down the equilibrium constant K_c and give its units.

   a. $2 SO_2 (g) + O_2 (g) \rightleftharpoons 2 SO_3 (g)$

   b. $2 NO (g) + O_2 (g) \rightleftharpoons 2 NO_2 (g)$

   c. $PCl_3 (g) + Cl_2 (g) \rightleftharpoons PCl_5 (g)$

   d. $CO (g) + NO_2 (g) \rightleftharpoons CO_2 (g) + NO (g)$

   e. $H_2 (g) + I_2 (g) \rightleftharpoons 2 HI (g)$

B1.5 (d) Equilibrium constant expressions (K_p, K_{sp}, K_a & K_w)

Equilibrium constant K_p

Equilibrium reactions in the gas phase will obey the equilibrium law (B1.5a) and it is usual to use the partial pressures of the individual gases in the mixture rather than their concentrations. It is much easier to measure the pressure of a gas, which is directly proportional to its concentration. K_p is defined in the same way as K_c (B1.5c) but partial pressures (p) are used instead of concentrations [ ].

$$a A + bB \rightleftharpoons c C + d D$$

When writing the equilibrium constant, K_p, each gas is, by convention, written inside round brackets. The subscript eq is written after the partial pressure of each species to indicate that we are dealing with equilibrium pressures.

$$K_p = \frac{p(C (g))_{eq}^c \, p(D (g))_{eq}^d}{p(A (g))_{eq}^a \, p(B (g))_{eq}^b}$$

In words, K_p is the product of the partial pressures of the products raised to the power of their coefficients divided by the product of the partial pressures of the reactants raised to the power of their coefficients. The only factor that affects the size of K_p is temperature, which is why it is always quoted with values of K_p. At a fixed temperature, changing the overall pressure for a gaseous equilibrium will change the equilibrium position, but will not change K_p.

In a mixture of gases, the contribution of each gas to the total pressure is called its **partial pressure**. The partial pressure of a gas can be calculated by multiplying its mole fraction by the total pressure.

$$\text{Mole fraction} = \frac{\text{Number of moles of a gas}}{\text{Total moles in the mixture}}.$$

The total pressure is the sum of the partial pressures of all the gases in the mixture. All of these definitions are neatly stated in **Dalton's law** which says: "that the sum of the partial pressures of the gases in an equilibrium mixture is equal to the total pressure." Pressure usually is quoted with the units in pascals (Pa).

Total pressure = partial pressure of A + partial pressure of B

Total pressure = $p (A (g)) + p (B (g))$

Using the particles in the boxes (below), the total number of particles in box **A** is 10 and the total number of particles in box **B** is 5. Therefore the total number of particles in the equilibrium mixture is 10 + 5 = 15. The mole fraction of A is $\frac{10}{15}$ and the mole fraction of B is $\frac{5}{15}$. Each gas in an equilibrium mixture behaves as if it is in the container (box) on its own.

A   B   Equilibrium mixture

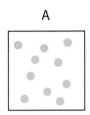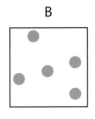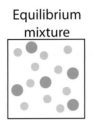

Example 5.14

What is the K_p expression for the following equilibrium?

$$N_2\,(g) + 3\,H_2\,(g) \rightleftharpoons 2\,NH_3\,(g)$$

$$K_p = \frac{p(NH_3\,(g))^2_{eq}}{p(N_2\,(g))_{eq}\,p(H_2\,(g))^3_{eq}}$$

To work out units replace each partial pressure with Pa.

This gives units $= \dfrac{(Pa)^2}{(Pa) \times (Pa)^3}$ so units $= \dfrac{1}{(Pa)^2} = Pa^{-2}$.

Questions 5.4

1. Show a proof, using the ideal gas equation (B1.6b), that the pressure of a gas is proportional to its concentration.

2. Write K_p expressions for the following equilibria.

   a. $2\,SO_2\,(g) + O_2\,(g) \rightleftharpoons 2\,SO_3\,(g)$

   b. $CO\,(g) + NO_2\,(g) \rightleftharpoons CO_2\,(g) + NO\,(g)$

   c. $H_2\,(g) + I_2\,(g) \rightleftharpoons 2\,HI\,(g)$

Equilibrium constant K_{sp}

When a heterogeneous equilibrium is set up between a sparingly soluble salt and its ions in solution, the equilibrium constant is called the **solubility product** (K_{sp}). The value of K_{sp} can be calculated from a salt's solubility (B1.5e). K_{sp} may be used to predict whether a precipitate will form for a sparingly soluble compound, This is particularly important when carrying out qualitative tests (A4.1a) that produce precipitates having characteristic colours. Like other equilibrium constants, K_{sp} is constant at a given temperature and the units depend on the stoichiometry of the equation.

Examples of solubility products (K_{sp})

Ionic compound	K_{sp}	units
$CaCO_3$	5.0×10^{-9}	$mol^2\,dm^{-6}$
$CaSO_4$	2.0×10^{-5}	$mol^2\,dm^{-6}$
$AgCl$	2.0×10^{-10}	$mol^2\,dm^{-6}$
$AgBr$	5.0×10^{-13}	$mol^2\,dm^{-6}$
AgI	8.0×10^{-17}	$mol^2\,dm^{-6}$
$PbBr_2$	3.9×10^{-5}	$mol^3\,dm^{-9}$

When silver chloride solid is placed into a beaker of water, an equilibrium is set up between the solid and the very small number of dissolved ions.

$$AgCl\,(s) \rightleftharpoons Ag^+\,(aq) + Cl^-\,(aq)$$

Cl⁻

Ag⁺

AgCl (s)

The concentration of the solid silver chloride is constant and, like other heterogeneous equilibria, the [solid] can be left out of the equilibrium expression for the solubility product.

$$K_{sp} = [Ag^+\,(aq)]_{eq}\,[Cl^-\,(aq)]_{eq}.$$

In words, K_{sp} is the product of the concentrations of the products raised to the power of their coefficients. The only factor that affects the size of K_{sp} is temperature, which is why it is always quoted with values of K_{sp}. At a fixed temperature, adding additional solid will not affect the position of the equilibrium because solubility products only apply if the solution in equilibrium with the solid is saturated. At 298 K, $K_{sp} = 2 \times 10^{-10}\ mol^2\,dm^{-6}$ for silver chloride.

Example 5.15

The solubility product of lead(II) iodide is $7.1 \times 10^{-9} \text{ mol}^3 \text{ dm}^{-9}$. Find the equilibrium and the equilibrium expression for K_{sp}.

The formula of lead(II) iodide is PbI_2 and it will form an equilibrium with its soluble ions. The very small value of K_{sp} tells us that lead(II) iodide is virtually an insoluble salt.

$$PbI_2 \text{ (s)} \rightleftharpoons Pb^{2+} \text{ (aq)} + 2 I^- \text{ (aq)}$$

$$K_{sp} = [Pb^{2+} \text{ (aq)}]_{eq} \times [I^- \text{ (aq)}]^2_{eq}$$

Question 5.5

1. Write K_{sp} expressions for the following equilibria remembering to give units.

   a. $CaCO_3 \text{ (s)} \rightleftharpoons Ca^{2+} \text{ (aq)} + CO_3^{2-} \text{ (aq)}$

   b. $BaSO_4 \text{ (s)} \rightleftharpoons Ba^{2+} \text{ (aq)} + SO_4^{2-} \text{ (aq)}$

   c. $PbS \text{ (s)} \rightleftharpoons Pb^{2+} \text{ (aq)} + S^{2-} \text{ (aq)}$

Equilibrium constant K_a

An equilibrium is set up when a weak acid (HA) dissolves in water. There are two ways to write this equilibrium, the longer version, which includes water, or the shorthand version which shows only the ionization of the weak acid.

$$HA \text{ (aq)} + H_2O \text{ (l)} \rightleftharpoons H_3O^+ \text{ (aq)} + A^- \text{ (aq)}$$

$$HA \text{ (aq)} \rightleftharpoons H^+ \text{ (aq)} + A^- \text{ (aq)}$$

The position of the equilibrium depends on the strength of the acid. For weak acids, the relative sizes of the equilibrium constant K_a indicate their relative strengths. Values of K_a typically vary from 1×10^{-2} to 1×10^{-10} mol dm^{-3}. Like other equilibrium constants K_a is temperature dependent and is usually quoted at 298 K.

Typical K_a values for some weak acids

Name of acid	Equilibrium in (aq) solution	K_a / mol dm^{-3} (298 K)
Sulfurous	$H_2SO_3 \rightleftharpoons H^+ + HSO_3^-$	1.5×10^{-2}
Phosphoric(V)	$H_3PO_4 \rightleftharpoons H^+ + H_2PO_4^-$	7.9×10^{-3}
Hydrofluoric	$HF \rightleftharpoons H^+ + F^-$	5.6×10^{-4}
Chloroethanoic	$CH_2ClCOOH \rightleftharpoons CH_2ClCOO^- + H^+$	1.3×10^{-3}
Nitrous	$HNO_2 \rightleftharpoons H^+ + NO_2^-$	4.7×10^{-4}
Methanoic	$HCOOH \rightleftharpoons HCOO^- + H^+$	1.6×10^{-4}
Benzoic	$C_6H_5COOH \rightleftharpoons C_6H_5COO^- + H^+$	6.3×10^{-5}
Ethanoic	$CH_3COOH \rightleftharpoons CH_3COO^- + H^+$	1.7×10^{-5}
Carbonic	$H_2CO_3 \rightleftharpoons H^+ + HCO_3^-$	4.5×10^{-7}

K_a is defined in the same way as K_c (B1.5c) but the solvent water is left out of the equilibrium expression because its concentration, $[H_2O]$, is considered to be constant as it is so large compared with the concentration of the other species. There is no need to write the subscript eq since these equilibria are reached so quickly. The equilibrium expression for the acid dissociation constant can be written in two ways and either is correct.

$$K_a = \frac{[H_3O^+ \text{ (aq)}] [A^- \text{ (aq)}]}{[HA \text{ (aq)}]}$$

or it can be expressed as:

$$K_a = \frac{[H^+ \text{ (aq)}] [A^- \text{ (aq)}]}{[HA \text{ (aq)}]}$$

The larger the value of K_a, the stronger the acid. Unlike some other equilibrium constants, which can have different units, K_a always has the units of mol dm^{-3}. K_a is a more useful way of representing acid strength than pH as, unlike pH, the equilibrium constant is unaffected by concentration changes. K_a for a weak acid can be determined (B1.5e) using the equilibrium equation and if its concentration and pH are both known. K_a can be used to calculate the $[H^+]$ for a weak acid and therefore its pH (B1.5f).

Example 5.16

What is the K_a expression for the following equilibrium?

$$C_6H_5COOH \text{ (aq)} \rightleftharpoons C_6H_5COO^- \text{ (aq)} + H^+ \text{ (aq)}$$

$$K_a = \frac{[H^+ \text{ (aq)}] \, [C_6H_5COO^- \text{ (aq)}]}{[C_6H_5COOH \text{ (aq)}]}$$

Questions 5.6

1. Why do stronger weak acids have large acid dissociation constants?

2. What types of substance are:

   methyl orange ($K_a = 2 \times 10^{-4}$ mol dm^{-3}) and

   phenolphthalein ($K_a = 7 \times 10^{-10}$ mol dm^{-3})?

3. Write the expression for K_a for:

   a. Methanoic acid

   b. Ethanoic acid

   c. Phenol

   d. Carbonic acid

Equilibrium constant K_w

Water dissociates according to this equilibrium:

$$H_2O \text{ (l)} \rightleftharpoons H^+ \text{ (aq)} + OH^- \text{ (aq)}$$

$$\Delta_r H = +57 \text{ kJ mol}^{-1} \text{ (endothermic)}$$

The equilibrium gives equal amounts of acid (H$^+$) and alkali (OH$^-$) and lies very much to the left hand side. In writing the equilibrium constant for this equilibrium the [H$_2$O] is omitted as it is effectively constant. This gives the ionic product of water K_w.

Ionic product: $K_w = [H^+] [OH^-]$

Since the pH of water at 298 K is 7.0:

$[H^+] = 1 \times 10^{-7}$ mol dm^{-3}.

For every molecule of water that ionizes it will produce one OH$^-$ for every H$^+$.

Therefore the [OH$^-$] also equals 1×10^{-7} mol dm^{-3}.

Therefore $K_w = 1 \times 10^{-7} \times 1 \times 10^{-7} = 1.0 \times 10^{-14}$ mol^2 dm^{-6} at 298 K.

The value of K_w increases as the temperature increases. This is because the ionization of water is endothermic. [OH$^-$] = [H$^+$] at all temperatures as both ions form in equal amounts every time a water molecule ionizes.

K_w / mol^2 dm^{-6}	Temperature / K
1.114×10^{-15}	273
1.00×10^{-14}	298
2.92×10^{-14}	313
5.13×10^{-13}	373

B1.5 (e) Equilibrium constant calculations

A series of calculations follow for each of the equilibrium constants. It will soon become apparent that there are a lot of similarities in the approach to the calculations for the different equilibrium constant expressions. Time needs to be invested in these exercises and familiarity with your particular type of calculator is essential.

Worked examples for K_p

Example 5.17

Write down the value of K_p for the following (homogeneous) gaseous equilibrium and give the units of K_p.

$$PCl_5 \text{ (g)} \rightleftharpoons PCl_3 \text{ (g)} + Cl_2 \text{ (g)}$$

$$K_p = \frac{p \, (PCl_3)_{eq} \times p \, (Cl_2)_{eq}}{p \, (PCl_5)_{eq}} \text{ and the units = Pa.}$$

Example 5.18

What is the value of K_p at 333K and 1 atmosphere pressure when the equilibrium mixture was found to consist of 30.4% N_2O_4 and 69.6% NO_2?

$$N_2O_4\,(g) \rightleftharpoons 2\,NO_2\,(g)$$

The partial pressure of each gas = (% of each gas ÷ 100%) × Total pressure

$$p\,N_2O_4 = \frac{30.4\%}{100\%} \times 100\text{kPa} = 30.4\text{ kPa}$$

$$p\,NO_2 = \frac{69.6\%}{100\%} \times 100\text{kPa} = 69.6\text{ kPa}$$

$$K_p = \frac{p\,(NO_2)^2_{eq}}{p\,(N_2O_4)_{eq}}$$

$$= \frac{(69.6)^2}{30.4}$$

$$= 159.3\text{ kPa}$$

Example 5.19

What is the total pressure and the value of K_p in an equilibrium mixture at constant temperature when the partial pressures are; H_2 $(2.2 \times 10^4$ Pa), I_2 $(0.5 \times 10^4$ Pa), and HI $(7.3 \times 10^4$ Pa)?

$$H_2\,(g) + I_2\,(g) \rightleftharpoons 2\,HI\,(g)$$

Total pressure = sum of all the partial pressures

Total pressure $= 2.2 \times 10^4$ Pa $+ 0.5 \times 10^4$ Pa $+ 7.3 \times 10^4$ Pa

$$= 10 \times 10^4\,\text{Pa}$$

$$K_p = \frac{p\,(HI)^2}{p\,(H_2) \times p\,(I_2)}$$

$$= \frac{(7.3 \times 10^4\,\text{Pa})^2}{(2.2 \times 10^4\,\text{Pa}) \times (0.5 \times 10^4\,\text{Pa})}$$

$$= 48.4\text{ (dimensionless)}$$

Example 5.20

Calculate K_p at 107°C and a total pressure of 1.5 MPa when the equilibrium mixture consists of carbon monoxide (0.122 mole), hydrogen (0.298 mole) and methanol (0.478 mole).

$$CO\,(g) + 2\,H_2\,(g) \rightleftharpoons CH_3OH\,(g)$$

Total moles in the mixture
$$= 0.122 + 0.298 + 0.478 = 0.898\text{ moles}$$

Partial pressure of CO $= \dfrac{0.122}{0.898} \times 1.5\text{ MPa}$

$$= 0.2038\text{ MPa}$$

Partial pressure of H_2 $= \dfrac{0.298}{0.898} \times 1.5\text{ MPa}$

$$= 0.4978\text{ MPa}$$

Partial pressure of $CH_3OH = \dfrac{0.478}{0.898} \times 1.5\text{ MPa}$

$$= 0.7984\text{ MPa}$$

$$K_p = \frac{p\,(CH_3OH)}{p(CO) \times p\,(H_2)^2}$$

$$= \frac{0.7984\text{ MPa}}{(0.2038\text{ MPa}) \times (0.4978\text{ MPa})^2}$$

$$= 15.81\text{ MPa}^{-2}$$

Questions 5.7

1. Write down the expression for K_p for the following (heterogeneous) equilibrium and give the units of K_p.

$$H_2O\,(g) + C(s) \rightleftharpoons H_2\,(g) + CO\,(g)$$

2. Calculate K_p at 650 K and a total pressure of 90 atmospheres when the equilibrium mixture consists of nitrogen (0.2 mole), hydrogen (0.6 mole) and ammonia (0.2 mole).

$$N_2\,(g) + 3\,H_2\,(g) \rightleftharpoons 2\,NH_3\,(g)$$

Worked examples for K_{sp}

Example 5.21

Calculate K_{sp} at 298 K when $CaCO_3$ has a solubility of 7.07×10^{-5} mol dm^{-3}.

Equation: $CaCO_3$ (s) $\rightleftharpoons$ Ca^{2+} (aq) + CO_3^{2-} (aq)

$K_{sp} = [Ca^{2+}] [CO_3^{2-}]$

The concentration of $[Ca^{2+}] = [CO_3^{2-}] = 7.07 \times 10^{-5}$ mol dm^{-3}

$$K_{sp} = (7.07 \times 10^{-5}) \times (7.07 \times 10^{-5})$$

$$= (7.07 \times 10^{-5})^2$$

$$= 5.0 \times 10^{-9} \text{ mol}^2 \text{ dm}^{-6}$$

Example 5.22

Calculate K_{sp} at 298 K when $CaSO_4$ has a solubility of 0.743 g dm^{-3}.

[A_r: Ca (40.1) S (32.1) O (16.0)].

There are two concentration units; mol dm^{-3} and g dm^{-3}.

The conversion to the more usual mol dm^{-3} concentration is g dm^{-3} ÷ M_r

M_r for $CaSO_4$ = 40.1 + 32.1 + (4 × 16.0) = 136.2 g mol^{-1}.

Solubility of $CaSO_4 = \dfrac{0.743}{136.2} = 5.46 \times 10^{-3}$ mol dm^{-3}

Equation: $CaSO_4$ (s) $\rightleftharpoons$ Ca^{2+} (aq) + SO_4^{2-} (aq)

$K_{sp} = [Ca^{2+}] [SO_4^{2-}]$

The concentration of $[Ca^{2+}] = [SO_4^{2-}] = 5.46 \times 10^{-3}$ mol dm^{-3}

$$K_{sp} = (5.46 \times 10^{-3}) \times (5.46 \times 10^{-3})$$

$$= (5.46 \times 10^{-3})^2$$

$$= 2.98 \times 10^{-5} \text{ mol}^2 \text{ dm}^{-6}$$

Example 5.23

Calculate the solubility in mol dm^{-3} of AgCl at 298 K if the solubility product $K_{sp} = 2.0 \times 10^{-10}$ mol^2 dm^{-6}.

Equation: AgCl (s) $\rightleftharpoons$ Ag^+ (aq) + Cl^- (aq)

$K_{sp} = [Ag^+] [Cl^-]$

$2.0 \times 10^{-10} = [Ag^+] [Cl^-]$ and since $[Ag^+] = [Cl^-]$

$\sqrt{2.0 \times 10^{-10}} = [Ag^+] = 1.41 \times 10^{-5}$ mol dm^{-3}.

Example 5.24

Calculate the solubility in mol dm^{-3} of $Ca(OH)_2$ at 298 K if the solubility product $K_{sp} = 1.43 \times 10^{-8}$ mol^3 dm^{-9}.

Equation: $Ca(OH)_2$ (s) $\rightleftharpoons$ Ca^{2+} (aq) + 2 OH^- (aq)

$K_{sp} = [Ca^{2+}] [OH^-]^2 = [Ca^{2+}](2[Ca^{2+}])^2$ (since $[OH^-] = 2[Ca^{2+}]$)

$1.43 \times 10^{-8} = 4[Ca^{2+}]^3$ and

$[Ca^{2+}] = \sqrt[3]{\dfrac{1.43 \times 10^{-8}}{4}} = 1.53 \times 10^{-3}$ mol dm^{-3}.

Questions 5.8

1. Calculate the solubility product at 298 K for $MgCO_3$ and AgBr.

   [A_r: Mg (24.3), C (12.0), O (16.0), Ag (108), Br (79.9)]

   Solubility of $MgCO_3$ is 0.267 g dm^{-3}

   Solubility of AgBr is 7.07×10^{-7} mol dm^{-3}

2. Calculate the solubility in mol dm^{-3} at 298 K of the following compounds:

   a. Ag_2S where its $K_{sp} = 6.3 \times 10^{-50}$ mol^3 dm^{-9}

   b. AgCNS where its $K_{sp} = 2.0 \times 10^{-12}$ mol^2 dm^{-6}

   c. SrF_2 where its $K_{sp} = 2.45 \times 10^{-9}$ mol^3 dm^{-9}

Worked examples for K_a

Example 5.25

The equilibrium between carbon dioxide and water helps buffer the blood.

$$CO_2\ (aq) + H_2O\ (l) \rightleftharpoons HCO_3^-\ (aq) + H^+\ (aq)$$

The acid dissociation constant $K_a = 4.5 \times 10^{-7}$ mol dm^{-3} at 310K.

If: $[HCO_3^-] = 1.3 \times 10^{-2}$ mol dm^{-3} and

$[CO_2] = 1.3 \times 10^{-3}$ mol dm^{-3}

calculate the $[H^+]$ and the pH of blood.

$$K_a = \frac{[HCO_3^-]\ [H^+]}{[CO_2]} \text{ and rearranging gives}$$

$$[H^+] = K_a \times \frac{[CO_2]}{[HCO_3^-]}$$

$$= 4.5 \times 10^{-7} \times \frac{1.3 \times 10^{-3}}{1.3 \times 10^{-2}}$$

$$= 4.5 \times 10^{-8} \text{ mol dm}^{-3}$$

$$pH = -\log_{10} [H^+]$$

$$= -\log_{10} 4.5 \times 10^{-8}$$

$$= 7.35$$

Example 5.26

Ethanoic acid with concentration 0.01 mol dm^{-3} has a pH of 3.38 at 298 K. What is its acid dissociation constant (K_a)?

$$CH_3COOH\ (aq) \rightleftharpoons CH_3COO^-\ (aq) + H^+\ (aq)$$

$$K_a = \frac{[CH_3COO^-]\ [H^+]}{[CH_3COOH]}$$

Since $\quad [H^+] = [CH_3COO^-]$

$$K_a = \frac{[H^+]^2}{[CH_3COOH]}$$

$$[H^+] = 10^{-pH}$$

$$[H^+] = 10^{-3.38}$$

$$[H^+] = 4.17 \times 10^{-4} \text{ mol dm}^{-3}$$

$$K_a = \frac{[4.17 \times 10^{-4}]^2}{[CH_3COOH]}$$

As ethanoic is a weak acid (partly ionized) and it is assumed that its concentration will be the same as that given for the acid.

$$K_a = \frac{[4.17 \times 10^{-4}]^2}{[0.01]}$$

$$= 1.74 \times 10^{-5} \text{ mol dm}^{-3}$$

Example 5.27

Hydrofluoric acid with concentration 0.0010 mol dm^{-3} has a $K_a = 1.7 \times 10^{-3}$ mol dm^{-3} at 298 K. What is its pH?

$$HF\ (aq) \rightleftharpoons H^+\ (aq) + F^-\ (aq)$$

$$K_a = \frac{[H^+]\ [F^-]}{[HF]}$$

Since $\quad [H^+] = [F^-]$

$$K_a = \frac{[H^+]^2}{[HF]}$$

rearranging this equation gives

$$[H^+] = \sqrt{K_a \times [HF]}$$

As hydrofluoric acid is a weak acid (partly ionized), it is assumed that its concentration will be the same as that given for the acid.

$$[H^+] = \sqrt{1.7 \times 10^{-3} \times 0.0010}$$

$$= 1.30 \times 10^{-3} \text{ mol dm}^{-3}$$

$$pH = -\log_{10} [H^+]$$

$$= -\log_{10} (1.30 \times 10^{-3})$$

$$= 2.9$$

Questions 5.9

1. What is K_a for 0.25 mol dm^{-3} of H_3PO_4 with a pH of 1.35 at 298K?

2. What is K_a for 0.05 mol dm^{-3} of HCO_2H with a pH of 2.55 at 298K?

3. What is K_a for 0.12 mol dm^{-3} of HOCl with a pH of 4.18 at 298K?

4. What is the pH of lactic acid (0.01 mol dm^{-3}) with $K_a = 1.29 \times 10^{-4}$ mol dm^{-3}?

5. What is the pH of propanoic acid (0.02 mol dm^{-3}) with $K_a = 1.3 \times 10^{-5}$ mol dm^{-3}?

6. What is the pH of benzoic acid (0.08 mol dm^{-3}) with $K_a = 6.3 \times 10^{-5}$ mol dm^{-3}?

Worked examples for K_W

The pH at which water is neutral varies with temperature. When water ionizes, there will always be the same number of H$^+$ ions and OH$^-$ ions.

Example 5.28

What is the pH at which water is neutral at 323 K when $K_w = 5.47 \times 10^{-14}$ mol^2 dm^{-6}?

$$K_w = [OH^-] \times [H^+]$$

$$5.47 \times 10^{-14} = [OH^-] \times [H^+] \text{ and since } [H^+] = [OH^-]$$

$$= [H^+] \times [H^+]$$

$$= [H^+]^2$$

$$[H^+] = \sqrt{5.47 \times 10^{-14}}$$

$$= 2.34 \times 10^{-7} \text{ moldm}^{-3}$$

and since $\text{pH} = -\log_{10} [H^+]$

$$= -\log_{10} 2.34 \times 10^{-7}$$

$$= 6.6.$$

So at a pH of 6.6 at 323 K, water is neutral.

Questions 5.10

1. Calculate the pH at which water is neutral at the different temperatures using the values for K_w.

K_w / mol^2 dm^{-6}	Temperature / K
0.114×10^{-14}	273
0.293×10^{-14}	283
1.00×10^{-14}	298
2.92×10^{-14}	313
51.3×10^{-14}	373

2. Explain what happens to the pH of pure water as the temperature increases.

B1.5 (f) pH and pK_a

pH can be measured with coloured indicators, which make up the universal indicator, or with pH electrodes. Modern pH meters have a digital read out, usually to one decimal place. A pH of exactly 7.0 is neutral. A pH less than 7 is acidic and a pH of greater than 7 is alkaline. The **p** in **pH** stands for the German word *potenz* which means power. This means that pH is an abbreviation for the power of hydrogen. The definition of pH is given by the equation pH = $-\log_{10}$ [H$^+$] and was first given by Søren Sørensen (1909).

For a pH less than seven, the smaller the pH number the stronger the acid. The larger the pH number greater than seven, the stronger the alkali (at a given concentration). The pH scale is logarithmic. This means that, if two solutions have a pH separated by one pH unit, they are different in concentrations of hydrogen ions by a factor of ten. Therefore, a solution of pH 2 is ×10 more acidic than a solution with pH 3. A solution of pH 4 is ×100 more acidic than a solution of pH 6. pH does not have a unit.

pH	Universal indicator colour (approx.)	[H$^+$] / mol dm^{-3}
0		1×10^{0}
1		1×10^{-1}
2		1×10^{-2}
3		1×10^{-3}
4		1×10^{-4}
5		1×10^{-5}
6		1×10^{-6}
7		1×10^{-7}
8		1×10^{-8}
9		1×10^{-9}
10		1×10^{-10}
11		1×10^{-11}
12		1×10^{-12}
13		1×10^{-13}
14		1×10^{-14}

pH of strong acids

Since strong acids fully ionize, the value of [H$^+$] will be the same as the value given for the concentration of a monoprotic acid. For a 0.1 mol dm^{-3} solution of hydrochloric acid the value of [H$^+$] will also equal 0.1 mol dm^{-3}. The pH of this acid will be pH = $- \log_{10}$ [0.1] = $-(-1)$ = 1. The pH for a 0.1 mol dm^{-3} solution of sulfuric acid will be pH = $- \log_{10}$ [0.2] = $-(-0.7)$ = 0.7. The concentration of H$^+$ ions for sulfuric acid is twice that for hydrochloric acid of the same concentration because sulfuric acid is diprotic. So, for every molecule of H$_2$SO$_4$, it will ionise to give two H$^+$ ions. A good rule of thumb is to give answers for pH values to the number of decimal places that equals the number of significant figures for the concentration of the acid.

Since pH = $- \log_{10}$ [H$^+$], it follows that [H$^+$] = 10^{-pH}. This latter equation is often used by technicians to check their dilutions when making acid for laboratory use. If a solution has a pH = 2.8, what is the value of [H$^+$]? Using [H$^+$] = 10^{-pH} the value of [H$^+$] = $10^{-2.8}$ = 1.58×10^{-3} mol dm^{-3}.

pH of weak acids

Since weak acids only partially ionize, the value of [H$^+$] will **not** be the same as the value given for the concentration of the acid. To calculate the pH of a weak acid, in addition to its concentration, you also need to have the value for its acid dissociation constant K_a.

Example 5.29

Lactic acid is a product of anaerobic respiration formed in the muscles where it is found at concentrations typically of around 0.01 mol dm^{-3}. What is the pH of this weak acid given that its K_a = 1.29×10^{-4} mol dm^{-3}

The equilibrium for lactic acid (2-hydroxypropanoic acid) is:

$$CH_3CH(OH)COOH \rightleftharpoons CH_3CH(OH)COO^- + H^+$$

Therefore the acid dissociation constant for lactic acid is:

$$K_a = \frac{[CH_3CH(OH)COO^-]\,[H^+]}{[CH_3CH(OH)COOH]}$$

Following all the assumptions explained in section B1.5d then the acid dissociation constant:

$$K_a = \frac{[H^+]^2}{0.01}$$

Rearranging gives:

$$[H^+] = \sqrt{1.29 \times 10^{-4} \times 0.01}$$

$$= 1.14 \times 10^{-3} \text{ mol dm}^{-3}$$

$$pH = -\log_{10} [H^+]$$

$$= -\log_{10} (1.14 \times 10^{-3})$$

$$= 2.94$$

pK_a

K_a values for weak acids are often very small and they can be conveniently converted into pK_a values to make the numbers easier to compare. There is the same relationship between pK_a and K_a as there is between pH and [H$^+$]. pK_a is a number which is the negative logarithm to the base ten of K_a.

$$pK_a = -\log_{10} K_a$$

pK_a is a measure of acid strength. The smaller the pK_a value, the stronger the acid.

The K_a for ethanoic acid is 1.7×10^{-5} mol dm^{-3}, therefore the pK_a of ethanoic acid is $-\log_{10} 1.7 \times 10^{-5} = 4.77$. Like pH, p$K_a$ has no units because they are both logarithmic.

pK_a values of some weak acids

Acid	pK_a	Acid	pK_a
HF	3.25	C_6H_5COOH	4.20
HNO_2	3.33	CH_3COOH	4.77
HCOOH	3.80	C_6H_5OH	9.89

$$pK_a = -\log_{10} K_a$$

and rearranging this equation gives:

$$K_a = 10^{-pK_a}$$

So if the pK_a of a weak acid is known, it is straightforward to work out its acid dissociation constant. The pK_a of nitrous acid is 3.33 so its $K_a = 10^{-3.33} = 4.68 \times 10^{-4}$ mol dm^{-3}.

pK_a from titration curves

The pK_a of a weak acid such as ethanoic acid can be determined experimentally from a titration curve. A 25 cm^3 sample of weak acid (0.1 mol dm^{-3}) is pipetted into a conical flask followed by the addition of a few drops of phenolphthalein. The strong alkali (0.1 mol dm^{-3}) is placed in the burette and the pH is recorded for every 0.5 cm^3 of alkali added. At the end point, the colour change will be from colourless to pale pink. Half way through the titration, exactly half of the ethanoic acid will have been converted into its conjugate base, sodium ethanoate.

Therefore, at this part of the titration, sometimes called the **half neutralization point**:

$$[CH_3CO_2H] = [CH_3CO_2^-]$$

Since:

$$K_a = \frac{[H^+][CH_3COO^-]}{[CH_3COOH]}$$

then:

$$K_a = [H^+]$$

as the other two concentrations cancel out to give one. Taking the negative logarithm to the base ten of both sides of $K_a = [H^+]$ gives pK_a = pH. This point has been marked on the titration curve.

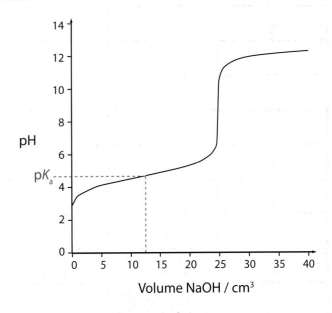

Titration of ethanoic acid *versus* a strong alkali

pH from pK_a

pH, pK_a and [weak acid] are related by the equation:

pH = ½pK_a – ½$\log_{10}$ [weak acid].

This equation is a useful short cut for solving pH from pK_a. For example, the pH of ethanoic acid (pK_a 4.8) of concentration 0.5 mol dm⁻³ is pH = ½ (4.8) – ½$\log_{10}$ (0.5) = 2.55.

Questions 5.11

1. Calculate the pH of the following strong acids.

   a. 0.001 mol dm⁻³ HCl (aq)

   b. 0.5 mol dm⁻³ HCl (aq)

   c. 0.02 mol dm⁻³ H_2SO_4 (aq) ✗ $H_2SO_4 \rightleftharpoons H^+ + HSO_4^-$ (only) c.

   d. 0.5 mol dm⁻³ H_2SO_4 (aq) ✗ $HSO_4^- \rightleftharpoons H^+ + SO_4^{2-}$ $K 10^{-2}$ d.

   $\varepsilon \approx 1 mol$ 0   0

   eq 0.01   0.1   0.1

2. What is the hydrogen ion concentration for solutions with the following pHs?

   a. 2.61

   b. 5.42

   c. 2.75

   d. –0.5

   e. 4.36

   f. 6.78

3. What is the pH of human blood given that the value of [H⁺] is 4.0 × 10⁻⁸ mol dm⁻³?

4. Calculate the pH of the following weak acids.

   a. 0.01 mol dm⁻³ propanoic acid
   (K_a = 1.3 × 10⁻⁵ mol dm⁻³)

   b. 0.25 mol dm⁻³ benzoic acid
   (K_a = 6.3 × 10⁻⁵ mol dm⁻³)

   c. 0.03 mol dm⁻³ methanoic acid
   (K_a = 1.6 × 10⁻⁴ mol dm⁻³)

   d. 0.40 mol dm⁻³ ethanoic acid
   (K_a = 1.7 × 10⁻⁵ mol dm⁻³)

   e. 0.40 mol dm⁻³ chloroethanoic acid
   (K_a = 1.3 × 10⁻³ mol dm⁻³)

5. What are the pK_a values for the following weak acids?

   Place the acids in order of their acidity starting with the most acidic and finishing with the least acidic.

   a. HOCl (K_a = 3.7 × 10⁻⁸ mol dm⁻³)

   b. HCN (K_a = 4.9 × 10⁻¹⁰ mol dm⁻³)

   c. C_2H_5COOH (K_a = 1.3 × 10⁻⁵ mol dm⁻³)

   d. H_3PO_4 (K_a = 7.9 × 10⁻³ mol dm⁻³)

6. What are the K_a values for these aromatic acids;

   benzoic (pK_a = 4.20)

   and phenol (pK_a =9.89)?

7. What is the pH of 0.6 mol dm⁻³ methanoic acid (pK_a 3.80)?

B1.5 (g) Acid–base titrations and indicators

A **titration** is a **volumetric analysis** used to determine the unknown concentration of a solution. In order to calculate the unknown concentration in an acid–base titration, you need to know the balanced formula equation and also the concentration of either the acid or the base.

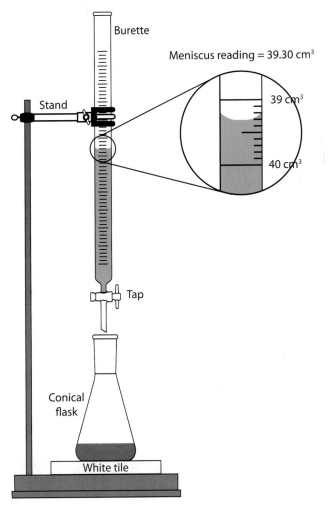

Meniscus reading = 39.30 cm³

Apparatus for an acid-base titration

Volumes of acid and base are accurately known as they are measured in either a pipette or a burette. When performing a titration, the burette is held vertically in a clamp with a white tile placed beneath the conical flask. A funnel is used to load the burette but should always be removed during the titration itself. Good experimenters will ensure that there is no air bubble trapped below the burette tap and they will not allow any liquid to enter the pipette filler. When reading volume scale marks, they will get their eye level with the meniscus to avoid parallax. During a titration it is good practice near the end point to add the liquid dropwise whilst swirling the contents of the conical flask.

The pH changes during an acid-base titration can be monitored using a pH electrode. If just the end point is needed, a few drops of a suitable indicator are added to the conical flask prior to addition of liquid from the burette. When carrying out a titration, a rough value for the end point is determined followed by at least two other titrations which agree to within 0.10 cm^3. The average is then taken from these results for the subsequent calculation and these results are often described as **concordant**, meaning **in agreement**. The table shows an efficient way of recording results for an acid-base titration.

Volume added from the burette / cm³	Rough	1st	2nd	Average titres (1st & 2nd)
Final	25.20	49.80	0.20	
Initial	0.10	25.20	24.80	
Titre	25.10	24.60	24.60	24.60

Titration curves

A titration curve is a plot of pH *versus* volume of acid or alkali added from the burette. There are four types of acid-base titration which give very different changes in pH as seen by their curves. It is clear that none of the titration curves change linearly.

The titration curve of the weak acid *vs.* strong alkali starts at ~ pH = 3 with a rapid change of pH in the neutralization reaction between pH 6.5 to pH 11 as it nears its equivalence point (pH 8.8) and finishes at ~pH = 13. The equivalence point is the point at which the number of moles of H^+ = number of moles of OH^-. The equivalence point is the part of the titration curve where the almost vertical part of the graph's gradient changes direction at a point called the point of inflection.

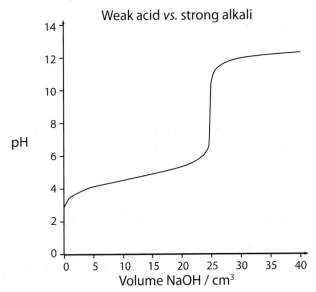

Weak acid *vs.* strong alkali

The titration curve of the strong acid *vs.* strong alkali starts at ~ pH = 1 with a rapid change of pH in the neutralization reaction between pH 3 to pH 11 as it nears its equivalence point (pH 7) and finishes at ~pH = 13.

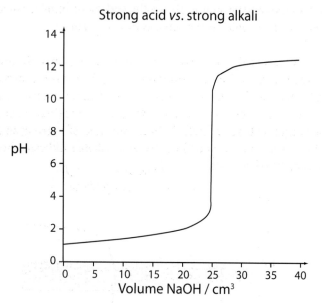

The titration curve of the strong acid *vs.* weak alkali starts at ~ pH = 1 with a rapid change of pH in the neutralization reaction between pH 3 to pH 7 as it nears its equivalence point (pH 5.2) and finishes at ~pH = 9.

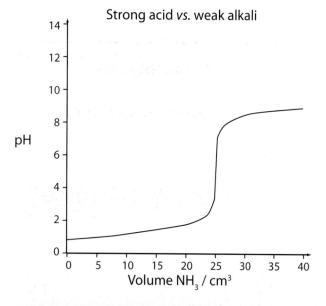

The titration curve of the weak acid *vs.* weak alkali starts at ~pH = 3 and there is no rapid change of pH in the neutralization reaction and it finishes at ~pH = 9.

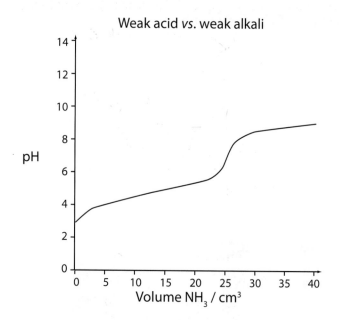

When drawing titration curves, start and finish in the right pH region and ensure that the vertical part is at the volume corresponding to the equivalence point. If 25 cm³ of 1.0 mol dm⁻³ hydrochloric acid is titrated against 1.0 mol dm⁻³ sodium hydroxide, the equivalence point will come at 25 cm³. But if 10 cm³ of 1.0 mol dm⁻³ sulfuric acid is titrated against 1.0 mol dm⁻³ sodium hydroxide, the equivalence point will come at 20 cm³.

Indicators

Indicators are water soluble dyes which are weak acids which have distinct and sharp colour changes over a narrow range of ~2 pH units. There are lots of examples of indicators and the two most useful for acid-base titrations are methyl orange and phenolphthalein.

Indicator	colour in acid (HIn)	pK_{in}	colour in alkali (In⁻)	Colour change pH range
Methyl orange	Red	3.7	Yellow	3.2–4.4
Methyl red	Red	5.1	Yellow	4.2–6.3
Aaolitmin (litmus)	Red	7.0	Blue	5.0–8.0
Bromothymol blue	Yellow	7.0	Blue	6.0–7.6
Phenol red	Yellow	7.9	Red	6.8–8.4
Phenolphthalein*	Colourless	9.3	Pink	8.2–10.0

* phenolphthalein is dissolved in ethanol.

The undissociated form of an indicator HIn (weak acid) will have a different colour from its dissociated conjugate base form (In⁻). The indicator phenolphthalein has two different structures corresponding to HIn (colourless) and In⁻ (pink).

Phenolphthalein (colourless)

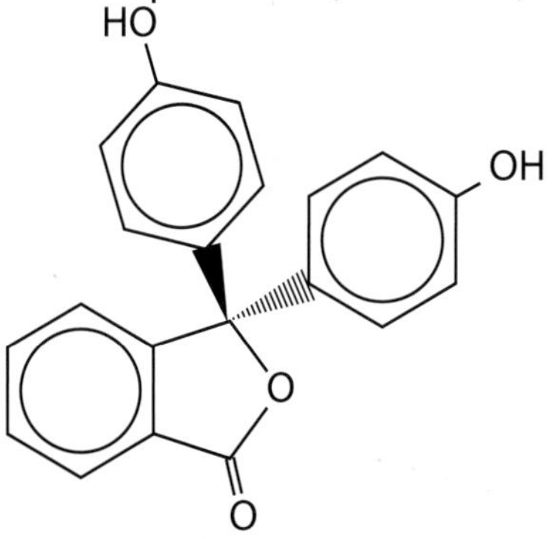

HO

OH

O

O

Phenolphthalein (pink)

O

OH

CO_2^-

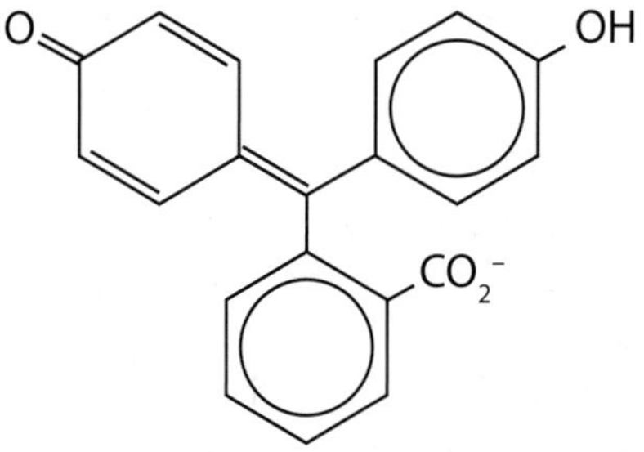

Colours of indicators in acid and alkali

Indicator	Colour in acid	Colour in alkali
Phenolphthalein		
Litmus		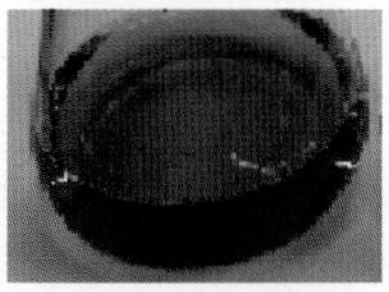
Methyl orange	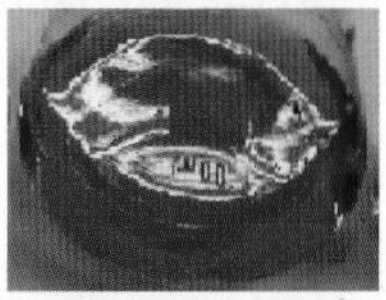	
Bromophenol blue	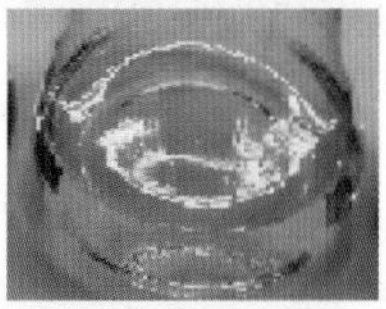	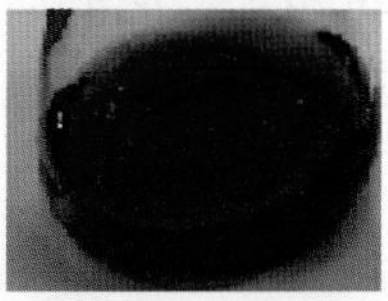
Bromothymol blue	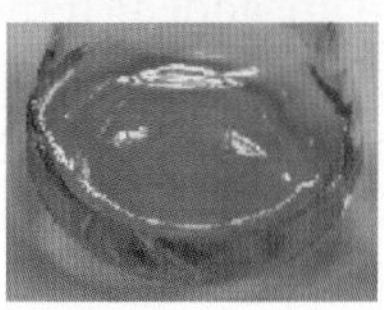	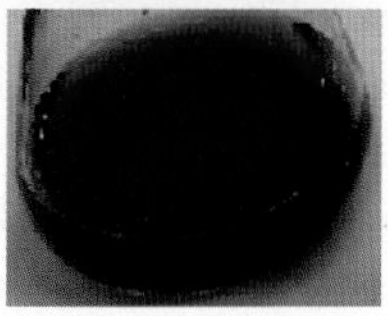

The choice of indicator for a titration depends on which type of acid-base pair is under investigation. The indicator chosen for a titration needs to change from one of its colours to the other where there is a large change in pH, *i.e.* the almost vertical part of the titration curve. The end point of a titration is when [HIn] = [In⁻], which is the same as the pK_{in} value.

If the value of pK_{in} and the colour change range for an indicator match the vertical part of titration curve, then it is a suitable indicator for the titration. This is why phenolphthalein is a suitable indicator but methyl orange is not for the titration of a weak acid with a strong alkali. In the titration of a strong acid with a weak alkali, methyl orange is a suitable indicator but phenolphthalein is not.

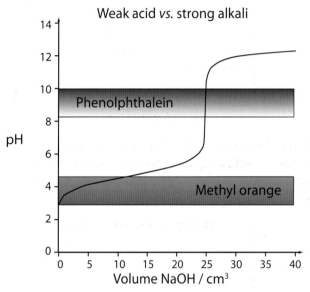

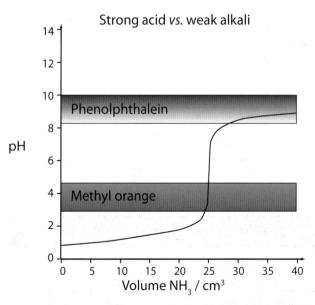

Can you work out what a suitable indicator will be for the titration of a strong acid *vs.* strong alkali and the titration of a weak acid *vs.* weak alkali? Find an indictor whose colour change coincides with the near vertical section of the titration curve. There is no sharp change in pH for the titration between a weak acid and a weak alkali.

	Weak acid	Strong acid
Weak alkali	No suitable indicator	Methyl orange
Strong alkali	Phenolphthalein	Methyl orange or Phenolphthalein

Questions 5.12

1. Which option shows a titration which will not show a sharp end point with either methyl orange or phenolphthalein?

    A   Strong acid *vs* weak alkali

    B   Strong acid *vs* strong alkali

    C   Weak acid *vs* strong alkali

    D   Weak acid *vs* weak alkali

2. What is a titration curve?

3. Complete the following table, which is helpful when drawing titration curves.

	Start the curve
Strong acid	pH = ?
Weak acid	pH = ?
	Finish the curve
Strong base	pH = ?
Weak base	pH = ?

4. What are the colours of these indicators in 1.0 mol dm^{-3} of hydrochloric acid?

    a.   Methyl orange

    b.   Phenolphthalein

    c.   Bromothymol blue

5. Sketch a titration curve for the addition of NaOH (0.1 mol dm^{-3}) to 10 cm^3 of 0.1 mol dm^{-3} of oxalic acid $(CO_2H)_2$ and explain any near vertical sections.

B1.5 (h) Buffer solutions

A buffer solution is one that resists changes in its pH on the addition of small amounts of acid or the addition of small amounts of alkali. There are two types of buffer:

- acidic buffers (pH < 7) and

- alkaline buffers (pH > 7).

The two types of buffer are compared and contrasted in the following table.

Acidic buffer	Alkaline buffer
Weak acid and its sodium salt (Weak acid and its conjugate base)	Weak alkali and its chloride salt (Weak alkali and its conjugate acid)
pH < 7	pH > 7
Ethanoic acid and sodium ethanoate	Ammonia solution and ammonium chloride
$CH_3CO_2H + H_2O \rightleftharpoons CH_3CO_2^- + H_3O^+$ (Equilibrium lies well over to the left hand side)	$NH_3 + H_2O \rightleftharpoons NH_4^+ + OH^-$ (Equilibrium lies well over to the left hand side)
High [CH_3CO_2H]	High [NH_3]
$CH_3CO_2Na + H_2O \rightarrow CH_3CO_2^- + Na^+$ (Sodium ethanoate fully ionizes)	$NH_4Cl + H_2O \rightarrow NH_4^+ + Cl^-$ (Ammonium chloride fully ionizes)

So how does an acidic buffer help to resist changes in its pH if small amounts of acid are added? If the [H_3O^+] is increased, the equilibrium will shift to the left hand side to minimise the applied change by removing the added acid, *i.e.* the added acid will combine with the ethanoate ion. So how does an acidic buffer help to resist changes in its pH if small amounts of alkali are added? If the [OH^-] is increased, the equilibrium will shift to the right hand side to minimise the applied change by replacing the H_3O^+ which is lost in its neutralization reaction with OH^-.

So how does an alkaline buffer help to resist changes in its pH if small amounts of acid are added? If the [H_3O^+] is increased, the equilibrium will shift to the right hand side to minimise the applied change by replacing the removed hydroxide which reacted with the additional acid to form water. So how does an alkaline buffer help to resist changes in its pH if small amounts of alkali are added? If the [OH⁻] is increased, the equilibrium will shift to the left hand side to minimise the applied change by removing the additional OH⁻ in its neutralization reaction with NH_4^+.

Buffers are used to control the pH in shampoos (citric acid and sodium hydroxide) and swimming pools (HOCl / ClO⁻) and to calibrate pH meters. Blood is buffered at pH = 7.4 which is important as it contains vital enzymes (B1.6e) which operate at this optimum pH. In blood, there is an equilibrium between carbonic acid (H_2CO_3) and hydrogen carbonate (HCO_3^-) and hydroxonium ion (H_3O^+).

$$H_2CO_3 \text{ (aq)} + H_2O \text{ (l)} \rightleftharpoons HCO_3^- \text{ (aq)} + H_3O^+ \text{ (aq)}$$
acid   *base*   *conjugate base*   *conjugate acid*

If a small amount of acid is added to blood, it will react with hydrogen carbonate forming carbonic acid and the equilibrium will shift to the left hand side (according to Le Chatelier's principle (B1.5a)) to remove the added acid. If a small amount of alkali is added to blood, it will react with the hydroxonium ion forming water and the equilibrium will shift to the right hand side (again according to Le Chatelier's principle (B1.5a)) to replace the removed hydroxonium. Another reaction which can take place when alkali is added to blood is the formation of carbonate by reaction of the hydroxide with hydrogen carbonate.

$$HCO_3^- \text{ (aq)} + OH^- \text{ (aq)} \rightleftharpoons CO_3^{2-} \text{ (aq)} + H_2O \text{ (l)}$$

In solution, amino acids (B3.11d) also act as buffer solutions due to the neutralizing effect of their acidic and basic groups. The addition of a small amount of acid or alkali to an amino acid solution will have little effect on its pH.

pH of buffers

The **Henderson-Hasselbach equation** is used for working out the pH of both acidic and basic buffers. The pH of an acidic buffer can be calculated if you know the pK_a (B1.5f) of the weak acid and the concentration of the weak acid and its conjugate base. The pH of a basic buffer can be calculated if you know the pK_a of the conjugate acid and the concentration of the weak base and its conjugate acid.

Henderson-Hasselbach equation

Acidic buffer: $pH = pK_a + \log_{10}\left(\dfrac{[\text{conjugate base}]}{[\text{weak acid}]}\right)$

Basic buffer: $pH = pK_a + \log_{10}\left(\dfrac{[\text{weak base}]}{[\text{conjugate acid}]}\right)$

Example 5.30

Calculate the pH of an acidic buffer with 0.1 mol dm⁻³ of sodium ethanoate and 0.1 mol dm⁻³ of ethanoic acid, where the pK_a of ethanoic acid is 4.8.

Since ethanoic acid is a weak acid (partially ionizes) the assumption is that $[CH_3COOH] = 0.1$ mol dm⁻³. As the salt fully ionizes we can assume that the $[CH_3COO^-] = 0.1$ mol dm⁻³. To calculate the pH of this acidic buffer you substitute the values into the Henderson-Hasselbach equation for an acidic buffer.

$$pH = pK_a + \log_{10}\left(\frac{[\text{conjugate base}]}{[\text{weak acid}]}\right)$$

$$= 4.8 + \log_{10}\left(\frac{0.1}{0.1}\right)$$

$$= 4.8 + \log_{10}(1)$$

$$= 4.8 + 0$$

$$= 4.8$$

Example 5.31

Calculate the pH of an acidic buffer formed when 2.53 g of sodium ethanoate is added to 1000 cm³ of ethanoic acid (0.08 mol dm⁻³). $K_a = 1.7 \times 10^{-5}$ mol dm⁻³.

[A_r: Na (23), C (12), O (16) H (1)]

M_r CH₃CO₂⁻Na⁺ = 82 g mol⁻¹.

$$HA \text{ (aq)} \rightleftharpoons H^+ \text{ (aq)} + A^- \text{ (aq)}$$

$$K_a = \frac{[H^+][A^-]}{[HA]}$$

and rearranging this equation gives

$$[H^+] = K_a \times \frac{[HA]}{[A^-]}$$

Assuming that sodium ethanoate fully ionizes (as it is a strong electrolyte):

Since $c = n \div \dfrac{V}{1000}$

it follows that:

$$[A^-] = \left(\frac{2.53}{82}\right) \div \left(\frac{1000}{1000}\right)$$

95

$$= 0.031 \text{ mol dm}^{-3}$$

Since ethanoic acid is a weak acid (partially ionizes), the assumption is that $[CH_3COOH] = 0.08 \text{ mol dm}^{-3}$.

Substituting the values into $[H^+] = K_a \times \dfrac{[HA]}{[A^-]}$

gives:

$$[H^+] = 1.7 \times 10^{-5} \times \frac{0.08}{0.031}$$

$$= 4.39 \times 10^{-5} \text{ mol dm}^{-3}$$

and since $\quad pH = -\log_{10}[H^+]$

$$pH = -\log_{10}[4.39 \times 10^{-5}]$$

$$= 4.36$$

Questions 5.13

1. Which options are examples of buffer solutions?

A   Weak acid and its conjugate acid

B   Weak base and its conjugate base

C   Weak acid and its conjugate base

D   Weak base and its conjugate acid

2. What is the pH of a buffer containing 0.1 mol dm^{-3} of CH_3CO_2Na and 0.2 mol dm^{-3} CH_3COOH? The pK_a of ethanoic acid is 4.8. What type of buffer does this mixture make?

3. What is in an acidic buffer and an alkaline buffer?

4. Derive the Henderson-Hasselbach equation using HA (aq) for the weak acid.

5. Which option shows the correct pH of a buffer with equimolar concentrations of weak acid and its salt?

A $pK_a + 1$

B pK_a

C $pK_a - 1$

D K_a

6. Which option is **not** a buffer?

A $H_2PO_4^- / HPO_4^{2-}$

B $H_2CO_3 / NaHCO_3$

C $NaOH / NH_4Cl$

D NH_3 / NH_4Cl

7. The general formula for an α-amino acid in solution is $H_3N^+–CHR–COO^-$.

Write equations to show how these amino acids can acts as buffers.

8. The titration curve is shown for the reaction between ammonia and hydrochloric acid. In which region **A**, **B**, **C** or **D** is the reaction mixture acting as a buffer? Explain your answer.

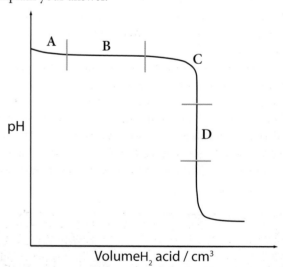

9. Calculate the pH of the buffer formed when 3.0 g of sodium ethanoate is added to 1000 cm^3 of 0.09 mol dm^{-3}

ethanoic acid ($K_a = 1.7 \times 10^{-5}$ mol dm^{-3}).

10. Calculate the mass of sodium ethanoate needed to make a buffer of pH 4.0 with 1000 cm^3 of 1.0 mol dm^{-3} ethanoic acid ($K_a = 1.7 \times 10^{-5}$ mol dm^{-3}).

B1.5 (i)
Quantitative electrolysis

Electrolysis is decomposing an ionic substance when it is molten or in aqueous solution by the passage of an electric current. The ionic compounds need to be in a state where the ions are free to move under the influence of an electric current (A1.0m). The **positive** electrode is the **anode** and the **negative** electrode is the **cathode**. The correct names of the electrodes can be remembered from the word **PANC**ake. During electrolysis, the anions (negative ions) are attracted to the anode and the cations (positive ions) are attracted to the cathode.

Michael Faraday who was, undoubtedly, one of the best experimentalists in the history of science, came up with two quantitative Laws of Electrolysis after conducting numerous experiments. His first law of electrolysis states that the mass of substance liberated at an electrode during electrolysis is proportional to the quantity of electricity that is passed through the electrolyte. His second law of electrolysis states that, for the same quantity of charge passed through different electrolytes, the extent of decomposition is inversely proportional to the charge on the ion. Twice as many moles of silver ($Ag^+ + e^- \rightarrow Ag$) will be deposited compared with copper ($Cu^{2+} + 2e^- \rightarrow Cu$) for the same quantity of current over the same time period. The charge carried by one mole of electrons is 96500 C and this is called the **Faraday constant**. Its value is 9.65×10^4 C mol^{-1}. One coulomb of charge is when one ampere of current flows for one second. The equation that relates these factors is: $Q = I \times t$, where Q = charge (C), I = current (A) and t = time (seconds). The following table illustrates Faraday's second law of electrolysis.

Metal	Ion charge	Charge needed to deposit one mole of metal (Coulombs)
Silver	+1	96500 × 1 = 96500
Copper	+2	96500 × 2 = 193000
Aluminium	+3	96500 × 3 = 289500

When performing electrolysis on a commercial scale, it is important for manufacturers to know how much current is required and for how long. One of the great costs of the 21st century is energy and this is a seriously important economic consideration for industrial chemists/metallurgists.

A simple quantitative electrolysis experiment is the electrolysis of aqueous copper(II) sulfate using copper electrodes. The diagram shows a typical experiment and what you might expect to observe. During the experiment, the following data need recording: the mass of electrodes (anode and cathode) before and after electrolysis, the current flowing (Amps), and the time the current flows for (seconds). A typical experiment lasts about 30 minutes with a current of 0.5 Amp. At the end of the experiment the electrodes are removed from the solution and they are washed first with deionised water then with propanone.

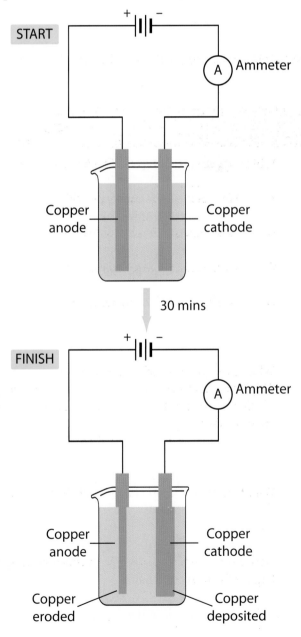

Quantitative electrolysis of CuSO$_4$ (aq) using copper electrodes

Interestingly, electrolysis experiments have allowed Avogadro's constant (L) to be determined. A quick look at units will allow you to realise that Faraday constant (F) = Avogadro's constant (L) × electronic charge (e).

$$F = L \times e$$

Rearranging this equation gives: $L = \dfrac{F}{e}$

Substituting in the values:

$$L = \dfrac{9.65 \times 10^4}{1.60 \times 10^{-19}}$$

$$= 6.03 \times 10^{23}$$

This value compares favourably (despite rounding errors) to the value used in calculations.

It is best to avoid naming the electrodes for an electrochemical cell (B1.5l) as it can be confusing because the signs of the anode and cathode in an electrochemical cell are opposite to those in an electrolytic cell.

Example 5.32

An aqueous solution of silver nitrate was electrolysed for 2 hours with a current of 0.050 amps. What mass of silver was deposited at the cathode?

$[F = 9.65 \times 10^4 \text{ C mol}^{-1} \text{ and } A_r \text{ Ag} = 108 \text{ g mol}^{-1}]$

Time: 2 hours = $2 \times 60 \times 60 = 7200$ seconds

Cathode equation: $Ag^+ (aq) + e^- \rightleftharpoons Ag (s)$

$$Q = I \times t$$

$$= 0.050 \times 7200$$

$$= 360 \text{ C}$$

Since the Faraday constant is $9.65 \times 10^4 \text{ C mol}^{-1}$:

The amount of silver deposited:

$$= \dfrac{360}{9.65 \times 10^4}$$

$$= 3.73 \times 10^{-3} \text{ mol.}$$

Mass of silver deposited $= n \text{ (Ag)} \times A_r \text{ (Ag)}$

Mass of silver deposited $= 3.73 \times 10^{-3} \times 108 = 0.403 \text{ g}$

Example 5.33

An aqueous solution of copper(II) sulfate was electrolysed for 4 hours with a current of 0.040 amps. What mass of copper was deposited at the cathode?

$[F = 9.65 \times 10^4 \text{ C mol}^{-1} \text{ and } A_r \text{ Cu} = 63.5 \text{ g mol}^{-1}]$

Time: 4 hours = $4 \times 60 \times 60 = 14400$ seconds

Cathode equation: $Cu^{2+} (aq) + 2 e^- \rightleftharpoons Cu (s)$

$$Q = I \times t$$

$$= 0.040 \times 14400$$

$$= 576 \text{ C}$$

The charge needed to deposit 1 mole of Cu:

$$= 9.65 \times 10^4 \text{ C mol}^{-1} \times 2$$

$$= 1.93 \times 10^5 \text{ C}$$

The amount of copper deposited:

$$= \dfrac{576}{1.93 \times 10^5}$$

$$= 2.98 \times 10^{-3} \text{ mol.}$$

Mass of copper deposited $= n \text{ (Cu)} \times A_r \text{ (Cu)}$

Mass of copper deposited:

$$= 2.98 \times 10^{-3} \times 63.5$$

$$= 0.19 \text{ g}$$

Example 5.34

How long will it take to deposit 2.0 g of chromium when an aqueous solution of chromium(III) sulfate is electrolysed with a current of 0.120 Amps ?

$[F = 9.65 \times 10^4 \text{ C mol}^{-1} \text{ and } A_r \text{ Cr} = 52.0 \text{ g mol}^{-1}]$

$Cr^{3+} (aq) + 3 e^- \rightleftharpoons Cr (s)$

$9.65 \times 10^4 \text{ C mol}^{-1} \times 3 = 289500 \text{ C}$ is needed to deposit 1 mole of Cr

The amount of chromium deposited:

$$= \frac{2.0}{52.0}$$

$$= 3.85 \times 10^{-2} \text{ mol}$$

Therefore the number of coulombs:

$$= 3.85 \times 10^{-2} \times 289500 \text{ C}$$

$$= 11145.75 \text{ C}$$

$Q = I \times t$ and rearranging gives

$$t = \frac{Q}{I}$$

$$= \frac{11145.75}{0.120}$$

$$= 92881 \text{ seconds}$$

$$\approx 25 \text{ hours } 48 \text{ mins}$$

Questions 5.14

1. What mass of copper is deposited at the cathode when an aqueous solution of copper(II) sulfate is electrolysed for 3 hours with a current of 0.15 Amps?

   [$F = 9.65 \times 10^4$ C mol^{-1} and A_r Cu = 63.5 g mol^{-1}]

2. What mass of silver is deposited at the cathode when an aqueous solution of silver nitrate is electrolysed for 120 minutes with a current of 40 mA?

   [$F = 9.65 \times 10^4$ C mol^{-1} and A_r Ag 108 g mol^{-1}]

3. How long will it take to deposit 0.50 g of copper when an aqueous solution of copper(II) sulfate is electrolysed with a current of 2.0 Amps ?

   [$F = 9.65 \times 10^4$ C mol^{-1} and A_r Cu = 63.5 g mol^{-1}]

B1.5 (j)
Redox and oxidation number

Redox is a contraction of the two words **red**uction and **ox**idation. In a reaction where there is a reduction there must also be an oxidation. A redox reaction consists of a reduction half and an oxidation half which, like the ancient Chinese *Yin Yang* symbol, are complementary opposites within a greater whole. When a redox reaction takes place, electrons are transferred from one species to another.

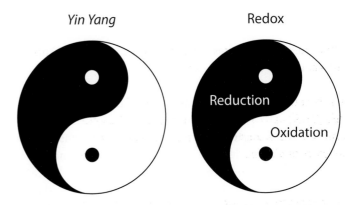

Yin Yang — Redox — Reduction — Oxidation

The concept of redox is best understood through oxidation numbers which help us to describe reactions. An oxidation number is a number given to an element when it is as the pure uncombined element, a simple ion or complex ion. Oxidation number is the number of electrons that need to be added or removed to or from an atom or ion to make a neutral atom. The oxidation number of elements is zero. The oxidation number of simple ions is the charge. A characteristic of transition elements is that they have variable oxidation numbers. Some common oxidation states are shown from −3 to +3. In the table below, where there are more than one element present, the one in bold has the oxidation state for that particular column.

Examples of oxidation numbers

Oxidation numbers						
−3	−2	−1	0	+1	+2	+3
N^{3-}	O^{2-}	F^-	Na	**HCl**	Mg^{2+}	Al^{3+}
P^{3-}	S^{2-}	Cl^-	Mg	Na^{1+}	Ca^{2+}	$H_3\mathbf{P}O_3$
As^{3-}	Se^{2-}	$H_2\mathbf{O}_2$	Cl_2	K^{1+}	Sr^{2+}	$H\mathbf{N}O_2$

A detailed set of rules which govern the assignment of oxidation numbers is found in section A2.1e. Information about the oxidation number of the metal is given in the form of a roman numeral immediately after the metal. The name copper(II) sulfate informs us that we have Cu^{2+}, and the name iron(III) chloride informs us that we have Fe^{3+}.

To recognise a redox reaction, you need to be familiar with the definitions of reduction and oxidation and to realise that they are opposites of each other in every definition. There is a special kind of redox reaction called **disproportionation** (A2.2n) where an individual element in a certain oxidation state is simultaneously oxidized and reduced.

Reduction	Oxidation
Gain of electrons	Loss of electrons
Decrease in oxidation number	Increase in oxidation number

Metals react with non-metals in redox reactions, *e.g.* sodium with chlorine.

$$Na\ (s) + \tfrac{1}{2}Cl_2\ (g) \rightarrow NaCl\ (s)$$

A redox reaction can be split into two half equations to show exactly which species gains electrons (reduced) and which species loses electrons (oxidised). Sodium is oxidised because its oxidation number increases and chlorine is reduced as its oxidation number decreases. It is often convenient to show the oxidation number above the species when assigning redox reactions.

$$\overset{0}{Na} - e^- \rightarrow +\overset{1}{Na^+}\ (\text{oxidation})$$

$$\tfrac{1}{2}\overset{0}{Cl_2} + e^- \rightarrow \overset{-1}{Cl^-}\ (\text{reduction})$$

The **thermite reaction** is used to weld together broken railway tracks and is the reaction between aluminium and iron(III) oxide. This reaction is a redox reaction where aluminium is oxidised and the iron(III) oxide is reduced. At the temperature of this highly exothermic reaction, the liquid iron will pour into the gaps between the rail tracks.

$$Fe_2O_3\ (s) + 2\ Al\ (s) \rightarrow Al_2O_3\ (s) + 2\ Fe\ (l)$$

$$\overset{+3}{Fe^{3+}} + 3e^- \rightarrow \overset{0}{Fe}\ (\text{reduction})$$

$$\overset{0}{Al} - 3e^- \rightarrow \overset{+3}{Al^{3+}}\ (\text{oxidation})$$

In a redox reaction the reducing agent loses electrons so, from the definition of oxidation, it is the reducing agent that gets oxidised. In a redox reaction, the oxidising agent gains electrons and it is the oxidising agent that gets reduced. Redox reactions involving complex ions appear, on first meeting, to be very difficult to balance. Redox reactions can be balanced from the two half equations. It is a matter of ensuring the electrons cancel on adding and checking that the equation balances for atoms as well as charges. The balancing of a redox reaction will be illustrated with the oxidising agent potassium

manganate(VII) which will oxidise iron(II) to iron(III) whilst itself getting reduced to manganese(II).

$$\overset{+7}{MnO_4^-}\ (aq) + 5\ e^- + 8\ H^+\ (aq) \rightarrow +\overset{2}{Mn^{2+}}\ (aq) + 4\ H_2O\ (l)$$

Five electrons are needed in this half equation to reduce the manganese from an oxidation number of +7 to +2. The oxygen in the manganate(VII) becomes part of the water. There need to be four moles of water since there are four oxygens in the manganate(VII). The hydrogen in the water comes from an acid (H^+) and there need to be eight of them to make the half equation balance.

The half equation for the iron species is much more straightforward.

$$\overset{+2}{Fe^{2+}}\ (aq) \rightarrow \overset{+3}{Fe^{3+}}\ (aq) + e^-$$

Before adding together the two half equations, the iron one needs multiplying by five so that the electrons in both half equations will cancel out.

$$5\ Fe^{2+}\ (aq) \rightarrow 5\ Fe^{3+}\ (aq) + 5\ e^-$$

This gives the balanced equation for this reaction as:

$$MnO_4^-\ (aq) + 5\ Fe^{2+}\ (aq) + 8\ H^+\ (aq)$$
$$\rightarrow Mn^{2+}\ (aq) + 5\ Fe^{3+}\ (aq) + 4\ H_2O\ (l)$$

Questions 5.15

1. What are the oxidation numbers of iron in ferric chloride and ferrous chloride?

2. Zinc reacts with copper(II) sulfate to form zinc sulfate and copper. Write the two half equations for this reaction and identify the oxidation and reduction processes.

3. For the following redox reactions, identify which species is oxidised and which species is reduced.

    a. $Cl_2\ (g) + 2\ Br^-\ (aq) \rightarrow 2\ Cl^-\ (aq) + Br_2\ (aq)$

    b. $CuO\ (s) + H_2\ (g) \rightarrow Cu\ (s) + H_2O\ (l)$

    c. $H_2\ (g) + \tfrac{1}{2}O_2\ (g) \rightarrow H_2O\ (l)$

    d. $2\ Fe^{3+}\ (aq) + 2\ I^-\ (aq) \rightarrow 2\ Fe^{2+}\ (aq) + I_2\ (aq)$

4. Write the balanced equation from the half equations for this redox reaction.

$$SO_2 \text{ (aq)} + 2 H_2O \text{ (l)} \rightarrow SO_4^{2-} \text{ (aq)} + 2 e^- + 4 H^+ \text{ (aq)}$$

$$Cr_2O_7^{2-} \text{ (aq)} + 6 e^- + 14 H^+ \text{ (aq)}$$
$$\rightarrow 2 Cr^{3+} \text{ (aq)} + 7 H_2O \text{ (l)}$$

B1.5 (k) Standard electrode potential and the standard hydrogen electrode

All metals have a tendency to give away their delocalised electrons (A1.0h). When a piece of metal is dipped into a solution of its ions, an equilibrium is set up between the metal and the aqueous metal ions.

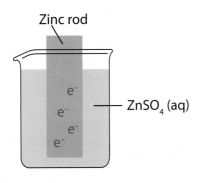

Zinc rod

ZnSO$_4$ (aq)

$$Zn \text{ (s)} \rightleftharpoons Zn^{2+} \text{ (aq)} + 2 e^-$$

If some zinc dissolves in a solution of its own ions, the equilibrium will move to the right hand side. When this happens, there will be a build up of negative electrical charge as electrons are left behind on the metal (electrode) surface. A metal dipping into a 1 mol dm^{-3} solution of its ions at 298 K is a **half cell**. When a half cell is connected to a standard hydrogen electrode you have an **electrochemical cell** (B1.5l) and a reduction potential which is usually referred to as a standard electrode potential ($E^{\ominus}$) is measured in volts. A list of important standard electrode potentials can be found in section B1.5m.

Standard hydrogen electrode

The **hydrogen electrode** is the standard electrode against which all other electrode potentials are measured in volts (V). Standard conditions for the hydrogen electrode are an acid with H$^+$ (aq) concentration of 1 mol dm^{-3}, 1 atmosphere pressure of hydrogen gas and a temperature of 298 K. The electrode is made of platinum with a foil end coated with platinum black. The platinum black increases the surface area at the surface of the catalyst to allow a very fast reaction. The hydrogen electrode under standard conditions is assigned a value of exactly zero volts (0.00 V).

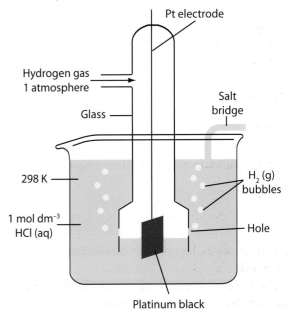

Standard hydrogen electrode

The hydrogen electrode is used as a reference cell against which all other half cells have their standard electrode potentials measured. The half equation for the standard hydrogen electrode like all other standard electrode potentials is written as a reduction.

$$2 H^+ \text{ (aq)} + 2 e^- \rightleftharpoons H_2 \text{ (g)} \qquad E^{\ominus}_{cell} = 0.00 \text{ V}$$

If the hydrogen electrode is connected to other half cells the measured voltage is called the electromotive force (emf) of the cell and this is called the standard potential of the cell with the symbol ($E^{\ominus}$) pronounced 'E standard'. Half cells with negative $E^{\ominus}$ values are better at releasing electrons than hydrogen, *i.e.* better reducing agents. Half cells with positive $E^{\ominus}$ values are better at accepting electrons than H$^+$, *i.e.* better oxidising agents. When the standard hydrogen electrode is connected to other half cells, they need to be connected by a salt bridge - an inert electrolyte such as potassium chloride in an agar gel or on filter paper (B1.5l).

In the figure labels: Pt electrode, Hydrogen gas 1 atmosphere, Glass, Salt bridge, 298 K, 1 mol dm^{-3} HCl (aq), H$_2$ (g) bubbles, Hole, Platinum black.

Questions 5.16

1. What equilibrium is set up when a piece of copper foil is dipped into an aqueous solution of copper(II) sulfate? Explain what is happening to the copper metal.

2. What is the potential of a standard hydrogen electrode?

3. What is the name of the process that holds the hydrogen gas at the surface of the platinum electrode?

4. What concentration would be needed if sulfuric acid was being used as part of a standard hydrogen electrode?

B1.5 (l) Measuring standard electrode potentials (practical)

Standard electrode potentials are measured when two half cells are joined together to make an electrochemical cell. The difference in the electric potential, also called the electromotive force (EMF), is a measure of the force that moves the electrons around the circuit and this is measured with a high resistance voltmeter which has the symbol V. A high resistance voltmeter is used because it draws very little current. The two half cells are connected by a salt bridge, which allows the flow of ions between the half cells and completes the circuit. The salt bridge does not allow electron flow. These only flow through the external circuit. A salt bridge is made by dipping a strip of filter paper into a saturated solution of a salt such as potassium chloride. During experiments, it is important to make sure the salt bridge does not dry out.

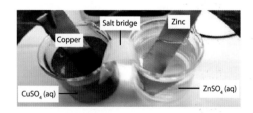

Electrochemical cell (two half cells connected *via* a salt bridge)

When measuring standard electrode potentials ($E^{\ominus}$), the standard conditions that are used are:

- all concentrations are 1.00 mol dm^{-3}

- temperature is 298 K

- any gases used are at a pressure of 1 atmosphere.

The standard electrode potential of all half-cells is obtained by connecting to the reference (0.00 V) standard hydrogen electrode. When the electrochemical cell is working, current is being generated by the cell, the reactions at the electrodes are no longer equilibria and will go in one direction. The direction of the reactions is governed by the standard electrode potentials of both half cells.

Metals

When measuring standard potentials of metals, the metal is dipped into a solution of its own ions and it is connected to a standard hydrogen electrode. The values obtained are listed in the electrochemical series. When zinc is connected to the positive terminal of the voltmeter under standard conditions, the standard electrode potential $E^{\ominus}$ is –0.76 V.

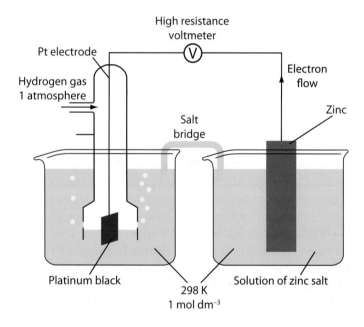

Apparatus for measuring $E^{\ominus}$ for zinc (–0.76 V)

Non-metals

When measuring standard potentials of gaseous non-metals, the gas is bubbled into a solution of its own ions with a platinum electrode and it is connected to a standard hydrogen electrode. This works for other non-metals as long as the non-metal is in contact with a solution of its aqueous ions. The values obtained are listed in the electrochemical series. When the platinum electrode is connected to the positive terminal of the voltmeter under standard conditions, the standard electrode potential for chlorine is $E^{\ominus}$ is +1.36 V. In all measurements of standard electrode/cell potential, the hydrogen is connected to the negative terminal of the voltmeter. In this case, from the electrochemical series, it is more negative (less positive) than chlorine.

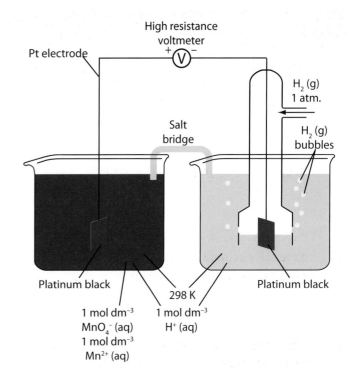

Apparatus for measuring $E^{\ominus}$ for MnO_4^- / Mn^{2+} (+1.51 V)

The standard electrode potentials tell us how easy it is to oxidise or reduce a particular species. Standard electrode potentials can also be used to predict the size of the standard electrode potential of electrochemical cells (B1.5m), the direction of electron flow and whether a particular reaction is feasible (B1.5o).

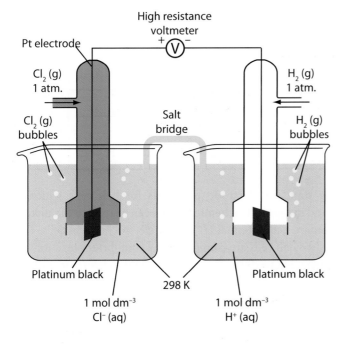

Apparatus for measuring $E^{\ominus}$ for chlorine (+1.36 V)

Ions of the same element

When measuring standard potentials of ions of the same element, e.g. manganate(VII) MnO_4^- and manganese(II) Mn^{2+}, they are placed together with acid. It is then possible to measure the standard electrode potential using a platinum electrode and connecting to a hydrogen electrode under standard conditions. The inclusion of the acid is necessary for the reduction of manganate(VII) to manganese(II). The standard electrode potential $E^{\ominus}$ is +1.51 V.

Questions 5.17

1. When is platinum used as the electrode in a half cell?

2. Which option shows the correct standard electrode potential for two identical Fe^{3+}/Fe^{2+} half cells connected via a salt bridge and a voltmeter under standard conditions?

   A   0.385 V

   B   1.54 V

   C   0.77 V

   D   0.00 V

3. Which option shows a salt which cannot be used to make a salt bridge?

   A   potassium chloride

   B   silver chloride

   C   ammonium chloride

   D   potassium nitrate

4. Draw diagrams to show how you would measure the standard electrode potential for half cells with the following equilibria.

   a. $Br_2 (aq) + 2\,e^- \rightleftharpoons 2\,Br^- (aq)$

   b. $Pb^{2+} (aq) + 2\,e^- \rightleftharpoons Pb (s)$

	$E^\ominus$ / V
$Zn^{2+} (aq) + 2\,e^- \rightleftharpoons Zn (s)$	−0.76
$Cr^{3+} (aq) + 3e^- \rightleftharpoons Cr (s)$	−0.74
$Fe^{2+} (aq) + 2\,e^- \rightleftharpoons Fe (s)$	−0.44
$Pb^{2+} (aq) + 2\,e^- \rightleftharpoons Pb (s)$	−0.13
$2\,H^+ (aq) + 2\,e^- \rightleftharpoons H_2 (g)$	0.00
$Cu^{2+} (aq) + e^- \rightleftharpoons Cu^+ (aq)$	+0.15
$Cu^{2+} (aq) + 2\,e^- \rightleftharpoons Cu (s)$	+0.34
$I_2 (aq) + 2\,e^- \rightleftharpoons 2\,I^- (aq)$	+0.54
$Fe^{3+} (aq) + e^- \rightleftharpoons Fe^{2+} (aq)$	+0.77
$Ag^+ (aq) + e^- \rightleftharpoons Ag (s)$	+0.80
$Br_2 (aq) + 2\,e^- \rightleftharpoons 2\,Br^- (aq)$	+1.09
$Cr_2O_7^{2-} (aq) + 14\,H^+ (aq) + 6\,e^- \rightleftharpoons 2\,Cr^{3+} (aq) + 7\,H_2O (l)$	+1.33
$Cl_2 (aq) + 2\,e^- \rightleftharpoons 2\,Cl^- (aq)$	+1.36
$MnO_4^- (aq) + 8\,H^+ (aq) + 5\,e^- \rightleftharpoons Mn^{2+} (aq) + 4\,H_2O (l)$	+1.51

B1.5 (m) Calculating standard cell potentials (theory)

The electrochemical series is a table of standard electrode potentials $E^\ominus$ (V). The convention is to have the most negative values at the top of the list and the most positive values at the bottom of the list. Somewhere in the middle is the standard electrode potential of hydrogen which is set at 0.00 V. The electrochemical series includes: metals, pairs of ions and non-metals, all written as reductions. Ions such as chromate(VI) and manganate(VII), which contain oxygen, also need H^+ in their half equations. The most powerful reducing agents appear at the top of the electrochemical series and the most powerful oxidising agents appear at the bottom of the electrochemical series. The number of electrons involved in the reduction does not affect the value of $E^\ominus$ and is ignored in calculations.

Electrochemical series

	$E^\ominus$ / V
$Li^+ (aq) + e^- \rightleftharpoons Li (s)$	−3.03
$Ca^{2+} (aq) + 2\,e^- \rightleftharpoons Ca (s)$	−2.87
$Na^+ (aq) + e^- \rightleftharpoons Na (s)$	−2.71
$Mg^{2+} (aq) + 2\,e^- \rightleftharpoons Mg (s)$	−2.37
$Al^{3+} (aq) + 3\,e^- \rightleftharpoons Al (s)$	−1.66

The standard electrode potentials for half cells which are found in the electrochemical series can be used to calculate the standard cell potential ($E^\ominus_{cell}$) for electrochemical cells. Once the two half cells are connected, the equilibrium reactions will go from left to right (reduction) or right to left (oxidation). So how do you decide on the direction? The more negative half cell (least positive) is the one that will release electrons more readily, so its equilibrium will go in the reverse direction (right hand side to left hand side). The more positive half cell (least negative) is the one that will gain electrons more readily so its equilibrium will go in the forward direction (left hand side to right hand side). There are several methods for arriving at the same value for the standard cell potential ($E^\ominus_{cell}$) for any electrochemical cell. The voltage obtained by connecting two half cells together is found from the difference between the two $E^\ominus$ values. The value obtained experimentally will be positive as long as the negative terminal of the voltmeter is connected to the half cell with the more negative $E^\ominus$.

Method 1

step 1: Draw three horizontal lines about 10 cm long directly above each other with sufficient gaps to write equilibria on each line.

step 2: Write the equilibria for the two half cells and the hydrogen electrode on the lines in a logical order in terms of their relative $E^{\ominus}$ values.

step 3: Use the diagram to work out the difference in V between the half cells

step 4: Write $E^{\ominus}_{cell}$ (remembering that cell voltages are always positive).

Method 2

step 1: Write out in full the half equations for both the two half cells.

step 2: Write next to the half equations their $E^{\ominus}$.

step 3: Assign the most negative half equation's voltage as $E_{\text{left hand side}}$.

step 4: Assign the most positive half equation's voltage as $E_{\text{right hand side}}$.

step 5: $E^{\ominus}_{cell} = E^{\ominus}_{\text{right hand side}} - E^{\ominus}_{\text{left hand side}}$ (remembering cell voltages are always positive).

Example 5.35

Calculate the standard cell potential $E^{\ominus}_{cell}$ for an electrochemical cell made up of zinc and copper half cells.

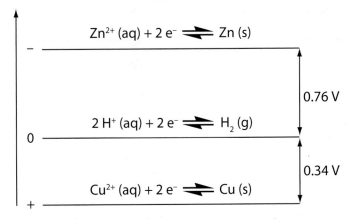

$$E^{\ominus}_{cell} = 0.76 \text{ V} + 0.34 \text{ V} = 1.1 \text{ V}$$

Example 5.37

Calculate the standard cell potential $E^{\ominus}_{cell}$ for an electrochemical cell made up of silver and copper half cells.

$$Ag^+ (aq) + e^- \rightleftharpoons Ag (s) \qquad E^{\ominus} = + 0.80 \text{ V} = E^{\ominus}_{\text{right hand side}}$$

$$Cu^{2+} (aq) + 2 e^- \rightleftharpoons Cu (s) \qquad E^{\ominus} = + 0.34 \text{ V} = E^{\ominus}_{\text{left hand side}}$$

$$E^{\ominus}_{cell} = E^{\ominus}_{\text{right hand side}} - E^{\ominus}_{\text{left hand side}}$$

$$= + 0.80 \text{ V} - + 0.34 \text{ V} = 0.46 \text{ V}$$

Example 5.36

Calculate the standard cell potential $E^{\ominus}_{cell}$ for an electrochemical cell made up of magnesium and lead half cells.

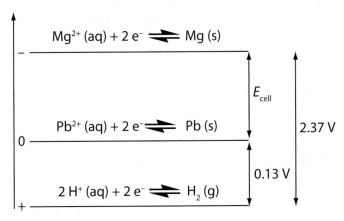

$$E^{\ominus}_{cell} = 2.37 \text{ V} - 0.13 \text{ V} = 2.24 \text{ V}$$

Example 5.38

Calculate the standard cell potential $E^{\ominus}_{cell}$ for an electrochemical cell made up of Fe^{3+}/Fe^{2+} and Cl_2/Cl^- half cells.

$$Fe^{3+} (aq) + e^- \rightleftharpoons Fe^{2+} (aq) \qquad E^{\ominus} = +0.77 \text{ V} = E^{\ominus}_{\text{left hand side}}$$

$$Cl_2 (g) + 2 e^- \rightleftharpoons 2 Cl^- (aq) \qquad E^{\ominus} = +1.36 \text{ V} = E^{\ominus}_{\text{right hand side}}$$

$$E^{\ominus}_{cell} = E^{\ominus}_{\text{right hand side}} - E^{\ominus}_{\text{left hand side}}$$

$$E^{\ominus}_{cell} = + 1.36 \text{ V} - + 0.77 \text{ V} = 0.59 \text{ V}$$

Method 3

An electrochemical cell can be shown as a cell diagram. The cell diagram for copper and zinc half cells is:

$$Zn\ (s)\ |\ Zn^{2+}\ (aq)\ ||\ Cu^{2+}\ (aq)\ |\ Cu\ (s).$$

The convention is to write the half cell with most negative value of $E^\ominus$ on the left of the cell diagram as an oxidation reaction. The half cell with the most positive $E^\ominus$ is written on the right of the cell diagram as a reduction reaction. A single vertical line (|) represents a phase boundary and a double vertical line (||) represents the salt bridge. The cell diagram shows the chemical changes and allows for $E^\ominus_{cell}$ to be calculated since:

$$E^\ominus_{cell} = E_{right\ hand\ side} - E_{left\ hand\ side}.$$

In the case of the copper and zinc electrochemical cell, $E_{right\ hand\ side}$ corresponds to the copper half cell as it is on the right hand side of the cell diagram. $E_{left\ hand\ side}$ corresponds to the zinc half cell as it is on the left hand side of the cell diagram.

step 1: Write down the cell diagram

step 2: Assign $E_{left\ hand\ side}$ to the equilibrium shown on the left hand side of the salt bridge

step 3: Assign $E_{right\ hand\ side}$ to the equilibrium shown on the right hand side of the salt bridge

step 4: $E^\ominus_{cell} = E_{right\ hand\ side} - E_{left\ hand\ side}$ (plug in the numbers from the electrochemical series)

If the calculated voltage for $E^\ominus_{cell}$ is positive the reaction is feasible (B1.5o).

Example 5.39

Calculate the standard cell potential $E^\ominus_{cell}$ for an electrochemical cell from the cell diagram: Cu (s) | Cu²⁺ (aq) || Ag⁺ (aq) | Ag (s) using the $E^\ominus$ for the equilibria.

$Ag^+\ (aq) + e^- \rightleftharpoons Ag\ (s)$ $E^\ominus = +0.80\ V$

$Cu^{2+}\ (aq) + 2\ e^- \rightleftharpoons Cu\ (s)$ $E^\ominus = +0.34\ V$

$$E^\ominus_{cell} = E^\ominus_{right\ hand\ side} - E^\ominus_{left\ hand\ side}$$

$$= +0.80\ V - +0.34\ V = +0.46\ V$$

Example 5.40

Calculate the standard cell potential $E^\ominus_{cell}$ for an electrochemical cell from the cell diagram: Al (s)|Al³⁺ (aq)||Cu²⁺ (aq)|Cu⁺ (aq) using the $E^\ominus$ for the equilibria.

$Al^{3+}\ (aq) + 3\ e^- \rightleftharpoons Al\ (s)$ $E^\ominus = -1.66\ V$

$Cu^{2+}\ (aq) + e^- \rightleftharpoons Cu^+\ (aq)$ $E^\ominus = +0.15\ V$

$$E^\ominus_{cell} = E^\ominus_{right\ hand\ side} - E^\ominus_{left\ hand\ side}$$

$$= +0.15\ V - -1.66\ V = +1.81\ V$$

Question 5.18

1. Calculate the standard cell potential $E^\ominus_{cell}$ for electrochemical cells made up of:

   a. Aluminium and copper half cells

   b. Magnesium and zinc half cells

   c. Aluminium and bromine half cells

   d. MnO_4^-/Mn^{2+} and copper half cells

   e. Chromium and chlorine half cells

B1.5 (n) Linking standard cell potential and Gibbs energy change

It is possible to calculate Gibbs energy change (ΔG) which is the maximum work obtained from a reaction from the standard cell potential ($E^\ominus_{cell}$). The equation which relates these two quantities is $\Delta G = -\ n\ F\ E^\ominus_{cell}$ where n = the number of electrons transferred during the redox reaction and F is the Faraday constant. ΔG is negative for all spontaneous changes (B1.4g) and is related to the equilibrium constant (K_p or K_c) by the equation $\Delta G = -\ RT \log_e K$ (B1.4f). Combining the two equations for ΔG leads to the **Nernst equation** which is:

$$E^\ominus_{cell} = \left(\frac{RT}{nF}\right) \log_e K$$

Example 5.41

Calculate the value of ΔG for the Daniell Cell:

$$Zn\ (s)\ |\ Zn^{2+}\ (aq)\ ||\ Cu^{2+}\ (aq)\ |\ Cu\ (s)$$

which has an $E^{\ominus}_{cell}$ = 1.10 V.

Equation: $Zn\ (s) + Cu^{2+}\ (aq) \rightarrow Zn^{2+}\ (aq) + Cu\ (s)$

Half equations:

$$Zn\ (s) - 2\ e^- \rightarrow Zn^{2+}\ (aq)$$

$$Cu^{2+}\ (aq) + 2\ e^- \rightarrow Cu\ (s)$$

Value of $n = 2$ (since two moles of electrons are transferred)

Equation: $\Delta G = -n\,F\,E^{\ominus}_{cell}$

Calculation: $\Delta G = -2 \times 96500 \times 1.10$ (CV mol^{-1} = J mol^{-1})

ΔG = −212300 J mol^{-1}
(divide by 1000 to convert J mol^{-1} to kJ mol^{-1})

$\Delta G = -212.3$ kJ mol^{-1}

Example 5.42

Calculate ΔG for the reaction $2\ Ag^+\ (aq) + Cu\ (s) \rightarrow 2\ Ag\ (s) + Cu^{2+}\ (aq)$ which has an $E^{\ominus}_{cell}$ = +0.46 V.

Half equations:

$$Cu\ (s) - 2\ e^- \rightarrow Cu^{2+}\ (aq)$$

$$2\ Ag^+\ (aq) + 2\ e^- \rightarrow 2\ Ag\ (s)$$

Value of n = 2 (since two moles of electrons are transferred)

Equation: $\qquad \Delta G = -n\,F\,E^{\ominus}_{cell}$

Calculation: $\qquad \Delta G = -2 \times 96500 \times 0.46$

$= -88780$ J mol^{-1}
(divide by 1000 to convert J mol^{-1} to kJ mol^{-1})

$\Delta G = -88.8$ kJ mol^{-1}

Questions 5.19

1. In the equation relating ΔG to $E^{\ominus}_{cell}$ what is ΔG?

2. Calculate ΔG for the reaction:

$$2\ MnO_4^-\ (aq) + 16\ H^+\ (aq) + 10\ I^-\ (aq)$$
$$\rightarrow 2\ Mn^{2+}\ (aq) + 5\ I_2\ (aq) + 8\ H_2O\ (l)$$
which has an $E^{\ominus}_{cell}$ = +0.97 V.

3. Calculate ΔG for the reaction:

$$Zn\ (s) + 2\ H^+\ (aq) \rightarrow Zn^{2+}\ (aq) + H_2\ (g)$$
which has an $E^{\ominus}_{cell}$ = +0.76 V.

4. Calculate $E^{\ominus}_{cell}$ for the reaction:

$$Zn\ (s) + Pb^{2+}\ (aq) \rightarrow Zn^{2+}\ (aq) + Pb\ (s)$$
which has an $\Delta G = -122$ kJ mol^{-1}

B1.5 (o) Electrochemical cells

In order to determine the direction of electron flow in an electrochemical cell, you need to look at the standard electrode potentials for the two relevant half equations in the electrochemical series. Electrons flow through the external circuit from the half cell with the more negative potential to the half cell with the more positive potential. In other words, the electrons will flow from the least positive half cell to the most positive half cell. The direction of electron flow is usually indicated by an arrow on the wire pointing away for the more negative half cell and another arrow on the wire pointing towards the more positive half cell and labelled 'electron flow', to avoid confusion with conventional current.

Example 5.43

What will be the direction of the electron flow if the following two equilibria are set up in half cells that make up an electrochemical cell?

$$Zn^{2+}\ (aq) + 2\ e^- \rightleftharpoons Zn\ (s) \qquad -0.76\ V$$

$$2\ H^+\ (aq) + 2\ e^- \rightleftharpoons H_2\ (g) \qquad 0.00\ V$$

The zinc half cell has the most negative standard electrode potential at −0.76V compared with the value of 0.00 V for the hydrogen electrode. Therefore the electrons flow from the zinc electrode through the external circuit (voltmeter) to the platinum electrode of the standard hydrogen electrode.

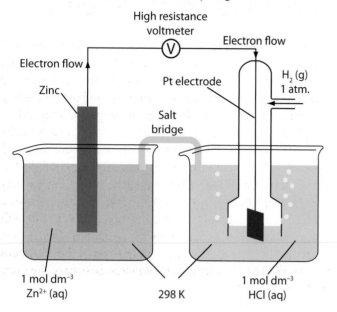

Direction of electron flow in an electrochemical cell

Example 5.44

What will be the direction of the electron flow if the following two equilibria are set up in half cells that make up an electrochemical cell?

$$Zn^{2+} (aq) + 2\ e^- \rightleftharpoons Zn\ (s) \qquad -0.76\ V$$

$$Cu^{2+} (aq) + 2\ e^- \rightleftharpoons Cu\ (s) \qquad +0.34\ V$$

The zinc half cell has the most negative standard electrode potential at −0.76V compared with the value of +0.34 V for the copper electrode. Therefore the electrons flow from the zinc electrode through the external circuit (voltmeter) to the copper electrode.

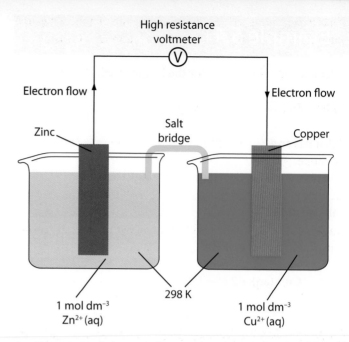

Direction of electron flow in an electrochemical cell

The overall reaction that takes place in the electrochemical cell is the same one that would happen if zinc was placed directly into a solution of copper(II) sulfate,

i.e. $Zn\ (s) + Cu^{2+} (aq) \rightarrow Zn^{2+} (aq) + Cu\ (s)$.

The difference being the electrons supplied by zinc flow through the external circuit to the Cu^{2+}/Cu half cell.

The feasibility of a reaction can be worked out from a cell diagram such as the one for the Daniell cell which is:

$$Zn\ (s)\ |\ Zn^{2+} (aq)\ ||\ Cu^{2+} (aq)\ |\ Cu\ (s)$$

The calculated value for $E^{\ominus}_{cell} = +1.10$ V and the fact that its value is positive informs us that the reaction is feasible. The reaction can be derived directly from the cell diagram. Substances to the left of the phase boundaries appear as reactants (left hand side) in the equation and substances that appear to the right of the phase boundaries appear as products (right hand side) in the equation.

Reactants are left of the phase boundaries
$$\textbf{Zn (s)}\ |\ Zn^{2+} \textbf{(aq)}\ ||\ \textbf{Cu}^{2+} \textbf{(aq)}\ |\ Cu\ (s)$$

Products are right of the phase boundaries
$$Zn\ (s)\ |\ \textbf{Zn}^{2+} \textbf{(aq)}\ ||\ Cu^{2+} (aq)\ |\ \textbf{Cu (s)}$$

This gives the overall equation as:

$$\textbf{Zn (s)} + \textbf{Cu}^{2+} \textbf{(aq)} \rightarrow \textbf{Zn}^{2+} \textbf{(aq)} + \textbf{Cu (s)}$$

If a cell diagram is written in such a way that it gives a negative value for its cell potential, then the reaction is not feasible:

$$e.g.\ 2\ Ag\ (s)\ |\ 2\ Ag^+\ (aq)\ ||\ Cu^{2+}\ (aq)\ |\ Cu\ (s)$$

which has an $E^{\ominus}_{cell} = -0.46$ V.

This would give an unfeasible reaction where silver is oxidised by copper:

$$i.e.\ 2\ Ag\ (s) + Cu^{2+}\ (aq) \rightarrow 2\ Ag^+\ (aq) + Cu\ (s).$$

Knowledge of the reactivity series would inform us that copper is more reactive than silver.

Questions 5.20

1. Which direction will electrons flow for these pairs of half equations which make up a series of electrochemical cells? Assume standard conditions and use data in the electrochemical series.

   a. Cu^{2+}/Cu^+ & Cl_2/Cl^-

   b. Ag^+/Ag & Zn^{2+}/Zn

   c. Fe^{3+}/Fe^{2+} & Cu^{2+}/Cu

   d. Li^+/Li & Pb^{2+}/Pb

2. Use the electrochemical series to decide if the following reactions are feasible. What do the reactions that are not feasible have in common?

   a. $I_2\ (s) + 2\ Br^-\ (aq) \rightarrow 2I^-\ (aq) + Br_2\ (l)$

   b. $2\ Ag\ (s) + 2\ H^+\ (aq) \rightarrow 2\ Ag^+\ (aq) + H_2\ (g)$

   c. $2\ Fe^{3+}\ (aq) + 2\ I^-\ (aq) \rightarrow 2\ Fe^{2+}\ (aq) + I_2\ (aq)$

   d. $Cu\ (s) + Ni^{2+}\ (aq) \rightarrow Cu^{2+}\ (aq) + Ni\ (s)$

B1.5 (p) Variation of cell potentials (equilibrium and non-standard conditions)

When the electrodes in the two half cells of an electrochemical cell are connected to each other, electrons will flow from the negative electrode to the positive electrode. If standard conditions are used, the equilibria established before the half cells were connected will become one way reactions and an $E^{\ominus}_{cell}$ is established. From experience, we know that batteries (collections of cells) do not supply a current indefinitely and, if they did, this would make my hobby of flying model electric aircraft even more fun. Eventually the batteries run flat and they need recharging or replacing. In the case of an electrochemical cell, chemical reactions take place at the electrodes and with time these cause the reduction in $E^{\ominus}_{cell}$ until it reaches 0.00 V. At this point, new equilibria are established at the electrodes and the reactions stop because both electrodes have the same electrical potential.

Non-standard conditions

What happens to $E^{\ominus}_{cell}$ when concentrations which are not 1.0 mol dm^{-3} are used, can be explained in terms of Le Chatelier's Principle (B1.5a). It has been demonstrated experimentally that changing the concentrations for electrochemical cells with large $E^{\ominus}_{cell}$ such as the zinc/copper electrodes has little effect on the size of $E^{\ominus}_{cell}$.

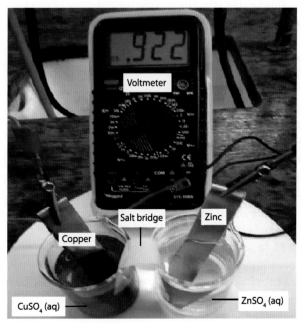

Electrochemical cell with non-standard concentrations of aqueous ions

For the half cell containing a zinc electrode dipping into a solution of its ions, a ten fold dilution only changes the half cell potential by 30 mV.

Concentration of ions / mol dm^{-3}	Equilibrium	Electrode potential / Volts
1.0	$Zn^{2+} (aq) + 2 e^- \rightleftharpoons Zn (s)$	−0.7318
0.1	$Zn^{2+} (aq) + 2 e^- \rightleftharpoons Zn (s)$	−0.7618

It has been found that, when comparing half cells with very similar standard electrode potentials (where $E^{\ominus}_{cell}$ is less than 0.2 V), changing the concentration does have a significant effect on the size of the electrode potential for the electrochemical cell. For these cells, a small change in concentration of ions could lead to the E_{cell} becoming negative and, therefore, no longer feasible.

We will use the Daniell cell [Zn (s) | Zn^{2+} (aq) || Cu^{2+} (aq) | Cu (s)] as the example to illustrate why decreasing the concentration of Zn^{2+} (aq) lowers the size of E_{cell}.

The equilibrium for the zinc half cell is:

$$Zn^{2+} (aq) + 2 e^- \rightleftharpoons Zn (s)$$

Decreasing [Zn^{2+} (aq)] from the standard 1.0 mol dm^{-3} will cause the equilibrium to shift towards the left hand side (according to Le Chatelier's Principle) to replace the removed ions. This has the effect of making the potential of this half cell more negative as more electrons are released.

Since $E^{\ominus}_{cell} = E^{\ominus}_{right\ hand\ side} - E^{\ominus}_{left\ hand\ side}$

and the value of $E^{\ominus}_{left\ hand\ side}$ becomes more negative. It then follows that the value of $E^{\ominus}_{cell}$ will reduce.

The Nernst equation gives the relationship between the concentration of ions and the size of the potential in the half cells. This equation is useful because it can be used to obtain the very small voltage obtained by connecting two half cells of the same metal but with different concentrations of ions. For example, two copper half cells where the [Cu^{2+} (aq)] are 1.0 mol dm^{-3} and 0.01 mol dm^{-3} gives an E_{cell} of +0.06 V. The Nernst equation can be used to work out the concentration of ions in very dilute solutions, e.g. silver chloride which leads to determining its solubility and, therefore, calculation of its solubility product (B1.5d).

Questions 5.21

1. Explain how $E^{\ominus}_{cell}$ will change if the value of [Zn^{2+} (aq)] is decreased for this electrochemical cell.

   [Mg (s) | Mg^{2+} (aq) || Zn^{2+} (aq) | Zn (s)]

2. Explain how $E^{\ominus}_{cell}$ will change if the value of [Cl^- (aq)] is increased in turn for each half cell of this electrochemical cell.

   [Ag (s) | Ag^+ (aq) || $\frac{1}{2}Cl_2$ (g) | Cl^- (aq)]

B1.5 (q)
Hydrogen/oxygen fuel cell

Fuel cells are electrochemical cells that convert chemical energy directly into electrical energy from a supply of fuel and oxygen. Fuel cells are another form of storage battery and are currently being produced for electric cars. Fuel cells were originally developed by NASA for the Apollo space programme where electricity and water for drinking were needed to fulfil the mission.

Hydrogen is considered by many to be a 'pollution free' fuel since its product of combustion is water.

$$H_2 (g) + \frac{1}{2}O_2 (g) \rightarrow H_2O (l)$$

Fuel cells do not need the high operating temperatures of traditional hydrocarbon based fuels which are also less efficient than fuel cells. Some of the advantages of this emerging green technology (A3.6b) are that the fuel cells are rechargeable (not disposed of) and are portable and convenient sources of power. It is hoped that fuel cells will allow us to move away from an oil based carbon economy and they should provide plenty of jobs in the twenty first century. The efficiency of fuel cells is ~70% at converting chemical energy into electrical energy compared with an efficiency of ~35% for wind turbines. The obvious disadvantage of fuel cells is the need for the generation, storage and transport of hydrogen, which is a highly explosive gas. The first successful transatlantic crossings for paying customers was in hydrogen filled airships called Zeppelins. This golden age of travel came abruptly to an end in May 1937 when the Hindenberg caught fire in New Jersey (USA) which inspired the name of the legendary rock band Led Zeppelin and their first album cover.

The Hindenberg disaster

In the fuel cell hydrogen is oxidised (loses electrons) and oxygen is reduced (gains electrons) and the product is water. The net result is that hydrogen gives electrons to oxygen and it is the movement of these electrons through the external circuit that is the electrical current that can be utilised. Electrons leave the fuel cell *via* the anode and enter the fuel cell *via* the cathode. Note that the electrodes are named contrary to the electrodes in electrolysis reactions (B1.5i).

When an aqueous solution of sodium hydroxide is used as the electrolyte in a fuel cell, the overall reaction is the same as for an acidic electrolyte. The anode and cathode reactions also include the hydroxide ion.

Anode: $2 H_2 (g) + 4 OH^- (aq) \rightarrow 4 H_2O (l) + 4 e^-$

Cathode: $O_2 (g) + 2 H_2O (l) + 4 e^- \rightarrow 4 OH^- (aq)$

Overall: $2 H_2 (g) + O_2 (g) \rightarrow 2 H_2O (l)$

All cells work by physically separating the two half-equations (B1.5j) so the reactants do not meet. This is what happens in hydrogen/oxygen fuel cells. The hydrogen is the fuel (anode side) and oxygen is the oxidant (cathode side). The two half equations result in electrons flowing through an external circuit from the anode to the cathode.

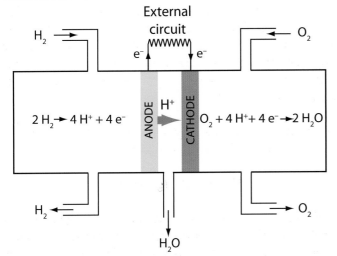

Hydrogen/oxygen fuel cell

Simulating a fuel cell

A simple experiment to simulate a fuel cell is to electrolyse acidified water for a few minutes with platinum electrodes. Once both the electrodes are obviously covered with bubbles of oxygen and hydrogen gas replace the power pack with a voltmeter. A voltage will be recorded as electrons transfer through the external circuit when the hydrogen at the anode reacts with oxygen produced from the cathode.

Fuel cells need a steady stream of gas bubbling over the surface of the platinum electrodes whilst they are in use. Between the platinum electrodes in an electrolyte there is a proton exchange membrane which allows the protons (H^+) to pass across the cell from the anode side where they are generated to the cathode side where they are consumed.

Anode: $2 H_2 (g) \rightarrow 4 H^+ (aq) + 4 e^-$

Cathode: $O_2 (g) + 4 H^+ (aq) + 4 e^- \rightarrow 2 H_2O (l)$

Overall: $2 H_2 (g) + O_2 (g) \rightarrow 2 H_2O (l)$

Questions 5.22

1. a. Write a balanced equation for the overall reaction taking place in a fuel cell.

   b. What is the opposite reaction to the fuel cell reaction?

2. In a methane/oxygen fuel cell the overall equation is $CH_4 + 2 O_2 \rightarrow CO_2 + 2 H_2O$. What are the equations taking place at the negative plate and the positive plate?

3. Why is it not currently practical for everyone to use electric cars powered by fuel cells?

6

Gases and Kinetics

Contents

Some of the first substances that students tend to meet are gases, *e.g.* oxygen, carbon dioxide, hydrogen and nitrogen. Substances exist exclusively as gas particles when the temperature is above their boiling points. About half of all non-metals are gases at room temperature and atmospheric pressure.

Non-metallic bromine is a volatile liquid at room temperature having a melting point of −7°C and a boiling point of 59°C. Putting a few drops of liquid bromine into a gas jar will illustrate the process of diffusion when gas particles spread out fill the container. The diffusion of the bright red colour of bromine vapour is easy to observe over a ten minute period.

One of the important things to learn about chemists is that they use a different temperature scale to that found on weather maps. The temperature scale used is called the kelvin scale after Lord Kelvin (William Thomson). A change of 1°C is equal to a change of 1 kelvin. Using water as an example it can be seen that to convert temperature from °C to K you need to add 273.

Water	°C	K (kelvin)
Melting point (m.p.)	0	273
Boiling point (b.p.)	100	373

For centuries, chemists have been working hard to explain the observed characteristics of chemical reactions. The study of their rates has led to great advances in the subject. Kinetics is a **quantitative** branch of chemistry which deals with the factors (temperature, pressure, concentration, catalysts, enzymes and surface area) that affect the rate (speed) of chemical reactions.

B1.6 (a)
Kinetic theory applied to an ideal gas

The kinetic theory is a mathematical model which can be applied to an ideal gas. It is a theory which is used to account for the properties of gases. The name of the theory comes from the Greek word *kinein*, which means 'to move', and was developed in the mid-nineteenth century by Rudolf Clausius and James Clerk Maxwell.

Kinetic theory is the foundation for the qualitative interpretation of the properties of ideal gases. There are five assumptions made in its development. It has been shown experimentally that any gas will closely obey the ideal gas laws at pressures < 1 atmosphere and temperatures > 273 K. The mathematics behind the kinetic theory is covered in undergraduate courses.

Assumptions of the kinetic theory

1. Gas particles are in continuous random motion.

2. Gas particles have negligible volume.

3. Gas particles are perfectly elastic.

4. Gas particles exert no attractive forces on each other.

5. Gas particles have an average kinetic energy that is proportional to absolute temperature.

Brownian motion experiments show that gas particles move randomly. It is possible to observe the random movement of lycopodium particles (pollen grains) on a drop of water placed under the lens of a microscope. Collisions with air particles are sufficiently energetic to jostle the pollen grains which float on the surface of the water. The random motion of the air particles is indicated by the random movement of the pollen grains as they collide with the invisible air particles. At 273 K, the average speeds for oxygen and nitrogen have been calculated at 424 ms^{-1} and 454 ms^{-1} respectively. The time gas particles spend in collision is very small compared with the time between collisions. This is because the particles in a gas are separated from each other by large distances compared with the size of the particles themselves.

The volume of a gas is usually tiny compared with the total volume that it occupies. Imagine a balloon filled with 1 mole of helium gas at 298K and 1 atmosphere of pressure. The molar volume of any gas is approximately 24 dm^3 at room temperature and pressure (A4.1e). Avogadro's constant is 6.02×10^{23} mol^{-1} and the atomic radius of helium is 0.05 nm = 5×10^{-10} dm.

Volume of a perfect sphere = $\frac{4}{3} \pi r^3$

Volume of a helium atom = $\frac{4}{3} \pi (5 \times 10^{-10})^3 = 5.24 \times 10^{-28}$ dm^3

Volume of a mole of helium atoms
$$= 5.24 \times 10^{-28} \text{ dm}^3 \times 6.02 \times 10^{23}$$

$$= 3.152 \times 10^{-4} \text{ dm}^3$$

Percentage volume of a mole of helium atoms

$$= \frac{3.152 \times 10^{-4} \text{ dm}^3}{24 \text{ dm}^3} \times 100\%$$

$$= 0.0013\%$$

This means that in a 24 dm^3 helium balloon, 99.9987% is empty space.

Describing gas particles as being 'perfectly elastic' assumes that, when they collide with each other and bounce apart, no energy is lost. This would lead to the assumption that the total kinetic energy of a gas is the same before and after a collision.

The assumption that gases exert no attractive force on each other is quite reasonable considering how much empty space there is compared with the volume of gas particles. The fact that particles of gas do have very small forces of attraction between them (called Van der Waals forces (A1.2j)) is one explanation of why gases can be liquefied.

Liquid nitrogen evaporating as it is poured from an insulated flask

The assumption that average kinetic energy is proportional to absolute temperature helps to explain why some helium balloons might pop as the room warms up at a children's party. The average speed of gas particles depends on their average kinetic energy. As the temperature increases, the average speed of the gas particles increase proportionately. The pressure of a gas can be explained in terms of the particles hitting the walls of a container. As temperature increases, the particles will hit the wall harder because they are moving faster. The increased force and frequency of collisions between gas particles and a container's walls will lead to an increase in pressure. With a flexible wall such as that of a rubber balloon, this increase pressure will lead to the balloon expanding.

Limitations of the kinetic theory

The ideal gas model is based on these five assumptions of the kinetic theory and it works well at fairly low pressures and fairly high temperatures. Deviations from ideal behaviour for gases are evident at high pressures and low temperatures, when the model breaks down (B1.7c). At high pressures, as the particles get closer and closer together, you can no longer ignore the attractive forces between particles. As the pressure increases, the gas particles will liquefy due to attractive forces holding the particles together. As gases are cooled, they will eventually liquefy and take up a much smaller volume. When the temperature of a gas is reduced and its boiling point approached, you can no longer ignore the volume of the particles themselves compared with the whole volume of the gas particles. The ideal gas equation (B1.6b) predicts that the volume of a gas is zero at absolute zero (0 K), which is clearly impossible.

Questions 6.1

1. How does the distance between helium atoms in a balloon compare with the atomic diameter?

2. Which option shows the factors that are most likely to lead to deviations from ideal gas behaviour?

	Temperature	Pressure
A	high	high
B	high	low
C	low	low
D	low	high

3. What are the assumptions made for the kinetic theory for an ideal gas?

B1.6 (b)
Boyle's law, Charles's law and the ideal gas equation

There are many additional gas laws such as **Raoult's Law** and **Henry's Law**, but we will restrict ourselves to the two most important laws, namely Boyle's and Charles's, which lead to the derivation of the ideal gas equation.

Boyle's Law

Robert Boyle is considered by many to be the founding father of modern chemistry. He wrote *The Sceptical Chymist*, a seminal book of the time (1661). This book helped put the subject on a firm footing as an evidence-based subject (B1.7a) which required controlled experimentation. Boyle was a great experimenter and believed all theories must be proved experimentally before being considered true. He is perhaps most famous for **Boyle's Law**. This is a quantitative (A4.1c) relationship between the volume (V) and pressure (P) of a gas. It states that the volume of a given mass of gas is inversely proportional to its pressure at constant temperature (T).

A simple experiment to illustrate Boyle's Law is to place a gas sample into a syringe and seal the end so that no gas can escape. The syringe is then held vertically and the volume of the gas can be compared as the pressure within the syringe is altered. The pressure in the syringe can be increased by placing weights on to the end of the syringe. As more weights are placed on the end of the syringe it will lead to a greater reduction in the gas volume and hence an increase in the gas pressure within the syringe.

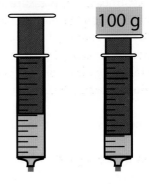

Increase in pressure leads to a reduction in gas volume

In terms of the kinetic theory (B1.6a), if the syringe contains a fixed amount of gas then there must be the same amount of gas if the volume is halved. If the volume is halved then, statistically, there will be twice the number of collisions with the wall of the syringe. So, at a constant temperature, the gas pressure will double.

The relationship between volume and pressure for a fixed mass of gas at a constant temperature can be shown graphically by plotting pressure against volume or pressure against $1/V$.

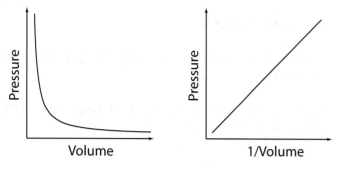

Graphs showing Boyle's Law

A visually interesting experiment to illustrate Boyle's Law is to place few marshmallows into a round bottom flask. When the round bottom flask is connected to a vacuum pump the pressure inside the flask can be reduced. For a constant mass of marshmallows at a fixed temperature, their volume will increase as the pressure of gas surrounding them is reduced.

Atmospheric pressure

Reduced pressure

Marshmallows at atmospheric pressure and at reduced pressure

Boyle's Law states that $V \alpha \frac{1}{P}$.

or V is inversely proportional to P.

Therefore $V = \frac{k}{P}$ where k is a proportionality constant.

Therefore another way of stating Boyle's Law is $PV =$ constant (k). A common way to express Boyle's Law is $P_1 V_1 = P_2 V_2$ where $P_1 =$ initial pressure and $V_1 =$ initial volume and $P_2 =$ final pressure and $V_2 =$ final volume. The expression $P_1 V_1 = P_2 V_2$ can be used to calculate the final volume or pressure of a gas when compressed (squashed) or expanded at a constant temperature.

Charles's Law

Charles's Law is a quantitative (A4.1c) relationship between the volume (V) and temperature (T) of a gas at a constant pressure. It states that the volume of a given mass of gas increases linearly with temperature at constant pressure. The volume is directly proportional to its absolute temperature (K).

A simple experiment to illustrate Charles's Law is to place a gas sample into a syringe and to seal the end of the syringe so that no gas can escape. The syringe is then held vertically and the volume of the gas can be compared as the temperature surrounding the syringe is altered. This can be done by placing the syringe into a beaker of water held at different temperatures. The volume of gas in the syringe can be increased by heating the water surrounding the syringe. The higher the temperature of the gas in the syringe the larger the volume it will occupy at the same pressure.

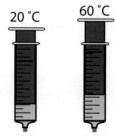

Increase in temperature leads to an increase in gas volume

In terms of the kinetic theory (B1.6a), if the syringe contains a fixed pressure of gas, then at higher temperatures the gas particles will have an increased average kinetic energy. As the gas particles speed up they will hit the walls of the syringe more energetically. This will cause the syringe's plunger to move upwards. If the volume of gas increases as the temperature increases, then the pressure will be maintained by the syringe moving position as the gas expands. Experiments have shown that, at temperatures of around 0°C, a gas changes its volume by $\frac{1}{273}$ of its volume for every 1°C change in temperature. This means that if a gas warms up by 1°C its volume will increase by $\frac{1}{273}$ its initial volume. Also if a gas cools down by 1°C its volume will decrease by $\frac{1}{273}$ of its initial volume. This does, of course, assume that the volume of a gas will be zero at absolute zero (0 K), which is another example of how the assumptions of the kinetic theory (B1.6a) break down at very low temperatures.

The relationship between volume and temperature for a fixed mass of gas at a constant pressure can be shown graphically by plotting volume against temperature. When volume (y-axis) is plotted against temperature in °C (x-axis) the graph extrapolates back to absolute zero.

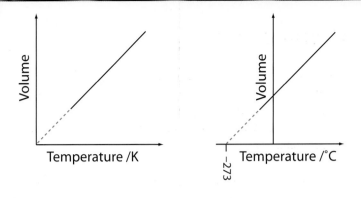

Graphs showing Charles's Law

The Charles's Law graphs of volume *vs.* temperature show that $\frac{V}{T}$ is a constant.

Therefore $\frac{V_1}{T_1} = \frac{V_2}{T_2}$

where:

- T_1 = initial temperature
- V_1 = initial volume and
- T_2 = final temperature and
- V_2 = final volume.

The equation:

$$\frac{V_1}{T_1} = \frac{V_2}{T_2}$$

can be used to calculate the final volumes of a gas when it is heated or cooled at constant pressure.

What is interesting is that, no matter what the pressure of a gas, the Charles's Law graphs always extrapolate back to −273 °C. There have been many attempts to reach absolute zero. One of the coldest temperatures ever recorded was by Nobel Laureate Wolfgang Ketterle's team in 2003 at the Massachusetts Institute of Technology. They cooled sodium gas to one billionth of a degree above absolute zero.

Ideal Gas equation

The ideal gas equation relates the three variables; pressure, volume and temperature.

The ideal gas equation is: $PV = nRT$ where R is the molar gas constant = 8.31 J K⁻¹ mol⁻¹ and n = amount of gas (mol). A gas that obeys the ideal gas equation is called an **ideal gas**. The ideal gas equation is obeyed by real gases at high temperatures and low pressures.

The ideal gas equation is derived from a combination of Boyle's Law ($P_1V_1 = P_2V_2$) and Charles's Law ($\frac{V_1}{T_1} = \frac{V_2}{T_2}$).

Combining the two equations gives:

$$\frac{P_1V_1}{T_1} = \frac{P_2V_2}{T_2}$$

Therefore $\frac{PV}{T}$ = constant.

The constant is the molar gas constant R (8.31 J K⁻¹ mol⁻¹) for one mole of gas.

Therefore $PV/T = nR$ and when this is rearranged you get the ideal gas equation $PV = nRT$.

Calculating relative molecular masses

The ideal gas equation can be used to calculate relative molecular masses (M_r) for gases. The ideal gas equation is $PV = nRT$ and since $n = m / M_r$ we can rewrite the equation as:

$$PV = \frac{m}{M_r} \times RT.$$

Therefore, if we know the mass and volume of a gas at any given temperature and pressure we can calculate its M_r in g mol⁻¹.

Example 6.1

1.20 g of a gas has a volume of 500 cm³ at 25°C & 100 kPa. [R = 8.31 J K⁻¹ mol⁻¹]

100 kPa = 100000 Pa

To convert volume from cm³ to m³, divide by 1 000 000.

To convert temperature °C to K, add 273.

$PV = \frac{m}{M_r} \times RT$ and rearranging gives $M_r = \frac{mRT}{PV}$.

$M_r = \frac{1.20 \times 8.31 \times 298}{100\ 000 \times 0.0005} = 59.4$ g mol⁻¹.

Calculating molar volume

One mole of any gas occupies approximately 24 dm³ (A4.1e) at room temperature (298 K) and at a pressure of 1 atmosphere (101325 Pa). The ideal gas equation $PV = nRT$ can be used to calculate the volume taken up by 1 mole of an ideal gas at room temperature and pressure.

Rearranging gives $V = \frac{nRT}{P}$ where V = volume in m³.

The conversion factor is m³ × 1 000 to become dm³.

$$V = \frac{1 \times 8.31 \times 298}{10\ 1325}$$

$$= 2.444 \times 10^{-2} \text{ m}^3$$

$$= 24.44 \text{ dm}^3$$

Avogadro's principle (that one mole of an ideal gas occupies the same volume under standard conditions) is rounded down and approximated to 24 dm³. One of the assumptions of the kinetic theory (B1.6a) does not hold true for real gases. The small differences in the attractive forces between gas particles (A1.2j) give them slightly different molar volumes. The differences are minimal, so 24 dm³ remains a good approximation for use in calculations. Molar volumes at 101 325 Pa and 20°C (293 K) for the main components of air have been determined experimentally as; nitrogen (24.3 dm³), oxygen (24.3 dm³), argon (24.0 dm³) and carbon dioxide (24.2 dm³).

Questions 6.2

1. Which option shows the correct relationship for Boyle's law?

    A V is proportional to $1/P$

    B PV is proportional to $1/V$

    C V is inversely proportional to $1/P$

    D P is inversely proportional to $1/V$

2. Which option does not show a plot representing Boyle's Law?

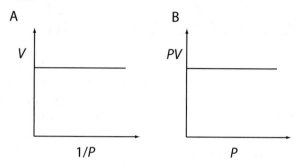

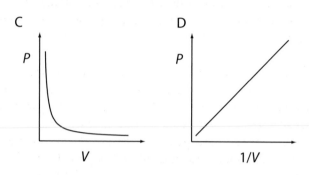

3. Which option shows the variable which is held constant for the gas laws?

	Boyle's Law	Charles's Law
A	Temperature	Volume
B	Temperature	Pressure
C	Pressure	Volume
D	Pressure	Temperature

4. Calculate the relative molecular mass for 48 cm³ of a gas that has a mass of 0.14 g and a pressure of 98400 Pa at 18°C. [$R = 8.31$ J K⁻¹ mol⁻¹].

5. What is the mass of 100 cm³ of laughing gas (N_2O) at 28°C and a pressure of 101.3 kPa? [Ar: N = 14.0 & O = 16.0].

B1.6 (c)
Boltzmann distribution

The rate of a chemical reaction depends on two important factors: the temperature at which the reaction is carried out and the size of the activation energy (A1.3g). Chemists use everything at their disposal to jump the energy hurdle of the activation energy (E_a). Reactions with large E_a are slow but the rate of their reactions will increase rapidly as the temperature is increased. Reactions with small E_a are fast and their rates of reaction do not increase as rapidly with temperature as reactions with high E_a.

The distribution of the molecular energy of particles is given by the **Boltzmann distribution** (A1.3h). The Boltzmann distribution shows that, in a known volume, gas particles are not all moving with the same kinetic energy but with a range of kinetic energies. Some particles will be moving slowly, perhaps because they have just collided with a particle travelling in the reverse direction. Some particles will be moving fast, perhaps because they have just been hit by a particle moving in the same direction. Note how the peak in the Boltzmann distribution moves to the right as the temperature increases and is lower in height. The total area under a curve in a Boltzmann distribution is proportional to the total number of particles present in the system.

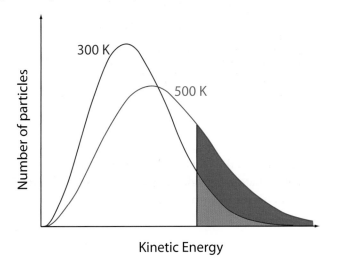

Boltzmann distribution of kinetic energies at 300 K & 500 K

The only particles which might react are those with energy equal to or exceeding the activation energy which is indicated by the shaded areas. The effect of increasing the temperature from 300 K to 500 K is to have more particles with higher energy and a greater proportion with energies exceeding the activation energy. There will be more energetic collisions at higher temperatures which break the reactants bonds, which is why the rate of reaction increases at higher temperatures.

Questions 6.3

1. What happens to reactant particles that collide with energy less than the activation energy?

2. What information is obtained from a Boltzmann distribution?

3. Which option shows the minimum energy needed for reaction to take place with a single molecule which collides head on with an identically fast molecule where:

   $E_a = 60$ kJ mol^{-1} and $L = 6.02 \times 10^{23}$ mol^{-1}?

   A 9.97×10^{-20} J

   B 4.98×10^{-23} J

   C 9.97×10^{-23} J

   D 4.98×10^{-20} J

B1.6 (d) Rate constant and the Arrhenius equation

For particles to react, they need to collide with energy equal to, or exceeding that of, the activation energy (E_a). The units of activation energy are kJ mol^{-1}. Activation energy is the minimum energy needed to break the bonds in the reactants on collision, leading to the formation of the products. Each reaction has a particular value for its activation energy, which range from ~3 kJ mol^{-1} to ~300 kJ mol^{-1}.

How often gas particles collide (collision frequency) depends on three main factors:

1. Size of molecules: the smaller the particles, the less the chance of collisions.

2. Mass of molecules: Kinetic energy, K.E. = ½mv². The larger the mass of the particles, the slower they will move at a particular temperature. Therefore, lighter particles are more likely to collide than heavier particles because they are moving faster.

3. Temperature: As the temperature is increased the kinetic energy of the particles increases, which is one of the assumptions of the kinetic theory (B1.6a). At higher temperatures, the proportion of particles with energy exceeding the activation energy will increase, and so will the collision frequency and consequently the rate of the reaction.

The first two factors are contrary (opposing), so it is temperature which is the main factor which determines how often particles will collide during a chemical reaction.

Quantitative experiments can determine the rate of a chemical reaction (B1.6f) and this leads to the calculation of a rate constant (k) with units such as dm^3 mol^{-1} s^{-1}. Faster reactions have larger values for the rate constant.

In 1889 the Swedish nobel laureate, Svante Arrhenius, produced an equation, named after him, that shows the effect of temperature on the rate constant.

Arrhenius equation: $k = A \exp\left(-\dfrac{E_a}{RT}\right) = A\, e^{\left(-\frac{E_a}{RT}\right)}$

Where:

k = rate constant,

A = pre-exponential factor,

E_a = activation energy,

R = molar gas constant (8.31 J K^{-1} mol^{-1}), and

T = thermodynamic temperature (K).

Taking $\log_e$ of both sides of the Arrhenius equation gives:

$\log_e k = \log_e A - \dfrac{E_a}{RT}$

Rearranging this equation gives:

$$\log_e k = -\dfrac{E_a}{R} \times \dfrac{1}{T} + \log_e A$$
$$y = m\,x + c$$

A plot of $\log_e k$ (y–axis) against $\dfrac{1}{T}$ (x-axis) gives a straight line plot.

The slope is $-\dfrac{E_a}{R}$ from which the activation energy can be calculated.

The pre-exponential A is found when $1/T = 0$ at the intercept on the vertical axis. Experimentally Arrhenius showed that A and E_a are constant over a large range of temperatures.

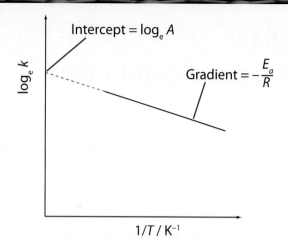

Arrhenius plot

In the Arrhenius equation, $e^{\left(-\frac{E_a}{RT}\right)}$ is the fraction of collisions with sufficient energy to react. This is the shaded area beyond the activation energy in a Boltzmann distribution curve (B1.6c). Take for example a reaction with an activation energy of 55 kJ mol^{-1} at 298 K.

The fraction of collisions giving reaction

$$= e^{\left(-\frac{55\,000}{8.31 \times 298}\right)}$$

$$= 2.3 \times 10^{-10}.$$

This means that only just over 2 in 10^{10} collisions have sufficient energy ($>E_a$) to give reaction. This does not seem a lot but, since each molecule collides at a rate of approximately 1×10^{11} collisions per second, it is a moderately fast reaction.

In addition to exceeding the activation energy, particles must also collide with the correct orientation (B3.9a) for the collision to lead to a reaction. Only a small proportion of gas particles will hit each other in a reaction with enough energy and in the right place within the molecule. The pre-exponential A in the Arrhenius equation is made up of the collision frequency (Z) and a steric factor (P), where $A = PZ$. It has been shown that for most reactions the steric factor $P < 1$.

Substituting PZ into the Arrhenius equation gives:

$$k = PZ \exp\left(-\dfrac{E_a}{RT}\right).$$

Without going into the mathematics, collision frequency (Z) has been shown to be proportional to $\frac{1}{M_r}$, d^2 and $\sqrt{T}$ (square root of temperature) where M_r = relative molecular mass, d = diameter of the molecule assuming it is spherical, and T = thermodynamic temperature.

Questions 6.4

1. What is meant by collision frequency?

2. What equation shows the relationship between temperature and rate constant?

3. Write down the Arrhenius equation and explain the significance of the negative sign in the exponential term.

4. Use the data for the decomposition of hydrogen iodide to calculate the activation energy for the reaction. Write an equation for this decomposition.

Temp / K	k / dm^3 mol^{-1} s^{-1}
630	1.80×10^{-5}
667	1.08×10^{-4}
698	5.00×10^{-4}
715	1.06×10^{-3}
780	1.50×10^{-2}

5. Which option shows the greatest activation energies from the Arrhenius plots?

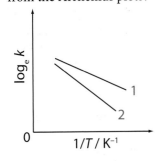 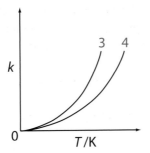

A   1 & 3

B   1 & 4

C   2 & 4

D   2 & 3

6. Which option shows a factor that is not present in the Arrhenius equation?

A   activation energy

B   collision frequency

C   pressure

D   steric factor

7. The rate constant is a product of collision frequency, steric factor and a Boltzmann term. Identify these factors in the Arrhenius equation.

8. Use the data to calculate the activation energy for the reaction between sodium thiosulfate and hydrochloric acid. Write a balanced formula equation for this reaction and explain how the rate of reaction might be measured.

Temperature / °C	Rate constant k / s^{-1}
25	0.040
35	0.052
45	0.080
55	0.111
65	0.152

9. Use the data to calculate the activation energy for the decomposition of dinitrogen pentoxide (N_2O_5). Suggest a balanced formula equation for this decomposition reaction.

Temperature / °C	Rate constant k / s^{-1}
25	3.4×10^{-5}
35	1.4×10^{-4}
45	5.0×10^{-4}
55	1.5×10^{-3}
65	4.9×10^{-3}

10. Use the Arrhenius equation and the data to calculate the rate constants (k) for the three reactions at 25 °C. Which is the slowest and which the fastest reaction?

Reaction #	A	E_a	k
1	4.3×10^{11}	89.5×10^3	
2	2.4×10^{11}	81.6×10^3	
3	7.9×10^8	10.5×10^3	

Step 2

Step 3 $+ H_2O + H^+$

Acid-catalysed esterification of methanoic acid

It is worth noting that the acid does not alter the position of the equilibrium (B1.5a) or the equilibrium constant K_c (B1.5c).

B1.6 (e) Homogeneous and heterogeneous catalysis

A key feature of catalysts is that they alter the rate of a chemical reaction without being chemically changed themselves. Catalysts do take part in the chemical reaction by making it easier to reach a transition state (B3.9b) which has a structure part way between that of reactant and product(s). Catalysts will also lower the activation energy (A1.3f) by providing a different pathway.

Catalysts can be divided into two groups called **homogeneous catalysts** and **heterogeneous catalysts**. The distinction is based on the states (phases) of the reactants and the catalyst. Homogeneous catalysts are in the **same** state as the reactants. Heterogeneous catalysts are in a **different** state from the reactants.

Homogeneous catalysis

Laboratory homogeneous catalysis reactions usually take place in solutions. An acid (H^+) is used as the homogeneous catalyst in acid-catalysed esterifications (B3.7b). Using an acid catalyst means that large scale production of esters takes place in several hours rather than the reaction taking place over many days. At the end of the reaction, the catalyst H^+ is regenerated and this is shown in the detailed reaction scheme called a mechanism (B3.9).

Step 1

Heterogeneous catalysis

Heterogeneous catalysis usually occurs at the surface of a transition metal catalyst. The reactants are often gases, so are in a different state from the solid catalyst. It is important that the catalysts have a very large surface area which is why the solids are often used as powders, pea-sized lumps or wire meshes. The mode of action of heterogeneous catalysis can be described in four steps.

Step 1: Gaseous reactant molecules diffuse and collide with the catalyst.

Step 2: Gaseous molecules are adsorbed onto the surface forming weak bonds.

Step 3: The reaction takes place with the accompanying molecular rearrangement.

Step 4: Products are desorbed from the surface of the catalyst.

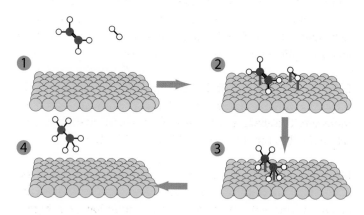

Reaction of ethene and hydrogen at nickel's surface

Transition metals make good heterogeneous catalysts because of the availability on their surfaces of 3d and 4s electrons and also the presence of unfilled d-orbitals (B2.4f). This is how transition metals form these new temporary bonds described in step 2. The adsorption onto the catalyst's surface weakens the reactants' bonds and also holds them in the correct orientation for reaction. The products form much weaker bonds to the catalyst than the reactants so are soon desorbed before diffusing away from the surface of the catalyst. Platinum is widely used as a heterogeneous catalyst for a number of reactions including hydrogenation to an alkene (A3.5b) because it has optimum adsorption, *i.e.* strong enough to bind the reactant but weak enough to release the product.

Modern motor vehicles use a catalytic converter to reduce levels of pollution emitted from their exhausts. The metals used are rhodium, platinum and palladium. The reason why leaded petrol cannot be used with vehicles fitted with a catalytic converter is because the lead atoms are adsorbed very strongly onto the surface, which poisons it.

Enzymes and active sites

Enzymes are biological catalysts, which are very large protein based molecules which often have a transition metal (B2.4c) bound within their structures. The names of enzymes are recognisable from biology as they often end (suffix) with *ase*. Enzymes increase rates of reaction by factors of 10^7-10^{14}. The rate increases due to enzymes often far exceed the levels of catalysts developed by chemists. This is one reason why only small amounts of these enzymes are needed for these very efficient catalysts. In nature, enzymes are found in solutions inside and outside cells along with aqueous reactants so they can be classified as homogeneous catalysts.

Enzymes greatly increase rates of reaction in living systems. Some of the numbers associated with them are incredible. For example, one molecule of a triose phosphate isomerase can catalyse up to 400,000 molecules per second. The limiting factor is, quite literally, the rate of diffusion.

Enzymes can be quite specific in their action which means that they only catalyse one reaction for one substrate (reactant) molecule. The enzyme *urease* will, for example, hydrolyse urea (H_2NCONH_2) but not ethanamide (CH_3CONH_2).

It is the shapes of enzymes which determine their catalytic activity. Any change in conditions which might alter the shape of an enzyme will affect its ability to function as a highly efficient catalyst. Experiments have determined that each enzyme has an optimum (best) temperature and an optimum pH for maximum catalytic activity. Within the 3D structure of enzymes there is a 'hollow' or 'cleft' part of the protein called

an **active site**. This is the place where the substrate will bind *via* intermolecular forces (A1.2j) and consequently react. The model often used to explain this concept is to think of the enzyme as being a lock and the substrate a key that exactly fits the lock.

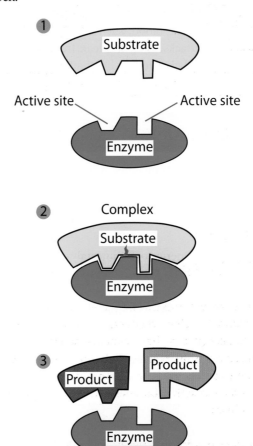

Substrate fitting into the active site of an enzyme

When a substrate forms a complex by binding in the active site of an enzyme, the activation energy (A1.3f) is lowered. The active site might consist of just a few amino acids which are locked into the correct orientation to accept and bind to the substrate. The products will bind less tightly to the active site and will soon diffuse away allowing more substrates to enter the active site and for the reaction to be repeated many times a second. The structures of enzymes have been solved using x-ray crystallography (B2.5b). It has been found that the highest quality crystals are grown by NASA (and other) scientists in space, on board the space shuttle. It is interesting to note that the active site perfectly complements the transition state (B3.9b).

Enzymes have been used for millennia to make alcohol from sugar and cheese and yoghurts from milk. The quite recent field of **biotechnology** is exploiting enzymes for use in medicines. Enzymes are used to make 'factor VIII', a drug for haemophiliacs and **insulin** for diabetics. Proteases are also finding extensive use in washing powders.

A lack, or an excess, of particular enzymes can have medical consequences. A lack of the enzyme tyrosinase is found in patients with the condition of albinism portrayed by the character Silas in Dan Brown's very readable *The Da Vinci Code*. A deficiency in the liver enzyme phenylalanine hydroxylase leads to a condition called **phenylketonuria** (PKU). Raised levels of enzymes in the blood, such as creatine kinase, are markers for heart attacks. Enzymes leak from cells in heart tissue when they are damaged by a heart attack.

Questions 6.5

1. The iodination of propanone is acid catalysed. Write an equation for this reaction and describe the catalyst.

2. The activation energy for the uncatalysed decomposition of nitrous oxide (N_2O) is 240 kJ mol^{-1}.

$$2 N_2O \, (g) \rightarrow 2 N_2 \, (g) + O_2 \, (g)$$

The reaction is catalysed by gold. Which option is the best description of the catalytic reaction?

	Activation energy / kJ mol^{-1}	Type of catalysis
A	120	heterogeneous
B	240	homogeneous
C	120	homogeneous
D	240	heterogeneous

3. For each of the following reactions, name and classify its catalyst.

   a. $N_2 + 3 H_2 \rightleftharpoons 2 NH_3$

   b. $SO_2 + \frac{1}{2}O_2 \rightleftharpoons SO_3$

   c. $H_2O_2 \rightarrow H_2O + \frac{1}{2}O_2$

   d. $CH_3CO_2H + CH_3OH$
   $\rightleftharpoons CH_3CO_2CH_3 + H_2O$

4. Write an equation for the hydrolysis of urea. [Hint: See section B3.8a). Name the enzyme that catalyses this transformation.

5. Which option about binding in an enzyme's active site is not true?

   A Activation energy is lowered and binding liberates energy.

   B Active site complements the shape of the transition state.

   C Substrate molecules are positioned in favourable orientations.

   D Substrates bind less tightly to the active site than the products.

6. Cross-sections are shown of the active sites of three different proteases forming complexes with three different amino acids (alanine, lysine, tyrosine). What are the major intermolecular forces holding these amino acids in place?

a. Elastase

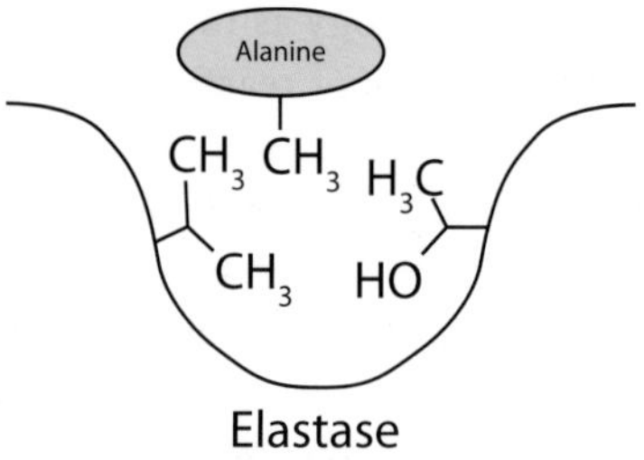

b. Trypsin

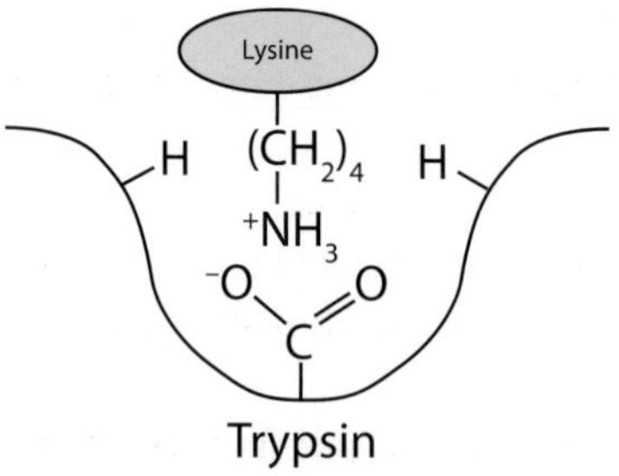

c. Chymotrypsin

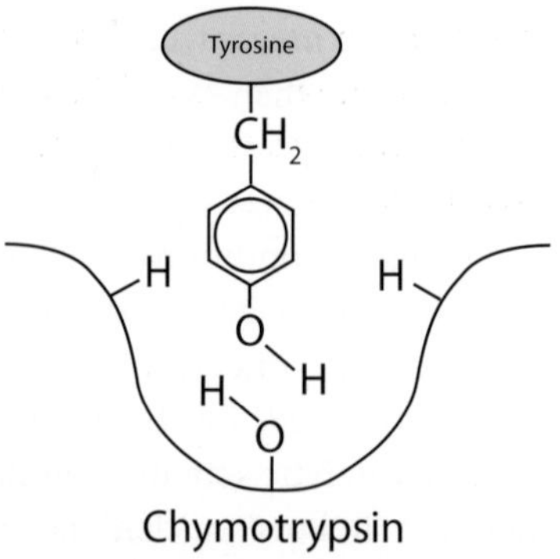

7. From the two equations, write the overall equation for the reaction and explain the role of bromine.

   $2NO + Br_2 \rightarrow 2\,NOBr$

   $2\,NOBr + Cl_2 \rightarrow 2\,NOCl + Br_2$

8. From the three equations write the overall equation for the reaction and explain which chemical species is the catalyst.

   $2\,KClO_3 + 2\,MnO_2 \rightarrow Cl_2 + 2\,KMnO_4 + O_2$

   $2\,KMnO_4 \rightarrow K_2MnO_4 + MnO_2 + O_2$

   $K_2MnO_4 + Cl_2 \rightarrow 2\,KCl + MnO_2 + O_2$

B1.6 (f)
Rate equations and orders

Rate equations take the form:

Rate = k [reactant A]^x [reactant B]^y [reactant C]^z

where k = rate constant and x, y and z are **orders** with respect to reactants A, B and C.

Orders and rate equations can only be determined experimentally and cannot be deduced from the balanced formula equation. The overall order for the reaction is the sum of the individual orders, *i.e.* $x + y + z$. Orders for reactants tend to be the integers 0, 1 and 2 and these are the powers to which the reactant concentrations are raised in rate equations.

Given a rate equation, it is a comparatively simple matter to correctly describe the order with respect to each reactant shown inside the square bracket. The order is the power to which the concentration is raised in the rate equation. The overall order is found by adding together all the orders for the individual reactants.

Example 6.2

The rate equation for a reaction was found to be:

Rate = k [A]^0 [B]^1 [C]^2.

The order with respect to A = 0, the order with respect to B = 1 and the order with respect to C = 2. The overall order for the reaction is the sum of the individual orders = 0 + 1 + 2 = 3.

Example 6.3

The rate equation for a reaction was found to be:

Rate = k [NO$_2$]^2 [CO]^0 [O$_2$]^0.

The order with respect to NO$_2$ = 2, the order with respect to CO = 0 and the order with respect to O$_2$ is 0. The overall order for the reaction is the sum of the individual orders = 2 + 0 + 0 = 2.

Example 6.4

The rate equation for a reaction was found to be:

Rate = k [HCrO$_4^-$]^1 [HSO$_3^-$]^2 [H$^+$]^1.

The order with respect to HCrO$_4^-$ = 1, the order with respect to HSO$_3^-$ = 2 and the order with respect to H$^+$ is 1. The overall order for the reaction is the sum of the individual orders = 1 + 2 + 1 = 4.

Units of rate and rate constants

Since rate is a change in concentration (mol dm^{-3}) of a reactant per unit time (s), the unit of rate, for the purposes of rate equations, is mol dm^{-3} s^{-1}. An explanation of how rate equations are arrived at is to be found in B1.6 (i). Using rate equations, it can be shown that the unit of rate constant depends on the total order of the reaction. The unit of rate constant for reactions with overall order 1, 2 and 3 is tabulated. The table summarises the rate constants for different orders. It is more important to be able to work out units rather than just learning them by rote.

Overall order	Unit of rate constant k
1st	s^{-1}
2nd	$mol^{-1}\, dm^3\, s^{-1}$
3rd	$mol^{-2}\, dm^6\, s^{-1}$

Example 6.5

Calculate the units of rate constant from the rate equation:

$$Rate = k\, [H_2O_2]$$

Units of rate = $mol\, dm^{-3}\, s^{-1}$ and units of concentration are $mol\, dm^{-3}$.

Replace all the quantities in the rate equation with their units.

$mol\, dm^{-3}\, s^{-1} = k\, mol\, dm^{-3}$ rearranging this equation gives

$$k = \frac{mol\, dm^{-3}\, s^{-1}}{mol\, dm^{-3}}$$

$k = s^{-1}$.

Example 6.6

Calculate the units of rate constant from the rate equation:

$$Rate = k\, [NO]^2\, [O_2]^1$$

Units of rate = $mol\, dm^{-3}\, s^{-1}$ and units of concentration are $mol\, dm^{-3}$.

Replace all the quantities in the rate equation with their units.

$mol\, dm^{-3}\, s^{-1} = k\, (mol\, dm^{-3})^2\, (mol\, dm^{-3})$

$mol\, dm^{-3}\, s^{-1} = k\, mol^3\, dm^{-9}$ rearranging this equation gives:

$$k = \frac{mol\, dm^{-3}\, s^{-1}}{mol^3\, dm^{-9}}$$

$k = mol^{-2}\, dm^6\, s^{-1}$.

Molecularity of a given step

The **molecularity** of a reaction step is the number of species that take part and are consumed in that step of the reaction. The molecularity of a given reaction step is always an integer and is probably going to be either one or two. When only one reactant takes part in a reaction step, it is described as **unimolecular** as its molecularity is one. When a reaction step involves two reactant species, it is described as **bimolecular** as its molecularity is two. The order of a reaction is determined experimentally, whereas the molecularity is a theoretical concept which can only be applied to simple reactions. Molecularity is not the same as the overall order for a reaction but they do sometimes match.

Example 6.7

What is the molecularity in each step for the alkaline hydrolysis of the tertiary halogenoalkane 2-bromo-2-methylpropane $(CH_3)_3CBr$?

Step 1: $(CH_3)_3CBr \rightarrow (CH_3)_3C^+ + Br^-$

Step 2: $(CH_3)_3C^+ + OH^- \rightarrow (CH_3)_3COH$

Since molecularity is the number of species involved in each step (the number of reactants), the molecularity is one for *step 1* and two for *step 2*.

Questions 6.6

1. What is the overall order of these reactions from the rate equations?

    a. Rate = $k\, [O_3]\, [C_2H_4]$

    b. Rate = $k\, [H_2O_2]\, [I^-]^2$

    c. Rate = $k\, [C_6H_5N_2Cl]$

    d. Rate = $k\, [H_2]\, [NO]^2$

    e. Rate = $k\, [Br^-]\, [H^+]^2\, [BrO_3^-]$

2. Which option shows the correct unit of rate of reaction used in a rate equation?

A $mol^{-1} dm^{-3} s^{-1}$

B $mol\ dm^{-3} s^{1}$

C $mol\ dm^{-3} s^{-1}$

D $mol^{-1} dm^{3} s^{-1}$

3. Calculate the units of rate constant from the rate equation; rate = k $[NO]^2$

4. Calculate the units of rate constant from the rate equation: rate = $k\ [H_2]^1 [I_2]^1$

5. Which option shows the correct units of k for reactions of order 1, 2 and 3?

	1st order	2nd order	3rd order
A	s^{-1}	$mol^{-1} dm^{-3} s^{-1}$	$mol^{-2} dm^6 s^{-1}$
B	$mol\ dm^{-3}$	$mol^2 dm^{-6}$	$mol^3 dm^{-9}$
C	$mol\ dm^{-3} s^{-1}$	$mol^2 dm^{-6} s^{-1}$	$mol^3 dm^{-9} s^{-1}$
D	s^{-1}	$mol^{-1} dm^3 s^{-1}$	$mol^{-2} dm^6 s^{-1}$

6. What is the molecularity of a reaction step which involves three reactant species and how might it be described?

7. What is meant by the 'overall order of a reaction'?

8. What is the molecularity of each step when dinitrogen pentoxide (N_2O_5) decomposes to give nitrogen dioxide (NO_2) and oxygen (O_2) given the mechanism involves the following three steps?

Step 1: $N_2O_5 \rightleftharpoons NO_2 + NO_3$

Step 2: $NO_2 + NO_3 \rightleftharpoons NO_2 + NO + O_2$

Step 3: $NO + NO_3 \rightleftharpoons 2\ NO_2$

B1.6 (g) Rate-determining step and mechanism

Chemical reactions often take place in a number of different steps. In these multi-step reactions, there is likely to be a fast step and a slow step. The overall rate of the reaction will be determined by the slow step. The slowest step in a chemical reaction is called the **r**ate **d**etermining **s**tep or **rds** for short. These different steps in going from reactants to products are called mechanisms and they are met again in the section on organic chemistry (B3.9).

The rate determining step can be thought of as a bottleneck in the traffic caused by speed restrictions where there are road works. You might do the first stage of your journey in good time but the overall time it takes to make a car journey will depend on how quickly you get through the road works.

Road works in Edinburgh, home to the famous crime writer Ian Rankin

It should be possible, given a mechanism, to identify the rate determining step and to be able to make predictions on orders and, therefore, the overall order of a reaction. For example in the upper atmosphere (stratosphere) there is an equilibrium between ozone (A2.2e) and its usual allotrope oxygen (O_2).

Mechanism for the destruction and formation of ozone

The slowest step is the second step and it is this which is the rate determining step. Adding the two steps of the mechanism together gives the overall equation for this pair of equilibria which is 2 $O_3 \rightleftharpoons$ 3 O_2. The molecularity in *step 1* is unimolecular and the molecularity in *step 2* is bimolecular. The rate equation will include [O] and [O_3] as both are present in the rate determining step. The orders of these substances will not be zero and it is reasonable to anticipate them to have values of one.

The rate equation for this reaction is rate $= k$ [O] [O_3] and the overall order is two. Even though it was not needed in this example, it is always worth bearing in mind that any reactant with zero order in the rate equation does not take part in the rate determining step (rds).

The acid catalysed iodination of propanone results in the formation of iodopropanone and hydrogen iodide.

$$CH_3COCH_3 \text{ (aq)} + I_2 \text{ (aq)} \xrightarrow[\text{(aq)}]{H^+} CH_3COCH_2I \text{ (aq)} + HI \text{ (aq)}$$

The inorganic hydrogen iodide will go on to react with the water to form hydroiodic acid HI (aq). The rate equation for this reaction, which has been determined experimentally, is rate $= k$ [CH_3COCH_3] [H^+] [I_2]^0.

Questions 6.7

1. There are four steps in the mechanism for the decomposition of dinitrogen pentoxide, with a slow first step followed by three fast steps. Suggest a rate equation for this reaction and identify the rate determining step.

   Step 1: $2 N_2O_5 \rightarrow 2 NO_2 + 2 NO_3$

   Step 2: $NO_2 + NO_3 \rightarrow NO + NO_2 + O_2$

   Step 3: $NO_2 + NO_3 \rightarrow 2 NO_2 + \frac{1}{2}O_2$

   Step 4: $NO + O_2 + NO_2 \rightarrow 2 NO_2 + \frac{1}{2}O_2$

2. There are three steps in the mechanism for the oxidation of iodide by hydrogen peroxide in the presence of acid, with a slow first step followed by two fast steps. Write a balanced formula equation for this reaction and suggest a rate equation given that the overall order is 2.

   Step 1: $H_2O_2 \text{ (aq)} + I^- \text{ (aq)} \rightarrow IO^- \text{ (aq)} + H_2O \text{ (l)}$

   Step 2: $IO^- \text{ (aq)} + H_3O^+ \text{ (aq)} \rightarrow HIO \text{ (aq)} + H_2O \text{ (l)}$

   Step 3: $HIO \text{ (aq)} + H_3O^+ \text{ (aq)} + I^- \text{ (aq)}$
   $\rightarrow I_2 \text{ (aq)} + 2 H_2O \text{ (l)}$

It should be possible to suggest a mechanism that is consistent with this given rate equation. The mechanism will include a rate determining step which does not contain iodine. The rate is zero order with respect to iodine and any reactant with order zero cannot take part in the rate determining step because its concentration does not affect the overall rate of the reaction. When building a mechanism from the rate equation, the final equation also needs to be consistent with the overall equation for the reaction. Propanone and the acid catalyst have order one so they both take part in the rate determining step.

The proposed mechanism has three steps with the first step, the protonation of propanone, being the rate determining step. You should also check that the three steps do add up to give the overall equation for this reaction.

Mechanism for the iodination of propanone

Questions 6.8

1. The acid catalysed hydration of ethene results in the formation of ethanol.

$$CH_2=CH_2 \, (g) + H_2O \, (g) \xrightarrow[\text{(l)}]{H^+} CH_3CH_2OH \, (g)$$
Ethene   Ethanol

Suggest a mechanism for this reaction from the rate equation:

Rate $= k \, [CH_2=CH_2] \, [H^+] \, [H_2O]^0$

2. The oxidation of nitrogen monoxide results in the formation of nitrogen dioxide. The equation for this reaction is $2 \, NO + O_2 \rightarrow 2 \, NO_2$. Suggest a mechanism for this reaction from the rate equation:

Rate $= k \, [NO]^2 \, [O_2]^0$

3. The reduction of nitrogen dioxide by carbon monoxide results in the formation of nitrogen monoxide and carbon dioxide. Write the equation for this reaction and suggest a mechanism from the rate equation:

Rate $= k \, [NO_2]^2 \, [CO]^0$

B1.6 (i)
Deducing rate equations

A simple experiment to measure the overall rate of reaction between a metal and an acid is to time how long it takes for a piece of magnesium ribbon to 'dissolve' in the acid. This method of following the rate of reaction is to measure the time it takes for the reactant to be consumed by excess acid.

$$Mg \, (s) + 2 \, HCl \, (aq) \rightarrow MgCl_2 \, (aq) + H_2 \, (g)$$

Another method to follow the rate of this redox reaction (B1.5j) is to measure the volume of hydrogen gas collected in a gas syringe every 10 seconds. This method of following the rate of reaction is to measure the time it takes for the product to be made in the reaction.

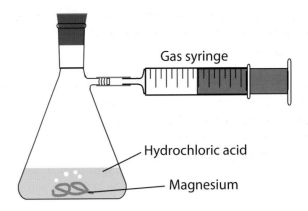

So the two simple ways to follow the rate of a reaction are measuring the rate at which a reactant is used up or measuring the rate at which a product is formed. Properties which change during the course of a reaction which can be used to measure the rate of reaction include; volume of gas, change in pH (B1.5f), change in conductivity, changes in mass if a gas is allowed to escape, and any colour change. The methods employed to follow these changes include use of gas syringes, titration, pH meter, conductivity meter, top pan balance and a colorimeter. These rates of reaction experiments can be efficiently managed with sensible use of datalogging instruments.

Initial rates method

Rates of reaction are generally fastest at the start of the experiment when there is the greatest concentration of reactants and therefore the greatest chance of successful collisions leading to reaction. The graph shows what typical results look like when volume of product is plotted against time.

The initial rate is measured from the gradient of a line taken from the tangent to the curve that goes through time $t = 0$ seconds.

The initial rate $= \dfrac{y}{x}$ in cm^3 s^{-1}.

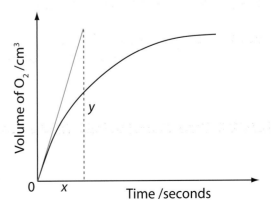

Usually, the only time the concentration of a reactant is accurately known is at the start of the experiment, before any of it is consumed. Methods designed to determine the rate of reaction at the start of the reaction are known as **initial rates methods**. Initial rates methods involve experiments where reactant or product concentrations are monitored against time. A simple experiment to carry out is the decomposition of hydrogen peroxide. This has water and oxygen as the products, according to the equation $H_2O_2 (aq) \rightarrow H_2O (l) + \frac{1}{2}O_2 (g)$. The volume of oxygen can be measured accurately in a gas syringe. If the temperature of the hydrogen peroxide is kept constant, it is possible to compare how the concentration of hydrogen peroxide affects the rate of decomposition. The graph shows how quickly oxygen is produced with four different concentrations of hydrogen peroxide. The steeper the slope of a tangent placed at the start of the reaction, the faster the initial rate.

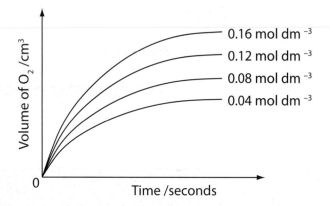

When the initial rate is worked out for each concentration (0.04 to 0.16 mol dm^{-3}), the data can be used to plot a second graph of initial rate *versus* concentration. In the case of the decomposition of hydrogen peroxide, the result is a straight line through the origin where the gradient is equal to the rate constant. This means that the reaction is first order with respect to hydrogen peroxide and the rate equation is rate = k [H$_2$O$_2$]. The slope is equal to the rate constant. By extrapolating the straight line, it is possible to work out the initial rate for untried concentrations such as 0.20 mol dm^{-3} of hydrogen peroxide.

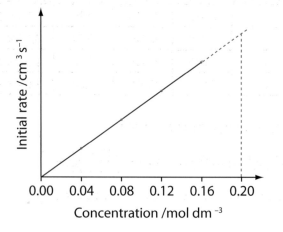

This type of experimental data allows the chemist to write a rate equation. The orders are usually the integers 0, 1 or 2. The orders give an idea how the individual reactant affects the rate of reaction. The orders can be determined by plotting graphs of initial rate *versus* concentration. The shape of the graph tells you the order with respect to the [reactant] on the x-axis. For a zero order reaction the graph is a straight line with a gradient of zero. For a first order reaction the graph is a straight line with a positive gradient starting at the origin. A second order reaction is a curved line pointing upwards that starts at the origin.

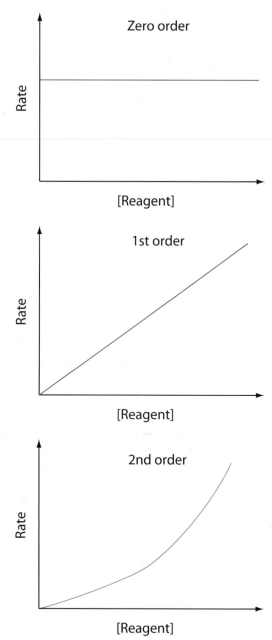

Data analysis is the bread and butter of the physical chemist and it is important not to be overwhelmed by numbers which look difficult. To work out the rate equation from initial rates data, you need to see how the rate changes as the concentration of one reactant is varied whilst **all** the other reactants' concentrations are kept constant.

If changing the concentration of a reactant has no effect on the rate, we say it has zero order. This is because any number raised to the power of zero = 1. If doubling the concentration of a reactant also doubles the rate, we say it has an order 1 with respect to this reactant. Whenever the rate changes by the same factor as the concentration, then this reactant is first order in the rate equation. If doubling the concentration of a reactant quadruples the rate, we say it has an order 2 with respect to this reactant, *i.e.* $2^2 = 4$. Whenever the rate changes by the square of the concentration factor, then this reactant is second order in the rate equation. Therefore tripling the concentration of the reactant will result in the rate multiplying by a factor of nine, *i.e.* $3^2 = 9$.

Once the orders have been worked out for each reactant, you are ready to write the rate equation, which then allows you to calculate the rate constant. Don't forget that the larger the rate constant (k) the faster the reaction. If you remember that order with respect to a particular reactant is the concentration raised to a power, then data analysis is often straightforward.

Rate equation

Rate = k [X]^1 [Y]^2

Calculating rate constant

Examiners tend to use the data from the first experiment!

Substituting in the value from experiment #1 into:

$$\text{rate} = k\,[X]^1\,[Y]^2 \text{ gives}$$

$$1.6 \times 10^{-5} = k\,[0.160]\,[0.25]^2$$

$$1.6 \times 10^{-5} = k \times 0.01$$

$$k = \frac{1.6 \times 10^{-5}}{0.01}$$

$$= 1.6 \times 10^{-3} \text{ dm}^6 \text{ mol}^{-2} \text{ s}^{-1}$$

Example 6.8

Analyse these data to determine the rate equation and the rate constant.

Experiment #	[X] / mol dm^{-3}	[Y] / mol dm^{-3}	Initial rate / mol dm^{-3} s^{-1}
1	0.160	0.25	1.6×10^{-5}
2	0.160	0.50	6.4×10^{-5}
3	0.080	0.50	3.2×10^{-5}
4	0.080	0.25	0.8×10^{-5}

Comparing experiments #1 and #2

As [Y] doubles, the rate quadruples $\left(\frac{6.4 \times 10^{-5}}{1.6 \times 10^{-5}} = 4\right)$.

Therefore the rate is 2nd order with respect to [Y].

This is also confirmed by comparing experiments #3 and #4.

Example 6.9

Analyse the data to determine the rate equation and the rate constant for this reaction:

$$H_2O_2 \text{ (aq)} + 2\,H^+ \text{ (aq)} + 2\,I^- \text{ (aq)} \rightarrow 2\,H_2O \text{ (l)} + I_2 \text{ (aq)}$$

Experiment #	[H$_2$O$_2$] / mol dm^{-3}	[I$^-$] / mol dm^{-3}	[H$^+$] / mol dm^{-3}	Initial rate / mol dm^{-3} s^{-1}
1	0.010	0.010	0.10	1.75×10^{-6}
2	0.030	0.010	0.10	5.25×10^{-6}
3	0.030	0.020	0.10	1.05×10^{-5}
4	0.030	0.020	0.20	1.05×10^{-5}

Comparing experiments #1 and #2

As [H$_2$O$_2$] triples the rate triples $\left(\frac{5.25 \times 10^{-6}}{1.75 \times 10^{-6}} = 3\right)$.

Therefore, the rate is 1st order with respect to [H$_2$O$_2$].

Comparing experiments #1 and #4

As [X] doubles the rate doubles $\left(\frac{1.6 \times 10^{-5}}{0.8 \times 10^{-5}} = 2\right)$.

Therefore, the rate is 1st order with respect to [X].

Comparing experiments #2 and #3

As [I⁻] doubles the rate doubles $\left(\dfrac{1.05 \times 10^{-5}}{5.25 \times 10^{-6}} = 2\right)$.

Therefore the rate is 1st order with respect to [I⁻].

Comparing experiments #3 and #4

As [H⁺] doubles the rate remains the same at 1.05×10^{-5} mol dm^{-3} s^{-1}

Therefore the rate is zero order with respect to [H⁺].

Rate equation

Rate $= k\,[H_2O_2]^1\,[I^-]^1\,[H^+]^0$

Calculating rate constant

Substituting in the value from experiment #1 into:

$$\text{Rate} = k\,[H_2O_2]^1\,[I^-]^1\,[H^+]^0$$

$$1.75 \times 10^{-6} = k\,0.010 \times 0.010 \times 0.10^0$$

$$1.75 \times 10^{-6} = k\,0.010 \times 0.010 \times 1$$

$$1.75 \times 10^{-6} = k \times 1 \times 10^{-4}$$

$$k = \frac{1.75 \times 10^{-6}}{1 \times 10^{-4}}$$

$$= 1.75 \times 10^{-2}\ \text{dm}^3\ \text{mol}^{-1}\ \text{s}^{-1}$$

Questions 6.9

1. What is meant by the term 'initial rate'?

2. Analyse the data to determine the rate equation and the rate constant.

Experiment #	[F] / mol dm^{-3}	[G] / mol dm^{-3}	Initial rate / mol dm^{-3} s^{-1}
1	1.25×10^{-2}	2.0×10^{-2}	1.4×10^{-6}
2	1.25×10^{-2}	4.0×10^{-2}	2.8×10^{-6}
3	2.50×10^{-2}	4.0×10^{-2}	11.2×10^{-6}

3. What is the 'initial rates method' and when and how is it useful?

4. Analyse the data to determine the rate equation and the rate constant.

What is [H⁺] in experiment #5?

Experiment #	[H⁺] / mol dm^{-3}	[I₂] / mol dm^{-3}	[CH₃COCH₃] / mol dm^{-3}	Initial rate / mol dm^{-3} s^{-1}
1	0.20	0.006	0.10	2.0×10^{-6}
2	0.20	0.006	0.30	6.0×10^{-6}
3	0.20	0.012	0.30	6.0×10^{-6}
4	0.40	0.006	0.10	4.0×10^{-6}
5	?	0.006	0.10	6.0×10^{-6}

5. Complete the table of data and calculate the rate constant given that the rate equation is:

Rate $= k\,[R]^1\,[S]^2$

Experiment #	[R] / mol dm^{-3}	[S] / mol dm^{-3}	Initial rate / mol dm^{-3} s^{-1}
1	0.20	0.10	0.142
2	0.20	0.20	
3	0.40	0.10	

6. Which option correctly describes the shape of a graph of rate *versus* [reagent]^2 for a second order reaction?

A   A straight line with a positive gradient through the origin.

B   A horizontal straight line with a gradient of zero.

C   A straight line with a negative gradient.

D   A curved line upwards through the origin.

B1.6 (j) First order reactions and half-life

Half-life is a concept usually first met in physics in terms of the radioactive decay of isotopes. Half-life in physics is the time it takes for the amount of a radioactive isotope to halve. This useful property of constant half-life for radioisotopes has allowed scientists to accurately date the Dead Sea scrolls (150 BC to 70 AD) found at Qumran (Israel) using levels of radioactive carbon-14 in these documents.

In chemistry half-life $(t_{1/2})$ is the time it takes for the concentration of a reactant to fall to half its original value. If the concentration of a reactant was 0.10 mol dm^{-3} and after 15 minutes its concentration was found to be 0.05 mol dm^{-3}, then the half-life would be 15 minutes.

Plotting a graph of concentration (*y*-axis) against time (*x*-axis) will allow the half-life to be found. It is suggested that, when measuring half-life, you measure two or more $t_{1/2}$ to confirm that the half-life is constant and therefore it is a first order reaction. When measuring more than one half-life, it is possible to distinguish between first and second order reactions, which look similar in concentration *vs.* time graphs (B1.6i). Analysis of the concentration *versus* time graphs show that half-life is constant for first order reactions. This constant half-life for first order reactions is because half-life is independent of concentration. For second order reactions the half-life is found to increase with time and for zero order reactions the half-life is found to decrease with time.

Example 6.10

A reactant had a concentration of 2.4 mol dm^{-3} at the start of the reaction when time = 0 and its concentration was measured every 150 seconds, with the following results:

Time / sec	[reactant] / mol dm^{-3}
0	2.400
150	1.200
300	0.600
450	0.300
600	0.150
750	0.075
900	0.0375
1050	0.0188
1200	0.0094

An analysis of the numbers will confirm the half-life and whether the reaction is first order. The time taken for the concentration to halve from 2.400 mol dm^{-3} to 1.200 mol dm^{-3} is 150 seconds. The time taken for the concentration to halve again from 1.200 mol dm^{-3} to 0.600 dm^{-3} is 300s - 150s = 150 seconds. The reaction is first order because it has a constant half-life (150 seconds).

When the numbers are more difficult a graph will soon allow the half-life to be solved. The workings are shown on the graph as a series of dashed lines. Three values of $t_{1/2}$ were obtained and all are shown to be 150 seconds.

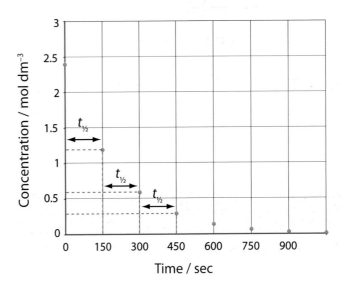

Working out $t_{1/2}$ from a concentration *vs.* time graph

First order rate constants

A first order rate constant can be calculated directly from a set of data.

The equation used in first order kinetics is: $\log_e\left(\dfrac{C_0}{C_t}\right) = k\,t$.

In this equation C_0 is the initial concentration at time $= 0$.

C_t is the concentration at time t and

k is the rate constant (s^{-1}).

This equation can also be written as $\log_e C_0 - \log_e C_t = k\,t$.

This can also be expressed as $\dfrac{C_0}{C_t} = e^{kt}$ or $C_t = C_0\,e^{-kt}$.

This last equation shows that the concentration decreases exponentially for a first order reaction.

Since the concentration C_t at $t_{\frac{1}{2}}$ will be half the original concentration, this means that:

$$\frac{C_0}{C_t} = 2.$$

Substituting this value 2 into the equation used in first order kinetics:

$$\log_e\left(\frac{C_0}{C_t}\right) = k\,t \text{ gives:}$$

$$\log_e 2 = k\,t_{\frac{1}{2}}$$

which works out as $0.693 = k\,t_{\frac{1}{2}}$.

This latter equation is very useful when working out the rate constant from the half-life for a first order reaction.

Questions 6.10

1. Which option gives a type of reaction that has a constant half-life?

    A   Second order

    B   Equilibrium

    C   First order

    D   Reversible

2. What happens to successive $t_{\frac{1}{2}}$ when the orders are zero, first and second with respect to reactants?

3. Which option is the best description of a first order reaction?

    A   The half-life $(t_{\frac{1}{2}})$ is variable and dependent upon initial concentration.

    B   The half-life $(t_{\frac{1}{2}})$ is constant and independent upon initial concentration.

    C   The half-life $(t_{\frac{1}{2}})$ is variable and independent upon initial concentration.

    D   The half-life $(t_{\frac{1}{2}})$ is constant and dependent upon initial concentration.

4. For a first order reaction with a half-life of 26 seconds and an initial concentration of 0.128 mol dm^{-3}, what will the concentration be after:

    a.   52 seconds?

    b.   104 seconds?

    c.   130 seconds?

5. Which option shows a correct relationship between rate constant and half-life?

    A $t_{\frac{1}{2}} = \dfrac{0.693}{k}$

    B $t_{\frac{1}{2}} = \dfrac{k}{0.693}$

    C $k = 0.693 \times t_{\frac{1}{2}}$

    D $k = \dfrac{t_{\frac{1}{2}}}{0.693}$

6.   Analyse these data to see if the reaction is first order.

Time / sec	[reactant] / mol dm^{-3}
0	0.5
10	0.375
20	0.281
30	0.21
40	0.158
50	0.118
60	0.089
70	0.066
80	0.05

7.   Analyse these data to show the reaction is first order. Find the half-life and rate constant.

Time / sec	[reactant] / mol dm^{-3}
0	108
100	75
200	52.5
300	36.6
400	25.5

7

Chemical Models and Evidence

Contents

The written work credited to Jabir, a 9th century alchemist, showed he was one of the first scientists to realize the need for systematic experiments. He did much for the long term future of chemistry by inventing familiar apparatus still used today for distillation and crystallization. He also developed repeatable methods for the production of the important mineral acids, hydrochloric and nitric acids. Jabir helped to turn alchemy into a science. Sadly it took western chemists another eight centuries to leave behind the dark age of magic and alchemy, by which time they also started to measure things and perform systematic experiments.

For chemistry to really come of age as a physical science, it had to wait until the development of accurate clocks and balances. Once the subject became quantitative it could make the paradigm shift to understanding how atoms are arranged and hence the solving of formulae.

John Dalton came up with his symbols for discovered elements and compounds. Dalton's formulae model was published in 1808 and was a useful way to visualise abstract ideas in support of his atomic theory. Can you see which compound(s) Dalton got wrong at a time when errors in weighing would have hidden the 'true' formulae of these compounds?

John Dalton's atoms and compounds

Scientific models have their limitations (B1.7c & B1.7d) and need to be revised as the frontiers are pushed forward with each generation of scientists. We have come a very long way since the time of Dalton and chemists are making ever more complicated structures using their imagination and laboratory skills. One beautiful example is the catenated molecules with interlocking rings called Borromean rings (front cover) which were developed in Sir Fraser Stoddart's (photo at right) research group.

An appreciation of the symmetry and three dimensional structures of molecules can be gained by building models of their structures or by close examination of their crystal structures.

B1.7 (a) Chemistry an evidence-based subject

In addition to developing a good understanding of the theories (B1.7b) and ideas that describe the world from a chemistry point of view, it is important to develop laboratory skills. This is because chemistry is an evidence-based subject and practical work is at the heart of the advances in the subject in laboratories around the world.

Once a student starts to get a bigger picture of a subject s/he soon discovers that it is the scientific method which, when applied rigorously, underpins the advances in our knowledge. The scientific method has four hierarchical and essential steps that are followed by researchers on every continent. The four steps for the scientific method are summarised and should form the background to all experiments that are carried out.

Scientific method

Step 1 is the observation and description of a phenomenon using practical skills. Step 2 is the formulation of a theory and or model to explain the phenomenon. Step 3 is using the theory and or model to make quantitative predictions or predict the existence of new phenomena. Step 4 is where experiments are carried out to test the predictions.

If the all the steps in the scientific method hold up to the scrutiny of independent experimenters, a paper[1] is written. This original work is peer reviewed[2] before the paper is accepted or rejected for publication in a scientific journal. The discoveries then become part of the body of knowledge of the area of science being investigated.

The power of this quantitative system should not be underestimated. If new observations or experiments conflict with a long standing theory, the model and theory will be modified or a new one proposed. The scientific method works best in situations where one can isolate the phenomenon of interest. This is why it is important during practicals to have careful control over the variables and why you should ensure

1   A 'paper' in this context is an essay or article.

2   'Peer review' means that the paper is read and commented on by other scientists working in the field (peers).

fair tests are carried out when making comparisons between test tube reactions.

Rate equations are solved experimentally by careful control of the concentrations of each reactant and measurement of their effects on rates (B1.6i). Rate equations (B1.6f) **cannot** be solved directly from the stoichiometry using the balanced formula equation. In each experiment there is only one variable, which is the concentration of either reactant. It is important for all other variables, such as temperature, to be controlled so that the data are reliable and repeatable.

$$2 \, NO \, (g) + O_2 \, (g) \rightarrow 2 \, NO_2 \, (g)$$

Experiment	Initial $[NO]$ / 10^{-3} mol dm^{-3}	Initial $[O_2]$ / 10^{-3} mol dm^{-3}	Initial rate / 10^{-4} mol dm^{-3} s^{-1}
1	10	10	8
2	20	10	32
3	30	10	72
4	20	20	64

By coincidence, the rate equation for the oxidation of nitrogen monoxide to form nitrogen dioxide does agree with the stoichiometry. Using the data from the four experiments the rate equation is rate = $k \, [NO]^2[O_2]$ and the rate constant is calculated as 800 dm^6 mol^{-2} s^{-1}.

Organic mechanisms (B3.9) are also solved experimentally using a number of different experimental techniques. For mechanisms to be accepted, they need to be consistent with the rate equation (B1.6h). The rate equation for the alkaline hydrolysis of tertiary halogenoalkanes (B3.9a), such as 2-bromo-2-methylpropane, is rate = k [halogenoalkane]. As the rate is independent of the concentration of hydroxide, shown by its absence from the rate equation, it does not take part in the slowest step of the reaction (B1.6g). This is in contrast to rate experiments for the alkaline hydrolysis of primary halogenoalkanes (B3.9a) which show that rate = k [RX][OH$^-$]. A different mechanism is used to explain the inclusion of the hydroxide in this rate equation.

Radioactive isotopes have also played an important part in solving organic mechanisms (B3.9). The isotope is used as a label to show which atoms from the reactants end up in which part of the product. Oxygen-18 has been used extensively in the solution of organic mechanisms in important biochemical reactions. An understanding of mechanisms is important to chemists if they are to understand what is happening in their reaction vessels.

Biochemists undertake mechanistic studies of enzymes where they have the ability to change a specific amino acid in a protein structure through genetic engineering. This demonstrates how far mechanistic studies have progressed since the first mechanism was solved back in 1902.

B1.7 (b) Theories, models, facts & definitions

Perhaps without realising it, science students will often have a fairly deep understanding of the fundamentals that underpin quantitative subjects such as chemistry. A 'science quiz' rewards those with a good memory for facts and definitions. The students who thrive in examinations will also have a good understanding of the models used to explain abstract ideas and will use appropriate theories in unfamiliar circumstances. We need to be clear about the distinction between theories/models (the skeleton) and facts/definitions (the flesh) which form the body of knowledge that is chemistry.

Theory

A theory, such as the **kinetic theory** (B1.6a), is an idea or set of ideas intended to explain thing(s). A theory can be tested practically and it explains the facts or is an interpretation of the facts. A theory will be superseded by a new or evolved theory as new facts are discovered. Even the greatest scientists made statements during their careers, based on the facts that they had at the time, which later proved incorrect. The most difficult of all theories, because of the level of complexity of the mathematics, must be **quantum theory**. Niels Bohr, who won the 1922 Nobel prize in Physics for his work on atomic structure and did important and fundamental work on quantum mechanics once said, "if anybody says he can think about quantum theory without getting giddy it merely shows that he hasn't understood the first thing about it."

Model

A **model** is a simplified description of a system or process, constructed as a way of looking at things. Models have no basis in reality but are designed to mimic the real world. Models are useful because they allow us to make predictions and do calculations. Models might be mathematical devices or physical constructs. A model will be adjusted as new facts are discovered. Models are excellent teaching aids as they can step in when a theory becomes too complex for most people to understand. The VSEPR model (A1.2g) is an excellent vehicle

for the understanding of the shape of molecules. Models play an important role within science and they have also proved extremely useful in the advancement of the public's understanding of science. Computer modelling is playing an important part in the search for new drugs to fit into active sites of enzymes. This work is vital in the fight against antiobiotic resistant bacteria such as **methicillin-resistant staphylococcus aureus** (MRSA) and *tubercle bacillus* (TB).

Facts

Facts are based on empirical evidence and are things which can be observed and/or measured.

Examples of facts are:

- The formula for fluorine is F_2 (A2.2j).

- The reaction between magnesium and hydrochloric acid is exothermic (A1.0i).

- Graphite is the best conductor of electricity of all carbon's allotropes (B2.3b).

- Copper(II) hydroxide is a blue solid (A4.1a).

Facts are pieces of information that are tried and tested and considered to be beyond doubt. Chemistry facts have been peer reviewed and are continuing to be published in journals and books which are increasingly available online. Facts are indisputable and fixed, unlike models and theories. There is, of course, the possibility that facts can be interpreted differently by scientists as seen by the 21st century battle to win the moral high ground on environmental issues.

Definitions

Students who make use of a subject dictionary will have a higher level of subject language and will make the most rapid progress. When learning something new, the dictionary definition is often the best starting point. A definition is a precise meaning of a word when applied in context. A definition is also an exact description of the meaning of something. Definitions need to be understood rather than just learned parrot fashion. Definitions in chemistry can be written in the form of words or equations, such as the first ionisation energy (A1.1i). This is the minimum energy needed to remove a mole of electrons from a mole of gaseous atoms to produce a mole of unipositive gaseous ions.

$$M \text{ (g) } (1 \text{ mole}) - e^- (1 \text{ mole}) \rightarrow M^+ \text{ (g) } (1 \text{ mole})$$

B1.7 (c) Breakdown of the ideal gas model

The ideal gas model (B1.6a) and the ideal gas equation (B1.6b) are models based on a series of assumptions (B1.6b) that break down under conditions of high pressure and low temperatures. The fact that real gases do not obey the ideal gas equation (*PV = nRT*) can be shown by plotting *PV/nRT versus P* for different gases.

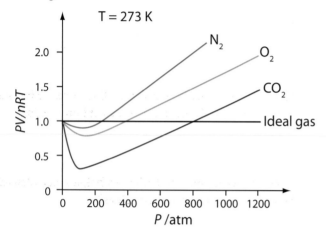

A graph to show deviation from ideal gas behaviour

PV/nRT is sometimes called the **compression factor** and an ideal gas is expected to have a value of 1.0. The graph shows that real gases do not obey the ideal gas law over a range of pressures. When a graph of *PV/nRT versus P* is made for any gas at different temperatures this non-ideal behaviour is also observed. Deviations from ideal behaviour are due to two factors. Firstly the attractive forces between gas molecules and secondly the volume of the molecules in a gas is not negligible, as assumed in the kinetic theory (B1.6a). Johannes van der Waals developed an equation to correct for non-ideal behaviour due to the breakdown of the kinetic theory by accounting for the volume of the gas molecules themselves and the attractive forces between particles. The van der Waals' equation is met at university and involves solving simultaneous equations.

Questions 7.1

1. Which option shows the conditions when ideal gases are most likely to deviate from the ideal gas equation?

	Temperature	Pressure
A	low	high
B	low	low
C	high	high
D	high	low

2. In a graph of PV/nRT *versus* P what has the value of 1.0 at all pressures?

    A   real gas

    B   noble gas

    C   ideal gas

    D   diatomic gas

B1.7 (d) Limitations of the ionic model

Lattice enthalpies derived from Born-Haber cycles (A1.3e) are considered to be experimental. Lattice enthalpies can also be calculated from crystal structures (B2.5f) using equations met at university (Born-Landé equation & the Kapustinskii equation). These theoretical lattice enthalpies are derived mathematically from crystal structure data (B2.5a). The largest differences between the experimental and theoretical lattice energies occur when there is an appreciable proportion of covalent bonding, *e.g.* silver halides.

The ionic model considers ions in a lattice to be hard incompressible, non-polarisable spheres that carry charge. The charge is always an integer multiple of the charge carried by an electron and is positive for cations and negative for anions. In the ionic model the charge is evenly distributed around the ions. The ionic model works well for alkali metal halides but begins to fall down with silver halides, as can be seen by the differences between their experimental and theoretical lattice enthalpies.

Binary compound	Experimental $\Delta_{latt}H$ / kJ mol^{-1}	Theoretical $\Delta_{latt}H$ / kJ mol^{-1}	Difference in lattice enthalpies
NaF	−923	−917	6
NaCl	−785	−775	10
NaBr	−747	−740	7
NaI	−710	−693	17
AgF	−963	−925	38
AgCl	−910	−838	72
AgBr	−896	−821	75
AgI	−894	−783	111

The larger difference between the experimental and theoretical lattice energies for the silver halides shows that the ionic model does not hold true. The model can be refined by explaining the differences in terms of polarisation of the halide by the smaller silver ions (B2.5f). This difference should not be surprising when one considers that the theoretical value for lattice enthalpy only considers the electrostatic contribution in terms of forces of attraction between spherical ions in a regular lattice.

An electron density map is determined using x-ray diffraction. The electron density map is shown for lithium fluoride. Each contour line joins regions of identical electron density, in the same way that contour lines on a map join regions at the same height above sea level. Electron density maps also illustrate the limitations of the ionic model. The lithium ion is not perfectly spherical and there is electron density between the lithium ions and fluoride ions. Distortion of the electron clouds leads to some sharing of electrons (some covalent character) as indicated by the shaded yellow areas.

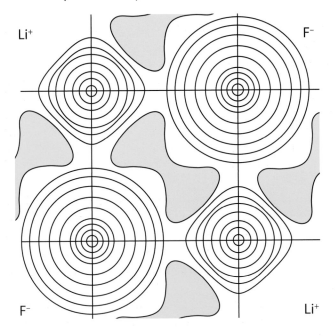

Li⁺   F⁻

F⁻   Li⁺

Electron density map for lithium fluoride

Questions 7.2

1. Which ionic compound has the largest lattice enthalpy?

    A   NaCl

    B   LiCl

    C $CaCl_2$

    D Al_2O_3

2. How large will the lattice enthalpy differences be for the experimental and theoretical values of boron oxide?

3. How are experimental lattice enthalpies calculated? What can be said about their values?

4. In terms of electronegativity differences between ions, when does the ionic model work best?

5. Which option most closely fits the ionic model as it has the smallest difference between its experimental and theoretical lattice enthalpies?

    A MgF_2

    B   NaF

    C SiF_4

    D AlF_3

8 | Periodic Table

Contents

A2.1 (a) Regions of the Periodic Table

The (Mendeleev) Periodic Table has 18 groups and 7 periods. Elements are arranged in order of increasing atomic number (proton number) starting with the universe's most abundant and first element, hydrogen ($_1H$). The atomic number is often written as a subscript before the symbol for the element. Vertical columns in the Periodic Table are known as **groups** (several have been given names) and horizontal rows are called **periods**. A new shell of electrons is added when moving from one period to the next.

Group	Name
1	Alkali metals
2	Alkaline earth metals
15	Pnictogens
16	Chalcogens
17	Halogens
18	Noble Gases

The main purpose of the Periodic Table is to classify elements, which assists in the study of them. Early Periodic Tables stimulated research to find the missing elements which were in the gaps left by Mendeleev. Going left to right across the Periodic Table the elements change from being metals to non-metals. Three quarters of the elements are metals, the familiar ones, and these are found to the left of the step which separates the Group 13 elements boron and aluminium. The division between metals and non-metals is a step (zig-zag) that runs from element 5 (boron) to element 84 (polonium) at the bottom right hand corner of the Periodic Table. Elements to the left of the step are electropositive and tend to form positive ions. Elements to the right of the step are electronegative (A1.2i), tend to form negative ions and are predominantly non-metals. The area of focus is the border region around the step where some elements might be 'fought over' as they might belong to more than one region. Around the step are the metalloids (B, Si, Ge, As, Sb, Te and probably At) which might be thought of as being autonomous regions like Kurdistan. An interesting but unusual book on the regions of the Periodic Table is *The Periodic Kingdom* by Peter Atkins.

	13	14	15	16	17
	B	C	N	O	F
	Al	Si	P	S	Cl
	Ga	Ge	As	Se	Br
	In	Sn	Sb	Te	I
	Tl	Pb	Bi	Po	At

The trends are that **metallic character**

- decreases across any period and

- increases on descending any group.

Metalloids are a number of elements towards the 'middle' of the Periodic Table which are neither strongly metallic nor strongly non-metallic in their properties.

Typical properties of metals and non-metals highlight their differences and some notable exceptions.

Metals	Non-metals
High density (except alkali metals).	Low density.
Shiny when freshly cut, malleable and ductile.	Dull (except graphite and silicon) and brittle.
High mp (except mercury, caesium & gallium).	Low mp (except carbon and silicon).
Good conductors of heat.	Poor conductors of heat (except diamond).
Good conductors of electricity.	Poor conductors of electricity (except graphite).

Question 8.1

1. In the Periodic Table, when does metallic character decrease?

	Periods	Groups
A	Left to Right	Descending
B	Right to Left	Ascending
C	Left to Right	Ascending
D	Right to Left	Descending

A2.1 (b)
Structures of the Elements

The table shows the four types of structure that are found at room temperature for the different elements. The Periodic Table divides neatly into distinct types by structure.

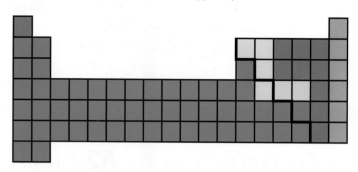

	Giant metallic lattice
	Giant molecular lattice
	Simple molecules
	Monatomic

Elements to the left of the metal non-metal dividing step have giant metallic structures, except for germanium. The gases; hydrogen, nitrogen and oxygen and all the halogens form simple diatomic molecules.

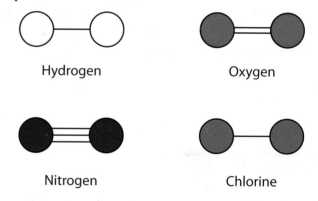

Hydrogen   Oxygen

Nitrogen   Chlorine

The other elements which form simple molecules are white phosphorus (P_4) and sulfur (S_8).

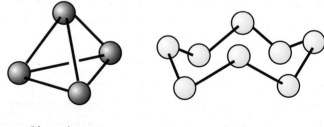

Phosphorus   Sulfur

Germanium forms a giant molecular structure with a tetrahedral diamond arrangement like two other members of Group 14 (carbon as diamond and silicon).

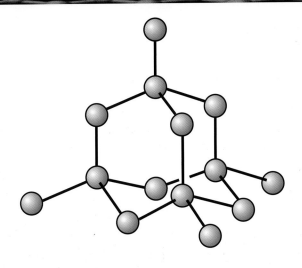

Germanium

Boron (B), arsenic (As) and selenium (Se) also have giant molecular structures.

The noble gases with their full outer shells exist as single atoms and are described universally as **monatomic**. They have very low boiling points and melting points as they only have very weak Van der Waals forces of attraction between atoms.

Question 8.2

1.   Using the Periodic Table on the previous page, identify which elements have a giant molecular structure.

A2.1 (c)
Period 3 trends in terms of structure and bonding

The structure and bonding of the Period 3 elements affects their physical properties such as melting point, boiling point and electrical conductivity. Across Period 3 the melting point and boiling points increase, peaking at silicon, and then rapidly decrease. M = monatomic, GM = giant metallic, GC = giant covalent and SC = simple covalent.

	Na	Mg	Al	Si	P *	S *	Cl	Ar
mp / K	371	922	933	1683	317	392	172	84
bp / K	1156	1380	2740	2628	553	718	238	87
structure	GM	GM	GM	GC	SC	SC	SC	M

* allotropes; P = white & S = monoclinic

Low values for melting points for the late Period 3 elements indicate that there are weak forces, such as Van der Waals forces (A1.2j), holding the molecules together in the solid state. Higher values for melting points for the mid-Period 3 elements indicate that there are stronger bonds within the giant metallic and giant covalent structures. Metallic bonds persist into the liquid phase which is why metals have boiling points significantly higher than their melting points. The increase in the strength of the metallic bonds from Na to Mg to Al is because there are more mobile outer electrons taking part in bonding as you cross Period 3. Silicon has a particularly high melting point because of the very strong giant covalent structure identical to that shown for germanium (A2.1b). Phosphorus and sulfur have higher melting and boiling points than chlorine as their relative molecular masses are higher and, with more electrons, there will inevitably be stronger Van der Waals forces of attraction between molecules. Chlorine and argon have very weak forces of attraction between their molecules and atoms even in the liquid phase, which explains the small differences between their individual melting and boiling points.

Electrical conductivity is another physical property that varies across Period 3 because of the differences in structure and bonding. Electrical conduction is the passage of electrical current through a solid, liquid or gas phase. Metals which are found in the s, d and f blocks (B2.4a) are, generally, the best electrical conductors with their mobile valence electrons. Interestingly, metals show a slow decrease in conductivity as their temperature increases. Non-metals are poor electrical conductors as their valence electrons are being used exclusively in covalent bonds. The notable exception is graphite, an allotrope of carbon (B2.3a). **Metalloids** are sometimes referred to as **semi-metals** and some have found use as **semi-conductors** (silicon). Metalloids have electrical conductivities which are much larger, particularly arsenic (As) and antimony (Sb) than the non-metals phosphorus and sulfur.

Electrical conductivity 10^6 /cm ohms

B	C	N	O	F
1.0×10^{-12}				
Al	Si	P	S	Cl
0.377	2.52×10^{-12}	1.0×10^{-17}	5.0×10^{-24}	
Ga	Ge	As	Se	Br
0.0678	1.45×10^{-8}	0.0345	1.0×10^{-12}	
In	Sn	Sb	Te	I
0.116	0.0917	0.0288	2.0×10^{-6}	
Tl	Pb	Bi	Po	At

Data from: www.environmentalchemistry.com

A2.1(d) Van Arkel diagrams

The **van Arkel diagrams** apply to binary substances. These might be binary compounds that contain two different elements, or they might be diatomic elements. The compounds can be ionic or covalent. Binary ionic compounds, which are inorganic, will consist of a metal and a non-metal, *e.g.* caesium fluoride (CsF). This is the most ionic of the binary compounds. Binary elements include the halogens, *e.g.* fluorine (F_2) the most electronegative element, and the diatomic gaseous elements (O_2, H_2 and N_2). Binary inorganic compounds which are covalent include the electron deficient boron trifluoride (BF_3). Binary metallic alloys include solder (50% Sn and 50% Pb) which has a low melting point compared to its constituent metals and is used to connect wires in electrical circuits.

The van Arkel diagram is a good way to unify the chemical bonding types: ionic, covalent and metallic. Ionic bonding was first proposed by Helmholtz in 1881. An ionic bond is the electrostatic attraction between oppositely charged ions, *e.g.* Na^+ and Cl^- in sodium chloride, and was first described in this way in 1929 by Anton van Arkel and Jan de Boer. Ionic bonds are formed when outer (valence) electrons transfer from a metal to a non-metal resulting in both ions achieving a noble gas configuration with empty or full outer shells.

Covalent bonding involves the sharing of outer electrons to fill the outer shell (complete the octet). Chlorine (Cl_2), by sharing an electron from each atom, forms a single covalent bond between the atoms. The theory of covalent bonding was developed early in the twentieth century and described in 1916 by Gilbert Lewis.

Metallic bonding was first described by Lewis in 1913 and the model can be used to explain conductivity as a sea of delocalised electrons surrounding the positively charged cations.

The physical properties of different types of substances, be they elements, compounds or alloys, can be explained by their internal workings, namely their bonding. Chemistry is interesting because substances have a full spectrum of properties as they might have bonding that is intermediate between the two extremes of 100% ionic bonding and 100% covalent bonding. This concept used to be shown as a line and students were merely told that most substances fell between the two extremes of bonding types. The **van Arkel triangle** serves to introduce the three quarters of the known elements that are metals. These diagrams also allow us to make predictions about unfamiliar substances which are at the cutting edge of technology, such as gallium nitride (GaN) which is used in flat screen televisions.

The van Arkel diagram (1941) below puts binary compounds onto a single graph.

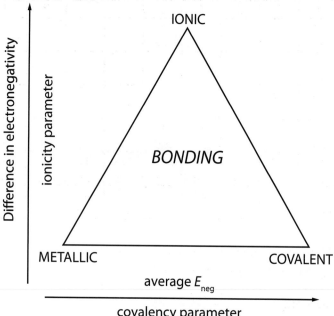

Intermediate bonding is found along the triangle edges. Compounds are found within the body of the triangle. The van Arkel triangle helps chemists to predict the structure and properties of compounds. The coordinate for each substance on the van Arkel diagram is calculated in terms of electronegativity. **Electronegativity** (E_{neg}) is the ability of a substance to attract electrons to itself (in a covalent bond). The electronegativity scale was devised and first used by Linus Pauling in 1932. The size of an element's E_{neg} is influenced by its atomic radius, proton number (nuclear charge) and shielding. There is no need to learn electronegativity values as they are given in questions. But it is important to know that fluorine is the most electronegative element with a value on the Pauling Scale of 4.0. It is also essential to know how electronegativity values change across periods (horizontal rows) and down groups (vertical columns). Think of the Periodic Table as a football (soccer) field, but ignoring the Noble gases. As you approach the corner flag of fluorine, the electronegativity increases.

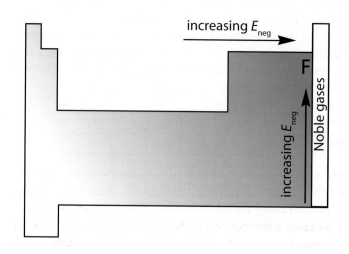

Periodic Table of the Elements with Electronegativity values

1	2	3	4	5	6	7	8	9	10	11	12	13	14	15	16	17	18
H 2.1																	He
Li 1.0	Be 1.5											B 2.0	C 2.5	N 3.0	O 3.5	F 4.0	Ne
Na 0.9	Mg 1.2											Al 1.5	Si 1.8	P 2.1	S 2.5	Cl 3.0	Ar
K 0.8	Ca 1.0	Sc 1.3	Ti 1.5	V 1.6	Cr 1.6	Mn 1.5	Fe 1.8	Co 1.9	Ni 1.9	Cu 1.9	Zn 1.6	Ga 1.6	Ge 1.8	As 2.0	Se 2.4	Br 2.8	Kr 3.0
Rb 0.8	Sr 1.0	Y 1.2	Zr 1.4	Nb 1.6	Mo 1.8	Tc 1.9	Ru 2.2	Rh 2.2	Pd 2.2	Ag 1.9	Cd 1.7	In 1.7	Sn 1.8	Sb 1.9	Te 2.1	I 2.5	Xe 2.6
Cs 0.7	Ba 0.9	La 1.1	Hf 1.3	Ta 1.5	W 1.7	Re 1.9	Os 2.2	Ir 2.2	Pt 2.2	Au 2.4	Hg 1.9	Tl 1.8	Pb 1.9	Bi 1.9	Po 2.0	At 2.2	Rn 2.4

Take caesium fluoride (CsF) as an example compound. The E_{neg} values are Cs (0.7) and F (4.0).

The average $E_{neg} = \dfrac{4.0 + 0.7}{2} = 2.35$

The difference in $E_{neg} = 4.0 - 0.7 = 3.3$

So on the van Arkel diagram the coordinates for CsF are (2.35,3.3).

What is the van Arkel triangle?

The van Arkel diagram is a plot of ΔE_{neg} of two elements on the y-axis and average E_{neg} on the x-axis. There is no need to consider the stoichiometry of the binary compound. So the oxides sulfur(IV)oxide (SO_2) and sulfur(VI) oxide (SO_3) will both appear at the same coordinate on the van Arkel diagram.

As the x-axis gives information on electronegativity average, it is a measure of the degree of localisation of the bonding electrons. It provides information on the **degree of covalency**. At the left hand side of the x-axis is found the most electropositive element (caesium). This is the element with the lowest E_{neg} value and is the metallic extreme with delocalised valence electrons. At the right hand side of the x-axis is found the most electronegative element (fluorine). In fluorine the bonding valence electrons in this purely covalent molecule are localised within the sigma bond. Noble gases are not considered for van Arkel diagrams as they don't bond with themselves (monatomic) or generally form binary compounds. Xenon tetrafluoride (XeF_4), first synthesized in 1962 by Neil Bartlett, being one of the exceptions.

As the y-axis gives information on electronegativity differences, it tells you how much the bonding electrons are unevenly (asymmetrically) distributed between the two bonding atoms. It provides information on the degree of **ionicity**. It is for this reason that at the bottom of the triangle, where $y = 0$,

the elements are found. At the top of the triangle there is the greatest degree of asymmetry of the electron distribution in the bond. This is where caesium fluoride (CsF) is to be found at the extreme of ionic bonding as the elements in this binary compound are the most electropositive and the most electronegative.

Example 8.1

Calculate where the chlorides of phosphorus will appear on a van Arkel diagram.

Solution:

Phosphorus(III) chloride (PCl_3) and phosphorus(V) chloride (PCl_5) will give the same coordinate on the van Arkel diagram. The E_{neg} values are P (2.1) and Cl (3.0).

The average $E_{neg} = \dfrac{2.1 + 3.0}{2} = 2.55$.

The difference in $E_{neg} = 3.0 - 2.1 = 0.9$

So, on the van Arkel diagram, the coordinates for PCl_3 or PCl_5 are (2.55,0.9).

Example 8.2

Calculate where the chloride of aluminium will appear on a van Arkel diagram.

Solution:

Aluminium chloride ($AlCl_3$). The E_{neg} values are Al (1.5) and Cl (3.0).

The average $E_{neg} = \dfrac{1.5 + 3.0}{2} = 2.25$.

The difference in $E_{neg} = 3.0 - 1.5 = 1.5$

So on the van Arkel diagram the coordinates for $AlCl_3$ are (2.25, 1.5).

In reading chemistry books and papers, it is always worth looking very closely at where the author has placed the three bonding types; I = Ionic, C = covalent and M = metallic because there are six possible van Arkel triangles. The original triangle was number 4 and the most convenient to use is triangle number 1.

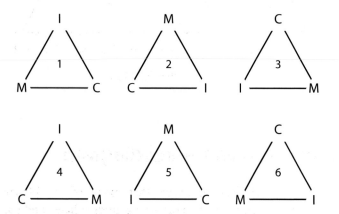

Simple Binary Compounds

There are 36 main group elements which are all the elements of Groups 1, 2, 13, 14, 15, 16 and 17, excluding francium and radium. The total possible number of binary compounds is 666. This figure is arrived at by considering that each element combines with each other and mathematically this is 36 + 35 + 34 + 33 ... +1. So 666 is the number of the binary compounds. In reality there are slightly fewer binary compounds formed from two different elements. Some combinations of elements result in several binary compounds. This is illustrated by some of the more familiar oxides of nitrogen, which have the generalised formula NO_x. The identified binaries for these two elements are;

$$NO,\ NO_2,\ N_2O,\ N_2O_3,\ N_2O_4\ \&\ N_2O_5$$

Students favouring inorganic chemistry may be interested to learn that not all binary compounds lead to the expected stoichiometry using the cross valency method for working out ionic formulae. The compound formed between boron and carbon is boron carbide and has the formula B_4C not the expected B_4C_3.

It is good practice for working out formulae to take the elements of a period and work out the possible binary compounds.

This has been done below with hydrogen and the elements of Period 2. When an element meets itself in the grid all you have to do is write down the element's symbol or, where it can bond to itself as a simple molecule, its formula.

	H	Li	Be	B	C	N	O	F
H	H_2							
Li	LiH	Li						
Be	BeH_2	Li_2Be	Be					
B	BH_3	Li_2B_3	Be_3B_2	B				
C	CH_4	Li_2C_2	Be_2C	B_4C	C			
N	NH_3	Li_3N	Be_3N_2	BN	C_3N_4	N_2		
O	H_2O	Li_2O	BeO	B_2O_3	CO_2	N_2O_3	O_2	
F	HF	LiF	BeF_2	BF_3	CF_4	NF_3	F_2O	F_2

Unexpected stoichiometries are shaded red in the table.

The elements caesium, fluorine and their resulting binary compound, caesium fluoride, illustrate the corners of a van Arkel triangle. Caesium is the most electropositive metal, fluorine the most electronegative non-metal and caesium fluoride the most ionic of compounds having the greatest electronegativity difference.

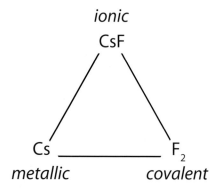

In terms of E_{neg} values the three bonding types are found in binary substances according to their average electronegativities and their electronegativity differences. The table summarises the findings.

Bonding	Size of E_{neg} values	Differences of E_{neg} values
Metallic	Small	Similar
Covalent	Large	Similar
Ionic	Small (metal), large (non-metal)	Different

Plotting points on van Arkel diagrams

It is important to practise plotting points on van Arkel diagrams.

It allows you to make predictions about bonding types for a binary compound as well its electrical properties. There are two approaches to plotting the point for a binary compound such as gallium nitride (GaN).

Method 1 (GaN)

Method 1 is a straightforward calculation giving an x,y plot of the calculated coordinates. It uses the electronegativity values provided to calculate the average E_{neg} value (x) and ΔE_{neg} (y) for the two elements.

The electronegativity values for the elements are Ga = 1.6 and N = 3.0.

Average $E_{neg} = \dfrac{1.6 + 3.0}{2} = 2.3$ and ΔE_{neg} is $3.0 - 1.6 = 1.4$

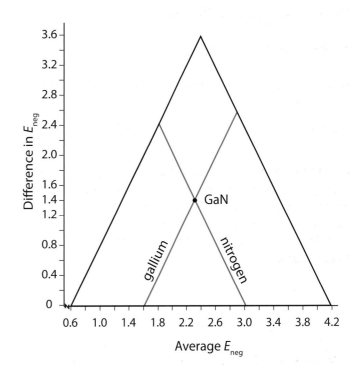

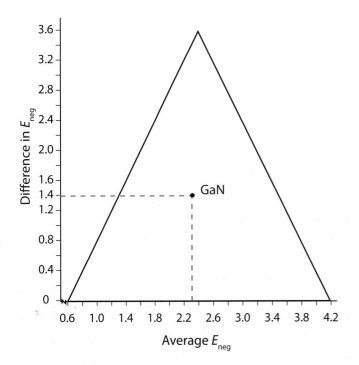

Method 2 (GaN)

Method 2 involves using the raw electronegativity values to draw two lines parallel to the left and right hand sides of the triangle and plotting the point where these lines cross over (intersect). The second method is a much quicker way of getting the answer.

Plots on a van Arkel diagram

The van Arkel diagram shows that many of the binary compounds can be considered as having intermediate bonding. Method 2 involves using the raw electronegativity values to draw intersecting lines. Good examples of intermediate substances in terms of their properties as well as their positions on a van Arkel diagram are silicon (Si), hydrogen fluoride (HF), caesium hydride (CsH) and mercury(II) chloride ($HgCl_2$).

Substance	Position	Metallic	Ionic	Covalent
Si	between	√		√
HF	between		√	√
CsH	between	√	√	
$HgCl_2$	Central part of the triangle			

Alchemists' van Arkel triangle

The early chemists (alchemists) were concerned with the two elements and the compound that results in the red triangle within the blue van Arkel triangle. It is apparent that they were playing with only a fraction of the modern day chemist's toolkit.

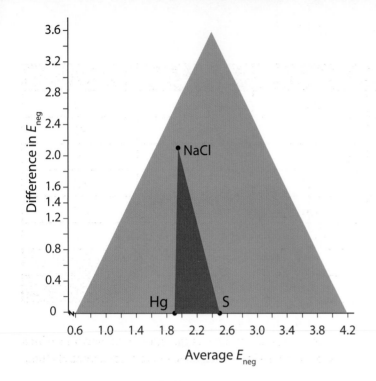

Advantages of the van Arkel triangle

The triangle gives a quantitative appreciation of intermediate bonding. It allows chemists to view the main models for chemical bonding in a single triangular shaped chart. It allows prediction in bonding for unfamiliar compounds. These predictions are easier when the resulting point plotted is close to one of the corners of the triangle.

Disadvantages of the van Arkel triangle

Like all models they tend to break down at some point and, whilst undoubtedly useful, they do have their limitations. The search by chemists for interesting new materials such as semiconductors and superconductors continues into the 21st century. It is not possible to use the van Arkel diagram to suggest new binary compounds that have these interesting properties. Whilst the van Arkel diagram provides information on bonding it does not really hint at the crystal structures of solids which depend on stoichiometry and electron configuration. This is clearly illustrated by elements with allotropes such as carbon, phosphorus and tin. Allotropes of the same element all have the same E_{neg} values but clearly by their very definition somewhat different structures. The same is also true when there are several forms of a binary compound because one of the elements is capable of existing in several oxidation states. A good example of multiple oxidation states are the chlorides of lead. Lead(IV) chloride ($PbCl_4$) is covalent whereas lead(II) chloride ($PbCl_2$) is ionic.

Question 8.3

1. Describe and explain the apparatus that would be used to prepare the anhydrous chloride of aluminium. Write a balanced formula equation for this reaction.

Predictions from the van Arkel diagrams

The Period 3 chlorides are quite different from one another. They range from high melting white solids to volatile colourless liquids and even a pale yellow solid. Their differences are a result of their bonding and structure. The reactions of the Period 3 chlorides will be dealt with elsewhere. All can be prepared by direct combination of the elements with chorine as shown in the equations.

	Van Arkel coordinate
$2 \, Na \, (s) + Cl_2 \, (g) \rightarrow 2 \, NaCl \, (s)$ [white solid]	(1.95, 2.1)
$Mg \, (s) + Cl_2 \, (g) \rightarrow MgCl_2 \, (s)$ [white solid]	(2.1, 1.8)
$2 \, Al \, (s) + 3 \, Cl_2 \, (g) \rightarrow 2 \, AlCl_3 \, (s)$ [white solid]	(2.25, 1.5)
$Si \, (s) + 2 \, Cl_2 \, (g) \rightarrow SiCl_4 \, (l)$ [colourless liquid]	(2.4, 1.2)
$P_4 \, (s) + 6 \, Cl_2 \, (g) \rightarrow 4 \, PCl_3 \, (l)$ [colourless liquid]	(2.55, 0.9)
$PCl_3 \, (l) + Cl_2 \, (g) \rightarrow PCl_5 \, (s)$ [pale yellow solid]	(2.55, 0.9)
$2 \, S \, (s) + Cl_2 \, (g) \rightarrow S_2Cl_2 \, (l)$ [golden yellow liquid]	(2.75, 0.5)
$S_2Cl_2 \, (l) + Cl_2 \, (g) \rightarrow 2 \, SCl_2 \, (l)$ [cherry red liquid]	(2.75, 0.5)

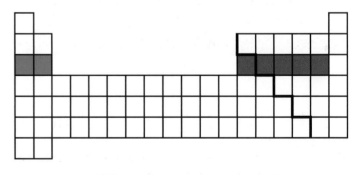

Ionic
Covalent

A look at the properties of the Period 3 chlorides shows how they are affected by their different types of bonding and structures.

Crystal structure	Formula	State at RT (298K)	m.p. / K	b.p. / K	S / J K^{-1} mol^{-1}
Cubic	NaCl	solid	1074	1686	72
Hexagonal	MgCl$_2$	solid	987	1685	90
Hexagonal	AlCl$_3$	solid	463 (at 2.5 atm)	451 (sublimes)	111
n/a	SiCl$_4$	liquid	203	331	240
n/a	PCl$_3$	liquid	161	349	217
Tetragonal	PCl$_5$	solid	435 (sublimes)	440 (decomposes)	167
n/a	SCl$_2$	liquid	195	332 (decomposes)	
n/a	S$_2$Cl$_2$	liquid	193	409	

The standard entropy values (rounded) are for molar amounts at 298K and 1 atmosphere. The high melting point of, for example, sodium chloride is due to the high energy needed to break the strong electrostatic forces (ionic bonds) holding the ions together in the lattice. The two Period 3 chlorides which stand out as being rather unusual are the two that sublime rather than melt. Aluminium chloride is often described as having an **intermediate structure**. The high charge density on Al^{3+} distorts the chloride anion sufficiently to make the bonding intermediate between ionic and covalent. Phosphorus(V) chloride is ionic and is in fact a mixture of PCl$_6^-$ and PCl$_4^+$ having an overall formula of PCl$_5$. The liquid chlorides (SiCl$_4$, PCl$_3$, SCl$_2$, S$_2$Cl$_2$) are simple molecular covalent structures. Chlorine exists as a diatomic molecule and it is also a simple covalent molecule that could be thought of as chlorine chloride.

Question 8.4

1. What observations would you make if excess chlorine gas were passed over solid white phosphorus (P$_4$)?

A2.1 (e) Oxidation number

Oxidation number is the number of electrons which must be added to a positive ion to form a neutral atom,

$$e.g. \ Na^+ + e^- \rightarrow Na$$

The oxidation number of sodium like all alkali metals is +1.

Also, the oxidation number is the number of electrons which must be removed from a negative ion to form a neutral atom,

$$e.g. \ O^{2-} - 2e^- \rightarrow O$$

The oxidation number of oxygen in an oxide ion is –2. In other words, the oxidation number is equal to the number of electrons lost or gained by an element.

There is a set of rules which needs to be applied in order to work out the oxidation number of individual elements in chemical species. Oxidation numbers are useful in identifying and balancing redox reactions. Oxidation numbers are written as Roman numerals and have replaced the old fashioned and less well understood suffix system. Traditional names often encountered and certainly worth learning are sulfate (SO$_4^{2-}$), sulfite (SO$_3^{2-}$), nitrate (NO$_3^-$), nitrite (NO$_2^-$), sulfurous acid (H$_2$SO$_3$) and nitrous acid (HNO$_2$).

Number	1	2	3	4	5	6	7
Roman Numeral	I	II	III	IV	V	VI	VII

So ferric chloride (FeCl$_3$) is now called iron(III) chloride and ferrous chloride (FeCl$_2$) is now called iron(II) chloride, which is unambiguous. Note there is no space between the roman numerals in brackets and the name of the metal. Other examples of oxidation numbers being used in nomenclature are sodium nitrate(V) (NaNO$_3$), where the oxidation number on the nitrogen atom is assigned as +5, whereas sodium nitrate(III) is NaNO$_2$ and nitrogen is +3. When there is only one possible oxidation number there is no need to write the number, e.g. NaCl is sodium chloride rather than sodium(I) chloride.

Oxidation numbers in Nomenclature

Name	Formula
Lead(II) oxide	PbO
Lead(IV) oxide	PbO_2
Sulfuric(IV) acid	H_2SO_3
Sulfuric(VI) acid	H_2SO_4
Phosphoric(V) acid	H_3PO_4
Nitric(V) acid	HNO_3
Nitric(III) acid	HNO_2
Copper(I) oxide	Cu_2O
Copper(II) oxide	CuO
Sodium chlorate(V)	$NaClO_3$

Rule	Examples
#1	H_2 (g) = 0, Na (s) = 0, F_2 (g) = 0, S_8 (s) = 0, C (s) = 0, Hg (l) = 0
#2	NaCl sum of oxidation numbers = +1 + −1 = 0 H_2SO_4 sum of oxidation numbers = (+1 × 2) + 6 + (−2 × 4) = 0
#3	NO_3^- sum of oxidation numbers = +5 + (−2 × 3) = −1 SO_4^{2-} sum of oxidation numbers = + 6 + (−2 × 4) = −2 NH_4^+ sum of oxidation numbers = −3 + (+1 × 4) = +1
#4	Oxidation number of oxygen = −2 in H_2O, K_2O, CO_2, CO, SO_2, SO_3, H_2SO_4 Oxidation number of oxygen = −1 in H_2O_2, Li_2O_2, Na_2O_2, K_2O_2 Oxidation number of oxygen = +2 in F_2O
#5	Oxidation number of fluorine = −1 in F_2O, NaF, CaF_2, HF, $CHClF_2$
#6	Oxidation number of hydrogen = +1 in HCl, H_2O, HF, HNO_3, $Ca(OH)_2$, H_2S Oxidation number of hydrogen = −1 in LiH, NaH, $LiAlH_4$, $NaBH_4$
#7	Oxidation number = +1 for alkali metals in LiH, NaCl, K_2O, KBr, KOH
#8	Oxidation number = +2 for alkaline earth metals in MgO, $CaCO_3$, $MgSO_4$, CaO
#9	Oxidation number of chlorine in ICl is −1 Oxidation number of bromine in IBr is −1 Oxidation number of fluorine in HF is −1

Oxidation Number Rules

Take time to learn the oxidation number rules so it is a trivial operation to apply them.

1. All elements have an oxidation number of zero (0).

2. The sum of the oxidation numbers in a compound is zero (0).

3. The sum of the oxidation numbers in ions is equal to the ion's charge.

4. The oxidation number of oxygen is −2 except in peroxides (−1) and F_2O.

5. The oxidation number of fluorine (the most E_{neg} element) is always −1.

6. The oxidation number of hydrogen is +1 except in metal hydrides (−1).

7. Group 1 oxidation number is +1.

8. Group 2 oxidation number is +2.

9. The most E_{neg} element gets the negative oxidation number.

Some elements have variable oxidation states, *e.g.* chlorine, nitrogen and most transition elements (B2.4c) such as chromium and manganese. Notice how the maximum oxidation states occur when elements combine with oxygen or fluorine. In the examples given, the oxidation number refers to the underlined element.

Oxidation Number	Examples
+7	$H\underline{I}O_4$, $HC\underline{l}O_4$, $KM\underline{n}O_4$, $\underline{Cl}_2O_7$, $KC\underline{l}O_4$, $\underline{Mn}_2O_7$
+6	$\underline{Cl}_2O_6$, $\underline{Cl}O_3$, $\underline{Cr}_2O_7^{2-}$, $\underline{S}O_3$, $I\underline{F}_6$, $\underline{Cr}O_4^{2-}$, $\underline{Cr}O_3$, $\underline{Mn}O_4^{2-}$, $\underline{S}F_6$
+5	$HC\underline{l}O_3$, $KC\underline{l}O_3$, $B\underline{r}F_5$, $\underline{P}Cl_5$, $\underline{N}_2O_5$, $H\underline{N}O_3$, $\underline{P}_2O_5$, $H_3\underline{P}O_4$, $\underline{V}_2O_5$
+4	$\underline{Cl}O_2$, $\underline{S}O_2$, $\underline{Mn}O_2$, $\underline{Pb}O_2$, $\underline{Sn}O_2$, $\underline{Si}Cl_4$, $\underline{Ti}O_2$, $\underline{N}O_2$, $\underline{S}O_3^{2-}$
+3	$\underline{Cl}F_3$, $HC\underline{l}O_2$, $\underline{Al}Cl_3$, $\underline{P}Cl_3$, $\underline{Ga}N$, $\underline{Cr}_2O_3$, $\underline{N}_2O_3$, $H\underline{N}O_2$, $\underline{Ti}Cl_3$
+2	$\underline{Cu}O$, $\underline{Pb}O$, $\underline{Cu}SO_4$, $\underline{Ca}CO_3$, $\underline{Ca}O$, $F_2\underline{O}$, $\underline{N}O$, $\underline{Mn}Cl_2$
+1	$HO\underline{Cl}$, $NaO\underline{Cl}$, $\underline{Cu}_2O$, $B\underline{r}Cl$, $\underline{I}Cl$, $\underline{N}_2O$, $\underline{Cl}O^-$
0	All elements ($\underline{Al}$, $\underline{Mg}$, $\underline{K}$, $\underline{Hg}$, $\underline{N}_2$, $\underline{P}_4$, $\underline{S}_8$, $\underline{F}_2$, $\underline{C}_{60}$, $\underline{U}$, $\underline{K}$, $\underline{He}$, $\underline{Be}$, $\underline{Zr}$)
−1	$H_2\underline{O}_2$, $H\underline{Cl}$, $Mg\underline{Cl}_2$, $C\underline{Cl}_4$, $Na\underline{F}$, $K\underline{Br}$, $Na\underline{H}$, $LiAl\underline{H}_4$, $NaB\underline{H}_4$
−2	$\underline{N}_2H_4$, $H_2\underline{O}$, $Cu\underline{O}$, $Cu\underline{S}O_4$, $H_2\underline{S}$, $H\underline{N}O_3$, $H_2\underline{S}O_4$, $\underline{O}H^-$
−3	$\underline{N}H_3$, $\underline{N}H_4^+$, $\underline{P}H_3$, $\underline{As}H_3$, $Li_3\underline{N}$, $Mg_3\underline{N}_2$

When an element decreases in oxidation number during the course of a reaction we say it has been **reduced**. When an element increases in oxidation number during the course of a reaction we say it has been **oxidised**. This is easy to work out when you use the acronym **OILRIG** which stands for **o**xidation **i**s **l**oss of electrons and **r**eduction **i**s **g**ain of electrons. In the reaction between sodium and chlorine to make sodium chloride (A1.2a), the sodium is being oxidised and the chlorine is being reduced. This is evident from oxidation numbers which are written above the balanced formula equation.

$$0 \qquad\qquad 0 \qquad\qquad +1 \quad -1$$

$$Na\,(s) \quad + \quad \tfrac{1}{2}Cl_2\,(g) \quad \rightarrow \quad Na\,Cl\,(s)$$

Example 8.3

What is the oxidation number of sulfur in sulfuric acid (H_2SO_4)?

Solution:

- Convert the formula into a sum ($2H + S + 4O$).

- Apply the appropriate oxidation number rules.

Rule 2: the sum of the oxidation numbers in a compound is zero.

$$2H + S + 4O = 0$$

Rule 4: the oxidation number of oxygen is −2 (except in peroxides).

$$2H + S + 4(-2) = 0$$

Rule 6: the oxidation number of hydrogen is +1 (except in metal hydrides).

$$2(1) + S + 4(-2) = 0$$

Calculation

$$2 + S - 8 = 0$$

Rearranging

$$S = 8 - 2 = 6$$

Answer: S = +6

Example 8.4

What is the oxidation number of chromium in sodium dichromate ($Na_2Cr_2O_7$)?

Solution:

- Convert the formula into a sum ($2Na + 2Cr + 7O$).

- Apply the appropriate oxidation number rules.

Rule 2: the sum of the oxidation numbers in a compound is zero.

$$2Na + 2Cr + 7O = 0$$

Rule 4: the oxidation number of oxygen is −2 (except in peroxides)

$$2Na + 2Cr + 7(-2) = 0$$

Rule 7: the oxidation number is +1 for alkali metals

$$2(1) + 2Cr + 7(-2) = 0$$

Calculation

$$2 + 2Cr - 14 = 0$$

Rearranging

$$2Cr = 14 - 2$$

$$2Cr = 12$$

$$Cr = \frac{12}{2} = 6$$

Answer: Cr = +6

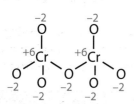

Questions 8.5

1. Cl_2O is a yellow-brown gas that is readily soluble in water and reacts to form hypochlorous acid (HOCl) according to the equation; $Cl_2O + H_2O \rightarrow 2$ HOCl. What is the change in oxidation number for chlorine in this reaction?

   A   −1

   B   0

   C   +1

   D   +2

2. Determine the oxidation number of chlorine in its reaction with sodium hydroxide. Give an explanation as to why this is not a typical redox reaction.

   $$6 \text{ NaOH} + 3 \text{ Cl}_2 \rightarrow 5 \text{ NaCl} + \text{NaClO}_3 + 3 \text{ H}_2\text{O}$$

3. Chlorine forms a number of oxoacids. Find the oxidation number of chlorine in all of these oxoacids; HOCl, $HClO_2$, $HClO_3$, $HClO_4$

4. Yellow chromate (CrO_4^{2-}) turns orange on the addition of acid to form dichromate ($Cr_2O_7^{2-}$). In this reversible reaction which is the correct option for the oxidation numbers of both chromium species?

   $$2 \text{ CrO}_4^{2-} + 2 \text{ H}^+ \rightleftharpoons \text{Cr}_2\text{O}_7^{2-} + \text{H}_2\text{O}$$

	CrO_4^{2-}	$Cr_2O_7^{2-}$
A	+6	+6
B	+7	+6
C	+6	+7
D	+7	+7

5. Determine the oxidation numbers for both iron and manganese in the following reaction. Use your answers to explain what is happening.

   $$10 \text{ FeSO}_4 + 2 \text{ KMnO}_4 + 8 \text{ H}_2\text{SO}_4 \rightarrow 5 \text{ Fe}_2(\text{SO}_4)_3 + \text{K}_2\text{SO}_4 + 2 \text{ MnSO}_4 + 8 \text{ H}_2\text{O}$$

A2.1 (f) Period 3 elements reactivity with oxygen

The first six Period 3 elements react directly with oxygen to form oxides. Chlorine forms oxides indirectly and argon does not react with oxygen.

Sodium burns with a bright yellow-orange flame to form sodium oxide (Na_2O).

$$4 \text{ Na (s)} + \text{O}_2 \text{ (g)} \rightarrow 2 \text{ Na}_2\text{O (s) [white solid]}$$

An additional reaction gives sodium peroxide (Na_2O_2).

$$2 \text{ Na (s)} + \text{O}_2 \text{ (g)} \rightarrow \text{Na}_2\text{O}_2 \text{ (s) [yellow solid]}$$

Magnesium oxidises slowly at room temperature. Magnesium burns with a brilliant white flame, which should not be looked at directly, when heated in air. Magnesium has found military uses because it burns so brightly.

$$2 \text{ Mg (s)} + O_2 \text{ (g)} \rightarrow 2 \text{ MgO (s)} \text{ [white solid]}$$

Aluminium reacts vigorously with oxygen at room temperature to form a protective layer of aluminium oxide (Al_2O_3).

$$4 \text{ Al (s)} + 3 O_2 \text{ (g)} \rightarrow 2 \text{ Al}_2O_3 \text{ (s)} \text{ [white solid]}$$

It is possible to remove the protective outer layer of Al_2O_3 from aluminium using an aqueous solution of mercury(II) chloride. This reaction has been described beautifully in a book entitled *Uncle Tungsten* by Oliver Sacks.

Silicon forms silicon(IV) oxide (SiO_2) slowly on heating in air.

$$\text{Si (s)} + O_2 \text{ (g)} \rightarrow SiO_2 \text{ (s)} \text{ [white solid]}$$

Silicon(IV) oxide is the stuff of many beaches (Boscombe, Bondi, Malibu) and also the material used by some sponges to make their skeletons.

Phosphorus can form two oxides on heating and burns with a very bright white light. Which oxide forms depends on how plentiful is the air supply. *Phosphoros* is the Greek word for 'bringer of light'. White phosphorus (P_4) is highly flammable and is stored under water.

In a limited air supply the lower oxidation state, phosphorus(III) oxide (P_2O_3) forms.

$$P_4 \text{ (s)} + 3 O_2 \text{ (g)} \rightarrow 2 P_2O_3 \text{ (s)} \text{ [white solid]}$$

In the presence of excess air the higher oxidation state, phosphorus(V) oxide (P_2O_5) forms.

$$P_4 \text{ (s)} + 5 O_2 \text{ (g)} \rightarrow 2 P_2O_5 \text{ (s)} \text{ [white solid]}$$

The structures of the oxides of phosphorus are quite similar. They consist of hexagonal rings of alternating phosphorus atoms (purple) and oxygen atoms (red) with a cage-like structure similar to diamond and germanium (A2.1b). The formulae are P_4O_6 and P_4O_{10} and it is their empirical formulae P_2O_3 and P_2O_5 which are often written in balanced formulae equations.

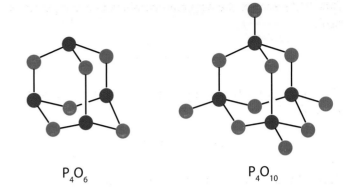

P_4O_6 P_4O_{10}

Sulfur burns with a pale blue flame to form the choking gas sulfur(IV) oxide (SO_2).

$$\text{S (s)} + O_2 \text{ (g)} \rightarrow SO_2 \text{ (g)}$$

Sulfur dioxide is an antioxidant and, because it kills bacteria, it is used in preserving foods.

Sulfur dioxide can be oxidised to sulfur(VI) oxide (SO_3) using platinum as the catalyst (A2.2g) or vanadium(V) oxide (V_2O_5) as part of the **Contact Process**.

$$2 SO_2 \text{ (g)} + O_2 \text{ (g)} \rightleftharpoons 2 SO_3 \text{ (g)}$$

Chlorine forms four oxides of varying stability but these cannot be made by direct combination with oxygen. The chlorine oxides have to be made indirectly.

Chlorine oxide	Colour	State at 298K
Cl_2O	yellow	gas
ClO_2	orange	gas
Cl_2O_2	red	liquid
Cl_2O_7	colourless	liquid

Argon is an inert gas that does not react with oxygen.

Question 8.6

1. Complete the table for some Period 3 oxides and explain the pattern with their formulae.

Element	Sodium	Magnesium			Phosphorus	Sulfur	Chlorine
Oxide	Na_2O				P_4O_{10}	SO_3	Cl_2O_7
Oxidation Number		+2	+3	+4			

A2.1 (f) Period 3 elements reactivity with water

Sodium is stored under oil because of its reactivity with water. As the first element in Period 3, sodium shows the most reactivity with water. Sodium reacts vigorously with water and typical observations are that the sodium floats, it melts into a ball and whizzes around and sometimes an orange flame is seen. The reaction is most impressive when the indicator phenolphthalein is added to the water and a purple alkaline trail is seen. In the reaction, the sodium is oxidised as seen by the increase in oxidation number (A2.1e) from zero in the element to +1 in sodium hydroxide (NaOH). The resulting solution is strongly alkaline and typically has a pH 12-14.

$$2 \, Na \, (s) + 2 \, H_2O \, (l) \rightarrow 2 \, NaOH \, (aq) + H_2 \, (g)$$

Magnesium reacts very slowly with cold water: only a few cm³ of hydrogen gas will be collected over several days. Magnesium sinks in water and by placing a funnel over a piece of magnesium ribbon the hydrogen gas can be collected as it will displace the water trapped in an inverted test tube. The weakly alkaline solution formed is ~ pH = 10.

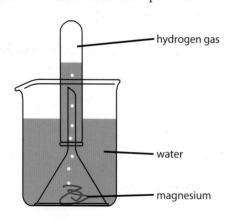

hydrogen gas

water

magnesium

$$Mg \, (s) + 2 \, H_2O \, (l) \rightarrow Mg(OH)_2 \, (aq) + H_2 \, (g)$$

Although magnesium only has a very slight reaction with cold water, it burns in steam. This reaction should only be demonstrated from behind a safety screen. Sometimes the hydrogen gas ignites spontaneously. When the magnesium reacts with steam it burns with a white flame as the white magnesium oxide forms.

$$Mg \, (s) + H_2O \, (g) \rightarrow MgO \, (s) + H_2 \, (g)$$

Aluminium does not react with cold water. However, aluminium powder will react in a similar manner to magnesium with steam. The reaction is very slow because the aluminium oxide formed prevents further reaction as the surface of the metal becomes coated with this protective oxide layer.

$$2 \, Al \, (s) + 3 \, H_2O \, (g) \rightarrow Al_2O_3 \, (s) + 3 \, H_2 \, (g)$$

Silicon, phosphorus, sulfur and argon have no reaction with cold water. Sulfur sinks because it is denser than water. Phosphorus is stored under water to prevent it reacting with oxygen.

The reaction of chlorine with water is very slow and hypochlorous acid (HOCl) and hydrochloric acid both form. HOCl, also known as chloric(I) acid, decomposes into hydrochloric acid and an oxygen free radical. This decomposition has been found to be catalysed by sunlight, metal oxides and platinum. The oxygen free radical disrupts the cell membranes of bacteria hence HOCl has found use as a powerful and versatile disinfectant.

$$Cl_2 \, (g) + H_2O \, (l) \rightarrow HCl \, (aq) + HOCl \, (aq)$$

$$HOCl \, (aq) \rightarrow HCl \, (aq) + O \, (g)$$

Question 8.7

1. Give the equations for the reaction between magnesium and water. How does the reactivity of magnesium compare with the other s-block metals in Period 3?

A2.1 (g) Period 3 oxides reactivity with water

Sodium oxide reacts vigorously with water to form a highly alkaline solution of pH ~13 (B1.5f).

$$Na_2O\ (s) + H_2O\ (l) \rightarrow 2\ NaOH\ (aq)$$

Sodium peroxide reacts with water to give an alkaline solution of sodium hydroxide and hydrogen peroxide (A2.2f).

$$Na_2O_2\ (s) + 2\ H_2O\ (l) \rightarrow 2\ NaOH\ (aq) + H_2O_2\ (aq)$$

Magnesium oxide is basic and it is much less soluble in water than sodium oxide. This is because magnesium oxide has a much higher lattice enthalpy than sodium oxide (A1.3e). The resulting solution has a pH ~8.

$$MgO\ (s) + H_2O\ (l) \rightarrow Mg(OH)_2\ (aq)$$

Aluminium oxide is completely inert in water and insoluble. Aluminium oxide is an **amphoteric oxide** which means it can react with both acids and bases. Examples to illustrate this somewhat unusual chemical property follow.

Aluminium oxide reacts as a base with sulfuric acid (H_2SO_4).

$$Al_2O_3\ (s) + 3\ H_2SO_4\ (aq) \rightarrow Al_2(SO_4)_3\ (aq) + 3\ H_2O\ (l)$$

Aluminium oxide reacts as an acid with hydroxides.

$$Al_2O_3\ (s) + 2OH^-\ (aq) + 3\ H_2O\ (l) \rightarrow 2\ Al(OH)_4^-\ (aq)$$

It is thought that because aluminium prefers to be six coordinate (B2.4d), $Al(OH)_4^-$ is probably hydrated, *i.e.* $[Al(OH)_4(H_2O)_2]^-$. So the overall equation for the reaction between aluminium oxide and hydroxide could be written as:

$$Al_2O_3\ (s) + 2OH^-\ (aq) + 7\ H_2O\ (l) \rightarrow 2\ [Al(OH)_4(H_2O)_2]^-$$

The same ion forms when Al^{3+}(aq) ions are tested for with excess hydroxide. See the data booklet of Qualitative Ions Tests.

Silicon dioxide (SiO_2) is a stable macromolecule which is completely inert in water giving no reaction. This question is a favourite at university interviews which you might like to think about next time you sit on a beach.

Silicon dioxide is weakly acidic and this property has been exploited when it is an impurity in the manufacture of iron. Silicon dioxide reacts with calcium oxide to form calcium silicate ($CaSiO_3$).

$$SiO_2\ (s) + CaO\ (s) \rightarrow CaSiO_3\ (l)$$

Phosphorus(III) oxide reacts slowly with cold water to make phosphonic acid (H_3PO_3) which can also be called phosphoric(III) acid.

$$P_2O_3\ (s) + 3\ H_2O\ (l) \rightarrow 2\ H_3PO_3\ (aq)$$

By contrast phosphorus(V) oxide reacts vigorously with cold water to make phosphoric(V) acid (H_3PO_4). It is often used as a powerful desiccant because of its affinity for water.

$$P_2O_5\ (s) + 3\ H_2O\ (l) \rightarrow 2\ H_3PO_4\ (aq)$$

The majority of manufactured H_3PO_4 is used to make fertilizers such as diammonium hydrogenphosphate(V) $(NH_4)_2HPO_4$. Both oxides of phosphorus are acidic in nature.

Sulfur dioxide (SO_2) reacts with water to make sulfurous acid (H_2SO_3).

$$SO_2\ (g) + H_2O\ (l) \rightarrow H_2SO_3\ (aq)$$

In the solid state, sulfur trioxide (SO_3) exists as a polymer. It reacts violently with water to make sulfuric acid (H_2SO_4).

$$SO_3\ (s) + H_2O\ (l) \rightarrow H_2SO_4\ (aq)$$

Dichlorine oxide (Cl_2O) reacts with water to make hypochlorous acid (HOCl).

$$Cl_2O\ (g) + H_2O\ (l) \rightarrow 2\ HOCl\ (aq)$$

Argon does not react with water.

The trend for the Period 3 oxides is that the s-block oxides are basic in character, aluminium oxide is amphoteric and the remaining p-block Period 3 oxides are acidic.

Period 3 oxides

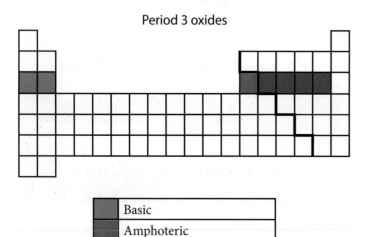

	Basic
	Amphoteric
	Acidic

Question 8.8

1. Complete the table for the Period 3 oxides

Element Symbol	Oxide formula	Oxide bonding	Nature of oxide's solution, *e.g.* acidity
Na			
Mg			
Al			
Si			
P			
S			
Cl			

A2.1 (h)
Period 3 chlorides and water

The trend is to change from ionic chlorides (NaCl and $MgCl_2$) to covalent chlorides ($AlCl_3$, $SiCl_4$, PCl_3, S_2Cl_2 and Cl_2) across Period 3. The covalent chlorides are more easily hydrolysed with increasing oxidation number (A2.1e) of the elements.

Period 3 chlorides

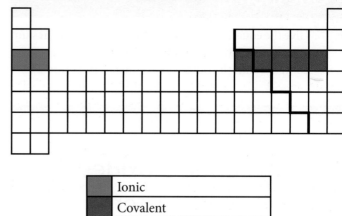

	Ionic
	Covalent

Sodium chloride does not react with water, but it does dissolve readily to form a neutral solution (pH = 7.0). An aqueous solution of sodium chloride is called brine and is often used in the food industry.

$$NaCl\ (s) + H_2O\ (l) \rightarrow Na^+\ (aq) + Cl^-\ (aq)$$

When the crystal lattice (A1.3e) of sodium chloride dissolves in water, each ion becomes surrounded by polar water molecules. The slightly positive (δ^+) hydrogen atoms of water are attracted to the negative chloride ions. The slightly negative (δ^-) oxygen atoms of water are attracted the positive sodium ions.

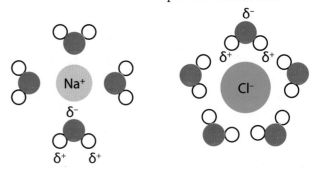

Magnesium chloride also dissolves in water with the formation of a weakly acidic solution (pH = 6.5) because it undergoes partial hydrolysis.

$$MgCl_2\ (aq) + 2\ H_2O\ (l) \rightarrow Mg(OH)_2\ (aq) + 2\ HCl\ (aq)$$

Aluminium chloride hydrolyses rapidly in water with the formation of a fairly strongly acidic solution of ~pH = 3.

$$AlCl_3\ (s) + 3\ H_2O\ (l) \rightarrow Al(OH)_3\ (aq) + 3\ HCl\ (aq)$$

The increased acidity across Period 3 from the NaCl to $AlCl_3$ is a result of the decreasing size and charge of the cation.

The chlorides of silicon and phosphorus all react with water to produce steamy white fumes of HCl (g). If a lot of water is added, this acid gas dissolves to create a strongly acidic solution of hydrochloric acid HCl (aq) with a pH = 2.

Silicon(IV) chloride ($SiCl_4$) is a volatile colourless liquid. It is prepared by heating silicon until it is red hot and then passing a stream of dry chlorine gas over it.

$$Si \text{ (s)} + 2\,Cl_2 \text{ (g)} \rightarrow SiCl_4 \text{ (l)}$$

Liquid silicon(IV) chloride fumes immediately on contact with moist air and the reaction is vigorous and exothermic. The reaction with water is described as a hydrolysis reaction.

$$SiCl_4 \text{ (l)} + 4\,H_2O \text{ (l)} \rightarrow Si(OH)_4 \text{ (aq)} + 4\,HCl \text{ (aq)}$$

Hydrolysis of silicon tetrachloride is a stepwise addition of H_2O *via* the lone pair followed by elimination of HCl. Each chlorine atom is replaced in turn until the final product tetrahydroxysilane $Si(OH)_4$ is formed.

$$SiCl_4 \text{ (l)} + H_2O \text{ (l)} \rightarrow SiCl_3(OH) \text{ (aq)} + HCl \text{ (aq)}$$

$$SiCl_3(OH) \text{ (aq)} + H_2O \text{ (l)} \rightarrow SiCl_2(OH)_2 \text{ (aq)} + HCl \text{ (aq)}$$

$$SiCl_2(OH)_2 \text{ (aq)} + H_2O \text{ (l)} \rightarrow SiCl(OH)_3 \text{ (aq)} + HCl \text{ (aq)}$$

$$SiCl(OH)_3 \text{ (aq)} + H_2O \text{ (l)} \rightarrow Si(OH)_4 \text{ (aq)} + HCl \text{ (aq)}$$

$$SiCl_4 \text{ (l)} + 4\,H_2O \text{ (l)} \rightarrow Si(OH)_4 \text{ (aq)} + 4\,HCl \text{ (aq)}$$

The hydrolysis of $SiCl_4$ is possible because silicon can expand its octet by holding more than eight electrons in its valence shell. It does this because its d-orbitals are available and can accept a lone pair of electrons from water. This nucleophilic attack is followed by the breaking of a Si-Cl bond. This is repeated until each Cl is replaced by an OH group.

Phosphorus pentachloride (PCl_5) is a pale yellow solid which can be prepared directly by reacting phosphorus with excess dry chlorine gas or by dropping phosphorus trichloride (PCl_3) into a flask containing dry chlorine.

$$P_4 \text{ (s)} + 6\,Cl_2 \text{ (g)} \rightarrow 4\,PCl_3 \text{ (l)}$$

$$PCl_3 \text{ (l)} + Cl_2 \text{ (g)} \rightarrow PCl_5 \text{ (s)}$$

Phosphorus trichloride hydrolyses in cold water with the formation of a strongly acidic solution of phosphonic acid (H_3PO_3) and hydrochloric acid at about pH = 2.

$$PCl_3 \text{ (l)} + 3\,H_2O \text{ (l)} \rightarrow H_3PO_3 \text{ (aq)} + 3\,HCl \text{ (aq)}$$

PCl_5 reacts violently with water to give hydrochloric acid and phosphoric(V) acid (H_3PO_4). The pale yellow solid reacts with water in a two stage hydrolysis reaction. The intermediate phosphorus oxychloride ($POCl_3$) is hydrolysed to phosophoric(V) acid which is sometimes called *ortho* phosophoric acid by chemical suppliers.

$$PCl_5 \text{ (s)} + H_2O \text{ (l)} \rightarrow POCl_3 \text{ (l)} + 2\,HCl \text{ (aq)}$$

$$POCl_3 \text{ (l)} + 3\,H_2O \text{ (l)} \rightarrow H_3PO_4 \text{ (aq)} + 3\,HCl \text{ (g)}$$

$$PCl_5 \text{ (s)} + 4\,H_2O \text{ (l)} \rightarrow H_3PO_4 \text{ (aq)} + 5\,HCl \text{ (aq)}$$

$POCl_3$ might well be formed after initial addition of the lone pair of H_2O to the vacant d-orbitals of phosphorus followed by elimination of two molecules of HCl.

$$PCl_5 \text{ (s)} + H_2O \text{ (l)} \rightarrow PCl_5(OH_2) \text{ (aq)}$$

$$PCl_5(OH_2) \text{ (aq)} \rightarrow POCl_3 \text{ (l)} + 2HCl \text{ (aq)}$$

$$PCl_5 \text{ (s)} + H_2O \text{ (l)} \rightarrow POCl_3 \text{ (l)} + 2HCl \text{ (aq)}$$

The reaction of equimolar amounts of PCl_5 and water leads to a less vigorous reaction that forms $POCl_3$ and HCl.

Hydrolysis of PCl_5 like $SiCl_4$ can also be thought of as a stepwise addition of H_2O *via* the lone pair followed by elimination of HCl. Each chlorine atom is replaced in turn until the final product phosophoric(V) acid is formed.

PCl_5 is used to replace OH groups in alcohols (ROH) and carboxylic acids (RCOOH) with a chlorine atom. So it should come as no surprise that it also replaces an OH group in HOH (water) with a chlorine atom. This is believed to happen for <u>all</u> five chlorine atoms. The unstable intermediate $P(OH)_5$, which has not been isolated, then eliminates water (dehydration) to produce H_3PO_4, phosphoric(V) acid.

$$PCl_5 \text{ (s)} + H_2O \text{ (l)} \rightarrow PCl_4(OH) \text{ (aq)} + HCl \text{ (aq)}$$

$$PCl_4(OH) \text{ (aq)} + H_2O \text{ (l)} \rightarrow PCl_3(OH)_2 \text{ (aq)} + HCl \text{ (aq)}$$

$$PCl_3(OH)_2 \text{ (aq)} + H_2O \text{ (l)} \rightarrow PCl_2(OH)_3 \text{ (aq)} + HCl \text{ (aq)}$$

$$PCl_2(OH)_3 \text{ (aq)} + H_2O \text{ (l)} \rightarrow PCl(OH)_4 \text{ (aq)} + HCl \text{ (aq)}$$

$$PCl(OH)_4 \text{ (aq)} + H_2O \text{ (l)} \rightarrow P(OH)_5 \text{ (aq)} + HCl \text{ (aq)}$$

$$P(OH)_5 \text{ (aq)} \rightarrow H_3PO_4 \text{ (aq)} + H_2O \text{ (l)}$$

This is analagous to the unstable hydroxyl group in geminal diols (A3.2h).

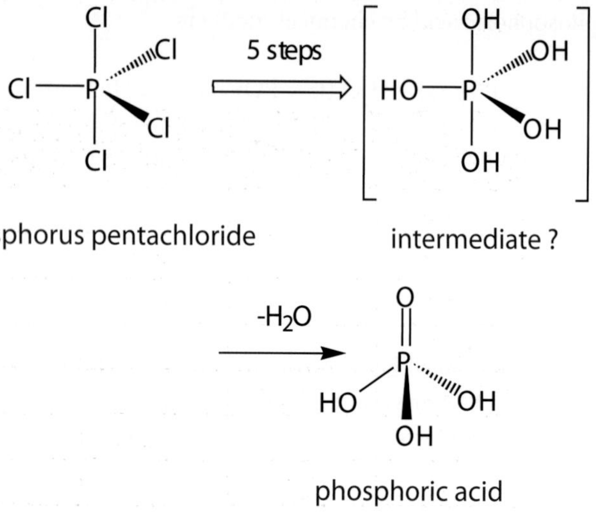

phosphorus pentachloride   intermediate ?

$$-H_2O$$

phosphoric acid

Sulfur forms a number of chlorides; sulfur dichloride (SCl_2) sulfur tetrachloride (SCl_4) and disulfuryl dichloride (S_2Cl_2). These sulfur chlorides hydrolyse slowly to give a variety of sulfur-containing compounds as well as hydrochloric acid. Equations for these reactions are:

$$SCl_4 \xrightarrow{-H_2O} [S(OH)_4] \xrightarrow{-H_2O} H_2SO_3 \rightarrow SO_2$$

$$S_2Cl_2 + 2\ H_2O \rightarrow 2\ HCl + H_2S + SO_2$$

followed by; $2\ H_2S + SO_2 \rightarrow 2\ H_2O + 3S$

or $2\ S_2Cl_2 + 2\ H_2O \rightarrow SO_2 + 3\ S + 4\ HCl$

$$2\ SCl_2\ (l) + 2\ H_2O\ (l) \rightarrow SO_2\ (g) + S\ (s) + 4\ HCl\ (aq)$$

Chlorine reacts slowly with water in a special type of redox reaction called a disproportionation (A2.2n) where chlorine is simultaneously oxidised and reduced.

$$Cl_2\ (g) + H_2O\ (l) \rightarrow HCl\ (aq) + HClO\ (aq)$$

The products are hydrochloric acid and chloric(I) acid (HClO) which gives swimming pools their characteristic smell.

Questions 8.9

1. What type of reaction occurs when chlorine reacts with water?

   $$Cl_2\ (g) + H_2O\ (l) \rightarrow HCl\ (aq) + HClO\ (aq)$$

   A   Decomposition.

   B   Oxidation.

   C   Disproportionation.

   D   Reduction.

2. Which Period 3 chloride does not undergo hydrolysis?

   A $AlCl_3$

   B PCl_3

   C PCl_5

   D   NaCl

3. Give the equation for the hydrolysis of aluminium chloride in moist air. Give a qualitative test for the gas produced.

4. Explain how careful hydrolysis of silicon(IV) chloride can result in the formation of $Cl_3SiOSiCl_3$.

5. Explain why $SiCl_4$ reacts with water but CCl_4 does not.

6. Phosphorus pentachloride (PCl_5) can be prepared by reacting phosphorus with excess dry chlorine gas. Write a balanced formula equation for the white phosphorus allotrope. What observations might you make when carrying out this reaction?

7. What observations would you make if $SiCl_4$ were added dropwise to water?

8. Phosphorus pentachloride reacts violently with water. Write an overall equation for this reaction and describe the observations expected.

9. The melting point of silicon tetrachloride is 203K and its boiling point is 331K. In what state of matter is $SiCl_4$ under standard conditions?

    A   Gas.

    B   Liquid.

    C   Aqueous.

    D   Solid.

10. Which option shows the correct outcome of adding some Period 3 chlorides to water?

	NaCl	$SiCl_4$	PCl_5
A	dissolving	hydrolysis	dissolving
B	dissolving	dissolving	hydrolysis
C	hydrolysis	hydrolysis	dissolving
D	dissolving	hydrolysis	hydrolysis

11. Which option best describes the phase change as PCl_5 is heated to above 162°C, the temperature at which it sublimes?

A	solid	→	gas
B	liquid	→	gas
C	solid	→	liquid
D	solid	→	aqueous

12. Phosphorus pentachloride has different structures in the solid and gaseous states. In the solid state it is made up of PCl_4^+ and PCl_6^- ions and in the vapour state it has been shown to be a simple covalent molecule with the formula PCl_5. Which option shows the correct shape of the phosphorus pentachloride molecules in the different states?

	PCl_4^+	PCl_6^-	PCl_5
A	trigonal bipyramidal	trigonal bipyramidal	octahedral
B	trigonal bipyramidal	octahedral	trigonal bipyramidal
C	tetrahedral	octahedral	trigonal bipyramidal
D	tetrahedral	trigonal bipyramidal	trigonal bipyramidal

13. Complete the table by filling in the gaps for the period 3 chlorides.

Formula	State (RT)	Bonding	Effect on moist air
NaCl	(s)		
$MgCl_2$		Ionic	
$AlCl_3$			
$SiCl_4$			
PCl_3 & PCl_5	(l) & (s)		
S_2Cl_2		Covalent	
Cl_2	(g)		

A2.1 (i) Mineral oxides

Minerals found in the Earth's crust are usually crystalline inorganic substances with definite formulae that have formed as a result of geological processes that have taken place over millions of years. Minerals are often conveniently divided into silicates and non-silicates. Most of the rock-forming minerals which make up a significant part of the rocks in the Earth's crust are silicates, *e.g.* quartz (SiO_2), which is about 59% of the Earth's crust followed by aluminium oxide (Al_2O_3) at about 15%. Quartz is found in granites and sandstones and both rocks have been used as building materials. The most important non-silicate group is the oxides, followed by the carbonates and then the sulfides.

Mineral	Formula
Bauxite	Al_2O_3
Magnetite	Fe_3O_4
Haematite	Fe_2O_3
Rutile	TiO_2
Quartz	SiO_2
Gypsum	$CaSO_4.2H_2O$

The proportion of different elements in the Earth's crust (pie chart) shows the importance and natural occurrence of mineral oxides. It should come as no surprise to see the high proportions of oxygen and silicon because silicates are the most common minerals in the Earth's crust.

Proportions of elements in the Earth's crust

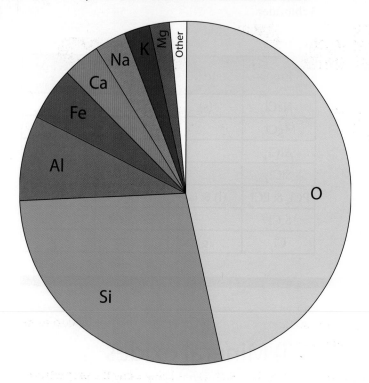

Mineral halides are minor in global terms compared with the more common oxide minerals. This should also come as no surprise when oxygen is 21% of our atmosphere. The two notable mineral halides are halite (NaCl) and fluorite (CaF_2) and their crystal structures are considered in B2.5e.

The thermodynamic preference of bonds for oxygen rather than chlorine is also a factor in the occurrence of oxides rather than halides in minerals. Comparing the relative lattice enthalpies of oxides and chlorides calculated from Born-Haber cycles (A1.3e) reveals the increased thermodynamic stability of the oxide compared with the chloride for the same metal.

$\Delta_{latt}H$ (kJ mol^{-1})		
Metal	Oxide	Chloride
sodium	−2478	−780
potassium	−2232	−711
magnesium	−3791	−2526
calcium	−3401	−2258

The high strength of the Si–O covalent bond in SiO_2 (s) at 466 kJ mol^{-1} is another factor to be considered to explain the large abundance of silicates in the Earth's crust.

9 Main Group Chemistry

Contents

Introduction

The remarkably diverse elements found in groups 15, 16 and 17 have led to some particularly interesting uses.

Group 15: For some years, Heston Blumenthal has being using the properties of liquid nitrogen in his dishes at his Michelin Star restaurant *The Fat Duck*. Nitrogen gas is also used as an inert atmosphere in crisp packets.

Liquid nitrogen used to freeze cream.

Nitrogen used in keeping crisps fresh.

Group 16: Sulfur is found in 2-furanmethanethiol (C_5H_6OS) which is the molecule responsible for the aroma of coffee.

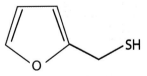

The smell of coffee.

Coffee beans.

Group 17: Bromine is found in the dye Tyrian Purple which has been used since ancient times. It was used by the Phoenicians, the Greeks and the Romans over two thousand years ago. The dye was extracted from the shells of the Murex sea snails (*Murex Brandaris*). Tyrian purple is the colour worn by emperors and cardinals.

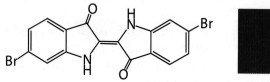

A2.2 (a)
Thermal decomposition of carbonates

Lithium carbonate (Li_2CO_3), and all the Group 2 carbonates, form the oxide and carbon dioxide on heating in a reaction which is known as a **thermal decomposition**. The reactions are shown for lithium carbonate and magnesium carbonate. The other Group 1 carbonates are thermally stable.

$$Li_2CO_3 \text{ (s)} \rightarrow Li_2O \text{ (s)} + CO_2 \text{ (g)}$$

$$MgCO_3 \text{ (s)} \rightarrow MgO \text{ (s)} + CO_2 \text{ (g)}$$

Thermal decomposition is the name given to reactions where substances decompose (break apart) when heat is applied. Decomposition of the Group 2 carbonates is perhaps the most familiar of the thermal decomposition reactions which are, more often than not, endothermic.

Thermal decompositions	Decomposition (°C)
$BeCO_3$ (s) unstable at 298 K	
$MgCO_3$ (s) → MgO (s) + CO_2 (g)	350
$CaCO_3$ (s) → CaO (s) + CO_2 (g)	832
$SrCO_3$ (s) → SrO (s) + CO_2 (g)	1340
$BaCO_3$ (s) → BaO (s) + CO_2 (g)	1450

The trend is that as Group 2 is descended, the decomposition temperature increases. The main factor that affects the decomposition temperature is the charge density of the cation which is related to its size by this equation:

$$\text{charge density} \propto \frac{\text{charge of ion}}{(\text{ionic radius})^2}$$

The charge on all the Group 2 ions is +2 as the elements have s^2 valence electrons. As Group 2 is descended, the ionic radius increases as there are more shells of electrons. Consequently there is a decrease in charge density as the ionic radius increases.

Ion	Ionic radius (pm)
Mg^{2+}	72
Ca^{2+}	100
Sr^{2+}	118
Ba^{2+}	135
CO_3^{2-}	135

The decomposition of a carbonate is concerned with the breaking of a C-O bond within the carbonate. This C-O bond is weakened by polarising cations. The most polarising cations are the ones with the highest charge density, *i.e.* the smallest cations. The smallest Group 2 ion in a stable carbonate is Mg^{2+} which gives the greatest polarisation of the carbonate ion. As the Mg^{2+} ion leads to the most distortion (polarisation) of the carbonate ion, it will break up more easily to give carbon dioxide and leave behind the oxide. Ba^{2+} is the largest of the stable Group 2 ions and it has little or no polarisation of the similarly sized CO_3^{2-} ion. Interestingly, these decomposition reactions are endothermic with high activation energies.

The smaller 2+ ion polarises the 2– ion more because it has greater attractions for its electrons. The size of the 'electron drift' is indicated by the size of the arrows.

Questions 9.1

1. Which option shows the correct order for the ease of thermal decomposition of the carbonates?

   A $MgCO_3 > CaCO_3 > SrCO_3 > Li_2CO_3$

   B $Li_2CO_3 < MgCO_3 < CaCO_3 < SrCO_3$

   C $MgCO_3 < CaCO_3 < SrCO_3 < Li_2CO_3$

   D $Li_2CO_3 > MgCO_3 > CaCO_3 > SrCO_3$

2. Which Group 1 carbonate is thermally unstable?

A K_2CO_3

B Li_2CO_3

C Rb_2CO_3

D Na_2CO_3

3. Why is lithium carbonate the only Group 1 carbonate that thermally decomposes?

4. Complete the table to show how the charge and size of cations affects carbonate stability.

carbonates	cation size	cation charge
most stable carbonates		
most unstable carbonates		

5. Which option shows the formula for a carbonate that exists under standard conditions?

A $Fe_2(CO_3)_3$

B $BeCO_3$

C $FeCO_3$

D $Al_2(CO_3)_3$

A2.2 (b)
Structures of nitrogen and white phosphorus

Nitrogen and phosphorus are the first two elements in Group 15. Nitrogen is a diatomic colourless gas with the formula N_2. White phosphorus (an **allotrope**) is a solid that has to be stored under water. It has the formula P_4.

The two atoms in a molecule of nitrogen are held together by a triple covalent bond, *i.e.* $N\equiv N$.

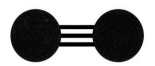

Nitrogen molecule

The triple bond of nitrogen consists of a single σ-bond and two π-bonds. The formation of π-bonds by sideways overlap of the 2p orbitals (A1.2d) in nitrogen is possible due to the small size of the nitrogen atoms. π-bonds are less stable with atoms of Group 15 elements larger than nitrogen, such as phosphorus.

White phosphorus (P_4) is the most reactive allotrope of phosphorus. It is also the allotrope with the simplest structure. Like nitrogen each phosphorus atom is trivalent. It does not form diatomic molecules $P\equiv P$ analogous to nitrogen. Instead it forms a P_4 structure which is a triangle based pyramid.

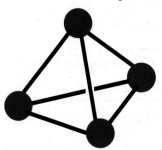

Structure of white phosphorus (P_4)

The four phosphorus atoms are to be found at the corners of a tetrahedron. Each phosphorus atom is bonded to the other three phosphorus atoms by single covalent bonds.

Questions 9.2

1. Which option shows the correct formula for white phosphorus and nitrogen?

	nitrogen	white phosphorus
A	N	P_4
B	N_2	P_2
C	N_2	P_4
D	N	P_2

2. Which option shows the correct bond order in nitrogen and white phosphorus?

	nitrogen	white phosphorus
A	3	1
B	2	4
C	1	3
D	3	3

A2.2 (c)
Unreactivity of nitrogen

About 78% of air in the atmosphere is the unreactive colourless gas nitrogen. It is found as the free element whereas all the other more reactive Group 15 elements occur in minerals. The only element to react with nitrogen under standard conditions is lithium, which forms lithium nitride (Li_3N).

$$N_2 \text{ (g)} + 6 \text{ Li (s)} \rightarrow 2 \text{ Li}_3N \text{ (s)}$$

Rhizobia are examples of nitrogen fixing bacteria found in the nodules of leguminous plants such as peas, clover and soy. They can 'fix' nitrogen directly from the air into water-soluble nitrates and nitrites.

Nitrogen is unreactive for several reasons. The triple bond of nitrogen has a very high bond enthalpy ($945.4 \text{ kJ mol}^{-1}$) and therefore a lot of energy is needed to break the sigma (σ) and two pi (π) bonds. Before the discovery of the reversible reaction (B1.5a) between nitrogen and hydrogen to make ammonia in the Haber-Bosch process, nitrogen was thought to be an inert gas.

$$N_2 \text{ (g)} + 3 \text{ H}_2 \text{ (g)} \rightleftharpoons 2 \text{ NH}_3 \text{ (g)}$$

Nitrogen's triple bond breaks when nitrogen adsorbs onto the surface of the iron catalyst (B1.3f).

Another reason for nitrogen's unreactivity is that it is a non-polar molecule (A1.2i) because the electrons in the triple bond are shared equally between the two nitrogen atoms which possess the same electronegativity (3.0). This is why it is one of the infra-red inactive gases (A4.3a). As nitrogen is non-polar it is not going to attract nucleophiles (B3.9g) or electrophiles (B3.10b). Each nitrogen atom in N_2 has a lone pair of electrons directed away from the internuclear axes. The lone pairs of electrons are in low energy bonding orbitals (A1.2b).

Uses of nitrogen

Pure nitrogen is obtained by fractional distillation of liquid air (**Linde process**). Liquid nitrogen is used extensively for freezing food because it can do so very quickly without water leaking from damaged cells caused by ice crystals. This inert substance prevents oxygen from reaching the surface of food which, in turn, prevents the growth of bacteria.

Nitrogen also provides an inert atmosphere in which chemical reactions can take place. The nitrogen gas takes the place of the air above the surface of solutions and is needed in the preparation of **Grignard reagents** (A3.4d).

Questions 9.3

1. Which option is not a factor in nitrogen's unreactivity?

A High electronegativity.

B Bond enthalpy.

C Triple bond.

D Non-polar.

2. Give three reasons why nitrogen is unreactive.

A2.2 (d) Acid-base behaviour of ammonia and the ammonium ion

Ammonia (NH_3) is the familiar hydride of nitrogen made in the Haber Process. Ammonia is a colourless gas which is less dense than air and which has a sharp, pungent smell. Ammonia is a weak base (proton acceptor) and is only partially ionised in aqueous solution. The majority of particles are molecules in an ammonia solution. The presence of hydroxide ions (OH^-) in an ammonia solution is confirmed by the reaction with cations (A4.1a).

$$NH_3 (aq) + H_2O (l) \rightleftharpoons OH^- (aq) + NH_4^+ (aq)$$

Ammonia is very soluble in water with 680 cm^3 of the gas dissolving in just 1 cm^3 of water. This high solubility can be shown by performing the 'fountain experiment'. In this experiment, dry ammonia dissolves in a small amount of water, creating a partial vacuum and a 'fountain' of water that dissolves the remaining gas (safety precautions are required!).

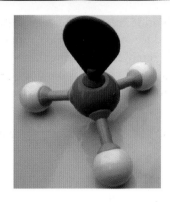

Molecular model of the ammonia molecule

Molecular model of the ammonium ion

Ammonia is neutralised by acids to form a salt as the exclusive product. Note the absence of water as a product in these neutralisation reactions. In these reactions, the ammonium ion (NH_4^+) is formed when the lone pair on nitrogen forms a dative covalent bond by accepting a proton.

$$NH_3 (aq) + HNO_3 (aq) \rightarrow NH_4NO_3 (aq)$$

$$2 NH_3 (aq) + H_2SO_4 (aq) \rightarrow (NH_4)_2SO_4 (aq)$$

Ammonia forms dense white fumes of ammonium chloride when it reacts with hydrochloric acid. This reaction can be demonstrated by dipping a glass rod into concentrated HCl (aq) and holding it near to a bottle of concentrated NH_3 (aq) with the stopper removed.

$$NH_3 (g) + HCl (g) \rightarrow NH_4Cl (s)$$

All the neutralisation reactions can be reversed when the ammonium salts are heated. The presence of ammonia can be detected by damp red litmus paper which turns blue.

Ammonium salts are acidic and they react with alkalis to form salts, water and ammonia. Ammonium chloride reacts with sodium hydroxide to produce sodium chloride, water and ammonia.

$$NH_4Cl + NaOH \rightarrow NaCl + H_2O + NH_3$$

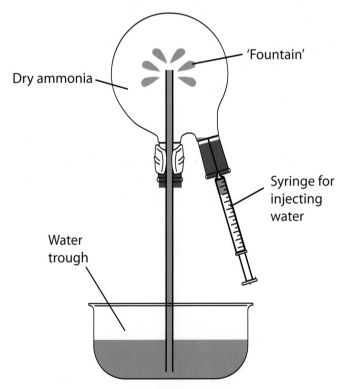

Apparatus for the 'fountain experiment' shown just after a small amount of water has been injected into the inverted flask

Ammonium chloride reacts when heated with calcium hydroxide to produce calcium chloride, water and ammonia. The water can be removed by passing through calcium oxide. This reaction is a convenient laboratory method for the preparation of ammonia when a gas cylinder is not available.

$$2\,NH_4Cl\,(s) + Ca(OH)_2\,(s)$$
$$\rightarrow CaCl_2\,(s) + 2\,H_2O\,(g) + 2\,NH_3\,(g)$$

Ammonia is a base (proton acceptor) and its conjugate acid is ammonium (proton donor). It is worth pointing out that, the weaker the base, the stronger its conjugate acid (B1.5b).

$$NH_3 \quad + \quad H^+ \rightleftharpoons \quad\quad NH_4^+$$

$$\textit{base} \quad\quad \textit{acid} \quad\quad\quad\quad \textit{conjugate acid}$$

Ammonium salts are all ionic, water soluble and, on heating with an alkali, give off ammonia. One useful ammonium salt is monohydrate ammonium carbonate $(NH_4)_2CO_3.H_2O$ which is an active ingredient in smelling salts. The small amount of ammonia given off helped people recover from "a fit of the vapours" - though the vapours they were recovering from were less salubrious than a trace of ammonia.

Ammonium salts behave as acids. This can be seen from the acid dissociation constant (B1.5d) for the ammonium ion, which is $K_a = 5.8 \times 10^{-10}\ mol\ dm^{-3}$.

$$NH_4^+ \rightleftharpoons \quad NH_3 \quad + \quad H^+$$

$$\textit{acid} \quad\quad \textit{conjugate base} \quad\quad \textit{conjugate acid}$$

This makes the ammonium ion less acidic than carbonic acid $(K_a = 4.5 \times 10^{-7}\ mol\ dm^{-3})$ but more acidic than phenol $(K_a = 1.3 \times 10^{-10}\ mol\ dm^{-3})$.

An example of an ammonium salt reacting as an acid is in the reaction of ammonium chloride with the base potassium amide.

$$NH_4Cl \quad + \quad KNH_2 \rightarrow KCl \quad + \quad 2\,NH_3$$

$$\textit{acid} \quad\quad\quad \textit{base} \quad\quad \textit{salt} \quad\quad \textit{solvent}$$

Ammonium salts have found use in fertilizers. Alone, these ammonium compounds would make the soil slightly acidic so, to overcome this tendency, they are mixed with limestone to make a mixture known as '**nitro-chalk**'.

Questions 9.4

1. Which option gives the correct description of the reactants and products in the reaction of ammonia with water?

$$NH_3\,(aq) + H_2O\,(l) \rightleftharpoons OH^-\,(aq) + NH_4^+\,(aq)$$

	NH_3 (aq)	H_2O (l)	OH$^-$ (aq)	NH_4^+ (aq)
A	base	amphi-protic	conjugate base	conjugate acid
B	base	acid	conjugate base	conjugate acid
C	base	acid	conjugate acid	conjugate base
D	acid	amphi-protic	conjugate acid	conjugate base

2. What is the ionic equation for any ammonium salt reacting with an alkali?

3. Write a balanced formula equation for the reaction between solid ammonium sulfate and solid calcium hydroxide. In this reaction, what is the role of ammonium sulfate? Describe a simple test for the gaseous product.

4. Write a balanced formula equation for the reaction between aqueous ammonia and hydrobromic acid with an explanation of the role of both reactants.

5. Ammonia solution precipitates metal ions from solution as metal hydroxides. Complete and balance the equations and suggest the colour for the precipitate.

$$FeSO_4\,(aq) + NH_3\,(aq) + H_2O\,(l) \rightarrow$$

$$Al_2(SO_4)_3\,(aq) + NH_3\,(aq) + H_2O\,(l) \rightarrow$$

6. Explain how you could compare the basicity of ammonia and sodium hydroxide solutions.

7. Which of the following statements are true?

A   Ammonia is the conjugate base for ammonium.

B   Ammonia is a strong base and ammonium a strong acid.

C   Ammonia is a weak base and ammonium a strong acid.

D   Ammonia is a strong base and ammonium a weak acid.

E   Ammonium is the conjugate acid of ammonia.

8. Self-ionization of a molecule is not restricted to just water ($2\,H_2O \rightleftharpoons H_3O^+ + OH^-$). Liquid ammonia also undergoes self-ionization. Predict the products in this reversible reaction. How might this reaction be described?

9. Explain why phosphine (PH_3) is not a base, but ammonia (NH_3) is a base.

10. Write the ionic equation for the reaction between aqueous ammonium solution and aqueous carbonate. What is the role of the ammonium ion?

Molecular model of Oxygen (O_2)

Molecular model of Ozone (O_3)

In 2001, chemists from Fulvio Cacace's research group at the University of Rome made and characterized a very unstable third allotrope tetraoxygen (O_4), using mass spectrometry.

For the last 200 million years, oxygen has been present in the Earth's atmosphere at levels of about 20%.

Ozone is formed in the part of the atmosphere at 25 km above the Earth's surface called the **stratosphere**. This is where the protective blanket of ozone filters out the majority of the harmful UV rays (220-290 nm) from the Sun. The concentration of ozone in this region is in the range 0-10 ppm. It is formed by homolytic fission of O_2.

A2.2 (e) Allotropes of oxygen

Allotropes are two or more forms of the same element in which the atoms are arranged in different ways. Allotropes have different properties because of their different structures. There are two main allotropes of oxygen: the familiar diatomic gas that rekindles a glowing splint (O_2) and the newsworthy triatomic gas ozone (O_3). The two oxygen atoms in O_2 are joined by a double O=O covalent bond. When drawing a dot and cross diagram for ozone the three oxygen atoms in O_3 are joined by a double O=O covalent bond and a single dative covalent bond. Ozone is a bent molecule (A1.2g) because of the presence of the lone pair of electrons on the central oxygen atom.

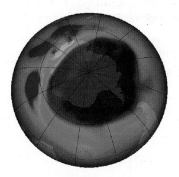

Ozone hole above the Antarctic photographed by NASA in September 2005

The overall equation for the equilibrium formation and destruction of ozone in the atmosphere:

$$3\,O_2 \rightleftharpoons 2\,O_3$$

$$\Delta H_f = +142\ kJ\ mol^{-1}\ \&\ \Delta G = 326.8\ kJ\ mol^{-1}$$

Ozone at street level is a harmful pollutant caused by the catalytic reaction between the car exhaust pollutant nitrogen dioxide (NO_2) and dioxygen.

$$NO_2 + O_2 \rightarrow O_3 + NO$$

$$NO + \tfrac{1}{2}O_2 \rightarrow NO_2$$

We can smell ozone at levels as low as 0.01 ppm which is fortunate because it is a very poisonous gas. Ozone takes its name from the Greek word *ozein* meaning 'to smell'.

The table compares the two allotropes of oxygen.

	Oxygen	Ozone
name	dioxygen	trioxygen
formula	O_2	O_3
reactivity / stability	reactive & stable	reactive & unstable
b.p. /°C	−183	−112
m.p. /°C	−219	−192
state at 298K	gas	gas
smell	odourless	electrical & pungent
colour of gas	colourless	pale blue
colour of liquid	pale blue	dark blue*
colour of solid	pale blue	violet-black*
magnetism	paramagnetic	diamagnetic
bonding	σ & π	σ, π & σ
bonds	O=O	O=O–O
shape	linear	bent (triangular)
bond angle	180°	117°
bond lengths / nm	0.121	0.128
Bond enthalpy / kJ mol⁻¹	498.3 (O=O)	302 (O–O)
solubility in 100 cm³ H_2O	3.08 cm³ (20°C) 2.08 cm³ (50°C)	0.105 g/100ml at 0°C
uses	medical, welding	bleaching, sterilizing, water purification

* (l) & (s) ozone are explosive.

Ozone is a powerful oxidising agent and it will react with many substances under conditions where its allotrope (O_2) remains unreactive. It is possible to determine the amounts of ozone quantitatively by its reaction with excess aqueous potassium iodide.

$$O_3 + 2\,KI + H_2O \rightarrow I_2 + 2\,KOH + O_2$$

The iodine that is produced in this reaction can be titrated against the primary standard (A4.1c) sodium thiosulfate (A2.2m), *i.e.*

$$2\,S_2O_3^{2-}\,(aq) + I_2\,(aq) \rightarrow S_4O_6^{2-}\,(aq) + 2\,I^-\,(aq)$$

Questions 9.5

1. Draw dot and cross diagrams for the two allotropes of oxygen.

2. Which option is isoelectronic with ozone?

   A   NO

   B NO_3^-

   C NO_2

   D NO_2^-

A2.2 (f) Redox properties of hydrogen peroxide

Pure hydrogen peroxide (H_2O_2) is a corrosive liquid which is pale blue in colour. '20 volume' solutions of hydrogen peroxide are generally used in the laboratory. A 20 volume solution is one which will produce 20 cm³ of oxygen gas on decomposition for each cm³ of hydrogen peroxide. A 20 volume solution of hydrogen peroxide has a concentration of 1.67 mol dm⁻³.

The order of atoms in hydrogen peroxide is easy to remember if you think of it as being like water but with an additional oxygen atom squeezed between an oxygen atom and a hydrogen atom. This makes its atom arrangement HOOH. The molecules are best described as a skewed chain. Each HOO angle is 97° and the angle between the two skewed H-O bonds is 94° in the liquid phase. The structure is adopted to minimise the repulsion between the lone pairs of electrons on the oxygen atoms.

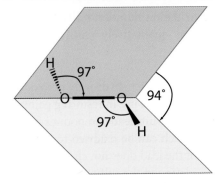

Decomposition of H_2O_2 with MnO_2

Hydrogen peroxide is unstable so, to slow down its rate of decomposition, it is often stored in bottles kept in a refrigerator. The decomposition of hydrogen peroxide is speeded up by light and a number of inorganic catalysts (MnO_2, PbO_2, iron filings) and biological catalysts (hydrogen peroxidase in blood, and catalase found in potatoes and celery).

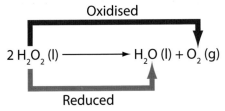

The decomposition of hydrogen peroxide is a good reaction to illustrate the unusual type of redox reaction called **disproportionation**. This is a reaction where the oxidation numbers for a particular element simultaneously increase and decrease from a single original value.

Name of Substance	Formula	Oxidation Number of Oxygen
Hydrogen peroxide	H_2O_2	−1
Hydrogen oxide (water)	H_2O	−2
Oxygen	O_2	0

During the decomposition of hydrogen peroxide, one oxygen atom gets reduced when it becomes water and the other gets oxidised when it becomes elemental oxygen. The O–O single bond is quite weak, like F–F (A2.2j), and hydrogen peroxide is prone to disproportionate. The addition of a detergent to hydrogen peroxide prior to catalytic decomposition leads to the generation of lots of foam. The oxygen gas evolved will relight a glowing splint.

Preparation of hydrogen peroxide

Barium peroxide is added to ice-cooled sulphuric acid. The precipitate of barium sulfate is filtered and the hydrogen peroxide in the filtrate can be concentrated by vacuum distillation.

$$BaO_2 \text{ (s)} + \text{dil. } H_2SO_4 \text{ (aq)} \rightarrow BaSO_4 \text{ (s)} + H_2O_2 \text{ (aq)}$$

Hydrogen peroxide has found uses as:

- a bleach

- a disinfectant

- improving the smell of drains and

- a source of oxygen for igniting fuel in rockets

Hydrogen peroxide is a difficult substance to handle and was put to devastating use by the 7/7 bombers in central London back in 2005.

In order to understand redox reactions, it is important to be familiar with the rules governing oxidation numbers (B1.4j). **Redox** is short hand for **red**uction-**ox**idation and in the reactions of hydrogen peroxide both reduction and oxidation happens. Reduction is where you get a decrease in oxidation number as electrons have been gained. Oxidation is the opposite reaction to reduction and is where there is an increase in oxidation number as electrons have been lost. A reminder of two ways to remember what happens with electrons are LEO says GER (**l**oss of **e**lectrons is **o**xidation and **g**ain of **e**lectrons is **r**eduction) or OILRIG (**o**xidation **i**s **l**oss of electrons and **r**eduction **i**s **g**ain of electrons). There are plenty of examples of redox reactions with hydrogen peroxide and they can be identified by looking at how the oxidation number for a particular element changes in going from reactants to products. One particularly important thing to remember is that oxidising agents get reduced during the course of a reaction because oxidising agents are electron acceptors.

The oxidation number of oxygen in hydrogen peroxide is –1. It is because of this 'intermediate' oxidation number that hydrogen peroxide can react as both an oxidising agent (more usual) and also a reducing agent depending on the reaction conditions and the oxidising power of the other reactant. A qualitative test for hydrogen peroxide is to add acidified potassium dichromate followed by extraction with ethoxyethane ($C_2H_5OC_2H_5$). A blue colour, due to Cr_2O_5, is the positive test.

Hydrogen peroxide as an oxidising agent

When hydrogen peroxide acts as an oxidising agent, water is produced. Hydrogen peroxide is a powerful oxidising agent in acidic solutions.

$$H_2O_2 + 2H^+ + 2e^- \rightarrow 2H_2O \quad E^\ominus = +1.77V$$

An example of hydrogen peroxide acting as an oxidising agent is its reaction with potassium iodide to liberate iodine in acidic solution. This reaction is the basis of one of the most crowd-pleasing iodine clock demonstrations and it is also very good for studying kinetics (B1.6f).

$$2\,KI\,(aq) + 2\,HCl\,(aq) + H_2O_2\,(aq)$$
$$\rightarrow I_2\,(aq) + 2\,KCl\,(aq) + 2\,H_2O\,(l)$$

The ionic equation for this reaction is:

$$2\,I^-(aq) + 2\,H^+\,(aq) + H_2O_2\,(aq) \rightarrow I_2\,(aq) + 2\,H_2O(l)$$

It is believed that this reaction actually takes place in two stages. In the first stage hydrogen iodide is formed and it is this which is oxidised by the hydrogen peroxide.

$$2\,KI\,(aq) + 2\,HCl\,(aq) \rightarrow 2\,KCl\,(aq) + 2HI\,(aq)$$

$$2\,HI\,(aq) + H_2O_2\,(aq) \rightarrow I_2\,(aq) + 2\,H_2O\,(l)$$

Hydrogen peroxide can also oxidise iron(II) to iron(III).

$$2Fe^{2+}\,(aq) + H_2O_2\,(aq) + 2H^+\,(aq) \rightarrow 2Fe^{3+}\,(aq) + 2H_2O\,(l)$$

The change in oxidation number of the transition metal ions can be confirmed qualitatively (A4.1a) by reactions with sodium hydroxide.

Another reaction in which hydrogen peroxide reacts as an oxidising agent has found use in restoring paintings. Pollution has slowly converted white lead compounds in paint into black lead(II) sulfide which can be oxidised to lead(II) sulfate. The oxidation state of the lead does not change but the addition of oxygen is an oxidation of the sulfur.

$$PbS\,(s) + 4\,H_2O_2\,(aq) \rightarrow PbSO_4\,(s) + 4\,H_2O\,(l)$$

$$\textit{black} \qquad\qquad\qquad \textit{white}$$

Hydrogen peroxide as a reducing agent

When hydrogen peroxide acts as a reducing agent oxygen is produced.

$$H_2O_2 \rightarrow O_2 + 2H^+ + 2e^- \quad E^\ominus = -0.68V$$

An example of hydrogen peroxide acting as a reducing agent is its reaction with sodium hypochlorite, which is a convenient laboratory method for the preparation of oxygen gas.

$$NaOCl + H_2O_2 \rightarrow O_2 + NaCl + H_2O$$

Hydrogen peroxide can be oxidised to elemental oxygen by powerful oxidising agents such as potassium manganate(VII). In this reaction, hydrogen peroxide is a reducing agent. This reaction is often used to accurately determine the concentration of solutions of hydrogen peroxide.

$$2\,MnO_4^-\,(aq) + 5\,H_2O_2\,(aq) + 6\,H^+\,(aq)$$
$$\rightarrow 2\,Mn^{2+}\,(aq) + 8\,H_2O\,(l) + 5\,O_2\,(g)$$

Hydrogen peroxide also acts as reducing agent in its reaction with another powerful oxidising agent silver oxide (Ag_2O). The evolution of oxygen gas can be detected with a glowing splint (A4.1a).

$$Ag_2O\,(s) + H_2O_2\,(aq) \rightarrow 2\,Ag\,(s) + H_2O\,(l) + O_2\,(g)$$

Hydrogen peroxide can be used as a reducing agent in the generation of chlorine dioxide for the pulp and paper industry. The most important application for hydrogen peroxide involves the bleaching of pulp and textile fibres. For many decades, the cosmetic business has used hydrogen peroxide in hair bleaching treatments.

Hydrogen peroxide to demonstrate catalysis

An unusual reaction where you can see a catalyst in action *via* a colour change is the reaction using Rochelle's salt (potassium sodium tartrate) and cobalt(II). Using a small measuring cylinder, carefully pour potassium sodium tartrate (10 cm³, 0.5 mol dm⁻³) into hydrogen peroxide (10 cm³, 2.0 mol dm⁻³). Bring this mixture gently to the boil whilst looking closely for signs of reaction, *i.e.* oxygen bubbles. Once boiling, remove the heat source and add 1 cm³ of an aqueous solution of cobalt(II) nitrate. What you will observe is that the initial mixture turns pink on the addition of the Co^{2+} (aq). There is a small period of time (induction period) when nothing seems to be happening. Then the solution fizzes whilst it darkens, turning first brown and then green due to the presence of Co^{3+} (aq). The solution is green in colour when the bubbles of oxygen gas are at a maximum. As the rate of oxygen evolved reduces, the green Co^{3+} (aq) fades to be replaced by the original Co^{2+} (aq) pink colour. This is a good reaction to show a change in oxidation number of a transition element during catalysis and to show, through a colour change, that the catalyst is regenerated at the end of the reaction.

Recently the presence of elevated levels of hydrogen peroxide in the body has been linked to the greying of hair in middle age.

Questions 9.6

1. Calculate the concentration (mol dm⁻³) of a 10 volume hydrogen peroxide solution.

2. Which option best describes the slow but spontaneous decomposition of hydrogen peroxide?

$$2 H_2O_2 \rightarrow 2 H_2O + O_2$$

   A   Double decomposition

   B   Reduction

   C   Oxidation

   D   Disproportionation

3. Write a balanced equation to show the oxidation of hydrogen peroxide by acidified manganate(VII). How could you demonstrate that the gas comes from hydrogen peroxide and not the manganate(VII)?

4. Write the ionic equation for the reaction between potassium iodide and hydrogen peroxide in acidic conditions. Describe the role of hydrogen peroxide in this reaction.

$$2 KI + H_2O_2 + H_2SO_4 \rightarrow I_2 + K_2SO_4 + 2 H_2O$$

5. Write the ionic equation for the reaction between potassium manganate(VII) and hydrogen peroxide in acidic conditions. Describe the role of hydrogen peroxide in this reaction.

$$2 KMnO_4 + 5 H_2O_2 + 3 H_2SO_4 \rightarrow K_2SO_4 + 5 O_2 + 2 MnSO_4 + 8 H_2O$$

6. Write the balanced formula equation for the decomposition of 100 vol. hydrogen peroxide. What factors could be investigated that would affect the rate of this decomposition? How could the rate be experimentally determined? What precautions should be taken?

7. What is the molar concentration in mol dm⁻³ of the following hydrogen peroxide solutions?

   a.   5 vol

   b.   20 vol

   c.   100 vol

A2.2 (g) Removing sulfur oxides (fuels and power stations)

The sulfur present in fossil fuels probably came from sulfur containing amino acids such as methionine and/or cysteine.

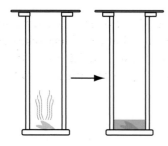

Methionine

Cysteine

Whilst efforts are increasing to develop renewable energy sources, carbon rich fossil fuels (natural gas, crude oil, and coal) are reliable sources of energy. Sulfur oxides are formed when fuels containing sulfur are combusted. The removal of the sulfur in these fuels did not happen during the early stages of the Industrial Revolution. Acidic lakes, damage to trees, stone work and lungs was found to be caused by **acid rain**.

Acid rain can be simulated by burning sulphur in a gas jar containing oxygen. Adding water and a small amount of universal indicator will demonstrate the acidic environment.

Once this was realised, two approaches were developed to reduce the acid rain caused by release of large amounts of SO_2 gas into the atmosphere. The first is to remove the sulfur before burning fuels as an energy source. The other approach is to burn the fuels in power stations and remove the sulfur dioxide which is produced as an unwanted by-product. This is discussed Chapter 18 (A3.6). Removal of sulfur dioxide in power station emissions is called **f**lue **g**as **d**esulfurisation (FGD). The cheapest method to remove this acidic gas is to pass the gases through a limestone (calcium carbonate) slurry. The sulfur dioxide gas reacts with the calcium carbonate to form calcium sulfite and carbon dioxide.

$$CaCO_3 \text{ (s)} + SO_2 \text{ (g)} \rightarrow CaSO_3 \text{ (s)} + CO_2 \text{ (g)}$$

The calcium sulfite can then be converted into calcium sulfate by heating in air.

$$CaSO_3 \text{ (s)} + \tfrac{1}{2} O_2 \text{ (g)} \rightarrow CaSO_4 \text{ (s)}$$

The calcium sulfate ($CaSO_4$) is used to make plaster board as well as plaster casts. When water is added to anhydrous calcium sulfate it forms gypsum which is $CaSO_4.2H_2O$. The energy released as the two waters of crystallisation form new bonds within the lattice causes the plaster to set.

An alternative method for the removal of sulfur dioxide makes use of magnesium carbonate. When magnesium carbonate is heated it thermally decomposes (A2.2a) to produce the base magnesium oxide and carbon dioxide.

$$MgCO_3 \text{ (s)} \rightarrow MgO \text{ (s)} + CO_2 \text{ (g)}$$

Sufur dioxide reacts with magnesium oxide to form magnesium sulfite.

$$MgO \text{ (s)} + SO_2 \text{ (g)} \rightarrow MgSO_3 \text{ (s)}$$

Magnesium sulfite is a neat way to store sulfur dioxide gas until it is needed. Heating magnesium sulfite releases sulfur dioxide and leaves behind magnesium oxide solid.

$$MgSO_3 \text{ (s)} \rightarrow MgO \text{ (s)} + SO_2 \text{ (g)}$$

The main use of sulfur dioxide is in the manufacture of sulfuric acid.

About 75% of the global sulfur dioxide in the atmosphere is from natural sources (volcanoes and dimethyl sulphide). The other 25% comes from power stations and vehicle emissions.

Questions 9.7

1. Which option shows the correct oxidation states for the sulfur in its oxide, sulfite and sulfate?

Oxidation states for sulfur			
	SO_2	$CaSO_3$	$CaSO_4$
A	+4	+6	+6
B	+2	+4	+6
C	+4	+4	+6
D	+2	+6	+6

2. It is believed that nitrogen dioxide catalyses the oxidation of sulfur dioxide in the atmosphere. Suggest equations that fit these atmospheric reactions.

3. Atmospheric sulfur dioxide can be detected by passing polluted air through aqueous hydrogen peroxide solution. Suggest an equation for this reaction and how it could be used to determine the amount of sulfur dioxide in the air.

4. Sulfur dioxide can be removed from power station emissions by passing waste gases through 'milk of lime' which is a solution of calcium hydroxide. Write a balanced equation for this reaction.

5. Sulfur dioxide gas reacts with hydrogen sulfide to form elemental sulfur and steam using Al_2O_3 as a catalyst. Which option best describes this reaction?

$$2\,H_2S\,(g) + SO_2\,(g) \rightarrow 3\,S\,(s) + H_2O\,(g)$$

A   Reverse disproportionation

B   Oxidation

C   Redox

D   Reduction

A2.2 (h) Properties and reactions of sulfuric acid

Introduction

Sulfuric acid (H_2SO_4) can be described as a strong involatile acid. It behaves as a typical strong acid in aqueous solution because the first dissociation of a proton is virtually complete. As the acid is diprotic it is capable of forming two salts depending on the amount of alkali present in the reaction mixture.

$$2\,NaOH\,(aq) + H_2SO_4\,(aq) \rightarrow Na_2SO_4\,(aq) + H_2O\,(l)$$

$$NaOH\,(aq) + H_2SO_4\,(aq) \rightarrow NaHSO_4\,(aq) + H_2O\,(l)$$

Great care is needed when handling c. H_2SO_4 and it is important that, if it is added to water, this is done slowly and whilst stirring. Never add water to c. H_2SO_4 as the reaction is extremely violent. At room temperature pure sulfuric acid (100%) is a covalent liquid.

A covalent molecule of sulfuric acid

Concentrated sulfuric acid is 98% pure (18.7 mol dm^{-3}) and is an oily viscous liquid with a density of 1.83 g cm^{-3}. It decomposes at its boiling point (330°C) and forms white fumes, $H_2SO_4\,(l) \rightarrow H_2O\,(g) + SO_3\,(g)$. The reverse reaction is a way of making sulfuric acid. Sulfuric acid tastes sour (it is poisonous!) and it turns blue litmus red, except when it is the covalent molecule.

Interestingly, sulfuric acid has been detected in Space. In 1999, solid (frozen) sulfuric acid was discovered on Europa, a moon of the planet Jupiter. Scientists have even identified solid sulfuric acid hydrates such as hemitriskaidecahydrate ($H_2SO_4.6\frac{1}{2}H_2O$).

Test for sulfuric acid

Firstly, add dilute HNO_3. This is to prevent precipitation of other insoluble barium compounds such as $BaCO_3$ or $BaSO_3$. Secondly, add $Ba(NO_3)_2\,(aq)$. If sulfuric acid or a sulfate is present, a white precipitate of $BaSO_4\,(s)$ will be immediately observed.

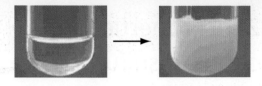

$$Ba^{2+} \text{ (aq)} + SO_4^{2-} \text{ (aq)} \rightarrow BaSO_4 \text{ (s)}$$

Dehydrating agent

Concentrated sulfuric acid has a very high affinity for water. On January 23rd, a small volume of c.H_2SO_4 was added to a beaker and left in a laboratory. By May 4th the volume in the beaker had more than doubled. The increase in volume was because c.H_2SO_4 had continued to absorb water from the air over a 14 week period.

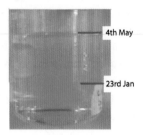

4th May

23rd Jan

Beaker of c.H_2SO_4 left for 14 weeks

Sulfuric acid's high affinity for water makes it a good dehydrating agent. It can be used to effect the dehydration of alcohols and ethene can be made from the dehydration of ethanol at 170°C.

$$C_2H_5OH \rightarrow C_2H_4 + H_2O$$

The dehydrating properties of sulfuric acid can be demonstrated by its reaction with sucrose ($C_{12}H_{22}O_{11}$) to leave a spongy column of carbon. A simplified equation for the reaction is:

$$C_{12}H_{22}O_{11} \text{ (s)} + n\, H_2SO_4 \text{ (l)}$$
$$\rightarrow 12\, C \text{ (s)} + 11\, H_2O \text{ (l)} + n\, H_2SO_4 \text{ (l)}$$

The carbon produced can then be oxidised to its common oxides with the result that the sulfuric acid is reduced to sulfur dioxide. An even more spectacular dehydration is the reaction between concentrated sulfuric acid and 4-nitroacetanilide ($CH_3CONHC_6H_4NO_2$) on gentle heating. The solid carbon sponge ejected from the small beaker can be up to 100 cm long and is affectionately called the furry caterpillar.

Furry caterpillar (30cm x 12cm)

When concentrated sulfuric acid dehydrates compounds, it does so with the evolution of a lot of heat. Examples of compounds that undergo dehydration are methanoic acid (HCOOH) and oxalic acid (CO_2HCO_2H). Both reactions need to be carried out in a fume-cupboard, as they release toxic and odourless carbon monoxide.

$$HCOOH \text{ (l)} \rightarrow CO \text{ (g)} + H_2O \text{ (l)}$$

$$CO_2HCO_2H \text{ (s)} \rightarrow CO \text{ (g)} + CO_2 \text{ (g)} + H_2O \text{ (l)}$$

Oxidising agent

Hot, concentrated sulfuric acid, which in equations is written as H_2SO_4 (l), is an oxidising agent. In its reactions as an oxidising agent, it accepts electrons. These are supplied by the reducing agent in the reaction.

$$2\, H_2SO_4 \text{ (aq)} + 2e^- \rightarrow SO_4^{2-} \text{ (aq)} + 2\, H_2O \text{ (l)} + SO_2 \text{ (g)}$$

When sulfuric acid reacts as an oxidising agent with metals, the sulfur in H_2SO_4 gets reduced from oxidation state **+6** to +4, 0 or −2. In these reactions, the respective reduction products are SO_2, elemental S_8 or H_2S. Despite what may have been taught early on in a chemistry career, copper does in fact react with concentrated sulfuric acid.

Examples of sulfuric acid reacting with metals where the products are metallic sulfates, water and sulfur dioxide include:

$$Mg \text{ (s)} + 2\, H_2SO_4 \text{ (l)} \rightarrow MgSO_4 \text{ (aq)} + 2\, H_2O \text{ (l)} + SO_2 \text{ (g)}$$

$$Zn \text{ (s)} + 2\, H_2SO_4 \text{ (l)} \rightarrow ZnSO_4 \text{ (aq)} + 2\, H_2O \text{ (l)} + SO_2 \text{ (g)}$$

$$Fe \text{ (s)} + 2\, H_2SO_4 \text{ (l)} \rightarrow FeSO_4 \text{ (aq)} + 2\, H_2O \text{ (l)} + SO_2 \text{ (g)}$$

$$Cu \text{ (s)} + 2\, H_2SO_4 \text{ (l)} \rightarrow CuSO_4 \text{ (aq)} + 2\, H_2O \text{ (l)} + SO_2 \text{ (g)}$$

Concentrated sulfuric acid also reacts with some non-metallic elements such as carbon and sulfur by oxidising them.

$$S \text{ (s)} + 2\, H_2SO_4 \text{ (l)} \rightarrow 2\, H_2O \text{ (l)} + 3\, SO_2 \text{ (g)}$$

$$C \text{ (s)} + 2\, H_2SO_4 \text{ (l)} \rightarrow 2\, H_2O \text{ (l)} + 2\, SO_2 \text{ (g)} + CO_2 \text{ (g)}$$

Sulfur dioxide can be detected (A4.1a) with a strip of filter paper moistened with potassium dichromate(VI) which turns from orange to green. Concentrated sulfuric acid also reacts with some compounds, such as sodium halides (A2.2l) (and hydrogen bromide and hydrogen iodide), by oxidising them.

$$2 \ HBr \ (g) + H_2SO_4 \ (l) \rightarrow 2 \ H_2O \ (l) + SO_2 \ (g) + Br_2 \ (l)$$

$$8 \ HI \ (g) + H_2SO_4 \ (l) \rightarrow 4 \ H_2O \ (l) + H_2S \ (g) + 4 \ I_2 \ (l)$$

Catalyst

Sulfuric acid is a catalyst in the synthesis of esters (B3.7b) from carboxylic acids and alcohols. When a carboxylic acid is heated under reflux with an equimolar amount of alcohol, a $1/10^{th}$ molar equivalent of c.H_2SO_4 is added as a catalyst. Instead of the esterification taking a week to reach equilibrium (B1.5), it is reached in several hours. The water formed as a product in esterifications is removed by reaction with sulfuric acid.

$$H_2SO_4 + H_2O \rightarrow H_3O^+ + HSO_4^-$$

Industrial importance

Millions of tonnes of sulfuric acid are manufactured in the UK each year. It is such an important industrial chemical that the wealth of a nation can be partly judged on the amount of sulfuric acid that the country produces. The biggest use of sulfuric acid is in the manufacture of sulfates such as gypsum $CaSO_4.2H_2O$, which is used to make plaster board as well as plaster casts. Another useful sulfate is the laxative 'epsom salt' $MgSO_4.7H_2O$. The manufacture of the fertiliser ammonium sulfate is another big consumer of sulfuric acid. Sulfuric acid is used for 'pickling' steel. This is where the metal alloy (steel) has any rust removed by dipping into c.H_2SO_4.

| Steel before pickling | Steel after pickling |

Sulfuric acid is also used in the manufacture of: hydrogen peroxide, hydrogen fluoride, and hydrogen chloride (**Mannheim Process**).

$$BaO_2(s) + H_2SO_4 \ (aq) \rightarrow BaSO_4 \ (s) + H_2O_2 \ (aq)$$

$$Ca_5F(PO_4)_3 + 5H_2SO_4 + 10H_2O$$
$$\rightarrow 5CaSO_4.2H_2O + HF + 3H_3PO_4$$

$$2 \ NaCl + H_2SO_4 \ (aq) \rightarrow Na_2SO_4 + 2 \ HCl$$

Sulfuric acid is also used in the manufacture of synthetic fibres (rayon), dyes, explosives, drugs and in the formation of sulfonates (A3.4b).

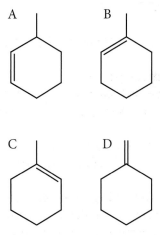

A2.2 (i) Trends in physical and chemical properties of the halogens

The halogens are Group 17 and include; fluorine, chlorine, bromine and iodine. Isotopes of astatine are formed in nuclear reactors and the longest lived isotope has a half-life of about 8 hours.

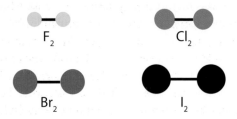

The trends in terms of the Group 17 physical properties are that as the Group is descended they get darker in colour and there is also an increase in melting and boiling points. The most volatile halogen is, therefore, fluorine. A substance which is described as volatile is one which evaporates easily due to the weak intermolecular forces. As Group 17 is descended, the halogens become less volatile as they have larger inter-molecular forces, called van der Waals forces (A1.2j).

Halogen	colour	mp /°C	bp / °C	state (298K)
Fluorine	pale yellow	−220	−188	gas
Chlorine	yellow-green	−101	−35	gas
Bromine	red-brown	−7	59	liquid
Iodine	grey-black	114	184	solid

As Group 17 is descended, the oxidising power of the halogens decreases, as seen by the vales for their standard electrode potentials (B1.5k).

Oxidising agent	$E^{\ominus}$ / V
Fluorine	2.87
Ozone	2.08
Hydrogen peroxide	1.77
Potassium manganate(VII)	1.70
Chlorine	1.36

Fluorine is so powerful an oxidising agent that it oxidises water to oxygen (A2.2i) whilst being reduced to hydrogen fluoride. The other halogens dissolve, forming aqueous solutions.

$$X_2 (g) + H_2O (l) \rightarrow X_2 (aq) \text{ [where X = Cl, Br or I]}.$$

$$2 F_2 (g) + 2 H_2O (l) \rightarrow 4 HF (aq) + O_2 (g)$$

A2.2 (j) Halogens' bond enthalpies

The bond energies for the covalently bonded elements is a major factor in their reactivities. The inertness of nitrogen under standard conditions is a reflection of the strength of its triple bond (945 kJ mol^{-1}). The diatomic halogens all possess a single (sigma) bond. The trend is that, as you descend Group 17, the bond enthalpy decreases from chlorine to bromine to iodine. Fluorine is exceptional as its bond enthalpy is similar to that of iodine. It is worth remembering that bond length for the halogens is twice their covalent radius.

Halogen	Bond enthalpy (kJ mol^{-1})	Bond length (nm)
F-F	158	0.142
Cl-Cl	243	0.199
Br-Br	193	0.228
I-I	151	0.267

The F–F bond is surprisingly weak. One might expect an F-F bond to be stronger than the Cl–Cl bond since there is less shielding of the bonding electrons in the fluorine atoms compared with the chlorine atoms. But since the fluorine atoms are so small and the bond length is also small, it means that there is an electrostatic repulsion between the lone pairs of each fluorine atom, which weakens the bond.

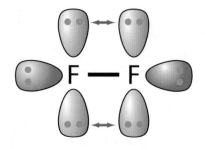

Lone-pair : lone-pair repulsion in F-F bond

Questions 9.9

1. How does oxidation state in interhalogen compounds affect bond enthalpy?

   FCl (255 kJ mol^{-1}) ClF_3 (176 kJ mol^{-1})

2. Predict how the bond enthalpies between **like atoms** will vary when comparing hydrazine (NH_2NH_2) with ethane (CH_3CH_3).

A2.2 (k) Trend in acidity of the hydrogen halides

All the halogens react with hydrogen, forming hydrogen halides. Hydrogen halides can be prepared safely by reacting concentrated sulfuric acid with a sodium halide (A2.2l). Fluorine reacts explosively with hydrogen even at the boiling point of hydrogen ($-253°C$) and chlorine reacts explosively with hydrogen in the presence of U.V. light. Each hydrogen atom in a hydrogen halide is joined by a single covalent bond to a halogen atom (Group 17). All the hydrogen halides are gases under standard conditions.

Hydrogen halide	Formula	Bond enthalpy (kJ mol^{-1})	K_a (mol dm^{-3})
Hydrogen fluoride	HF	562	5.62×10^{-4}
Hydrogen chloride	HCl	431	1×10^7
Hydrogen bromide	HBr	366	1×10^9
Hydrogen iodide	HI	299	1×10^{11}

When the hydrogen halides react with water they form hydrohalic acids, *i.e.* hydrofluoric acid (HF), hydrochloric acid (HCl), hydrobromic acid (HBr) and HI, (hydroiodic acid). Group 17 hydrohalic acids are strong acids except HF (aq).

$$HF (g) + H_2O (l) \rightleftharpoons H_3O^+ (aq) + F^- (aq)$$

$$HCl (g) + H_2O (l) \rightarrow H_3O^+ (aq) + Cl^- (aq)$$

$$HBr (g) + H_2O (l) \rightarrow H_3O^+ (aq) + Br^- (aq)$$

$$HI (g) + H_2O (l) \rightleftharpoons H_3O^+ (aq) + I^- (aq)$$

As Group 17 is descended, the hydrogen halides become stronger acids, as shown by their increasing acid dissociation constants (K_a). The trend is that the weaker the hydrogen-halogen bond the stronger the acid. As the bond strength weakens (as it gets longer) from hydrogen fluoride to hydrogen iodide, the tendency to ionise and form H^+ (aq) increases.

Hydrogen fluoride is a fuming liquid in a cold laboratory as it has a boiling point of $20°C$ and a melting point of $-80°C$. Despite being highly corrosive, hydrofluoric acid is the only hydrohalic acid that is a weak acid. Hydrofluoric acid is stored in polythene, not glass, bottles. Hydrofluoric acid is a weak acid due to the very strong hydrogen-fluorine bond. This factor outweighs the reduced hydration energy (A1.3a) from F^- to I^-. Another reason HF is a weak acid is because of the extensive and very strong hydrogen bonds (125 kJ mol^{-1}) that it forms in the liquid and vapour phases. These abnormally large hydrogen bonds help to explain hydrogen fluoride's relatively high melting and boiling points. The strong hydrogen bonds between hydrogen fluoride molecules reduce the likelihood that the molecules will ionize. This, along with the bond enthalpy, is a contributing factor in it being a weak acid.

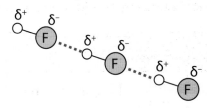

Hydrogen bonding in hydrogen fluoride

Hydrogen chloride does not form hydrogen bonds despite the hydrogen being attached to the highly electronegative chlorine atom. In chlorine, the lone pair of electrons is in the third shell (principal quantum number = 3). The electron density is less (more diffuse) in the 3s and 3p orbitals where chlorine's lone pairs are found.

Questions 9.10

1. Hydrogen fluoride attacks the silicon(IV) oxide component of glass, so it can be used in the manufacture of glass artefacts. Complete and balance the equation and suggest a use for this reaction.

   $$SiO_2 (s) + HF (l) \rightarrow$$

2. Write an equation for the reaction between magnesium and hydrobromic acid. How would the reaction appear different if this acid was replaced by hydrofluoric acid of the same concentration?

3. Which option gives the correct order for bond enthalpy and acidity?

	Bond enthalpy	Acid strength
A	HF > HCl > HBr > HI	HF > HCl > HBr > HI
B	HF < HCl < HBr < HI	HF < HCl < HBr < HI
C	HF < HCl < HBr < HI	HF > HCl > HBr > HI
D	HF > HCl > HBr > HI	HF < HCl < HBr < HI

4. Which option gives the correct order for polarity and magnitude of hydration enthalpy?

	Polarity	Hydration enthalpy
A	HF > HCl > HBr > HI	$F^- > Cl^- > Br^- > I^-$
B	HF < HCl < HBr < HI	$F^- < Cl^- < Br^- < I^-$
C	HF < HCl < HBr < HI	$F^- > Cl^- > Br^- > I^-$
D	HF > HCl > HBr > HI	$F^- < Cl^- < Br^- < I^-$

A2.2 (l) Reaction of halides with concentrated H_2SO_4

Reactions of the halides with concentrated sulfuric acid should always be performed in a fume cupboard because of the toxic nature of the gases produced. As you descend Group 17 the halides react more vigorously with concentrated sulfuric acid.

Reactions between sodium halides and $c.H_2SO_4$

NaCl · · · · · · · · · · · · · · NaBr · · · · · · · · · · · · · Nal

Fluorides and chlorides

Hydrogen fluoride and hydrogen chloride can both be prepared by the reaction between the relevant halide salt with concentrated sulfuric acid. In these reactions the sulfuric acid is transformed into sodium hydrogen sulfate ($NaHSO_4$). Neither hydrogen fluoride nor hydrogen chloride are oxidised further by $c.H_2SO_4$, no matter what the increase in temperature.

$$NaF\ (s) + c.H_2SO_4\ (l) \rightarrow HF\ (g) + NaHSO_4\ (s)$$

$$NaCl\ (s) + c.H_2SO_4\ (l) \rightarrow HCl\ (g) + NaHSO_4\ (s)$$

The misty fumes of hydrogen chloride gas are seen. The reason chlorine gas is not formed is because sulfuric acid is **not** powerful enough to oxidise chloride ions.

Bromides

Bromide ions are a stronger reducing agent than chloride ions. As bromide ions are larger than chloride ions their electrons are easier to remove. Bromide ions reduce sulfuric acid into sulfur dioxide in two steps.

$$NaBr\ (s) + c.H_2SO_4\ (l) \rightarrow HBr\ (g) + NaHSO_4\ (s)$$

$$2\ HBr\ (g) + c.H_2SO_4\ (l) \rightarrow Br_2\ (l) + 2\ H_2O\ (l) + SO_2\ (g)$$

The generation *in situ* of hydrogen bromide by the reaction of sodium bromide with concentrated sulfuric acid is used in the synthesis of halogenoalkanes (A3.3b).

Iodides

Iodide ions are even larger than bromide ions and iodide's electrons are even easier to remove. Iodide ions will react with concentrated sulfuric acid to produce hydrogen iodide gas, which will reduce sulfuric acid in three ways at room temperature.

$$NaI\ (s) + c.H_2SO_4\ (l) \rightarrow HI\ (g) + NaHSO_4\ (s)$$

Equation 1:

$$8\ HI\ (g) + c.H_2SO_4\ (l) \rightarrow 4\ I_2\ (s) + H_2S\ (g) + 4\ H_2O\ (l)$$

Equation 2:

$$6\ HI\ (g) + c.H_2SO_4\ (l) \rightarrow 3\ I_2\ (s) + S\ (s) + 4\ H_2O\ (l)$$

Equation 3:

$$2\ HI\ (g) + c.H_2SO_4\ (l) \rightarrow I_2\ (s) + SO_2\ (g) + 2\ H_2O\ (l)$$

You might expect to observe the following if concentrated sulfuric acid is added to solid sodium iodide:

- a smell of bad eggs due to toxic H_2S (equation 1)

- purple iodine vapour (equations 1-3)

- a brown colouration due to triiodide formation $(I_2 + I^- \rightarrow I_3^-)$

- a dark grey iodine solid condensing on cold glassware.

The chloride, bromide and iodide ions can be identified qualitatively by their reactions with concentrated sulfuric acid. In high concentration, sulfuric acid behaves as quite a strong oxidising agent. The trend is that, as Group 17 is descended, the hydrogen halides are more easily oxidised. Sulfuric acid oxidises iodide and bromide ions to their elemental state, but it is not a strong enough oxidising agent to oxidise chloride to chlorine.

Sulfuric acid is reduced to a different extent by iodide and bromide, reflecting the relative reducing power of these halides.

$H_2SO_4 + 2 H^+ + 2 e^- \rightarrow SO_2 + 2 H_2O$ *(reaction with bromide)*

$H_2SO_4 + 8 H^+ + 8 e^- \rightarrow H_2S + 4 H_2O$ *(reaction with iodide)*

Questions 9.11

1. Which option shows the two halogens which can be prepared by dropping c.H_2SO_4 onto a solid halide?

   A Cl_2 & I_2

   B Cl_2 & Br_2

   C F_2 & Cl_2

   D Br_2 & I_2

2. Write an equation for the reaction between calcium chloride and concentrated sulfuric acid.

A2.2 (m) Reaction of iodine with sodium thiosulfate

Sodium thiosulfate ($Na_2S_2O_3$) is used as a standard reducing agent. The thiosulfate ion $S_2O_3^{2-}$ can be thought of as being like a sulfate SO_4^{2-} in which one oxygen atom has been replaced by one sulfur atom. Sodium thiosulfate has found use in photography where it 'fixes' photographic negatives. The thiosulfate reacts with any unreacted silver bromide forming the complex ion $[Ag(S_2O_3)_2]^{3-}$. Thiosulfate is unstable in acid and its reaction with acid is perhaps familiar as the 'disappearing cross' experiment in which the rate at which sulfur is produced is taken as a measure of the reaction rate.

$$S_2O_3^{2-} (aq) + 2 H^+ (aq) \rightarrow H_2O (l) + SO_2 (g) + S (s)$$

Sodium thiosulfate is a good primary standard (A4.1c) because it can be obtained as a very pure solid. It dissolves readily in water and has a high relative formula mass (M_r). Also, its reactions are instantaneous and go to completion. Sodium thiosulfate reacts with iodine in a redox reaction and is often used to determine the concentration of iodine solutions in volumetric analyses. The sulfur atoms in thiosulfate **catenate** (join in chains) to form tetrathionate in which four sulfur atoms are linked *via* single bonds, *i.e.* S-S-S-S. Sodium thiosulfate + iodine → sodium iodide + sodium tetrathionate

$$2 Na_2S_2O_3 + I_2 \rightarrow 2 NaI + Na_2S_4O_6$$

In this reaction, iodine is reduced as its oxidation number decreases from 0 (I_2) to –1 (I^-). The thiosulfate is oxidised as the oxidation number of sulfur increases from +2 ($S_2O_3^{2-}$) to +2.5 in tetrathionate ($S_4O_6^{2-}$). In the titration between sodium thiosulfate (burette) and iodine (conical flask) the brown colour of iodine fades to a pale yellow as the end point (A4.1c) of the reaction is near. At this point a few drops of 1% starch solution are added to give an intense blue-black colour. This indicator sharpens up the end point which is reached when the solution in the conical flask turns colourless.

A primary standard is used as the starting point for determining the concentration of other solutions. When excess potassium iodide is added to an oxidising agent of unknown concentration, *e.g.* Cl_2, Fe^{3+}, IO_3^-, MnO_4^- or Cu^{2+} iodine is released. The amount of iodine can be determined accurately in a titration with thiosulfate and, therefore, the amount of oxidising agent can also be determined. The molar ratio of oxidising agent to thiosulfate can be calculated from the stoichiometry of the balanced formula equations. When faced with questions in the less familiar concentration unit of $g\ dm^{-3}$, divide this by $g\ mol^{-1}$ to convert into the more familiar unit of concentration, $mol\ dm^{-3}$.

Oxidising agent	Balanced formula equation
Cl_2	$Cl_2 + 2\,I^- \rightarrow 2\,Cl^- + I_2$
Fe^{3+}	$Fe^{3+} + I^- \rightarrow Fe^{2+} + \frac{1}{2}\,I_2$
IO_3^-	$IO_3^- + 6\,H^+ + 5\,I^- \rightarrow 3\,I_2 + 3\,H_2O$
MnO_4^-	$MnO_4^- + 8\,H^+ + 5\,I^- \rightarrow 2\frac{1}{2}\,I_2 + 4\,H_2O + Mn^{2+}$
Cu^{2+}	$Cu^{2+} + 2\,I^- \rightarrow CuI + \frac{1}{2}\,I_2$

Example 9.1

When excess potassium iodide was added to 25 cm³ of potassium iodate(V) having a concentration of 0.0150 mol dm⁻³ the iodine liberated required 22.3 cm³ of sodium thiosulfate at the end point. Calculate the concentration of the sodium thiosulfate.

Solution:

$$IO_3^- + 6\,H^+ + 5\,I^- \rightarrow 3\,I_2 + 3\,H_2O$$

$$n(IO_3^-) = c \times \frac{v}{1000}$$

$$= 0.0150 \times \frac{25}{1000}$$

$$= 3.75 \times 10^{-4}\ \text{mol}$$

$$n(I_2) = 3 \times n(IO_3^-)$$

$$= 3 \times 3.75 \times 10^{-4}\ \text{mol}$$

$$= 1.125 \times 10^{-3}\ \text{mol}$$

Since, $2\,S_2O_3^{2-}\,(aq) + I_2\,(aq) \rightarrow 2I^-\,(aq) + S_4O_6^{2-}\,(aq)$

$$n(S_2O_3^{2-}) = 2 \times n(I_2)$$

$$= 2 \times 1.125 \times 10^{-3}\ \text{mol}$$

$$= 2.25 \times 10^{-3}\ \text{mol}$$

$$[S_2O_3^{2-}] = \frac{n}{\left(\dfrac{v}{1000}\right)}$$

$$= \frac{2.25 \times 10^{-3}}{\left(\dfrac{22.3}{1000}\right)}$$

$$= 0.10\ \text{mol dm}^{-3}$$

Example 9.2

3.03 g of brass was dissolved in excess concentrated nitric acid.

$$Cu\,(s) + 4\,HNO_3\,(aq)$$
$$\rightarrow Cu(NO_3)_2\,(aq) + 2\,H_2O\,(l) + 2\,NO_2\,(g)$$

The excess acid was neutralised with aqueous sodium carbonate and then made up to 250 cm³ with distilled water in a volumetric flask. 25 cm³ of the Cu^{2+} (aq) was placed in a conical flask and then excess potassium iodide was added. Zn^{2+} does not react.

$$2\,Cu^{2+}\,(aq) + 4\,I^-\,(aq) \rightarrow 2\,CuI\,(s) + I_2\,(aq)$$

The white precipitate of copper(I) iodide was dissolved in ethanoic acid.

The iodine released was titrated against 0.110 mol dm⁻³ $Na_2S_2O_3$ (aq) and the average titre was found to be 29.5 cm³. [A_r for Cu = 63.5].

$$2\,S_2O_3^{2-}\,(aq) + I_2\,(aq) \rightarrow 2I^-\,(aq) + S_4O_6^{2-}\,(aq)$$

What is the percentage (%) of copper and zinc in the brass?

Solution:

The ratio of Cu to Cu^{2+} is 1:1 and the ratio of Cu^{2+} to I_2 is 2:1 and the ratio of $S_2O_3^{2-}$ to I_2 is 2:1, therefore the ratio of Cu to $S_2O_3^{2-}$ is 2:2 *i.e.* 1:1

$$n(S_2O_3^{2-}) = 0.110 \times \frac{29.5}{1000}$$

$$= 3.245 \times 10^{-3}\ \text{mol}$$

since $n(S_2O_3^{2-}) = n(Cu)$

$$n(Cu) = 3.245 \times 10^{-3}\ \text{mol}$$

mass of Cu $= 3.245 \times 10^{-3} \times 63.5$ in 25 cm³

$$= 0.206\ \text{g in 25 cm}^3$$

$$= 2.06\ \text{g in 250 cm}^3$$

$$\%\ Cu = \frac{2.06}{3.03} \times 100\%$$

$$= 68\%$$

$$\%\ Zn = 100 - 68 = 32\%$$

Questions 9.12

1. **a.** Write the ionic equation for the reaction between sodium thiosulfate and iodine.

b. What are the half equations in the reaction between iodine and thiosulfate?

c. Describe how the end point can be detected.

2. 16.8 g of hydrated copper(II) sulfate ($CuSO_4.5H_2O$) was dissolved in deionised water and made up to 500 cm^3 in a volumetric flask. 25.0 cm^3 of the Cu^{2+} (aq) was placed in a small beaker and excess potassium iodide was added. A white precipitate formed and was removed by filtration and the resulting filtrate was titrated against 0.200 mol dm^{-3} sodium thiosulfate. Use the titration results to calculate the percentage (%) copper in the original sample and to calculate the purity of the copper(II) sulfate.

Volume $S_2O_3^{2-}$ / cm^3	Rough	1st	2nd
Final	16.70	33.20	49.70
Initial	0.10	16.70	33.20

3. Use the equations to give the relative oxidising powers of the halogens.

$$4\,Cl_2\,(g) + 5\,H_2O\,(l) + S_2O_3^{2-}\,(aq)$$
$$\rightarrow 2\,SO_4^{2-}\,(aq) + 10\,H^+\,(aq) + 8\,Cl^-\,(aq)$$

$$I_2\,(aq) + 2\,S_2O_3^{2-}\,(aq) \rightarrow S_4O_6^{2-}\,(aq) + 2I^-\,(aq)$$

A2.2 (n) Reactions of the halogens with cold NaOH (aq)

All the halogens react with cold aqueous solutions of sodium hydroxide. As iodine is not very soluble in water, it is reacted with iodide to set up this equilibrium.

$$I_2\,(s) + I^-\,(aq) \rightleftharpoons I_3^-\,(aq)$$

Solutions of sodium hydroxide are considered to be 'cold' when their temperature is held at or below 15°C. Chlorine, bromine and iodine react with sodium hydroxide in a reaction called a disproportionation (special redox reaction). This is a reaction in which the halogen is simultaneously reduced and oxidised. The reactions of the halogens with cold NaOH (aq) are shown. The trend is for the reactivity to decrease as the group is descended.

$$2\,F_2\,(g) + 2\,NaOH\,(aq) \rightarrow 2\,NaF\,(aq) + F_2O\,(g) + H_2O\,(l)$$

$$Cl_2\,(g) + 2\,NaOH\,(aq) \rightarrow NaCl\,(aq) + NaOCl\,(aq) + H_2O\,(l)$$

$$Br_2\,(aq) + 2\,NaOH\,(aq) \rightarrow NaBr\,(aq) + NaOBr\,(aq) + H_2O\,(l)$$

$$I_2\,(aq) + 2\,NaOH\,(aq) \rightleftharpoons NaI\,(aq) + NaOI\,(aq) + H_2O\,(l)$$

The reaction between fluorine and sodium hydroxide gives sodium fluoride, water and difluorine monoxide (F_2O) also known as oxygen difluoride. This gas reacts very slowly with water to form hydrofluoric acid.

$$F_2O\,(g) + H_2O\,(l) \rightarrow 2HF\,(aq) + O_2\,(g)$$

Chlorine and sodium hydroxide are both produced in the chlor-alkali industry from the electrolysis of solutions of brine. The reaction between chlorine and sodium hydroxide is commercially important and is used to make bleach for domestic use. The products are sodium chloride, water and sodium chlorate(I) (NaOCl), which is also known as sodium hypochlorite. Bleach works because the sodium chlorate(I) decomposes to give sodium chloride and oxygen atoms (radicals).

$$NaOCl \rightarrow NaCl + O$$

It is the oxygen atoms which disrupt the cell membranes of bacteria, making it an effective bactericide.

Bromine and iodine both react with cold sodium hydroxide to give sodium halide, sodium halate(V) and water as the products. The only difference is that iodine reacts reversibly with chlorine. In both reactions, one of the initial products is sodium bromate(I) (or sodium iodate(I)). These are unstable and decompose at room temperature to give the corresponding sodium halate(V).

$$3\ NaOI \rightarrow NaIO_3 + 2\ NaI$$

Colour changes can be observed in the reactions between sodium hydroxide and bromine and also sodium hydroxide and iodine. Practically, this involves adding a few drops of NaOH (1.0 mol dm^{-3}) to a few cm^3 of Br$_2$ (aq) or I$_2$ (aq).

Questions 9.13

1. Chlorine reacts with sodium hydroxide to give different products at different temperatures. Assign oxidation states to the chlorine containing products in both equations 1.1 and 1.2.

   cold $2\ NaOH + Cl_2 \rightarrow NaCl + NaOCl + H_2O$ (1.1)

   hot $6\ NaOH + 3\ Cl_2 \rightarrow 5\ NaCl + NaClO_3 + 3\ H_2O$ (1.2)

2. Why can the reaction between chlorine and water be classified as a disproportionation reaction?

   $Cl_2 + H_2O \rightarrow HOCl + HCl$

3. What type of reaction is this: $3\ NaOI \rightarrow NaIO_3 + 2\ NaI$?

4. Which option shows an ion in which chlorine could not undergo disproportionation?

   A ClO$^-$

   B ClO$_3^-$

   C Cl$^-$

   D Cl$_2$O

5. The chlorate(I) ion is a strong oxidising agent in acidic solution. Write balanced formula equations for the reaction between acidified chlorate(I) and:

   a. iodide b. iron(II)

6. Suggest, with a reason, why it is dangerous to add acid to bleach which has been made using the reaction between sodium hydroxide and chlorine.

A2.2 (o) Fluorine: anomalous reactivity & high oxidation state fluorides

Fluorine is the most reactive of the non-metals. Fluorine reacts readily with all metals, even gold and platinum, which are considered particularly unreactive metals. Fluorine has anomalous reactivity compared with the other halogens (X = halogen) and will react explosively with hydrogen at −252°C.

$$H_2\ (g) + X_2\ (g) \rightarrow 2\ HX\ (g)$$

Halogen	Reaction with hydrogen
Fluorine	Explosive under all conditions
Chlorine	Slow in the dark, explodes in direct sunlight
Bromine	Needs heat (300°C) and catalyst (Pt)
Iodine	Reacts slowly and partially (reversibly) needs heat (300°C) and catalyst (Pt)

Fluorine's highly exothermic reactions are a result of its low enthalpy of atomisation (A1.3a) which, in turn, is a result of the lone-pair repulsion (A2.2j).

$\Delta H^{\ominus}_{atom}$ (kJ mol^{-1})	F	Cl	Br	I
½ X$_2$ (g,l,s) → X (g)	79	122	112	107

Fluorine's highly exothermic reactions are also a result of the strong bonds that it forms with other elements. The effect that differences in atomisation enthalpy and bond enthalpy have on enthalpies of formation can be seen using the enthalpy cycle.

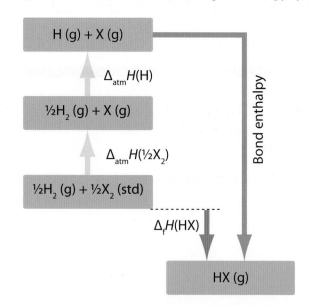

Fluorine is a very powerful oxidising element with a standard electrode potential (B1.4l) of +2.87 V. Fluorine oxidises all non-metals except helium, nitrogen, neon and argon. Fluorine oxidises water to oxygen (A2.2i) and is itself reduced to hydrogen fluoride rather than dissolving in water, like all the other halogens.

$$2 \text{ F}_2 \text{ (g)} + 2 \text{ H}_2\text{O (l)} \rightarrow 4 \text{ HF (aq)} + \text{O}_2 \text{ (g)}$$

As fluorine is such a powerful oxidising agent, it tends to oxidise elements to their highest possible oxidation states, e.g. PF_5, SF_6, UF_6, IF_7 and XeF_6. This ability is partly favoured by its low F-F bond dissociation enthalpy (A2.2j) and partly because fluorine forms strong bonds with other elements. Fluorine's small size leads to strong bonds and also allows many fluorine atoms to fit around a central atom.

Sulfur hexafluoride (SF_6) is a gas that finds use as an electrical insulator. When counting the twelve valence electrons around sulfur, it is clear that the 'octet rule' has been broken. The octet rule informs us that atoms react and they tend to attain an outer shell containing eight electrons. As sulfur is Period 3, it has a Principal Quantum Number of 3 and so sulfur atoms can have up to eighteen electrons in their outer shells by using the 3d sub-shell.

Uranium hexafluoride (UF_6) is a white crystalline solid at room temperature and has proved to be an important molecule as it has enabled nuclear scientists to separate the isotopes uranium-235 and uranium-238. UF_6 sublimes at 56.5°C and separation of $^{235}UF_6$ and $^{238}UF_6$ is achieved by diffusion of the vapour through porous membranes. The lighter $^{235}UF_6$ molecules diffuse slightly faster than the $^{238}UF_6$ molecules.

Questions 9.14

1. Why can fluorine help elements to achieve their highest oxidation states, e.g. XeF_6, SF_6 and UF_6?

2. Which halogen cannot be obtained by chemical oxidation of its halide ion? How might this halogen be obtained?

10

Group 14

from non-metals to metals

Contents

Group 14 contains some very familiar elements, starting with carbon at the top, through, silicon, germanium, tin to the last member lead. The chemistry of the group varies enormously and there are no clear patterns such as those found with the non-metallic halogens (Group 17). The group starts with a non-metal (carbon), then there are two metalloids (silicon and germanium) either side of the zigzag, followed by two metals (tin and lead) which have been known since ancient times. Other metalloids are identified in A2.1a.

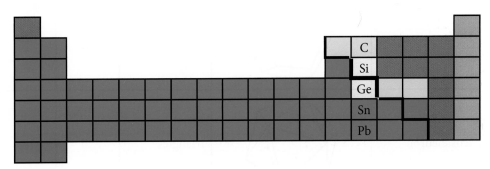

Group 14 does not have a name precisely because it is the most diverse Group of the Periodic Table with a wide range of properties in the elements and their compounds. Each element of Group 14 has important uses which reflects its structure. The importance of dimensional shapes was realised in ancient Greece by the great philosophers Plato and Archimedes who considered how two dimensional shapes, *e.g.* triangles and squares, could be made into three dimensional shapes, *e.g.* cubes and tetrahedra. The first Nobel prize winner in chemistry, Jacobus van't Hoff (1901), also realised the importance of shape in chemicals. He came up with the idea of carbon being tetrahedral. Van't Hoff's contributions were mostly theoretical but he had the foresight to make models out of wood to illustrate his ideas. Today we take for granted these ideas and have models made out of plastic and animations of crystal structures on websites (http://www-teach. ch.cam.ac.uk/links/3Dindex.html).

Students of mathematics will have probably met **Euler's Law**.

This is a formula ($F + C - E = 2$) for 3D shapes (polyhedra) formed by putting together polygonal faces, where F = number of faces, C = number of corners and E = number of edges. The cube has six identical faces and is known as a platonic solid. There are only five platonic solids.

The Platonic solids:

Platonic solid		Shapes	Faces	Corners	Edges	F + C − E = 2
Tetrahedron	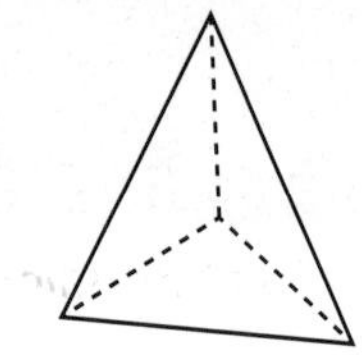	triangles	4	4	6	4 + 4 − 6 = 2
Cube	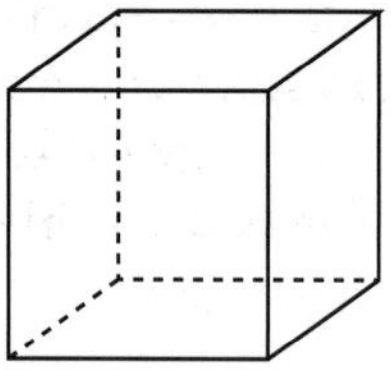	squares	6	8	12	6 + 8 − 12 = 2
Octahedron	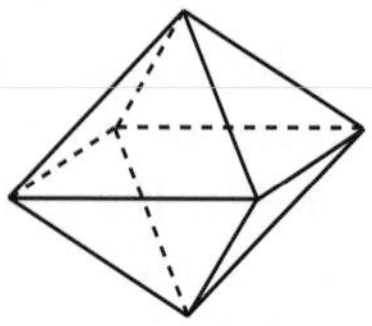	triangles	8	6	12	8 + 6 − 12 = 2
Dodecahedron	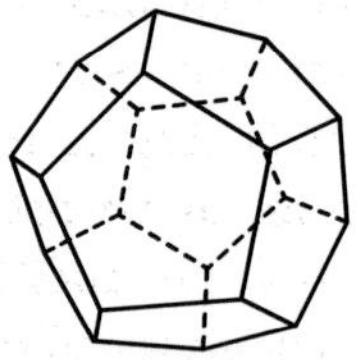	pentagons	12	20	30	12 + 20 − 30 = 2
Icosahedron	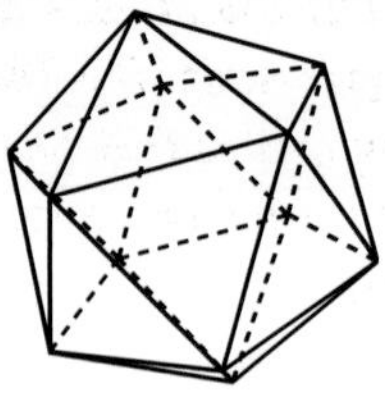	triangles	20	12	30	20 + 12 − 30 = 2

B2.3 (a) Allotropes of carbon

Like oxygen (A2.2e), carbon also exists in different forms called **allotropes**. The most abundant allotrope of carbon is graphite. Another allotrope of carbon which is less common is diamond. Since 1988 chemists around the world have been able to synthesize another allotrope of carbon called **buckminsterfullerene**, also called **buckyball** (C_{60}). The structures of the three allotropes of carbon are quite different. The differences in bonding in the carbon allotropes affect their structures and consequently their physical properties.

The picture opposite is of C_{540}.

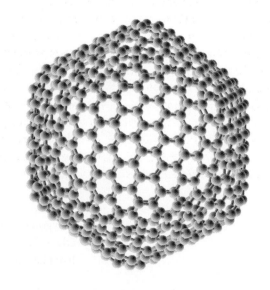

Graphite

Graphite has a honeycomb structure composed of hexagonal layers of carbon atoms where each carbon atom is bonded to three other carbon atoms. The sheets of adjacent hexagonal layers are held together by weak van der Waals forces (A1.2j). The name graphite comes from the Greek *graphein* meaning 'to write'.

Graphite (mineral)

Graphite is a more thermodynamically stable allotrope than diamond at low pressures and this is because graphite has the lower Gibbs free energy (B1.4f). The different densities of graphite and diamond are hinted at in their different entropy values; graphite ($S = 5.7$ J K^{-1} mol^{-1}) and diamond ($S = 2.4$ J K^{-1} mol^{-1}).

Bee honeycomb made of wax

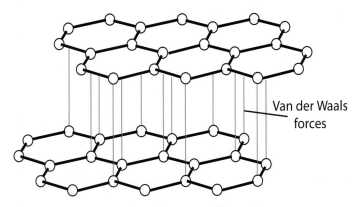

Graphite (hexagonal layers)

Within the layers, the carbon-carbon bond lengths are all identical (0.142 nm) and are found to be shorter than a normal carbon-carbon bond length (0.154 nm). Only three of the four valence electrons of carbon are tied up in single covalent bonds. This means that there is one delocalised electron for each carbon atom. These 'free' electrons allow graphite to conduct electricity through the layers, hence its use in electrodes. Since the layers of graphite can slide over each other when a force is applied, graphite has found use as a writing material in pencils and as a lubricant. Each carbon in graphite has trigonal planar symmetry with each layer stacked upon other layers with an interlayer distance of 0.335 nm. The mineral graphite is a shiny dark grey solid that feels greasy when touched.

Diamond

The name diamond comes from the Latin *adamans* meaning 'very hard substance'. Diamond is a colourless crystal which sparkles in light. The main sources of diamonds are South Africa, Congo, Namibia, Angola, Brazil, Australia and Siberia. Diamond is the hardest known natural substance with a value of 10 on the Moh scale. In addition to its use in jewellery, diamond is used to cut glass and rocks. Rocks can be cut and drilled through with diamond studded saws or drills with diamond tips. In her song *The Fear*, Lily Allen reminds us not only of the high price that people pay for diamonds but also the price that people pay mining for them, often in very difficult conditions.

Diamond is composed of tetrahedral carbon atoms where each carbon atom is bonded to four other carbon atoms. The structure of diamond is similar to that found in ice (A1.2k). A diamond is a single giant molecule made almost entirely of carbon atoms. Within the layers, the carbon-carbon bond lengths are all identical (0.155 nm) and very close to the average found for other carbon-carbon bonds (0.154 nm).

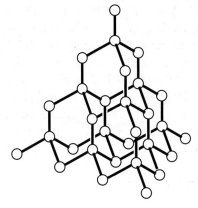

Diamond (tetrahedral carbons)

189

Diamond has a more compact structure than graphite hence it has a greater density. Diamond is relatively unreactive because of its stable structure. It might be surprising to learn that, since diamond is a form of carbon, it will burn in air (600-800°C) to form carbon dioxide. This was an expensive but important experiment first performed by the English chemist Smithson Tennant, who also discovered osmium and iridium.

Industrial diamonds can be made by applying heat and pressure to graphite. Paul May (Bristol University) makes thin films of diamond by another method called chemical vapour deposition (CVD). This involves passing hydrocarbons such as methane (CH_4) and ethyne (C_2H_2) mixed in hydrogen over a metal filament at 2000°C in a vacuum chamber. The high temperatures cause the hydrocarbon molecules to break apart, freeing the carbon which then deposits onto a nearby surface as a layer of diamond. Each diamond is a single crystal with a giant lattice composed of only carbon atoms. A question commonly asked by students is what happens at the surface of a diamond? At the surface of a diamond there is a layer of hydrogen atoms which bond to the lattice *via* C-H bonds. Chemists have even managed to replace all the surface hydrogen atoms with fluorine atoms.

Buckminsterfullerene

Buckminsterfullerene (C_{60}) is a spheroidal molecule which has sixty carbon atoms where each carbon atom is bonded to three other carbon atoms. The result is a football-like structure with twelve pentagons and twenty hexagons. In a soccer ball, the pentagons are coloured black and the stitching represents the single covalent bonds found in buckminsterfullerene.

Soccer ball

The molecule buckminsterfullerene is named after the architect R. Buckminster Fuller who constructed geodesic domes. His buildings enclose the greatest possible volume using hexagons and pentagons with less construction materials than alternative building structures. Buckminsterfullerene is moderately soluble in benzene, toluene and carbon tetrachloride. Dilute solutions are purple and this colour is due to $\pi-\pi^*$ electronic transitions (A1.2b). The sigma bonds of buckminsterfullerene are more stressed than those found in graphite and, consequently, it is a less stable allotrope than graphite. When buckminsterfullerene is heated to above 1500°C in the absence of air, it converts exothermically into graphite.

$$C_{60} \rightarrow C_{graphite} \quad \Delta_r H = -38.0 \text{ kJ mol}^{-1}$$

This allotropic interconversion is essentially opposite to the preparation of buckminsterfullerene by the vaporisation of graphite on an electric arc for which Harold Kroto, Richard Smalley and Robert Curl were awarded the Nobel prize in chemistry in 1996.

To encourage three dimensional thinking why not make a net of buckminsterfullerene and then build a paper model. The whole process is made easier if a regulation football (soccer) is available. Commercial model kits (Buckybox®) are being sold by Dynamic Enterprises Ltd. The net for making this model can be found on this book's website.

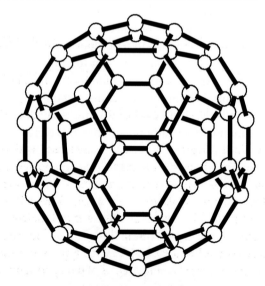

Buckminsterfullerene (C_{60})

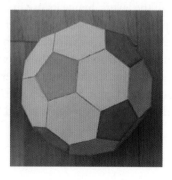

Paper model of C_{60}

The allotropes of carbon have different physical properties, *e.g.* density, because of the differences in their structures. The allotropes of carbon also have very different electrical conductivities (B2.3b). Graphite is the only non-metal which is an electrical conductor because of its delocalised electrons.

	Graphite	Diamond	Buckminster-fullerene
Density / g cm^{-3}	2.26	3.51	1.72
Melting point / °C	3800	3820	> 360
Electrical conductivity S m^{-1}	7×10^4	1×10^{-11}	1.7×10^{-6}

Diamond has the highest thermal conductivity of any known natural substance and it is five times higher than that of copper. This is the reason why diamonds feel cold to the touch.

Other fullerenes

Since the discovery of buckminsterfullerene (C_{60}) other all carbon molecules have been isolated. These compounds belong to a class of molecules called fullerenes and these are all closed hollow cages with even numbers of carbon atoms. At the start of 2009 Aldrich, a chemical supplier, was selling 25 mg of C_{60} for £55.50 and 10 mg of C_{70} for £38.80 in addition to C_{76}, C_{78} & C_{84}.

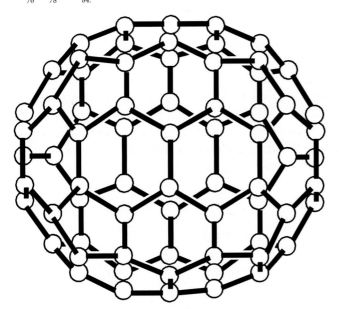

Rugby ball shaped C_{70}

In order to form hollow cages, these all carbon molecules (fullerenes) must have twelve pentagons. Like other platonic shapes which are regular polyhedra (like cubes and octahedrons), the fullerenes also fit Euler's Law (F+C–E=2) which relates the number of faces (F), corners (C) and edges (E).

Fullerene	C_{60}	C_{70}
Pentagons	12	12
Hexagons	20	25
Faces	32	37
Corners	60	70
Edges	90	105
F + C – E = 2	32 + 60 – 90 = 2	37 + 70 –105 = 2

Questions 10.1

1. What are the different forms of the element carbon?

2. Which option shows the allotrope of carbon with the greatest thermal conductivity?

    A   soot

    B   buckminsterfullerene

    C   diamond

    D   graphite

B2.3 (b) Transition from non-metal to metalloid to metal

The metallic character of the elements increases as Group 14 is descended. Carbon is a non-metal, silicon and germanium are metalloids and tin and lead are metals. Metalloids have properties of both metals and non-metals. Silicon is a shiny silver solid that looks very much like a metal. Silicon is not cold to touch as it is a poor thermal conductor and feels quite light because of its low density, which is a typical non-metallic property. The electrical conductivities of pure germanium and pure silicon are poor at room temperature.

To make the metalloid elements (Si and Ge) better at conducting electricity, traces of Group 3 elements (Ga or In) or Group 5 elements (As or Sb) are added. In electronic devices where these elements are added as controlled impurities it is known as **doping**. The result is either (n-type) semi-conductors with an excess of electrons in the lattice when Group 5 elements are added, or (p-type) semiconductors with a deficiency of electrons in the lattice when Group 3 elements are added.

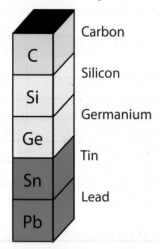

Transition from non-metal (C) to metalloids (Si, Ge) and metals (Sn, Pb)

As Group 14 is descended, the bonds between atoms become weaker with increasing atomic radius (A1.1i) which results in an increasing delocalisation of outer shell electrons. With increasing delocalisation of electrons there is an increase in electrical conductivity. As the conductivity of the elements increases, their metallic character increases. The exception to this increasing conductivity down Group 14 is graphite (B2.3a). The structure of carbon's allotropes has been outlined earlier (B2.3a). Silicon and germanium have diamond-like covalent macromolecular structures and tin and lead have cubic close packed (B2.5a) metallic structures (A1.0h).

Element	m.p. / °C	Density / g cm^{-3}	Electrical conductivity (Qualitative)	Electrical conductivity (Quantitative) 10^6/ Ω cm^{-1}
carbon (graphite)	3652	2.25	fair	700
carbon (diamond)	>3550	3.51	nil	10^{-13}
silicon	1410	2.33	semi-conductor	2.52×10^{-12}
germanium	937	5.35	semi-conductor	1.45×10^{-8}
tin (white)	232	7.28	good	0.0917
lead	328	11.34	good	0.0481

Tin and lead are often described as being weakly metallic in terms of their relative electrical conductivities. Copper has an approximately seven times higher electrical conductivity than tin and a twelve times a higher electrical conductivity than lead. With tin and lead, orbitals overlap and metallic lattices are formed. White tin (refined metallic tin) and lead are normal metallic conductors of electricity. There is a clear trend from the typical non-metallic lack of electrical conductivity of carbon (diamond) to the typically metallic behaviour of white tin and lead.

The transition from non-metal to metal in Group 14 can also be seen in the products formed when these elements react with nitric acid. Carbon, silicon and germanium do not react with dilute nitric acid. Tin and lead are above hydrogen in the reactivity series so will react with dilute nitric acid to form tin(II) nitrate and lead(II) nitrate. Carbon, silicon and germanium react with concentrated nitric acid to form hydrated dioxides.

Questions 10.2

1. Which option shows Group 14 elements used in the electronics industry as semi-conductors?

   A   germanium and silicon

   B   silicon and tin

   C   graphite and silicon

   D   germanium and tin

2. Which option shows a property that does not increase on descending Group 14?

   A   electrical conductivity

   B   melting point

   C   density

   D   metallic character

3. Which option shows the number of Group 14 elements with giant molecular structures?

A   4

B   2

C   3

D   1

B2.3 (c) Lead chemistry (mainly +2 oxidation state)

Lead is a soft metal that has been used in pipes since Roman times and is found at the bottom of Group 14. Lead is found in the ore galena (PbS) which is exceptionally heavy for its size because of the density of lead (B2.3b).

Galena: the main ore of lead

Lead does not form allotropes and its high density is partly due to its cubic close packed crystal structure. Lead has found uses in the alloys solder (50% Pb: 50% Sn) and pewter (25% Pb: 75% Sn) and as a shield against X-rays and radioactivity. Lead pipes carrying water supplies should only be used in areas with hard water as the pipes soon get a protective coating of lead(II) carbonate ($PbCO_3$). There is an increasing tendency down Group 14 for a pair of valence electrons ns^2 to be 'inert' and for ionic bonds to be formed by M^{2+}. The chemistry of lead is dominated by the +2 oxidation state. If heated gently in air, lead will get a surface coating of yellow lead(II) oxide.

$$Pb \ (s) + \tfrac{1}{2}O_2 \ (g) \to PbO \ (s)$$

The formation of the preferred +2 oxidation state in PbO is due to the $6s^2$ electrons of lead being rather inert and difficult to remove during chemical reactions.

Commercially, lead is extracted by first crushing galena (PbS) then roasting it in air to make lead(II) oxide.

$$2 \ PbS \ (s) + 3 \ O_2 \ (g) \to 2 \ PbO \ (s) + 2 \ SO_2 \ (g)$$

Finally, the oxide is reduced with coke (carbon).

$$2 \ PbO \ (s) + C \ (s) \to 2 \ Pb \ (s) + CO_2 \ (g)$$

The last reaction can be carried out in a laboratory by mixing lead(II) oxide (litharge) with carbon powder in the hollow of a charcoal block. The mixture is then heated strongly with a Bunsen burner and air is blown into the hollow using a blow pipe. After about ten minutes, silver looking globules of lead become visible in the reaction mixture. The reduction of lead(II) oxide to the metal also takes place with hydrogen or carbon monoxide as the reducing agent.

$$PbO \ (s) + CO \ (g) \to Pb \ (s) + CO_2 \ (g)$$

The stability of the +2 oxidation state in Group 14 compounds increases as you descend the group.

Relative Stability of Group 14 oxidation states			
Name	Symbol	2+	4+
Carbon	C	Low	High
Silicon	Si		
Germanium	Ge		
Tin	Sn		
Lead	Pb	High	Low

One consequence of the preferred oxidation state of lead being lead(II) is that lead(IV) compounds are oxidising agents. Concentrated hydrochloric acid can be oxidised to give chlorine with lead(IV) oxide.

$$PbO_2 \ (s) + 4 \ c.HCl \to Cl_2 \ (g) + PbCl_2 \ (s) + 2 \ H_2O \ (l)$$

Lead does form the +4 oxidation state, but these compounds often decompose to give the more stable +2 oxidation state on heating. Lead(IV) chloride decomposes into lead(II) chloride at room temperature.

$$PbCl_4 \ (s) \to PbCl_2 \ (s) + Cl_2 \ (g)$$

The dark chocolate coloured lead(IV) oxide decomposes into yellow lead(II) oxide at 300°C.

$$2 \ PbO_2 \ (s) \to 2 \ PbO \ (s) + O_2 \ (g)$$

Another lead oxide known trivially as red lead (Pb_3O_4) also decomposes into lead(II) oxide at 470°C. This oxide is a combination of 2 PbO : 1 PbO_2.

$$2\ Pb_3O_4\ (s) \rightarrow 6\ PbO\ (s) + O_2\ (g)$$

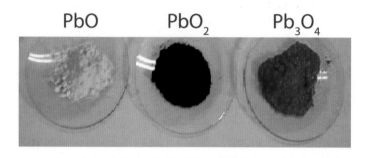

PbO PbO_2 Pb_3O_4

The three oxides of lead

Lead(IV) carbonate and lead(IV) nitrate also decompose on heating to form the more stable +2 oxidation state in the form of yellow lead(II) oxide.

$$PbCO_3\ (s) \rightarrow PbO\ (s) + CO_2\ (g)$$

$$2\ Pb(NO_3)_2\ (s) \rightarrow 2\ PbO\ (s) + 4\ NO_2\ (g) + O_2\ (g)$$

Other lead(IV) compounds react to give more stable lead(II) compounds. Lead(IV) oxide reacts with concentrated hydrochloric acid to make lead(II) chloride, which is difficult to make by reacting the metal directly with hydrochloric acid.

$$PbO_2 + 4\ c.HCl \rightarrow PbCl_2 + Cl_2 + 2\ H_2O$$

Preparation of lead(II) compounds

Quite a few lead(II) compounds are insoluble (B1.5d) and the preparation of lead(II) hydroxide, lead(II) chloride, lead(II) iodide and lead(II) sulfate are characteristic qualitative tests (A4.1a) for Pb^{2+} (aq). Many insoluble lead(II) compounds are white. Others, for example lead(II) iodide, are yellow.

$$Pb^{2+}\ (aq) + 2\ OH^-\ (aq) \rightarrow Pb(OH)_2\ (s)$$

white precipitate which dissolves in excess hydroxide

$$Pb(OH)_2\ (s) + 2\ OH^-\ (aq) \rightarrow PbO_2^{2-}\ (aq) + 2\ H_2O\ (l)$$

$$Pb^{2+}\ (aq) + 2\ Cl^-\ (aq) \rightarrow PbCl_2\ (s)$$

white precipitate with dilute HCl (aq)

$$PbCl_2\ (s) + 2\ Cl^-\ (aq) \rightarrow PbCl_4^{2-}\ (aq)$$

colourless solution with concentrated HCl (aq)

$$Pb^{2+}\ (aq) + 2\ I^-\ (aq) \rightarrow PbI_2\ (s)$$

yellow precipitate

$$Pb^{2+}\ (aq) + SO_4^{2-}\ (aq) \rightarrow PbSO_4\ (s)$$

white precipitate with H_2SO_4 (aq)

A reliable source of aqueous lead(II) ions is lead(II) nitrate which is made by reacting elemental lead with dilute nitric(V) acid (HNO_3) in a typical displacement reaction where hydrogen gas is also evolved. Lead(II) nitrate is also obtained with concentrated nitric acid but with different inorganic products.

$$Pb\ (s) + 2\ HNO_3\ (aq) \rightarrow Pb(NO_3)_2\ (aq) + H_2\ (g)$$

$$Pb\ (s) + 4\ HNO_3\ (aq)$$
$$\rightarrow Pb(NO_3)_2\ (aq) + 2\ NO_2\ (g) + 2\ H_2O\ (l)$$

Testing for Pb^{2+}

Addition of potassium chromate(VI) (K_2CrO_4) or potassium iodide (KI) to an aqueous solution of lead(II) ions (Pb^{2+}) gives bright yellow precipitates of lead(II) chromate ($PbCrO_4$) or lead(II) iodide (PbI_2) respectively.

Stability of Pb^{2+}

For lead, the +2 oxidation state is the most stable. This is in contrast to the rest of the Group 14 elements where the +4 oxidation state is the most stable. In the case of carbon a 2s electron is promoted to the $2p_z$ orbital, allowing for the commonly encountered tetravalency in its compounds. Lead has an atomic number of 82 and, being in Group 14, its valence electrons will be s^2p^2. The shorthand version of its electronic configuration is [Xe] $4f^{14}\ 5d^{10}\ 6s^2\ 6p^2$. It is the $6p^2$ electrons which are most often used in forming ionic bonds, whereas the 'inert pair' $6s^2$ tend not to be used in the formation of ionic bonds. The reason why the s^2 electrons are less likely to be involved in bonding the further down you go in Group 14 is due to the shape of the inner $4f^{14}$ and $5d^{10}$ orbitals. Their shapes mean that they do not completely shield the outer electrons as effectively as s and p orbitals would do in earlier members of Group 14, such as carbon or silicon. The result is that the outer $6s^2$ electrons of lead are pulled more strongly to towards the nucleus and are, consequently, less available for bonding.

At university, this phenomenon is described as the **Lorentz-Fitzgerald relativistic contraction**. X-ray crystallography has shown the electrons to be closer to the nucleus than might have been expected. In the case of lead, the energy released when it forms four covalent bonds or forms a lattice does not compensate for the additional energy needed to promote a 6s electron into an empty p-orbital and change the electron's spin. The difference in stability between the two oxidation states (+4 & +2) of lead is shown by their standard electrode potentials (B1.5l).

Questions 10.3

1. What is the correct oxidation state of the Group 14 element in these compounds?

	CH_4	CCl_4	$SnCl_2$	PbO
A	+4	+4	+2	+2
B	-4	+4	+2	+2
C	-4	-4	+2	+4
D	-4	+4	+4	+2

2. Which of the following statements about Group 14 elements is correct?

   A   They have outer shell arrangements of $ns^2\, np^2$ and zero unpaired electrons.

   B   They have outer shell arrangements of $ns^2\, np^2$ and two unpaired electrons.

   C   They have outer shell arrangements of $ns^2\, np^2$ and one unpaired electron.

   D   They have outer shell arrangements of $ns^2\, np^2$ and four unpaired electrons.

3. Which of the following **increases** as Group 14 is descended?

   A   The stability of the +2 oxidation state.

   B   The first ionisation energy of the elements.

   C   The stability of the hydrides.

   D   The acidity of the dioxide.

4. The first four elements of Group 14 form oxides with an oxidation state of +4 by heating the elements in air. But lead(IV) oxide cannot be prepared by this method. Suggest which lead oxide is prepared by heating lead in air and why the +4 oxidation state oxide is not formed. Give the formulae of the four Group 14 oxides with +4 oxidation states.

5. Red lead is an unusual oxide with the formula Pb_3O_4 which reacts chemically as if it is a mixture of two lead oxides. At temperatures exceeding 470°C it decomposes into lead(II) oxide and oxygen according to the equation;

   $$2\ Pb_3O_4\ (s) \rightarrow 6\ PbO\ (s) + O_2\ (g)$$

   What two oxides of lead might constitute Pb_3O_4 and in what proportions? How would you test for the gas evolved in this reaction?

6. A student was comparing the reactions of lumps of lead with the three commonly met mineral acids. She carefully selected three similar sized pieces of lead and chose to use 10 cm³ of 0.5 mol dm⁻³ of nitric acid, 10 cm³ of 0.25 mol dm⁻³ of sulfuric acid and 10 cm³ of 0.5 mol dm⁻³ of hydrochloric acid.

   Give equations for all three reactions, explain the choice of concentrations and explain which two reactions were much slower than expected.

7. Complete the table to show the colours of these lead(II) salts and solutions.

	Lead salt or solution	Colour
(a)	$PbSO_4$ (s)	
(b)	$PbCl_2$ (s)	
(c)	$PbCrO_4$ (s)	
(d)	PbI_2 (s)	
(e)	PbO_2^{2-} (aq)	
(f)	$PbCl_4^{2-}$ (aq)	
(g)	$Pb(OH)_2$ (s)	

B2.3 (d)
Transition from covalent oxides to ionic oxides

The oxides at the top of Group 14 are essentially covalent. The three oxides of carbon are all covalent molecules, *i.e.* carbon monoxide (CO), carbon dioxide (CO_2) and carbon suboxide (C_3O_2). Carbon monoxide and carbon dioxide are the more familiar oxides of carbon which exist as discrete linear molecules (A1.2g).

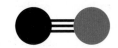

Carbon monoxide

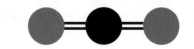

Carbon dioxide

Carbon suboxide

Carbon monoxide has a triple bond in which one of the bonds is a dative covalent bond (A1.2a) with a pair of electrons being donated from the oxygen atom to the carbon atom. Carbon suboxide can be synthesized by warming a dry mixture of phosphorus pentoxide (P_4O_{10}) and propanedioic acid.

Silicon monoxide (SiO) is an amorphous brown solid which is only stable at high temperatures. It has been detected in stellar objects (stars) using spectroscopy (A4.3c). It has recently found use as a coating material with films of silicon monoxide being deposited on aluminium surface mirrors, lenses and gratings to protect against corrosion and wear. The surface of the silicon monoxide will oxidise in air to give a protective silicon(IV) oxide layer. At temperatures between 400-800°C silicon monoxide has been found to **disproportionate** (A2.2n).

$$2 \text{ SiO (s)} \rightarrow \text{SiO}_2 \text{ (s)} + \text{Si (s)}$$

The important oxide of silicon is silicon(IV) oxide (SiO_2), also called silica. Known as sand or quartz, it is the most abundant mineral in the earth's crust. Flint is a particularly hard form of the mineral quartz which is used as a building material, *e.g.* Chernocke House in Winchester.

Chernocke House (Winchester College)

Silicon dioxide (SiO_2) has a giant covalent macromolecular structure which is diamond-like. Each silicon atom is surrounded tetrahedrally by four oxygen atoms joined *via* single covalent bonds (Si-O). Silicon dioxide as quartz has a high melting point of 1610°C which reflects the large number of strong covalent bonds within its structure.

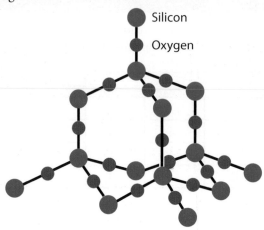

Silicon(IV) oxide (diamond-like structure)

Despite the similarity in their formulae, SiO_2 forms quite a different structure to CO_2. Silicon only forms single covalent compounds as it cannot form stable π-bonds. The Si-O bond is stronger than the C-O bond despite being longer and the C=O bond releases a lot of energy when formed (A1.0i).

	Si-O	C-O	C=O
Bond length / nm	0.161	0.143	0.116
Bond strength / kJ mol^{-1}	466	358	805

Germanium forms two oxides; germanium(II) oxide GeO, which sublimes at 710°C, and the more stable germanium(IV) oxide (GeO_2) which melts at 1115°C. Both oxides of germanium are ionic solids. Germanium(II) oxide is unstable in the presence of oxygen so has to be stored under an inert atmosphere.

Tin forms two oxides; the relatively rare dark green solid tin(II) oxide (SnO), which decomposes at 1080°C, and the white tin(IV) oxide (SnO_2) which melts at 1633°C. Tin(II) oxide can be prepared by thermal decomposition (A2.2a) of tin(II) hydroxide or tin(II) nitrate.

$$\text{Sn(OH)}_2 \text{ (s)} \rightarrow \text{SnO (s)} + \text{H}_2\text{O (g)}$$

Tin(IV) oxide occurs naturally as the ore cassiterite. Some of the earliest tin mines were in Cornwall (UK). When the ore was partially exhausted, the mines closed and many miners emigrated to countries where their expertise was highly valued. There are Cornish communities in many mining areas around the World including Canada, Australia and Mexico. In the early part of the twenty-first century the price of tin rose sufficiently to make commercial tin mining viable again in Cornwall (Kernow). Legend says that the Cornish flag, which is a white cross on a black background, reflects the shape formed by the smelting of tin in St Piran's hearth stone.

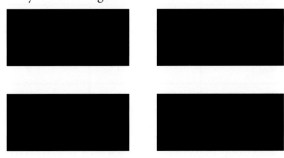

Cornish Flag

At the bottom of Group 14, the oxides are largely ionic. Lead(II) oxide (PbO) forms a layer lattice and has a melting point of 886°C. In fact, bonding is ionic in lead(II) compounds. Lead(IV) oxide (PbO_2) is also a solid which decomposes at 290°C. The electronegativity of lead is not certain because it forms no stable covalent compounds. The electronegativity difference between Pb and O is 1.6. This means that its bonding should be borderline ionic/covalent and the increasing covalency in lead(IV) compounds is indicated by their lower melting points in comparison with the lead(II) analogues.

Pb_3O_4 also has a layered structure with layers of PbO_2 sandwiched between layers of PbO. Red lead can be thought of as dilead(II) lead(IV) oxide $(Pb^{2+})_2(PbO_4^{4-})$ and behaves as $PbO_2.2PbO$.

In conclusion, the ability to form stable dioxides decreases as Group 14 is descended. The ability to form stable monoxides increases as Group 14 is descended.

Questions 10.4

1. Which option is an incorrect description of the structure for a Group 14 oxide?

    A CO_2 is a simple triatomic molecule with a linear structure.

    B SiO_2 is a giant macromolecule with a diamond like structure.

    C   CO is a simple diatomic molecule with a linear structure.

    D SiO_2 is a giant macromolecule with a graphite like structure.

2. Explain why there may be some ionic character in the covalent silicon(IV) oxide.

3. When germanium(II) oxide is heated, it disproportionates to form germanium(IV) oxide and germanium. Write a balanced formula equation for this reaction and describe what is happening.

4. Write a balanced formula equation for tin(II) oxide being oxidised into tin(IV) oxide on standing in air. Why does this reaction happen?

5. Which option shows the preferred oxidation state of tin and lead?

    A   Sn(II) & Pb(II)

    B   Sn(IV) & Pb(IV)

    C   Sn(IV) & Pb(II)

    D   Sn(II) & Pb(IV)

B2.3 (e) Bonding in divalent and tetravalent oxides

Valency is a measure of the number of chemical bonds formed by a given element. The majority of Group 14 oxides are divalent (two bonds) or tetravalent (four bonds). The divalent Group 14 oxides are monoxides with the Group 14 element in the +2 oxidation state, *e.g.* silicon(II) oxide, germanium(II) oxide, tin(II) oxide, and lead(II) oxide. Carbon monoxide is not an example of a divalent oxide because there is a triple bond between the carbon and the oxygen in this diatomic oxide

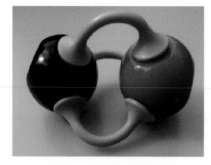

Model of carbon monoxide (C≡O)

The tetravalent Group 14 oxides are dioxides with the Group 14 element in the +4 oxidation state, *e.g.* carbon dioxide, germanium(IV) oxide, tin(IV) oxide, and lead(IV) oxide. Carbon and lead both have additional tetravalent oxides in the form of carbon suboxide (C_3O_2) and the mixed oxide, red lead (Pb_3O_4).

	CO_2	C_3O_2
SiO	SiO_2	
GeO	GeO_2	
SnO	SnO_2	
PbO	PbO_2	Pb_3O_4

Group 14 divalent and tetravalent oxides

Van Arkel triangles (A2.1d) are plots that can be made for binary compounds such as the Group 14 oxides with average E_{neg} (*x*-axis) *versus* ΔE_{neg} (*y*-axis). For each Group 14 element, the position for their divalent and tetravalent oxides in the Van Arkel Triangle will be identical (A2.1d). Using the electronegativity values (A1.2i) for oxygen and the Group 14 elements, the coordinates are tabulated.

Group 14 oxides	Average E_{neg}	ΔE_{neg}
CO, CO_2, C_3O_2	3.00	1.0
SiO_2	2.65	1.7
GeO, GeO_2	2.65	1.7
SnO, SnO_2	2.65	1.7
PbO, PbO_2, Pb_3O_4	2.70	1.6

When the Group 14 oxides are plotted on a Van Arkel triangle, there are only three points for the five elements because silicon, germanium and tin have identical electronegativity values. The oxides of carbon are covalent as seen by their position on the Van Arkel triangle. Carbon dioxide and carbon suboxide do have dipoles but with dipole moments (A1.2i) that cancel as they are acting in opposite directions. The covalent nature of the bonding in the oxides of carbon is indicated on the Van Arkel triangle because of the large E_{neg} values but similar E_{neg} values for oxygen and carbon.

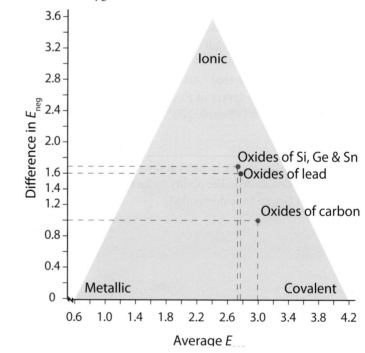

Van Arkel triangle for the Group 14 oxides

The bonding in the Group 14 tetravalent oxides (MO_2) is predicted to be intermediate between ionic and covalent, from their plots in the Van Arkel triangle. In fact the bonding in the

Group 14 tetravalent oxides is found to be mostly covalent. One explanation that can be used to explain why tetravalent oxides are covalent is that a large amount of energy is required to remove four electrons (A1.1i) from any Group 14 element. Using PbO_2 as an example, the covalent bonding can also be explained in terms of the increased charge density on the Pb^{4+} cation compared to the Pb^{2+} cation. This leads to increased polarisation of the oxide O^{2-} anion (A2.2a) by Pb^{4+}. This increased polarisation by M^{4+} (Group 14 ions) leads to greater sharing of electron density between the Group 14 element and oxygen in their tetravalent oxides.

The bonding in the divalent oxides of tin (SnO) and lead (PbO) is found to be predominantly ionic. This can be explained in terms of the reduced polarising power of M^{2+} compared with M^{4+}, so there is less sharing of electrons and ionic bonding predominates in these divalent oxides.

Questions 10.5

1. Which option is not a covalent Group 14 oxide?

   A   lead(IV) oxide

   B   tin(II) oxide

   C   carbon monoxide

   D   silicon(IV) oxide

2. What information is given by the following standard electrode potentials?

   Sn^{4+}/Sn^{2+} (+0.15 V) and Pb^{4+}/Pb^{2+} (+1.5 V)

3. When germanium, tin, and lead form divalent compounds, which electrons are said to be an inert pair?

11 Transition Elements

Contents

The transition elements are the elements of Group 3 to Group 12. This region of the periodic table is known as the d block (A1.1d). The first row transition elements are found in Period 4, the second row of transition elements are in Period 5, and the third row of transition elements are in Period 6.

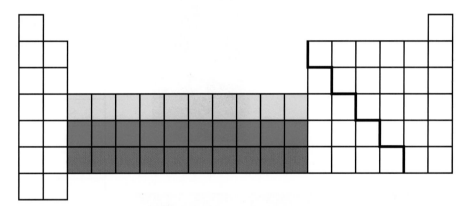

	1st row
	2nd row
	3rd row

Transition elements have four characteristic properties:

- they form complexes

- they form coloured compounds

- they have more than one oxidation state and

- they act as catalysts.

To be a transition element, there must be at least one ion which has an incomplete set of 3d electrons. Transition elements form ions by losing their 4s electrons first. Copper is [Ar] $4s^1$ $3d^{10}$ and Cu^{2+} is [Ar] $3d^9$. A transition element is a d-block element that forms at least one or more stable ion with partially filled d subshell. Scandium and zinc are not 'technically' transition elements since they only form one ion each; Sc^{3+} [Ar] $4s^0$ and Zn^{2+} [Ar] $3d^{10}4s^0$.

Different coloured solutions of transition metal compounds

A number of transition elements have been known since Ancient times. The magnificent statue of King Alfred (871-899), the first King to unite England, is located in Winchester, the ancient capital. The statue (pictured) is made of bronze, which is an alloy of copper and tin.

Questions 11.1

1. Why is vanadium placed in the d block in the Periodic Table?

2. Give the electronic configurations for the following transition elements / ions.

   a.   Zn   b. Zn^{2+}

   c.   Fe   d. Fe^{3+}

   e.   Cu   f. Cu^{1+}

   g. Cu^{2+} h. Mn^{2+}

   i.   Cr   j. Cr^{3+}

B2.4 (a)
Comparing properties of transition elements and the s-block

The transition elements have very similar properties to one another and these typical metals are hard, dense, good conductors of heat and good conductors of electricity. Their properties contrast sharply with the soft, low density s-block alkali metals (Group 1). In the table below, the characteristic properties of the transition elements are compared with s-block elements in the same period in terms of their atomic radii, melting and boiling points and first ionisation energies (A1.1i). Scandium and zinc are included in the table of properties to complete the picture.

Period 4 elements	Block	Atomic radius / nm	m.p. / K	b.p. / K	ΔH_{i1} / kJ mol^{-1}
K	s	0.235	336	1033	419
Ca	s	0.197	1112	1757	590
Sc	d	0.164	1814	3104	631
Ti	d	0.147	1933	3560	658
V	d	0.135	2163	3653	650
Cr	d	0.129	2130	2943	653
Mn	d	0.137	1517	2235	717
Fe	d	0.126	1808	3023	759
Co	d	0.125	1768	3143	758
Ni	d	0.125	1728	3003	737
Cu	d	0.128	1356	2840	746
Zn	d	0.137	693	1180	906

Atomic radii

The s block elements, potassium and calcium, have larger atomic radii than the transition elements of Period 4. The atomic radii of the transition elements would be expected to be smaller than those of s block elements because of the increasing nuclear charge due to increasing numbers of protons in the nucleus. What might be surprising is that there is no clear trend for the atomic radii of the transition elements which have similar sized atomic radii.

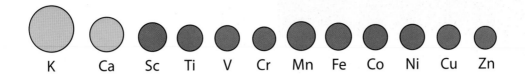

Relative atomic radii for the s block and transition elements of Period 4

In moving across the first series of transition elements, the nuclear charge increases, but additional electrons are being added to the inner 3d sub-shells. These inner 3d electrons effectively shield the outer 4s electrons from the increasing nuclear charge. The consequence of this is that the transition elements have fairly similar atomic radii.

It is interesting to note that manganese has a slightly larger atomic radius than the other transition elements in Period 4. This might be explained by considering the electron arrangement of manganese with its five 3d electrons with parallel spins which result in maximum shielding of the nucleus and an increased atomic radius. This slight increase in the atomic radius of manganese hints at weaker metallic bonding which leads to a lower melting point.

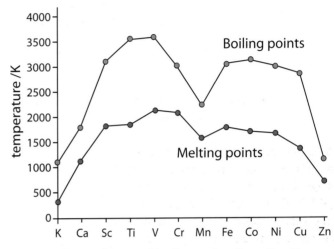

Trend in melting and boiling points from K to Zn

Melting and boiling points

The melting points and boiling points of the first row of d-block metals are much higher than the s-block elements, with the notable exception of zinc. The high melting points of the d-block elements suggest that, in addition to the 4s electrons, delocalized 3d electrons are involved in metallic bonding. The higher the melting point, the stronger the metallic bonding. When boiling point *versus* atomic number is plotted, the two maxima are for vanadium and cobalt. When melting point is plotted against atomic number, this time the two maxima are for vanadium and iron. There is a noticeable minimum for manganese for both the melting and boiling point plots. Manganese has a half-filled subshell ($3d^5$) and its lower melting point suggests that its electrons are not as available for metallic bonding. Hence the lower melting point compared with the adjacent elements (chromium and iron). Chromium also has a $3d^5$ configuration as one of its 4s electrons is promoted to the 3d subshell (A1.1g). It is thought that the effect on melting point is lessened by its lower effective nuclear charge compared with manganese. Zinc has a full 3d subshell ($3d^{10}$) and this electron arrangement results in its valence electrons being held more tightly by the nucleus and, as a consequence, being less available for metallic bonding. This is reflected in its much lower melting point and boiling point compared with the other first row transition elements.

Ionisation energies

The first ionisation energies of the transition elements are larger than those found for s-block elements in the same period. The graph shows how the size of the first ionisation energies of the transition elements is similar. This is because the addition of electrons into the 3d sub-shell shields the 4s electron(s) from the increasing nuclear charge so their first ionisation energies remain similar. It is an electron from the 4s orbital that is removed from transition elements when one electron is removed. The overall trend is for a small increase in first ionisation energies across the period. This increase in ΔH_{i1} across the first row of transition elements is small compared with that observed for Period 3 (A1.1i).

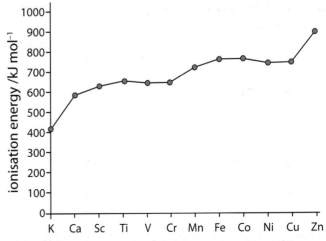

Graph of first ionisation energy *vs.* proton number

203

Questions 11.2

1. The graph shows the first ionisation energies *versus* atomic number for successive Period 4 elements. Identify the transition elements labelled, **A**, **B**, **C** and **D**.

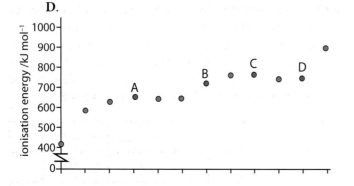

2. Which options about the first row transition elements (Sc to Zn) are true? Explain your answers.

   a. Their ions have partially filled d sub-shells.

   b. They all have high densities and boiling points.

   c. They have decreasing first ionisation energies as proton numbers increase.

   d. They form coloured metal ions in aqueous solutions.

3. Explain why transition elements in the same period have atoms of similar size.

4. Which option gives properties which are similar for transition elements in Period 4?

   A atomic radii and melting point

   B melting point and boiling point

   C first ionisation energy and boiling point

   D first ionisation energy and atomic radii

5. Which option shows the maxima and minima in the plot of melting point *versus* atomic number for the first row transition elements?

	minima	maxima
A	Mn & Zn	V & Cr
B	Mn	V & Cr
C	Mn & Zn	V & Fe
D	Zn	V & Fe

B2.4 (b) Variation of properties across the series

There is little variation in the atomic radii of the p-block elements of Period 4 compared with the d-block elements. The diagram shows how similar the atomic radii are for the d-block and p-block elements. Krypton has the smallest atomic radius of all the Period 4 elements because it has the largest nuclear charge.

Relative atomic radii for the transition elements of Period 4 and the p-block

Gallium has a very low melting point and a sample of it in a glass ampoule will melt in the hand since its melting point is below body temperature. The metalloid germanium (A2.1a) has a high melting and boiling point quite similar to the transition elements. The melting point of grey arsenic is reported as 1090°C at 28 atmospheres of pressure. Its boiling point is lower than the melting point as it sublimes at 886°C at 1 atmosphere of pressure. The non-metallic elements have characteristically low melting and boiling points. Bromine is a volatile liquid at room temperature and krypton is a gas at room temperature.

Period 4 elements	Block	Atomic radius / nm	m.p. / K	b.p. / K	ΔH_{i1} / kJ mol^{-1}
Ga	p	0.120	303	2676	579
Ge	p	0.122	1210	3103	762
As	p	0.122	1090	886	947
Se	p	0.117	490	958	941
Br	p	0.114	266	332	1140
Kr	p	0.110	116	121	1351

For the p-block elements, there is a general increase in their first ionisation energies as the proton number increases. There is a slight decrease in first ionisation energy from As to Se which can be accounted for by the spin-pair effect (A1.1i). Krypton has the highest first ionisation energy for the fourth period. The p-block elements from gallium to selenium have first ionisation energies similar to the d-block elements which reflect the size of their atomic radii. The first ionisation energies of bromine and krypton are larger than the other p-block elements due to their increasing nuclear charges and shielding, but still quite similar to the d-block elements.

B2.4 (c)
Characteristic properties of transition elements

Characteristic properties of transition elements include variable oxidation states, formation of stable complexes and catalysis. They are also dense metals which form coloured compounds (B2.4g).

Variable oxidation states

Most transition elements form several oxidation states (B1.5j) in their compounds. Notable exceptions from the first series are the first member (scandium) and the last member (zinc). The highest oxidation states occur when compounds are formed with the most electronegative non-metals, *e.g.* fluorine (A2.1e), oxygen, and chlorine. The maximum oxidation states from Sc to Mn correspond to the loss of all their 4s and 3d electrons. The variable oxidation states are shown from scandium to zinc with the most common oxidation states highlighted.

Sc	Ti	V	Cr	Mn	Fe	Co	Ni	Cu	Zn
	1+	1+	1+	1+	1+	1+	1+	1+	
	2+	2+	2+	2+	2+	2+	2+	2+	2+
3+	3+	3+	3+	3+	3+	3+	3+	3+	
	4+	4+	4+	4+	4+	4+	4+		
		5+	5+	5+	5+	5+			
			6+	6+	6+				
				7+					

First row transition elements' oxidation states

With the exception of scandium, all first row transition elements have an oxidation state of +2 which usually corresponds to the loss of the 4s^2 electrons. With the exception of zinc, all first row transition elements have an oxidation state of +3. The number of oxidation states increases from titanium to manganese which achieves the highest possible oxidation state of +7 since its electron configuration is [Ar]4s^{2}3d^5. After manganese, each subsequent metal has a smaller maximum oxidation state decreasing by one across the series. This decrease, shown by the elements with more than five 3d electrons, reflects the increase in nuclear charge.

Potassium manganate(VII), known trivially as potassium permanganate, has the formula $KMnO_4$. As potassium is in Group 1, the manganate(VII) ion has the formula MnO_4^-. The oxidation state of manganese is +7 which does not mean that it exists as Mn^{7+}. The removal of seven electrons from manganese would require 38,108 kJ mol^{-1}.

	Sc	Ti	V	Cr	Mn	Fe	Co	Ni	Cu	Zn
1		*a	*b	*c	$Mn(CN)_6^{5-}$	*d	$[Co(NCCH_3)_5]^+$	NiCN	Cu_2O	
+2		$TiCl_2$	VCl_2	$CrCl_2$	MnO	$FeCl_2$	$CoCl_2$	NiO	CuO	ZnS
+3	Sc_2O_3	Ti_2O_3	V_2O_3	Cr_2O_3	Mn_2O_3	Fe_2O_3	CoF_3	Ni_2O_3	CuF_6^{3-}	
+4		TiO_2	VO^{2+}	$CrCl_4$	MnO_2	Sr_2FeO_4	CoO_2	NiO_2		
+5			V_2O_5	CrF_5	MnO_3^-	FeO_4^{3-}	K_3CoO_4			
+6				CrO_3	MnO_4^{2-}	FeO_4^{2-}				
+7					Mn_2O_7					

Examples of variable oxidation states for the 1st row transition elements

*a = $[Ti(NR_2)_2(N_2)]^{2-}$ where R = $SiMe_3$ *b = $[V(bipy)_3]^{1+}$ where bipy = bipyridine, i.e.

*c = $[Cr(CNR)_6]^+$ where R = CH_3, C_2H_5 etc.   *d = $[Fe(NO^+)(H_2O)_5]^{2+}$

The lowest oxidation states are rarer and often difficult to prepare as they are easily oxidised into more stable higher oxidation states. Low oxidation states are stabilized by ligands such as NO^+, CN^- and bipy which accept electrons from the metal (and form π bonds).

Stable complexes

Transition elements form stable complexes in which a central metal ion or metal is surrounded by molecules or anions containing lone pairs called ligands which form dative covalent bonds (A1.2a).

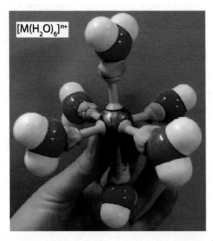

$[M(H_2O)_6]^{n+}$

Molymod of an hexaaqua complex with six water molecules around a metal ion

Ligand comes from the Latin word *ligare* which means to bind. In transition metals these dative covalent bonds

between the ligand and the metal are known as coordinate bonds. In transition metal complexes the lone pairs of electrons are donated from the ligands into vacant orbitals of the transition element.

Ligands are classified by the number of lone pairs that they possess that can form coordinate bonds to the transition metal. Monodentate ligands use one lone pair and bidentate ligands use two lone pairs to coordinate to the transition metal (see below).

Formula	Name of molecule / ion	Name of ligand	Type of ligand
H_2O	water	aqua	neutral
NH_3	ammonia	ammine	neutral
CO	carbon monoxide	carbonyl	neutral
NO	nitrogen monoxide	nitrosyl	neutral
NO_2^-	nitrite ion	nitro	anion
F^-	fluoride ion	fluoro	anion
Cl^-	chloride ion	chloro	anion
Br^-	bromide ion	bromo	anion
I^-	iodide ion	iodo	anion
OH^-	hydroxide ion	hydroxo	anion
CN^-	cyanide ion	cyano	anion
SCN^-	thiocyanate ion	thiocyanato	anion
$S_2O_3^{2-}$	thiosulfate ion	thiosulfato	anion

Bidentate ligands (B2.4f) can form two bonds because they have two lone pairs, *e.g.* 1,2-diaminoethane ($H_2NCH_2CH_2NH_2$) which bonds through the lone pairs on the nitrogen atoms.

The formula of the complex is enclosed inside a square bracket. In the formula for a complex, the central metal ion is written first followed by the ligands. Polyatomic ligands, *e.g.* H_2O are placed inside parentheses (round brackets). The overall charge on the complex is placed as a superscript after the square brackets. There are four rules needed when naming complex ions. Complexes with an overall positive charge, *e.g.* $[Cu(H_2O)_6]^{2+}$ are cationic complex ions. Complexes with an overall negative charge, *e.g.* $[CuCl_4]^{2-}$ are anionic complex ions. It is important to be able to name complex ions from their formulae and also to be able write the formulae of complex ions from their names.

Rules for naming complex ions

Step 1: Identify the number of each type of ligand.

Greek prefixes are used to identify the number of particular types of ligand.

Number	1	2	3	4	5	6
Greek prefix	mono	di	tri	tetra	penta	hexa

Step 2: Name the ligands alphabetically

Neutral ligands are called by their correct names, *e.g.* aqua for water.

Anion ligands end in **o**, *e.g.* F^- = fluor**o** & CN^- = cyan**o**.

Step 3: Name the metal ion

With neutral or positive (cationic) complexes, the English name is used for the metal. With negative (anionic) complexes, the metals end their names with **ate** and some metals take their latin names, *e.g.* ferr**ate** (iron), cupr**ate** (copper), aur**ate** (gold), and argen**ate** (silver).

Step 4: Show the metal's oxidation state in bracketed roman numerals

Number	1	2	3	4	5	6	7
Roman numerals	I	II	III	IV	V	VI	VII

Examples of complex ions include; hexaaquacopper(II) ion $[Cu(H_2O)_6]^{2+}$, hexacyanoferrate(II) ion $[Fe(CN)_6]^{4-}$, hexacarbonylvanadium(0) $[V(CO)_6]^0$, tetracyanonickelate(II) ion $[Ni(CN)_4]^{2-}$ and diaquatetrafluoroferrate(III) ion $[FeF_4(H_2O)_2]^-$.

Example 11.1

Name this metal complex: $[Co(NH_3)_6]^{2+}$

Step 1: six ammonia ligands need the prefix hexa

Step 2: ligand is ammonia whose name is ammine

Step 3: metal is cobalt

Step 4: metal ion is Co^{2+} so it is named cobalt(II)

	step 1	step 2	step 3	step 4
Name	hexa	ammine	cobalt	(II)

Answer: hexaamminecobalt(II) ion.

Example 11.2

Name this metal complex: $[CuCl_4]^{2-}$

Step 1: four chloride ligands need the prefix tetra

Step 2: ligand is chloride whose name is chloro

Step 3: copper metal is named cuprate as it is an anionic complex

Step 4: metal ion is Cu^{2+} so it is named cuprate(II)

	step 1	step 2	step 3	step 4
Name	tetra	chloro	cuprate	(II)

Answer: tetrachloro cuprate(II) ion.

Example 11.3

Name this metal complex: $[Fe(OH)(H_2O)_5]^{2+}$

Step 1: one OH^- ligand and five water ligands prefix penta

Step 2: OH^- ligand is hydroxo and the water ligand is aqua

Step 3: metal is iron as it is a cationic complex

Step 4: metal ion is Fe^{3+} so it is named iron(III)

	step 1	step 2	step 3	step 4
Name	penta	aqua hydroxo	iron	(III)

Answer: pentaaquahydroxo iron(III) ion.

Example 11.4

Name this metal complex: $[PtCl_4]^{2-}$

Step 1: four chloride ligands need the prefix tetra

Step 2: ligand is chloride whose name is chloro

Step 3: metal is platinate as it is an anionic complex

Step 4: metal ion is Pt^{2+} so it is named platinate(II)

	step 1	step 2	step 3	step 4
Name	tetra	chloro	platinate	(II)

Answer: tetrachloroplatinate(II) ion

Coordination number

The coordination number for a metal complex is the total number of dative covalent bonds from the ligand(s) to the transition metal atom/ion. For most complexes the coordination number is four or six. Coordination number is sometimes abbreviated to C.N. not to be confused with the ligand CN^- (cyanide). The diagrams illustrating coordination number are shown in two dimensions (2D) to introduce the concept. When drawing complexes you will need to draw them in three dimensions (3D).

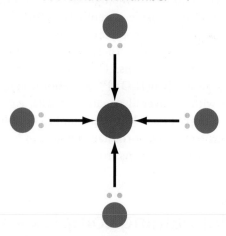

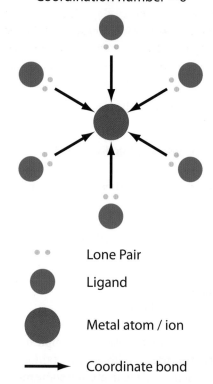

Metal complexes with different coordination numbers

Tollens' reagent (A3.4c), $[Ag(NH_3)_2]^+$, is an example of a transition metal complex with a coordination number of two. Nickel tetracarbonyl $[Ni(CO)_4]^0$, formed in the Mond Process for the purification of nickel, has a coordination number of four. A solution of aqueous copper sulfate contains the metal complex hexaaqua copper(II) $[Cu(H_2O)_6]^{2+}$, which has a coordination number of six.

When a ligand has more than one lone pair of electrons for coordination to the metal atom/ion the coordination number does not equal the number of ligands. The green transition metal complex $[Ni(EDTA)]^{2-}$ formed between the ligand EDTA (**e**thylene**d**iamine**t**etr**a**acetic acid) and Ni^{2+} has a coordination number of six.

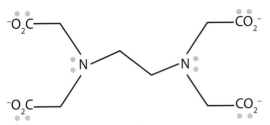

Skeletal diagram of the ligand EDTA

Catalysts

There are many important examples of transition elements and their compounds being used as industrial and laboratory catalysts. These catalysts speed up specific reactions by lowering the activation energy and providing a different reaction pathway (A1.3f). Transition elements are heterogeneous catalysts (B1.6e) as they are in a different phase from the reactants.

Haber Process

$$N_2 + 3H_2 \rightleftharpoons 2NH_3$$

Product: ammonia

Catalyst: Fe

Contact Process

$$SO_2 + \frac{1}{2}O_2 \rightleftharpoons SO_3$$

Product: sulfur trioxide

Catalyst: V_2O_5

Ostwald Process

$$4\,NH_3 + 5\,O_2 \rightarrow 4\,NO + 6\,H_2O$$

Product: nitric oxide leading to nitric acid

Catalyst: Pt/Rh alloy

Hydrogenation Process

$$CH_2=CH_2 + H_2 \rightarrow CH_3CH_3$$

Product: saturated fats

Catalyst: Ni

Vanadium(V) oxide (V_2O_5) is the catalyst used in the Contact process to turn sulfur dioxide into sulfur trioxide before its eventual conversion into sulfuric acid. The catalytic activity of transition elements such as vanadium is thought to depend on their variable oxidation states and also their ability to form complexes with different coordination numbers.

Sulfur dioxide is oxidised by vanadium(V) oxide into sulfur trioxide with reduction, for example, to vanadium(IV) oxide.

Equation 1:

$$2\,SO_2\,(g) + 2\,V_2O_5\,(s) \rightleftharpoons 2\,SO_3\,(g) + 4\,VO_2\,(s)$$

Vanadium(IV) oxide then reacts with oxygen to regenerate the catalyst, vanadium(V) oxide.

Equation 2:

$$4\,VO_2\,(s) + O_2\,(g) \rightleftharpoons 2\,V_2O_5\,(s)$$

Addition of **equations 1 & 2** gives **equation 3**, which is the overall equation for the reaction.

Equation 3:

$$2\,SO_2\,(g) + O_2\,(g) \rightleftharpoons 2\,SO_3\,(g)$$

The equations show how the heterogeneous catalyst (B1.6e) vanadium(V) oxide can take part in the reaction and yet is recovered unchanged. The availability of 3d and 4s electrons helps to explain the ready adsorption of reactant molecules onto the catalyst's surface. This adsorption onto the catalyst surface weakens the reactant molecules' bonds which reduces the activation energy (B1.6c).

It has been found that the peroxodisulfate(VI) ion $[S_2O_8]^{2-}$ slowly oxidises aqueous iodide ions to form sulfate (SO_4^{2-}) ions. This reaction can be speeded up by the presence of certain d-block ions.

$$2\,I^-\,(aq) + [S_2O_8]^{2-}\,(aq) \rightarrow 2\,SO_4^{2-}\,(aq) + I_2\,(aq)$$

The oxidation of iodide ions by peroxodisulfate(VI) can be speeded up by the addition of iron(II) ions. In this example the aqueous iron(II) ion is acting as a homogeneous catalyst (B1.6e).

$$2\,Fe^{2+}\,(aq) + S_2O_8^{2-}\,(aq) \rightarrow 2\,Fe^{3+}\,(aq) + 2\,SO_4^{2-}\,(aq)$$

$$2\,Fe^{3+}\,(aq) + 2\,I^-\,(aq) \rightarrow 2\,Fe^{2+}\,(aq) + I_2\,(aq)$$

Questions 11.3

1. Which option shows d-block elements with only one oxidation state in their compounds?

A   Zn & Sc & Ag

B   Cu & Zn & Sc

C   Zn & Ag & Cu

D   Ni & Sc & Ag

2. Which option shows the coordination number, ligand and shape of the complex potassium hexacyanoferrate(III) $K_3Fe(CN)_6$?

	Coordination number	Ligand	Shape
A	4	:CN	octahedral
B	6	:CN⁻	tetrahedral
C	9	:CN	tetrahedral
D	6	:CN⁻	octahedral

3. Name the following complex ions.

Formula	Name of complex ion
$[Cu(NH_3)_4(H_2O)_2]^{2+}$	
$[Fe(SCN)(H_2O)_5]^{2+}$	
$[Co(H_2O)_6]^{2+}$	
$[CoCl_4]^{2-}$	
$[CrCl_2(NH_3)_4]^+$	
$[Co(NH_3)_6]^{3+}$	
$[Pt(NH_3)_4(NO_2)Cl]^{2+}$	
$[Ni(CO)_4]^0$	

4. Give the formulae of the following complex ions

Name of complex ion	Formula
Hexacarbonyl chromium(0)	
Tetrahydroxo zincate(I) ion	
Diammine silver(I) ion	
Hexaammine nickel(II) ion	
Diamminedichloro platinum(II) ion	
Hexacyano ferrate(III) ion	
Hexaaquamanganese(II) ion	
Diaquatetrafluoro ferrate(III) ion	
Dithiosulfato argentate(I) ion	

5. a.   What is a complex ion?

   b.   What is a ligand?

   c.   What is meant by coordination number?

6. Give the formula of titanium nitrate when titanium is in its maximum oxidation state.

B2.4 (d)
Octahedral, tetrahedral and square planar complexes

The co-ordination number of a complex is the number of lone pairs bonded (dative covalently) to the central ion from ligands. The coordination number is the same as the number of unidentate ligands which bond through one lone pair *e.g.* H_2O, NH_3, Cl^-, SCN^-, and CN^-. Coordination numbers around metals and metal ions are typically six or four. The shapes of transition metal complexes follow the VSEPR theory (A1.2g) and have been confirmed by x-ray crystallography (B2.5).

Octahedral complexes

When there is six-fold coordination, *i.e.* six dative bonds, the complex is octahedral in shape with bond angles of 90°. An example is the hexaaqua copper(II) ion which has six water molecules bonded *via* lone pairs from the oxygen atom of water. Examples of octahedral complexes include; $[Co(H_2O)_6]^{3+}$, $[Mn(H_2O)_6]^{2+}$, $[Fe(CN)_6]^{3-}$, $[Ni(NH_3)_6]^{2+}$, $[Cu(NH_3)_4(H_2O)_2]^{2+}$ and $[Ni(EDTA)]^{2-}$.

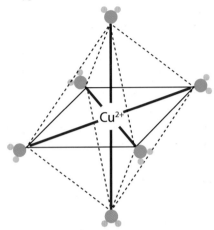

The octahedral complex $[Cu(H_2O)_6]^{2+}$

Tetrahedral complexes

When there is four-fold coordination, there are two possible geometries. Larger ions such as chloride (Cl⁻) tend to form tetrahedral complexes with bond angles of 109.5°. Examples of tetrahedral complexes include; $[CoCl_4]^{2-}$, $[FeCl_4]^{2-}$, $[CuCl_4]^{2-}$, $[Cu(CN)_4]^{3-}$, $[NiBr_4]^{2-}$, $[Ni(CO)_4]$, CrO_4^{2-}, and MnO_4^-.

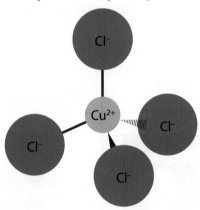

The tetrahedral complex $[CuCl_4]^{2-}$

In the diagram of tetrachlorocuprate(II) ion, the chloride and copper ions have been drawn approximately to scale, based on ionic radii. The chloride ions are so much larger than the copper ion that the coordination number is four rather than six.

Square planar complexes

Group 10 metals nickel, palladium and especially platinum form square planar complexes with bond angles of 90°. Examples of square planar complexes include; $[NiCl_2(NH_3)_2]^0$, $[AuCl_4]^-$, $[Ni(CN)_4]^{2-}$, $[Cu(NH_3)_4]^{2+}$ and $[Pt(Cl)_2(NH_3)_2]^0$.

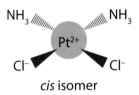

cis isomer

The square planar complex $[PtCl_2(NH_3)_2]^0$

Cis-diamminedichloroplatinum(II) $[PtCl_2(NH_3)_2]^0$, known trivially as *cis*-platin, is a square planar complex which was first described in 1845. Its structure was finally elucidated (solved) in 1893 by Alfred Werner who was the first inorganic chemist to be awarded the Nobel Prize in Chemistry in 1913. Interest in this metal complex followed the discovery in 1962 by Barnett Rosenberg that it had an interesting effect on the bacterium *Escherichia coli* (*E. coli*). The compound was then tested on various cancers in rats before finding use in treating human testicular cancer. One of the world's most brilliant cyclists, Lance Armstrong, who won seven consecutive Tour de France competitions ('99-'05), was treated with *cis*-platin which is an anti-cancer drug. *Cis*-platin is believed to work by strongly binding onto DNA (deoxyribonucleic acid) at any point where there are two adjacent guanine bases. *Cis*-platin is not subsequently dislodged by DNA repair enzymes. This results in distortion in the tumour's DNA, which helps to prevent it from replicating further.

B2.4 (e)
Geometric and Optical isomerism in complexes

The two types of isomerism that can occur with transition metal complexes are geometric (*cis-trans*) isomerism and optical isomerism. Metal complexes which are isomeric will have the same molecular formulae but a different arrangement of their ligands in space. Isomers of metal complexes are best drawn in three-dimensions and where possible molecular models should be used to aid understanding.

Geometrical isomers

It is possible to have geometrical isomers with square planar complexes (B2.4d) and octahedral complexes (B2.4d) but not tetrahedral complexes. The two geometric isomers are given the prefix *cis* or *trans*. The prefix *cis* indicates that two identical ligands are next to each other. The prefix *trans* indicates that two identical ligands are diagonally opposite each other. The bond angle between identical ligands and the metal in *cis* isomers is 90°. The bond angle between identical ligands and the metal in *trans* isomers is 180°.

Example 11.5

Diamminedichloro nickel(II) is a square planar complex with the formula $[Ni(NH_3)_2Cl_2]^0$. This complex fits the general formula MX_2Y_2 where $M = Ni^{2+}$, $X = NH_3$ and $Y = Cl^-$. Therefore it can form *cis* and *trans* isomers because there are four ligands which are two identical pairs of monodentate ligands.

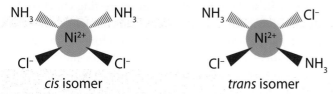

cis isomer   *trans* isomer

The *cis* isomer has the chloride ligands next to each other and the *trans* isomer has the chloride ligands diagonally opposite each other.

Example 11.6

Chlorocarbonylbis(triphenylphosphine) iridium(I) known as **Vaska's complex** is a square planar complex with the formula $[IrCl(CO)(P(C_6H_5)_3)_2]^0$. This complex fits the general formula $MXYZ_2$ where $M = Ir^{1+}$, $X = Cl^-$, $Y = C{\equiv}O$ and $Z = P(C_6H_5)_3$. Therefore it can form *cis* and *trans* isomers because there are two ligands which are identical monodentate ligands.

$(C_6H_5)_3P$ $P(C_6H_5)_3$ $O{\equiv}C$ $P(C_6H_5)_3$

$O{\equiv}C$ Cl^- $(C_6H_5)_3P$ Cl^-

cis isomer   *trans* isomer

The *cis* isomer has the triphenylphosphine ligands next to each other and the *trans* isomer has the triphenylphosphine ligands diagonally opposite each other.

Example 11.7

Diamminetetraaqua cobalt(II) ion is an octahedral complex with the formula $[Co(H_2O)_4(NH_3)_2]^{2+}$. This complex fits the general formula MX_2Y_4 where $M = Co^{2+}$, $X = NH_3$ and $Y = H_2O$. Therefore it can form *cis* and *trans* isomers because there are four ligands, two of which are identical pairs of monodentate ligands.

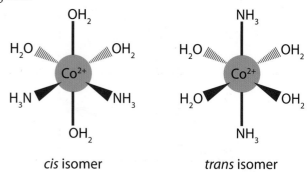

cis isomer   *trans* isomer

The *cis* isomer has the ammonia ligands next to each other and the *trans* isomer has the ammonia ligands diagonally opposite each other.

Optical isomers

It is possible to have optical isomers with octahedral complexes (B2.4d) when there are two or more bidentate ligands. A bidentate ligand is one with two binding sites that bond to the same metal to form a ring *via* two lone pairs. When ligands form ring structures with the central metal ion in a complex this is known as the chelate effect. The word chelate comes from the Greek word *chela*, meaning "crab's claw." **Ethylenediamine** ($H_2NCH_2CH_2NH_2$) is a bidentate ligand often abbreviated to **en** which binds *via* the nitrogen lone pairs of the amine (NH_2) group.

Crab's claw	Bidentate ligand ethylenediamine
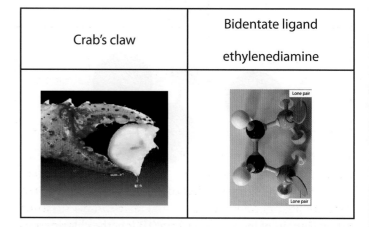	

Ligands with two lone pairs that can form two coordinate bonds to the transition metal are classified as bidentate ligands.

Bidentate ligands

Structure of ligand	Name of ligand	Type of ligand
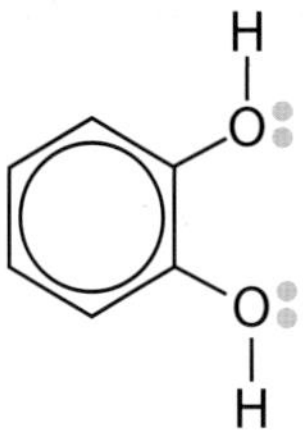	benzene-1,2-diol (catechol)	neutral
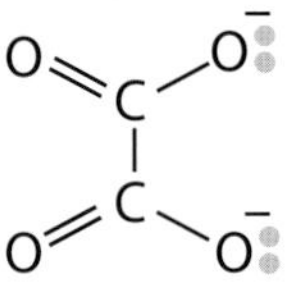	ethanedioate (oxalate)	anion
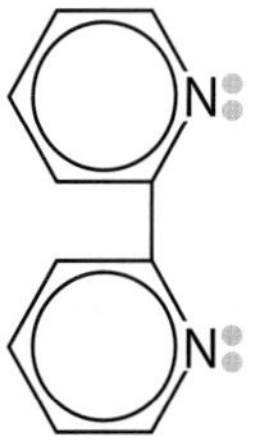	bipyridyl	neutral
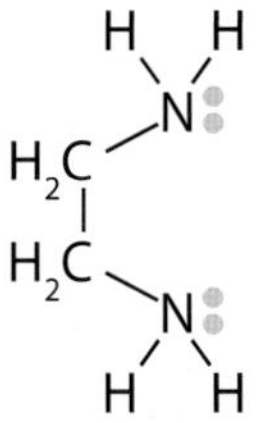	ethane-1,2-diamine (en)	neutral
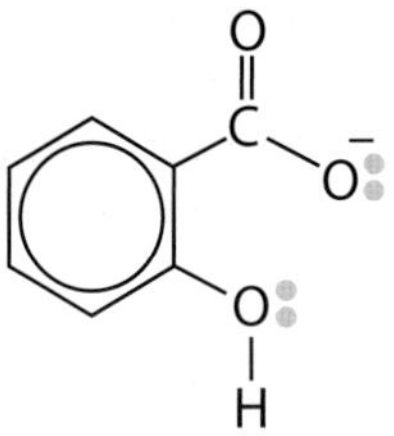	2-hydroxybenzoate (salicylate)	anion
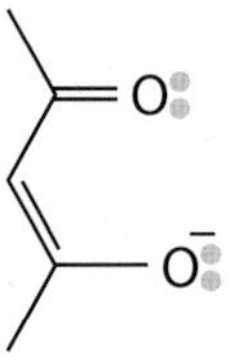	acetylacetonate (acac)	anion

Pairs of optical isomers are molecules that are non-superimposable mirror images. Optical isomers are more commonly met in organic chemistry (A3.1e) where they have different pharmacological effects. The metal complexes which are optical isomers will have identical chemical properties. When separated, solutions of identical concentration will rotate plane polarised light (B3.12b) in equal but opposite directions.

Example 11.8

Tris(ethylenediamine) nickel(II) ion is an octahedral complex with the formula $[Ni(H_2NCH_2CH_2NH_2)_3]^{2+}$. This complex has three bidentate ligands therefore it can form optical isomers.

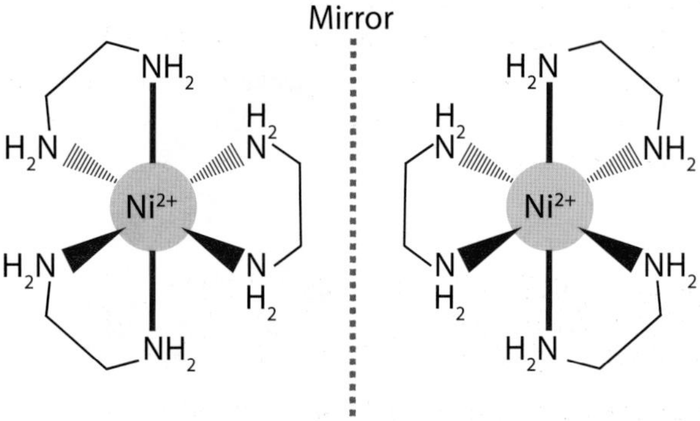

The optical isomers are non-superimposable mirror images and will form in equal amounts in solution. A convenient shorthand formula for this complex is $[Ni(en)_3]^{2+}$.

Example 11.9

Dichlorodiethylenediamine chromium(III) ion is an octahedral complex with the formula $[CrCl_2(H_2NCH_2CH_2NH_2)_2]^{1+}$. This complex has two bidentate ligands therefore it can form optical isomers.

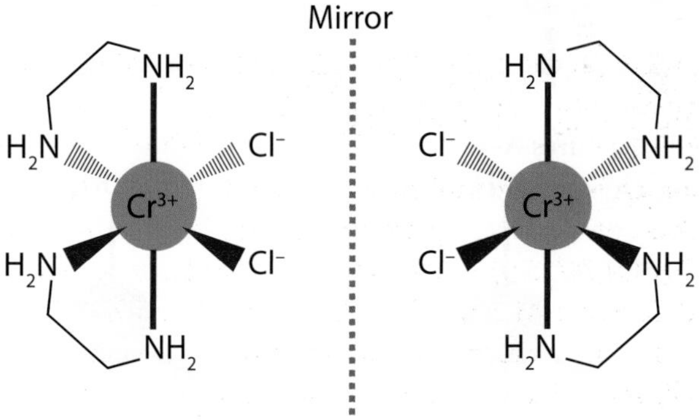

The two optical isomers are non-superimposable mirror images. A convenient shorthand formula for this complex is $[CrCl_2(en)_2]^+$. The molymods of this complex are shown for both of the optical isomers and the *trans*-isomer.

Optical isomer 1	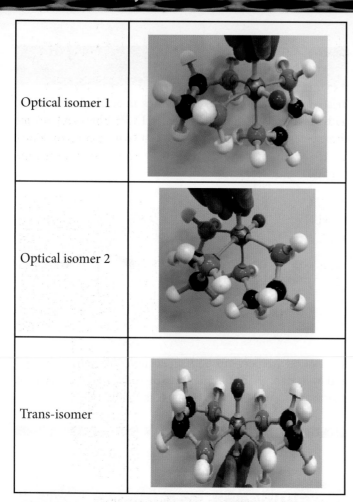
Optical isomer 2	
Trans-isomer	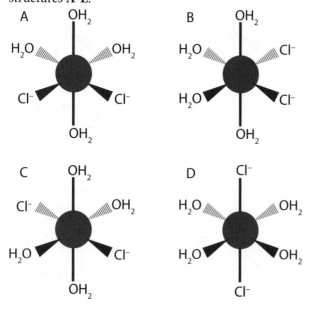

Questions 11.4

1. Tetraaquadichlorochromium(III) forms geometric isomers. Identify the *cis* and *trans* isomers from structures **A**-**E**.

A OH$_2$

B OH$_2$

C OH$_2$

D Cl$^-$

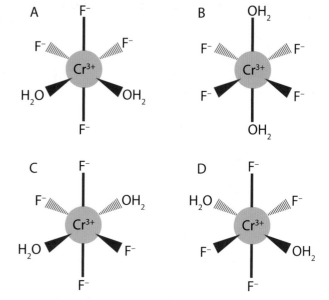

E OH$_2$

2. Which option is isomeric with this complex?

A F$^-$

B OH$_2$

C F$^-$

D F$^-$

3. Which option shows the general formula for a metal complex which can form geometric isomers? M = metal ion, X = one type of ligand and Y = another type of ligand.

	Formula of complex	Geometry
A	MX_2Y_2	tetrahedral
B	MX_3Y	square planar
C	MX_2Y_2	square planar
D	MXY_3	tetrahedral

4. Which option is not a name for the bidentate ligand $H_2NCH_2CH_2NH_2$?

   A   Ethylene diamine

   B   1,2-diaminoethane

   C   Ethane-1,2-diamine

   D   Ethylene diammine

5. Why does hydrazine (H_2N-NH_2) not act as a chelating agent?

6. The square planar complex $[Pt[Cl]_2(NH_3)_2]^0$ can form geometric isomers. Draw both isomers and explain which one will have zero dipole moment.

7. Which option is a metal complex that does **not** show optical isomerism?

   A $[Cr(en)_2(NH_3)_2]^{2+}$

   B $[Cr(C_2O_4)_2Cl_2]$

   C $[Cr(C_2O_4)_3]^{3+}$

   D $[Cr(en)(NH_3)_4]^{3+}$

8. The dichlorodiethylenediamine chromium(III) ion $[CrCl_2(H_2NCH_2CH_2NH_2)_2]^{1+}$ forms optical isomers. Draw the third possible isomer for this complex.

9. For the complex $[Pt(NH_3)_2Cl_2]^0$ what is the:

   a.   name?

   b.   oxidation state of the metal?

   c.   geometry?

   d.   coordination number?

   e.   name of the different types of ligands?

B2.4 (f) d-orbital splitting in transition metal complexes

The valence electrons are located in 3d orbitals (A1.1e) for the transition elements of Period 4. Their d-orbitals either point along the Cartesian axes ($3d_{x^2-y^2}$ & $3d_{z^2}$) or between the Cartesian axes ($3d_{xy}$, $3d_{yz}$ & $3d_{xz}$).

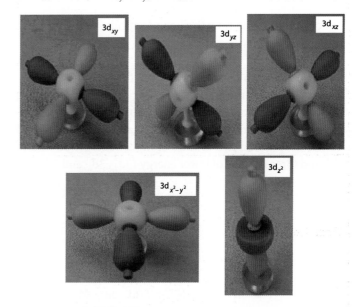

Molymods of the five d orbitals

When transition elements form octahedral complex ions (B2.4c), the central metal atom/ion is bonded to ligands along the Cartesian axes (x, y & z). The diagram shows the orientations in space of the five 3d orbitals for an octahedral complex with the orbitals of the ligands approaching along the Cartesian axes. The ligands' orbitals contain the lone pairs of electrons that form the coordinate bonds to the metal atom/ion.

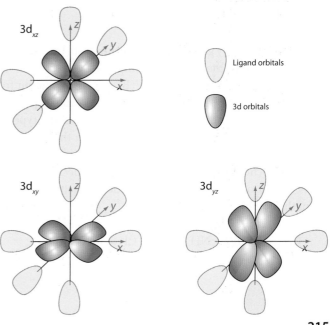

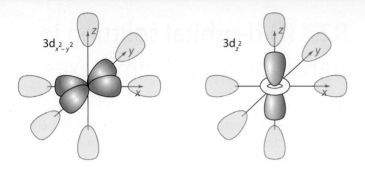

Diagrams showing how the ligands approach the five 3d orbitals

In an isolated atom or gaseous ion, the five sets of 3d orbitals have exactly the same amount of energy. Chemists often use the word 'degenerate' to describe orbitals having the same energy. In octahedral complexes, the ligands cause the five 3d orbitals to split into two orbitals of higher energy ($3d_{x^2-y^2}$ and $3d_{z^2}$) and three orbitals of lower energy ($3d_{xy}$, $3d_{yz}$ and $3d_{xz}$).

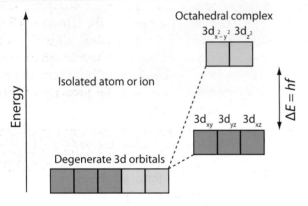

d-orbital splitting in an octahedral complex

Since the $3d_{x^2-y^2}$ and $3d_{z^2}$ orbitals are directed towards the ligands' orbitals, they will have additional electrostatic repulsion and are pushed into slightly higher energy levels. The $3d_{xy}$, $3d_{yz}$ and $3d_{xz}$ orbitals lie between the ligands' orbitals, so they are at lower energy levels than the other two as they have smaller electrostatic repulsions.

The size of the energy gap (ΔE) which results from the d-orbital splitting in transition element complexes corresponds to frequencies in the visible spectrum (B2.4g). The equation for this is $\Delta E = hf$ (A4.3b). The amount of the d-orbital splitting depends upon the metal ion, its oxidation state, the type of ligand(s) and the coordination number. When the metal ion and coordination number are the same, the size of ΔE matches the **spectrochemical series** (B2.4h). The spectrochemical series is a list of ligands arranged in order of their Lewis base strength (B1.5b):

$$CN^- > EDTA^{4-} > NH_3 > H_2O > Cl^- > SCN^- > Br^- > I^-$$

The d-orbital splitting is greatest when the ligand is cyanide (CN^-) and smallest when iodide (I^-) is the ligand.

In tetrahedral complexes, the splitting of the orbitals is the opposite way round to that found for octahedral complexes. The splitting is such that the five 3d orbitals will split into three orbitals of higher energy ($3d_{xy}$, $3d_{yz}$ and $3d_{xz}$) and two orbitals of less high energy ($3d_{x^2-y^2}$ and $3d_{z^2}$).

In transition element complexes where the energy levels are split (d-orbital splitting), there is the possibility of electrons being promoted from a low energy d-orbital to a high energy d-orbital. This promotion of electrons happens when there are unfilled d-orbitals of higher energy when transition element complexes absorb light in the visible region of the electromagnetic spectrum (B2.4g).

Radiation in the visible region of the spectrum can therefore be absorbed when an electron moves from a d-orbital of lower energy to one of higher energy.

Questions 11.5

1. What leads to d-orbital splitting in a first row transition element octahedral complex?

2. Explain, in terms of the first law of thermodynamics, how the 3d orbitals split in octahedral complexes.

3. What is meant by promotion of an electron in a first row transition element complex?

B2.4 (g) Origin of colour in transition metal complexes

The majority of transition metal complexes are coloured and this is one of their characteristic properties. The table shows a few examples of coloured compounds and white compounds in their solid state.

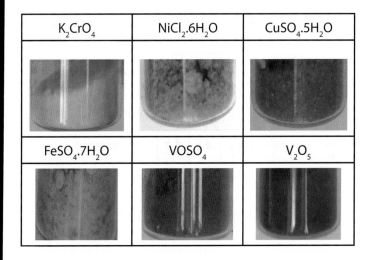

K_2CrO_4	$NiCl_2.6H_2O$	$CuSO_4.5H_2O$
$FeSO_4.7H_2O$	$VOSO_4$	V_2O_5

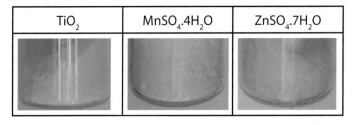

TiO_2	$MnSO_4.4H_2O$	$ZnSO_4.7H_2O$

These complexes are different colours because they absorb different wavelengths of visible light. It is unlikely that many students or teachers will remember all the colours of all the metal complexes shown in the next table. What this table does illustrate, with many examples, is how transition metal complexes can provide us with all the different colours across the full visible spectrum. This colourful property has been made use of for centuries by artists.

Colour	Example #1	Example #2	Example #3	Example #4
red	$[Cr(H_2O)_5(OH)]^{3+}$	$[Co(NH_3)_5(H_2O)]^{3+}$	$[Fe(H_2O)_5SCN]^{2+}$ (blood)	
pink	$[Co(H_2O)_6]^{2+}$	$Mn^{2+}(aq)$ (pale)	$[Co(H_2O)_6]^{2+}$	
orange	$Cr_2O_7^{2-}(aq)$	$[Co(NH_3)_6]^{2+}$ (straw)	$[Co(NH_3)_5(NO_2)]^{2+}$	
yellow	$[Fe(H_2O)_5(OH)]^{2+}$	$[CuCl_4]^{2-}$	$VO_2^{+}(aq)$ $VO_3^{-}(aq)$	$CrO_4^{2-}(aq)$
green	$V^{3+}(aq)$ $Ni^{2+}(aq)$	$[Co(NH_3)_4Cl_2]^{+}$	$Fe^{2+}(aq)$ (pale)	$[Cr(OH)_6]^{3-}$
blue	$[Cu(H_2O)_6]^{2+}$ (pale)	$[Cr(H_2O)_6]^{2+}$ $VO^{2+}(aq)$	$[Cu(H_2O)_6]^{2+}$ $[Cu(NH_3)_4(H_2O)_2]^{2+}$	$[CoCl_4]^{2-}$ $Co^{3+}(aq)$
purple	$V^{2+}(aq)$ $Ti^{3+}(aq)$	$MnO_4^{-}(aq)$ $Mn^{3+}(aq)$ (violet)	$Cr^{3+}(aq)$ (violet) $[Cr(NH_3)_6]^{3+}$	$[Fe(C_6H_5O^{-})_3]$ $[Co(NH_3)_5Cl]^{2+}$

Not all transition metal complexes are coloured. The exceptions are those complexes where the transition metals have no electrons in their d-orbitals ($3d^0$) such as Sc^{3+} and Ti^{4+}. The other exceptions are those complexes with full d-orbitals ($3d^{10}$) such as Zn^{2+} and Cu^{1+} in copper(I) iodide.

Colour	Example #1	Example #2	Example #3
colourless	Zn^{2+} (aq)	Sc^{3+} (aq)	
white (s)	CuI	TiO_2	$ZnSO_4.7H_2O$

Colour in transition metal complexes is due to having partially filled d-orbitals. This fact is illustrated by some examples of transition metal ions having electron configurations from $3d^1$ to $3d^9$.

	Example	Colour
$3d^0$	Sc^{3+}	
$3d^1$	Ti^{3+}	
$3d^2$	V^{3+}	
$3d^3$	Cr^{3+}	
$3d^4$	Mn^{3+}	
$3d^5$	Mn^{2+}	
$3d^6$	Fe^{2+}	
$3d^7$	Co^{2+}	
$3d^8$	Ni^{2+}	
$3d^9$	Cu^{2+}	
$3d^{10}$	Zn^{2+}	

Visible light is light having wavelengths from 400 nm to 750 nm. The different wavelengths of light correspond to different colours of visible light. Violet has the shortest wavelength and red the longest.

colour	violet	blue	green	yellow	orange	red
Absorbed λ / nm	400	470	540	590	640	700

Two useful equations are $E = hf$ (where E = photon energy, h = Planck's constant, 6.63×10^{-34} Js and f = frequency of light) and $v = f\lambda$ (where $v = c$ = speed of light 3.00×10^8 ms^{-1} and λ = wavelength of light).

Colour is associated with changes in energy levels of electrons (A4.3a). When light is absorbed it causes an electronic transition. In the case of an octahedral complex of Cu^{2+}, absorption of light might cause promotion of an electron from the $3d_{yz}$ orbital to the $3d_{z^2}$ orbital. For a complex to be coloured, at least one electron in a lower orbital and at least one gap in a higher energy orbital after d-orbital splitting (B2.4f) are required.

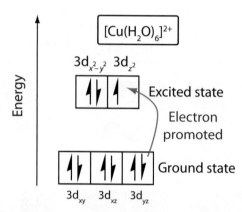

Promotion of an electron in an octahedral complex

The (hydrated) ion Cu^{2+} appears blue-green because red light has been absorbed during the promotion of an electron from a low energy orbital to a high energy orbital. This means that blue and green light are transmitted and what we see is a mixing of these two colours when we observe a solution containing copper(II) ions such as $[Cu(H_2O)_6]^{2+}$ (aq). The same explanation for colours of complexes is given in a bit more detail at university as the **crystal field theory**.

The test tube diagrams show what happens when one of the primary colours of light (red, green and blue) is absorbed when visible light (white light) is shining on a transition metal complex. When one colour is absorbed you get the (subtractive) colours: magenta, cyan and yellow which are the colours used in colour ink printers.

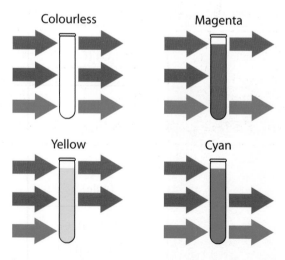

How absorption of different colours affects the colour of a complex

In the case of titanium(III) Ti^{3+}, green light is absorbed. This means that red and blue light are reflected (transmitted) and consequently the solution looks purple (magenta).

The precise colour of metal complexes depends on the size of the d-orbital splitting caused by the ligand and the charge on the metal ion. A strong ligand (CN^-) will lead to a large splitting and a large value for ΔE. A weaker ligand (I^-) will lead to a smaller splitting and a smaller value for ΔE. A more highly charged ion (Fe^{3+}) will lead to greater splitting than a less highly charged ion (Fe^{2+}) for the same transition element.

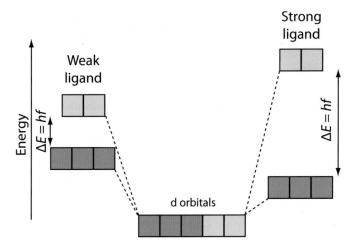

Differences in splitting (ΔE) for weak and strong ligands

Greater splitting within the d-subshell means those more energetic photons are used to promote electronic transitions. A summary of how a large ΔE and small ΔE will affect the colour of the complex. A qualitative understanding of the colours will suffice.

Property	Larger ΔE	Smaller ΔE
Energy of light absorbed	Higher energy	Lower energy
Frequency	Higher	Lower
Wavelength	Smaller	Longer
Colour of light absorbed	Blue end of spectrum	Red end of spectrum
Colour observed	Yellow or red	Cyan or blue

Colour wheel and complementary colours

The colour wheel is a device to help you work out the colour of a complex. When a particular colour is absorbed by a metal complex it will take on the colour of its complementary colour in the colour wheel. A complementary colour is the one directly opposite a particular colour.

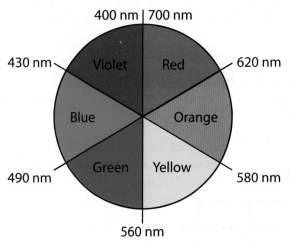

Colour wheel showing opposite complementary colours

For example, $[Ti(H_2O)_6]^{3+}$ absorbs yellow light so it is violet in colour. Using the colour wheel, it is possible to quickly work out all the complementary colours for the six main colours. The following pairs of complementary colours can be used to predict the colour of a complex. This table is a good guide but, as colours can be quite subjective, the maximum absorbance (λ_{max}) is often given for a complex to avoid ambiguity.

Table of complementary colours

Colour absorbed	Colour observed
Red	Blue-green
Orange	Blue
Yellow	Violet
Green	Red-purple
Blue	Yellow-orange
Violet	Yellow

A colorimeter measures the absorption of visible light radiation as it passes through a sample in a small plastic container called a **cuvette**. A violet solution of $[Ti(H_2O)_6]^{3+}$ will have maximum absorption with yellow light as it is violet's complementary colour. During colorimetry experiments, the filter selected will match a complex's complementary colour. Therefore, in experiments with a violet complex like $[Ti(H_2O)_6]^{3+}$, a yellow filter is used in the colorimeter.

Colorimeter for studying metal complexes

Since colorimetry is used for measuring the intensity of the colour of a complex ion in solution, it can be used to determine a complex's formula. Experiments involve measuring the absorbance of light by a metal complex in a colorimeter when solutions of a metal ion and a ligand are mixed in different ratios. The most intense colour, *i.e.* greatest absorbance, occurs when the ratio of metal ion to ligand matches the formula in the complex. For example, the ratio of Co^{2+} to NH_3 that produces the most intense colour is when a 1:6 mixture is placed in the colorimeter to produce the complex $[Co(NH_3)_6]^{2+}$.

Colours of vanadium ions

Vanadium has different colours in its four different oxidation states. These can be seen in turn by the reaction between acidified ammonium vanadate(V) and zinc. A spatula of ammonium vanadate(V) NH_4VO_3 is dissolved in 20 cm^3 of dilute hydrochloric acid. The resulting yellow solution contains vanadium in the +5 oxidation state as the ion VO_2^+. Addition of zinc granules will lead to the stepwise reduction of vanadium from the +4 oxidation state to the +3 oxidation state. Sometimes gentle heating is needed to reduce +3 to +2.

Oxidation state	+5	+4	+3	+2
colour	yellow	blue	green	violet
ion	VO_2^+	VO^{2+}	V^{3+}	V^{2+}

Colours of vanadium in its different oxidation states

A look at the standard electrode potentials tells us that other reducing agents will not reduce vanadium all the way to +2 if their electrode potentials are more positive than that of zinc.

$$Zn^{2+} (aq) + 2\ e^- \rightleftharpoons Zn\ (s)$$
$$E = -0.76\ V$$

$$V^{3+} (aq) + e^- \rightleftharpoons V^{2+} (aq)$$
$$E = -0.26\ V$$

$$Sn^{2+} (aq) + 2\ e^- \rightleftharpoons Sn\ (s)$$
$$E = -0.14\ V$$

$$VO^{2+} (aq) + 2\ H^+ (aq) + e^- \rightleftharpoons V^{3+} (aq) + H_2O\ (l)$$
$$E = +0.34\ V$$

$$S_4O_6^{2-} (aq) + 2\ e^- \rightleftharpoons 2\ S_2O_3^{2-} (aq)$$
$$E = +0.47V$$

$$VO_2^+ (aq) + 2\ H^+ (aq) + e^- \rightleftharpoons VO^{2+} (aq) + H_2O\ (l)$$
$$E = +\ 1.00\ V$$

Comparing the electrode potentials of the oxidising agents and the different oxidation states for the vanadium ions shows how far each reducing agent will affect vanadium +5. A tick ($\sqrt{}$) indicates that this oxidation state is reduced by the reducing agent.

Reducing agent	Oxidation state of vanadium			Allowable O.S. changes
	+5	+4	+3	
Zn	$\sqrt{}$	$\sqrt{}$	$\sqrt{}$	+5 to +2
Sn	$\sqrt{}$	$\sqrt{}$		+5 to +3
$S_2O_3^{2-}$	$\sqrt{}$			+5 to +4

Questions 11.6

1. Which option shows the 3d arrangements for two different colourless transition metal complexes X and Y?

	d-subshell for X	d-subshell for Y
A	full	half full
B	empty	full
C	half full	half full
D	empty	half full

2. Why is only one colour of visible light absorbed to supply the energy needed for electron promotion in transition metal complexes?

3. How much energy is absorbed for visible light of frequency 6×10^{14} Hz?

   [Planck's constant $h = 6.63 \times 10^{-34}$ Js]

4. How do changes in the energy gap (ΔE) for the split d-orbitals affect the colour of transition metal complexes?

B2.4 (h) Ligand exchange and observed colour changes

A ligand exchange reaction is a reaction where one or more ligands in a metal complex are replaced by different ligand(s). These ligand exchange reactions are essentially substitution reactions as one type of ligand is swapped for another type of ligand. The general equation for ligand exchange with a hexaaqua complex is shown where L = ligand.

$[M(H_2O)_6]^{n+}$ (aq) + L $\rightleftharpoons$
$\qquad$ $[M(H_2O)_5(L)]^{n+}$ (aq) + H_2O (aq)

In ligand exchange reactions, for example involving hexaaqua complexes, there may be exchange of one or more water molecules in the complex ion. If ligands are neutral and similar in size there will be no change in coordination number. This is the case when ammonia replaces all the water molecules in hexaaqua cobalt(II) when it reacts with an aqueous ammonia solution. Remember to include the six water molecules after the new metal complex when writing balanced equations.

$[Co(H_2O)_6]^{2+}$ (aq) + 6 NH_3 (aq)
pink $\rightleftharpoons$ $[Co(NH_3)_6]^{2+}$ (aq) + 6 H_2O (l)
$\qquad$ *pale yellow/brown*

If ligands are not similar in size or charge, there will be a change in coordination number and hence geometry around the metal ion will change during the ligand exchange reaction. This is the case when chloride replaces all the water molecules in hexaaqua cobalt(II) when it reacts with a saturated sodium chloride solution or hydrochloric acid.

$[Co(H_2O)_6]^{2+}$ (aq) + 4 Cl^- (aq)
pink $\rightleftharpoons$ $[CoCl_4]^{2-}$ (aq) + 6 H_2O (l)
$\qquad$ *blue*

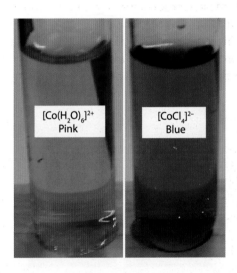

$[Co(H_2O)_6]^{2+}$ Pink $\qquad$ $[CoCl_4]^{2-}$ Blue

Ligand exchange reactions have found use as qualitative tests (A4.1a) because most of them involve a change in colour with the formation of a new complex ion.

Ligands can be described as Lewis bases (B1.5b) because they have lone pairs of electrons which they donate to the transition metal. The strength of ligands as Lewis bases varies because of differences in electron density in their lone pairs of electrons. Consequently different ligands will lead to different amounts of d-orbital splitting (B2.4f) with different relative energies (ΔE) of the d-orbitals. This is why there is often a colour change associated with ligand exchange reactions.

The order of ligands' strengths as Lewis bases, known as the **spectrochemical series** is:

$$CN^- > EDTA^{4-} > NH_3 > H_2O > Cl^- > SCN^- > Br^- > I^-$$

A strong base, such as the ligand ammonia, can displace a weaker base, such as the ligand water, from a complex ion. EDTA will displace ammonia, water and chloride from a complex ion. The cyanide ion will displace all other ligands, which is why it has such high toxicity at low concentrations. Cyanide binds almost irreversibly to Fe^{2+} in haemoglobin (B2.4j) preventing the carriage of oxygen and failure of respiration.

Examples of ligand exchanges

The qualitative test for the presence of iron(III) ions (Fe^{3+}) is a ligand exchange reaction with thiocyanate ion (SCN^-) by the addition of a small amount of a solution of potassium thiocyanate (KSCN). The presence of very small amounts of Fe^{3+} will be detected by the formation of the blood red complex pentaaquathiocyanato iron(III).

$[Fe(H_2O)_6]^{3+}$ (aq) + SCN^- (aq) $\rightleftharpoons$
yellow-brown $\qquad [Fe(H_2O)_5(SCN)]^{2+}$ (aq) + H_2O (l)
$\qquad\qquad\qquad\qquad$ *blood red*

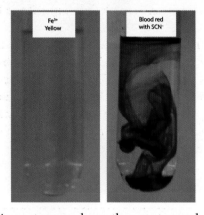

Ammonia is a stronger base than water and its reaction with aqueous copper(II) sulfate solution is perhaps one of the most familiar ligand exchange reactions. It can be used as a qualitative test for copper(II) ions. With a few drops of ammonia solution pale blue copper(II) hydroxide is formed (A4.1a). When excess ammonia is added, a dark blue solution of tetraamminediaqua copper (II) ion is formed.

$[Cu(H_2O)_6]^{2+}$ (aq) + 4 NH_3 (aq) $\rightleftharpoons$
$\qquad$ *blue* $\qquad\qquad [Cu(H_2O)_2(NH_3)_4]^{2+}$ (aq) + 4H_2O(l)
$\qquad\qquad\qquad\qquad$ *dark blue*

Chloride is a weaker base than water. When concentrated hydrochloric acid is added to an aqueous solution of copper(II) ions, ligand exchange does take place due to the presence of large amounts of chloride ion. The colour of the resulting

tetrachlorocuprate(II) ion is yellow. The solutions often look green as the yellow colour is masked by some residual blue hexaaqua copper(II) complex.

$[Cu(H_2O)_6]^{2+}$ (aq) + 4 Cl^- (aq) $\rightleftharpoons$
$\qquad$ *blue* $\qquad\qquad\qquad\qquad [CuCl_4]^{2-}$ (aq) + 6 H_2O (l)
$\qquad\qquad\qquad\qquad\qquad\qquad$ *yellow*

Chloride is a weaker base than ammonia and water. When excess ammonia is added to an aqueous solution of tetrachlorocuprate(II) ion, ligands exchange and the product is tetraamminediaqua copper(II) ion. The coordination number changes from four to six and all four chloride ions are replaced by two water molecules and four ammonia molecules.

$[CuCl_4]^{2-}$ (aq) + 4 NH_3 (aq) + 2 H_2O (l) $\rightleftharpoons$
yellow $\qquad\qquad [Cu(H_2O)_2(NH_3)_4]^{2+}$ (aq) + 4 Cl^- (aq)
$\qquad\qquad\qquad\qquad$ *dark blue*

For example, ammonia ligands cause a larger difference than water molecules in the relative energies. This factor results in the colour change from blue to blue-violet when ammonia is added to an aqueous solution of a copper(II) salt.

Different coloured copper(II) complexes with different ligands

Questions 11.7

1. Two chromium(III) complexes have different colours. $[Cr(H_2O)_6]^{3+}$ $3Cl^-$ is violet and $[CrCl_2(H_2O)_4]^+$ Cl^- is dark green. How could a colour blind technician show that he had labelled the samples correctly?

2. Describe what would happen when aqueous solution of cyanide ions is added to the hexaaqua iron(II) complex ion. Include a balanced equation.

3. Explain what you would expect to observe if water is added to $[CuCl_4]^{2-}$ (aq).

4. Which option shows the correct colours for these copper compounds?

	$[Cu(H_2O)_6]^{2+}$ (aq)	$Cu(OH)_2$ (s)	$[CuCl_4]^{2-}$ (aq)	$[Cu(H_2O)_2(NH_3)_4]^{2+}$ (aq)
A	blue	pale blue	yellow	purple
B	pale blue	blue	green	dark blue
C	blue	pale blue	yellow	dark blue
D	blue	blue	green	purple

5. Write a balanced formula equation for the ligand exchange reaction between Co^{2+} (aq) and excess NH_3 (aq), giving colour changes.

6. Write a balanced formula equation for the reaction between Ni^{2+} (aq) and excess 1,2-diaminoethane.

a. What type of reaction is this?

b. What changes might be observed during this reaction?

c. How many metal complexes are formed in this reaction?

d. What is the sign of ΔS for this reaction?

B2.4 (i) Redox chemistry Fe^{3+}/Fe^{2+}; MnO_4^-/Mn^{2+}; $Cr_2O_7^{2-}/Cr^{3+}$; Cu^{2+}/Cu^+

Transition elements can undergo redox reactions (B1.5j) because they have more than one oxidation state. During a redox reaction, electron(s) pass from the reducing agent to the oxidising agent. A simple redox reaction which can easily be carried out in the laboratory is the reaction between zinc and copper(II) ions. In this reaction, you can quickly observe that copper is deposited at the surface of a piece of zinc that has been dipped into an aqueous solution of copper(II) sulfate. The ionic equation for this reaction is:

$$Zn\ (s) + Cu^{2+}\ (aq) \rightarrow Zn^{2+}\ (aq) + Cu\ (s)$$

In this reaction, Cu^{2+} is being reduced, as its oxidation number decreases by two, and zinc is being oxidised, as its oxidation number increases by two. Therefore the zinc is the reducing agent (as it is being oxidised) and it provides electrons to reduce the Cu^{2+} ions. Like all redox reactions, this process can be split into two half-equations to represent separately the oxidation and reduction processes in a redox reaction.

$$Zn\ (s) - 2e^- \rightarrow Zn^{2+}\ (aq)\ \&\ Cu^{2+}\ (aq) + 2\ e^- \rightarrow Cu\ (s)$$

The redox chemistry of Fe^{3+}/Fe^{2+}, MnO_4^-/Mn^{2+}, $Cr_2O_7^{2-}/Cr^{3+}$ and Cu^{2+}/Cu^+ will be explored below. Much of the chemistry of these ions can be used to determine the concentration of a reducing or oxidising agent in solution as redox titrations (B1.5g) and are often met in practical examinations. It is important to learn the colours of the ion pairs so that the end point of a titration is recognised.

Fe^{3+} (aq)	yellow
Fe^{2+} (aq)	pale green
MnO_4^- (aq)	purple
Mn^{2+} (aq)	pale pink
$Cr_2O_7^{2-}$ (aq)	orange
Cr^{3+} (aq)	green
Cu^{2+} (aq)	blue
Cu^+ (s)	white

Redox chemistry of Fe³⁺/Fe²⁺

The two common oxidation states of iron are +2 and +3 found in its ions Fe^{2+} and Fe^{3+}. Fe^{3+} is the most stable oxidation state for iron since its electron arrangement contains a half-filled $3d^5$ subshell. It has been observed that solutions containing Fe^{2+} are unstable in air and soon get oxidised to Fe^{3+}. A solution of iron(II) forms a green precipitate with aqueous solutions of ammonia and sodium hydroxide. The resulting Fe^{2+} turns brown on contact with air (A4.1a) as it is oxidised to Fe^{3+}.

$$Fe^{2+} - e^- \rightarrow Fe^{3+}$$
green   *brown*

Additional examples of the redox chemistry of Fe^{3+}/ Fe^{2+} are given where iron(II) is oxidised to iron(III):

$$2\,Fe^{2+}\,(aq) + Cl_2\,(g) \rightarrow 2\,Cl^-\,(aq) + 2\,Fe^{3+}\,(aq)$$

$$6\,Fe^{2+}\,(aq) + Cr_2O_7{}^{2-}\,(aq) + 14\,H^+\,(aq)$$
$$\rightarrow 2\,Cr^{3+}\,(aq) + 6\,Fe^{3+}\,(aq) + 7\,H_2O\,(l)$$

$$5Fe^{2+}\,(aq) + MnO_4{}^-\,(aq) + 8\,H^+\,(aq)$$
$$\rightarrow 5\,Fe^{3+}(aq) + Mn^{2+}\,(aq) + 4\,H_2O\,(l)$$

Redox chemistry of MnO₄⁻/Mn²⁺

Solutions of potassium manganate(VII) are purple and they contain manganese in its highest oxidation state of +7. Potassium manganate(VII) is stored in brown bottles because, in the presence of light, it will oxidise water to oxygen. The manganate(VII) ion is a powerful oxidising agent which is reduced in its redox reactions to its lowest oxidation state of +2. The +2 oxidation state is the most stable oxidation state of manganese in aqueous solution with its $3d^5$ electron arrangement. Mn^{2+} (aq) is usually written as this shorthand form but it is actually the pale pink complex ion $[Mn(H_2O)_6]^{2+}$ (aq).

$$MnO_4{}^-\,(aq) + 8\,H^+\,(aq) + 5\,e^- \rightleftharpoons Mn^{2+}\,(aq) + 4\,H_2O\,(l)$$
purple   *pale pink*   1.51 V

Manganate(VII) is sometimes used in the preparation of chlorine gas by reacting solid potassium manganate(VII) with hydrochloric acid. In aqueous solution, the redox reaction shows how the manganese is reduced from +7 to +2 whilst the chloride is oxidised from –1 to 0 in elemental chlorine.

$$MnO_4{}^-\,(aq) + 8\,H^+\,(aq) + 5\,Cl^-\,(aq)$$
$$\rightleftharpoons Mn^{2+}\,(aq) + 4\,H_2O\,(l) + 2\tfrac{1}{2}\,Cl_2\,(g)$$

This method for the preparation of chlorine needs care as solid manganate(VII) explodes violently if the wrong acid (sulfuric acid) is accidentally used. Potassium manganate(VII) is often used in redox titrations to measure the concentration of reducing agents. There is no need for an indicator as these titrations are self-indicating because the colour change from purple $(MnO_4{}^-)$ to pale pink (Mn^{2+}) is quite dramatic. It can be quite difficult to read the burette when it contains potassium manganate(VII). If possible try to select a burette with white writing rather than one with blue writing.

Additional examples of the redox chemistry of $MnO_4{}^-/Mn^{2+}$ are given where manganese(VII) is reduced to manganese(II).

$$MnO_4{}^-\,(aq) + 8\,H^+\,(aq) + 5Fe^{2+}\,(aq)$$
$$\rightarrow Mn^{2+}\,(aq) + 4\,H_2O\,(l) + 5\,Fe^{3+}(aq)$$

$$2\,MnO_4{}^-\,(aq) + 6\,H^+\,(aq) + 5\,H_2O_2\,(aq)$$
$$\rightarrow 2\,Mn^{2+}\,(aq) + 8\,H_2O\,(l) + 5\,O_2\,(g)$$

$$2\,MnO_4{}^-\,(aq) + 6\,H^+\,(aq) + 5\,(CO_2H)_2\,(aq)\ \textit{[ethanedioic acid]}$$
$$\rightarrow 2\,Mn^{2+}\,(aq) + 8\,H_2O\,(l) + 10\,CO_2\,(g)$$

Sometimes during the titration of $KMnO_4$ vs Fe^{2+}, a brown precipitate of MnO_2 is observed in the conical flask. If this happens, the brown solid will redissolve when additional acid is supplied to the mixture.

Redox chemistry of Cr₂O₇²⁻/Cr³⁺

The two most common oxidation states of chromium are +6 and +3. Two examples of chromium in the +6 oxidation state are the bright yellow sodium chromate(VI) (Na_2CrO_4) and the bright orange sodium dichromate(VI) $(Na_2Cr_2O_7)$.

Solid sodium chromate(VI) & solid sodium dichromate(VI)

These two different coloured forms of chromium in the +6 oxidation state exist in an equilibrium reaction (B1.5a) in solution. The equilibrium mixture is yellow in alkaline solutions and orange in acidic solutions. Chromium(III) compounds are often green, although $[Cr(H_2O)_6]^{3+}$ is purple. Acidified dichromate(VI) is a powerful oxidising agent and has found use in organic chemistry (A3.3d). Looking at the standard electrode potentials for iodine and chlorine, which of the halides will be oxidised by dichromate(VI)?

$$I_2 (aq) + 2 e^- \rightleftharpoons 2 I^- (aq) \qquad +0.54 \text{ V}$$

$$Cl_2 (aq) + 2 e^- \rightleftharpoons 2 Cl^- (aq) \qquad +1.36 \text{ V}$$

$$Cr_2O_7^{2-} (aq) + 14 H^+ (aq) + 6 e^-$$
$$\rightleftharpoons 2 Cr^{3+} (aq) + 7 H_2O (l) \qquad +1.33 \text{V}$$

Dichromate(VI) is powerful enough to oxidise iodide to iodine as it has a more positive standard electrode potential.

$$Cr_2O_7^{2-} (aq) + 14 H^+ (aq) + 6 I^- (aq)$$
$$\rightleftharpoons 2 Cr^{3+} (aq) + 3 I_2 (aq) + 7 H_2O (l)$$

However, dichromate(VI) is not powerful enough to oxidise chloride to chlorine since it has a lower positive standard electrode potential.

Ethanedioate ions being oxidised to carbon dioxide on reaction with acidified dichromate(VI) is another example of the redox chemistry of $Cr_2O_7^{2-}/Cr^{3+}$.

$$Cr_2O_7^{2-} (aq) + 3 C_2O_4^{2-} (aq) + 14 H^+ (aq)$$
orange   *oxalate*
$$\rightleftharpoons 2 Cr^{3+} (aq) + 6 CO_2 (g) + 7 H_2O (l)$$
            green

A redox titration which can be used to estimate the amount of iron(II) in solution is its reaction with dichromate(VI). A suitable indicator for this titration is diphenylamine sulfonate.

$$Cr_2O_7^{2-} (aq) + 6 Fe^{2+} (aq) + 14 H^+ (aq)$$
$$\rightleftharpoons 2 Cr^{3+} (aq) + 6 Fe^{3+} (aq) + 7 H_2O (l)$$

Redox chemistry of Cu^{2+}/Cu^+

The two common oxidation states of copper are +1 and +2 found in its ions Cu^+ and Cu^{2+}. The colour of copper(I) compounds is often white because of its full $3d^{10}$ subshell. The notable exception is copper(I) oxide (Cu_2O) which is red. The colour of most copper(II) compounds is blue in aqueous solution. The relative instability of Cu^{1+} compared with Cu^{2+} is illustrated by its disproportionation (A2.2n) in aqueous solution. Cu^{1+} is simultaneously oxidised to Cu^{2+} and reduced to Cu.

$$2 Cu^+ (aq) \rightarrow Cu (s) + Cu^{2+} (aq)$$

The instability of copper(I) can be explained in terms of standard electrode potentials for these half equations;

$$Cu^+ + e^- \rightarrow Cu \ (+0.52 \text{ V})$$

$$\& \ Cu^{2+} + e^- \rightarrow Cu^+ \ (+0.15 \text{ V})$$

The analysis of brass, which is an alloy of copper and zinc, provides the opportunity to meet some Cu^{2+}/Cu^+ redox chemistry.

$$2 Cu^{2+}(aq) + 4 I^- (aq) \rightarrow 2 CuI (s) + I_2 (aq)$$
blue   *white*

In this reaction, copper(II) is reduced by iodide into copper(I). The reducing agent, iodide, is oxidised to iodine since its oxidation number increases from −1 to 0. The half equation for the reduction is $Cu^{2+} + e^- \rightarrow Cu^{1+}$. The mixture of copper(I) iodide and iodine looks brown with white pieces of copper(I) iodide as a suspension.

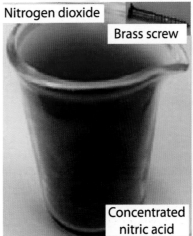

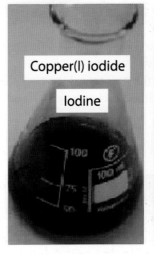

Colour changes during brass analysis

Questions 11.8

1. Which option is the only one which is a reducing agent in redox reactions?

    A Fe^{2+}

    B MnO_4^-

    C Fe^{3+}

    D $Cr_2O_7^{2-}$

2. Using electron configuration arguments, explain why Fe^{2+} is easily oxidised into Fe^{3+} whereas Mn^{2+} is not readily oxidised to Mn^{3+}. Which pair of ions are isoelectronic?

3. Mohr's salt is a hexahydrate of ammonium iron(II) sulfate which is more stable to air than iron(II) sulfate. Give the formula for Mohr's salt, suggest how it might be prepared and state the likely colour of its crystals.

4. What colour changes would you expect to observe in the following reaction and what is the role of hydrogen peroxide?

$2 [Cr(OH)_6]^{3-} (aq) + 3 H_2O_2 (aq)$
$\rightarrow 2 CrO_4^{2-} (aq) + 2 OH^- (aq) + 8 H_2O (l)$

5. Which option shows the correct explanation for the reaction between acidified dichromate(VI) and zinc metal?

$Cr_2O_7^{2-} + 14 H^+ + 3 Zn \rightarrow 2 Cr^{3+} + 7 H_2O + 3 Zn^{2+}$

	oxidised	reduced	oxidising agent	reducing agent
A	Zn^{2+}	Cr^{3+}	Zn^{2+}	Cr^{3+}
B	Zn	$Cr_2O_7^{2-}$	$Cr_2O_7^{2-}$	Zn
C	Zn^{2+}	$Cr_2O_7^{2-}$	$Cr_2O_7^{2-}$	Zn
D	Zn	Cr^{3+}	Zn	Cr^{3+}

6. Explain what is happening when copper(I) oxide is warmed with dilute sulfuric acid. What observations might you expect to make?

$Cu_2O (s) + H_2SO_4 (aq) \rightarrow Cu (s) + CuSO_4 (s) + H_2O (l)$

7. Write a balanced formula equation for the reaction between ethanol and dichromate(VI) where the organic product is ethanoic acid. Explain why this is a redox reaction.

8. 0.97 g of steel was dissolved in concentrated sulfuric acid and made up to 250 cm³ with distilled water in a volumetric flask. 25 cm³ of the iron solution was pipetted into a conical flask and titrated against a 0.01 mol dm⁻³ dichromate(VI) solution. Calculate the percentage of iron in the steel given that the average titre was 22.85 cm³. [A_r = Fe 55.8 g mol⁻¹].

9. Two tablets of Iron(II) sulfate had a combined mass of 0.960 g. The tablets were crushed and dissolved in dilute sulfuric acid and made up to 100 cm³ in a volumetric flask. 10 cm³ of the iron solution was pipetted into a conical flask and titrated against a 0.006 mol dm⁻³ potassium manganate(VII) solution. Calculate the percentage of iron in the tablets given that the average titre was 10.40 cm³. What is the colour change at the end point? [A_r = Fe 55.8, S = 32.1 & O = 16.0].

B2.4 (j)
Biological role of three important iron complexes

Haemoglobin, myoglobin and ferritin are three iron complexes which have essential biological roles. In all three cases the iron ion is held in its least stable oxidation state, namely iron(II) Fe^{2+}. Iron as an ion in its lowest oxidation state (Fe^{2+}) takes the name 'ferrous' and iron in its highest oxidation state (Fe^{3+}) takes the name 'ferric'.

Haemoglobin

Haemoglobin is a **tetrameric protein** which carries oxygen around the body for release into tissues. There are four subunits in haemoglobin each of which contains a haem molecule capable of binding oxygen. This means that each molecule of haemoglobin binds up to four oxygen molecules. The binding of oxygen by haemoglobin is reversible.

Haem consists of four hetrocyclic pyrrole rings in a square joined at the corners by methylyne (CH) bridges.

Bovine haemoglobin is a red-brown solid	Structure of haem found in haemoglobin showing its hydrophobic and hydrophilic parts
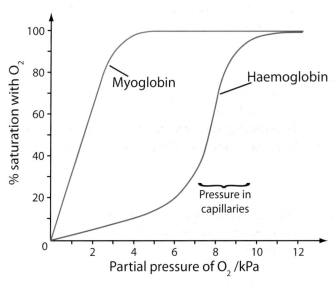	

Myoglobin

Myoglobin is a water-soluble monomeric protein which acts as an emergency store of oxygen in muscle tissue. Its tertiary structure is a single polypeptide chain with eight alpha helices joined by short loops which forms a pocket into which the haem group fits. The haem group has Fe^{2+} at its centre which reversibly binds to oxygen. The simplest way to think of myoglobin is as an oxygen storage protein that only relinquishes the oxygen molecule (O_2) when there are relatively low concentrations of oxygen in muscles during periods of strenuous exercise. The concentration of oxygen becomes low when the muscle oxygen demand outpaces the supply of oxygen from the blood. Deoxygenated myoglobin is called deoxymyoglobin.

$$\text{deoxymyoglobin} + \text{oxygen} \rightleftharpoons \text{myoglobin}$$

Myoglobin contains a porphyrin ring with a ferrous ion (Fe^{2+}) at its centre. There is a histidine group nearby (proximal), which is attached directly to the iron centre, and a distal histidine group on the opposite face, not bonded to the iron. The shape of the myoglobin curve is hyperbolic and the shape of the haemoglobin curve is sigmoidal.

Oxygen saturation curve (dissocation curve) for myoglobin and haemoglobin

Haemoglobin picks up oxygen in the alveoli of the lungs where it becomes almost fully saturated with oxygen at these high pressures. Conversely at the lower oxygen pressures found in the capillaries, haemoglobin releases most of its oxygen where it can be described as being unsaturated.

Myoglobin has a dissociation curve well to the left of that shown for haemoglobin. This shows that myoglobin has a much higher affinity for oxygen than does haemoglobin. Myoglobin only releases oxygen at very low partial pressures of oxygen which allows the muscle to continue respiring aerobically (to continue contracting) at low levels of oxygen.

Ferritin

Most of the iron stored in the body is as ferritin in the cells of the liver, spleen, skeletal muscles and bone marrow. **Ferritin** is a complex of the protein apoferritin and inorganic iron. Iron bound to ferritin inside cells is a major store of iron that your body can use later in haemoglobin and myoglobin. The iron is in the form of iron(II) oxide (FeO). There is only a small amount of ferritin in the blood, but enough for it to be quantified in the **ferritin test**. The normal amount of iron in your blood, measured as serum ferritin levels, is 12-300 ng/ml for males or 12-150 ng/ml for females. Low levels of iron indicate an iron deficiency which might be a sign of anaemia or the liver conditions cirrhosis or hepatitis. High levels of iron indicate alcoholism (liver disease), thalassemia or rheumatoid arthritis.

Ferritin has recently been used as a catalyst in the growth of carbon nanotubes. Scientists are making use of nature's scaffolding as templates to make their own structures as they strive to make molecules with applications for devices such as molecular computers.

Questions 11.9

1. Which option is **not** a metalloprotein?

    A   ferritin

    B   ferrocene

    C   haemoglobin

    D   myoglobin

2. Studies have shown that, when carbon dioxide levels increase, *e.g.* when tissues become more active, the haemoglobin dissociation curve shifts to the right. Explain the significance of this phenomenon, which is known as the Bohr shift.

3. Explain the consequences of smokers having up to 9% carboxyhaemoglobin in their blood

B2.4 (k)
Stability of Co^{2+} and Co^{3+} with different ligands

Cobalt forms many compounds and it has been found that +2 and +3 are the two main oxidation states. In solution, the +2 oxidation state is usually the most stable, except when strong complexing agents such as ammonia and cyanide are present.

Aqueous solutions of cobalt(II) ions are characteristically pink. The hexaaqua cobalt(II) ion is a stable octahedral ion having the formula $[Co(H_2O)_6]^{2+}$ (aq). It is possible to form the hexaaqua cobalt(III) ion $[Co(H_2O)_6]^{3+}$ which is blue, but it is easily reduced to $[Co(H_2O)_6]^{2+}$ as seen from the standard electrode potentials for iodide and silver metal. This transformation is a reduction because there is a decrease in the oxidation state of cobalt from +3 to +2.

	$E^{\ominus}$ / V
$[Co(H_2O)_6]^{3+} + e^- \rightleftharpoons [Co(H_2O)_6]^{2+}$	+1.81
$Ag^+ + e^- \rightleftharpoons Ag$	+0.80
$I_2 + 2 e^- \rightleftharpoons 2I^-$	+0.54

The reduction by silver is:

$$[Co(H_2O)_6]^{3+} + Ag \rightleftharpoons [Co(H_2O)_6]^{2+} + Ag^+.$$

Don't forget when writing balanced equations to check that atoms and charges balance on both sides of the equation.

Cobalt (III) has enhanced stability when the ligand is ammonia. A solution of hexaammine cobalt(II) will oxidise to hexaammine cobalt(III) when left to stand in air. The observed colour change will be from pale yellow (straw) $[Co(NH_3)_6]^{2+}$ to orange-brown $[Co(NH_3)_6]^{3+}$. The enhanced stability of Co^{3+} with ammonia is because this ligand is a stronger ligand than water forming stronger coordinate bonds. At university, this is explained in terms of it having high crystal field stabilisation energy. $[Co(NH_3)_6]^{2+}$ can also be oxidised by hydrogen peroxide (A2.2f) according to the equation:

$$2 [Co(NH_3)_6]^{2+} (aq) + H_2O_2 (aq)$$
$$\rightarrow 2 [Co(NH_3)_6]^{3+} + 2 OH^- (aq)$$

Solutions of cobalt(III) ions are characteristically blue. Although hexaammine cobalt(III) ion is a stable complex ion $[Co(NH_3)_6]^{3+}$, it is possible to reduce it to hexaammine cobalt(II) ion $[Co(NH_3)_6]^{2+}$ with stronger reducing agents than were needed for the reduction of $[Co(H_2O)_6]^{3+}$. The standard electrode potentials are shown for iron and vanadium(II). These reducing agents will decrease the oxidation state of cobalt from +3 to +2.

$$E^{\ominus} / V$$

$$[Co(NH_3)_6]^{3+} + e^- \rightleftharpoons [Co(NH_3)_6]^{2+} \quad +0.11$$

$$Fe^{2+} + 2e^- \rightleftharpoons Fe \quad -0.44$$

$$V^{3+} + e^- \rightleftharpoons V^{2+} \quad -0.26$$

The reduction by iron is:

$$2[Co(NH_3)_6]^{3+} + Fe \rightleftharpoons 2[Co(NH_3)_6]^{2+} + Fe^{2+}.$$

Questions 11.10

1. What are the electron configurations for cobalt and its two main oxidation states?

2. Write a balanced formula equation for the reduction of $[Co(H_2O)_6]^{3+}$ by iodide.

3. Which option shows the most stable oxidation states for the hexaaqua and hexaammine ions for cobalt(II) and cobalt(III)?

   A $[Co(H_2O)_6]^{2+}$ & $[Co(NH_3)_6]^{3+}$

   B $[Co(H_2O)_6]^{2+}$ & $[Co(NH_3)_6]^{2+}$

   C $[Co(H_2O)_6]^{3+}$ & $[Co(NH_3)_6]^{2+}$

   D $[Co(H_2O)_6]^{3+}$ & $[Co(NH_3)_6]^{3+}$

4. Cobalt(III) fluoride is a brown solid used as a fluorinating agent which reacts instantly with water to form oxygen gas as one of its products. Write a balanced formula equation for this reaction.

5. Write a balanced formula equation for the reduction of $[Co(NH_3)_6]^{3+}$ by V^{2+}.

6. Name the following cobalt complexes and predict their stability in the presence of water.

   a. $[Co(CN)_6]^{3-}$

   b. $[Co(CN)_5]^{3-}$

12 Crystallography

Contents

Most solids found in nature are crystalline and some of them are highly prized. Crystals have a highly organised regular arrangement of their atoms or ions in three dimensions. Nature has provided us with many examples of beautiful crystals from the snow flakes of winter to the salt crystals in Death Valley (USA). Some crystals such as diamonds, found in the mineral kimberlite (South Africa), are very expensive. It is possible to cut crystals using the planes that exist within their regular and repeating internal structures. One of my favourite crystals is the cubic iron pyrites, more commonly known as fool's gold.

Examples of crystals (left: iron pyrites, middle: bismuth[1], right: diamond)

High purity bismuth produces hollow form crystals with rainbow colours in about ten minutes when molten bismuth is super-cooled. The iridescent metallic colours are caused by light scattering from the thin layer of bismuth oxide.

How particles are arranged in a crystal lattice can be solved using x-ray crystallography. Pioneering work was carried out by the father and son team of William Henry Bragg and William Lawrence Bragg, for which they were awarded the 1915 Nobel Prize in Physics. The first structure they solved was for zinc blende (ZnS).

The wavelength of x-rays (~ 0.1 nm) is similar to the distances between atoms/ions in a crystal lattice. Crystals contain regular layers of atoms/ions and x-rays are diffracted by these layers. The diffraction of the x-rays is due to electrons around the atoms/ions. More electrons around an atom/ion leads to greater scattering of the x-rays. It took the world's top scientists many months/years to solve the structures of crystals from x-ray diffraction patterns. Today, with a good quality crystal and a supercomputer, a crystal's structure can be solved in a matter of hours. From a crystal structure, the size of the unit cell (B2.5b) and distance between atoms/ions can be determined.

---

1   Image from Wiki Commons under GNU license.

Building models of crystals by sticking together polystyrene spheres is very helpful to the understanding of this topic. There are also online resources where three dimensional computer models can be examined and the structures rotated. One particularly good resource built for the Pre-U chemistry course is designed and managed by Chas McCaw. At the time of publication, this can be found at *http://www-teach.ch.cam. ac.uk/links/3Dindex.html.*

Questions 12.1

1. Which option shows the technique used to solve a crystal structure?

   A   Mass spectrometry

   B   X-ray diffraction

   C   Infra-red spectroscopy

   D   Nmr spectroscopy

2. Which option shows a substance that does not have a layered structure?

   A   Glass

   B   Graphite

   C   Sodium chloride

   D   Magnesium

B2.5 (a)
Crystal structures of metals

The arrangements of metal atoms in which the gaps are kept to a minimum are called close-packed arrangements and the two types are cubic-close packed (CCP) and hexagonal close-packed (HCP). The periodic table shows, by position, thirty metals and which type of closed-packed structure they have. There is no obvious relationship between a metal's position in the periodic table and its structure type, CCP or HCP. The other metals left as blank squares in the Periodic Table have the more complex body centred cubic structures which are best left to university.

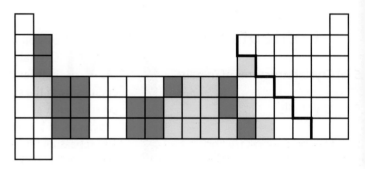

| | Hexagonal close packed |
| | Cubic close packed |

Close-packed metallic elements in the Periodic Table

When considering the CCP and HCP crystal structures in metals, it is helpful to think of the atoms in the crystal as being like hard spheres. The properties of the crystals (and indeed the substances) depend very much on the strength of the forces within the crystal and how the particles are arranged, which is partly a result of the size of the particles

If you take sixteen spheres (marbles, polystyrene balls) and arrange them in neat 4×4 rows and in columns, the result looks like this:

Inefficient packing

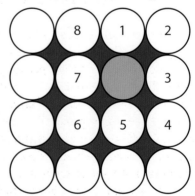

This line up leads to rather inefficient packing. The amount of 'space' between the spheres in this one layer is shown by the green colour (48%). But if you take sixteen spheres and pack them like the bricks in a wall they pack far more efficiently. The amount of 'space' between the spheres in this one layer is shown to be considerably smaller by the red colour (39%). Efficient packing places six spheres around an atom compared with the eight spheres with inefficient packing. Close-packed atoms in layers will adopt the efficient packing where each sphere in a layer is surrounded by six others in a hexagon.

Efficient packing

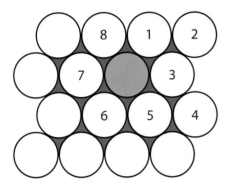

The close-packing of spheres is similar to the arrangement of the red balls on a snooker table or the spots and stripes on a pool table.

Close-packing of freshly racked pool balls

Now let us consider what will happen when another layer is added on top of a 4×4 first (lower) layer which has been packed with maximum efficiency, *i.e.* efficient packing. This second layer adds another dimension to our understanding of crystal structures. The first layer is the bottom layer onto which a second set of 4×3 spheres can be placed. By removing one row from the second layer the bottom layer is still 'visible'. Things get a little more complicated when you add a 4×3 layer on top of this lower original 4×4 layer of spheres. The first thing to realise is that, in the second layer, it is extremely difficult to stack spheres directly above the spheres of the first layer. What

happens in metals is that the second layer rests on the hollows of the first layer. The different colours have been used to show the arrangements of atoms in the two layers.

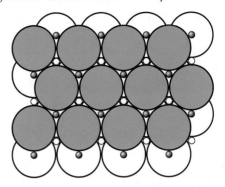

2nd layer in green

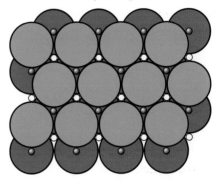

1st layer in red

Now the second layer is in place it is possible to spot that there are two types of hollow still visible. These hollows are where spheres in a third layer are going to rest, depending on whether the metal adopts the CCP or HCP structure. Once again, the third layer will be a set of sixteen spheres arranged in a 4×4 arrangement.

ABC and AB representation

One type of hollow (○) is found in the spaces of the first layer. If the third layer spheres rest here, all three layers are stacked in such a way that not one sphere in any of the three layers is directly above another sphere. This type of packing is often referred to as **ABC**.

The other type of hollow (◉) is found directly above the spheres of the first layer. If the third layer spheres rest here, then alternate layers are stacked in such a way that they are directly above each other. This type of packing is often referred to as **ABAB**.

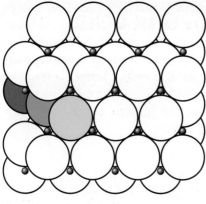

ABC

3rd layer directly above
the hollows ○ in the 1st layer **ABC**

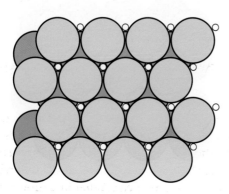

ABAB

3rd layer directly above
the hollows ● in the 2nd layer **ABA**

The next diagram shows only the first layer and the hollows (shown as ●) which result from the addition of a second layer of spheres. This time I have made the hollows, which are available to a third layer of spheres, the same colour to allow the hexagon patterns connecting the hollows to be seen. Nature has found strength in this hexagon shape elsewhere with the honeycomb found in bee hives.

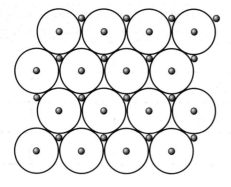

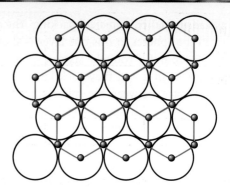

Modelling crystal structures is made easier if you have access to polystyrene balls and blue tac and a good imagination (see this book's website for some photographs). It is important to understand packing within crystals as it affects physical properties such as melting point, boiling point, density and hardness. Three of the most malleable (bendy) metals are gold, silver and copper and they all possess planes of atoms allowing deformation when a force is applied.

This mnemonic might prove useful when trying to remember which arrangement represents which close packed structure.

ABC = CCP *[A big cat could cause panic]*

ABAB = HCP *[A big African buffalo has chased people]*

It is worth pointing out that, in some cases, the structure of a metal can change with temperature. For example, iron has a body centred cubic structure below 906°C and a CCP structure above 906°C until the lattice is broken when the iron melts. Napoleon Bonaparte was a great supporter of the sciences but his scientists were unaware of the change in the structure of tin at the low temperatures achieved in a typical Russian winter. This meant that the buttons on French soldiers' uniforms soon fell off on cold days as it transformed to a weaker allotrope.

Questions 12.2

1. Use the periodic table, which gives the structures of metallic elements, to complete the following table, identifying which are hexagonal close-packed (HCP) and which are cubic-close packed (CCP).

Metal	HCP	CCP
Cadmium		
Silver		
Platinum		
Magnesium		
Cobalt		

Metal	HCP	CCP
Nickel		
Zinc		
Gold		
Copper		

2. What do the letters A, B & C represent in the diagram of one layer of close-packed spheres?

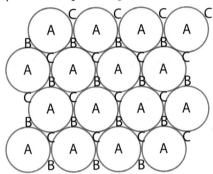

3. Which option shows which layer is directly above the 1st layer in close-packed crystals?

	HCP	CCP
A	2nd	3rd
B	3rd	4th
C	3rd	2nd
D	4th	3rd

4. A hexagonal close packed structure is shown for a metal. What is the coordination number of an atom in this structure and what is the stacking arrangement (ABC or ABAB)?

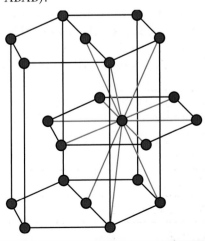

B2.5 (b) Unit cells

Patterned wall paper is made by repeating a unit pattern in two dimensions. This makes it possible for a good decorator to cover a wall without making any obvious mistakes in the overall pattern. Can you spot the repeating unit in this wall paper from the 1950s?

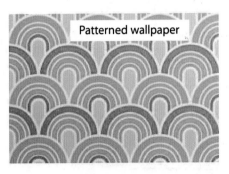

Patterned wallpaper

Repeating pattern

Patterned wall paper from the 1950s with a repeating pattern

Crystals are made up of repeating units in three dimensions called **unit cells**. A unit cell is defined as the simplest repeating unit of the lattice which shows the full symmetry of the crystal. A crystal is composed of many thousands of unit cells stacked side by side and on top of each other in a three dimensional lattice.

A crystallographer will work out the distances between atoms/ions in a crystal in addition to the unit cell. This is important because the formula for a compound can be worked out from the unit cell. The unit cell will often contain many more ions than are found in the formula of ionic compounds, as seen with the unit cells for halite (NaCl) and fluorite (CaF_2). A unit cell may also contain part of an atom/ion. How much of the atom/ion is in the unit cell depends on its position. An atom/ion can be in the centre of a unit cell, at a corner, at the centre of an edge or in the centre of a face. The table shows what fraction an atom/ion is in the unit cell depending on its position.

Position of atom / ion in unit cell	Fraction of atom / ion within the unit cell
Centre	1
Centre of face	$\frac{1}{2}$
Centre of edge	$\frac{1}{4}$
Corner	$\frac{1}{8}$

A particle at the corner of a cube is found in eight unit cells, so one eighth is to be found in a particular unit cell. You might have to play with cubes to see how this works. A particle at the

235

centre of an edge is found in four unit cells, so one quarter is to be found in a particular unit cell. A particle at the centre of a face is found in two unit cells, so one half is to be found in a particular unit cell.

Unit cell (CCP)

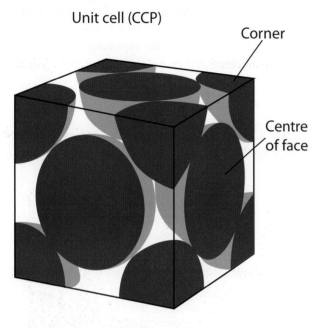

Corner

Centre of face

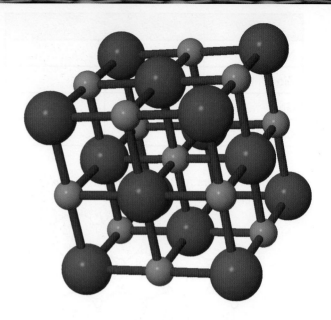

Unit cell of sodium chloride (green = Cl^- & silver = Na^+)

Unit cell of sodium chloride

The unit cell of sodium chloride has a CCP arrangement which is also the structure of many other salts, *e.g.* potassium bromide, magnesium oxide and silver chloride. The microscopic structure of table salt is reflected in the macroscopic structure of sodium chloride crystals which are often grown to capture the imagination of the younger chemists. The cubic structure of this natural sodium chloride crystal is clear to see and reflects the inner ionic arrangements within the crystal lattice. Unit cells are usually shown using ball-and-stick models which show the arrangement of atoms/ions. The blue lines do not represent a chemical bond, but are used to help hold physical models together and to help in the visualisation of diagrams.

The unit cell of sodium chloride, shown above, was drawn from crystallographic data by Chas McCaw and is also found online as a 3D applet at http://www-teach.ch.cam.ac.uk/links/3Dindex.html. In the unit cell, which is a cube, there are six faces, twelve edges and eight corners. A count of the ions in the unit cell reveals that there are 14 chloride ions and 13 sodium ions at least partly within the unit cell.

Cell occupancy is a term which refers to the number of ions within the unit cell. How many sodium ions are in the unit cell? Twelve sodium ions are at the centre of an edge ($12 \times \frac{1}{4} = 3$) and there is one sodium ion at the centre of the unit cell ($1 \times 1 = 1$) giving a total of 4 sodium ions. How many chloride ions are in the unit cell? Eight chloride ions are at the corners ($8 \times \frac{1}{8} = 1$) and six chloride ions are in the centre of each face ($6 \times \frac{1}{2} = 3$) giving a total of 4 chloride ions in the unit cell. The cell occupancy is $4 + 4 = 8$. The ratio of ions is 4:4 which cancels down to give a stoichiometry of 1:1. Hence the formula is Na_1Cl_1 usually written as NaCl.

Unit cell of calcium fluoride

The unit cell of calcium fluoride has an HCP arrangement and was drawn from crystallographic data by Chas McCaw. Fluorite crystals have the interesting property of fluorescence when placed under UV light. There are some wonderful examples of fluorescing crystals in the Natural History Museum (London).

Crystal of sodium chloride (salt)

White light

UV light

Crystals of fluorite

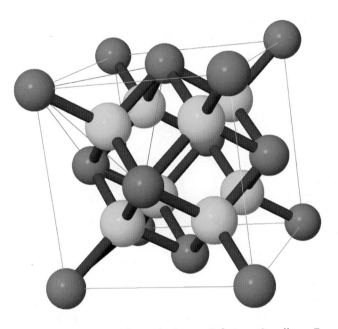

Unit cell of calcium fluoride (grey: Ca²⁺ ions & yellow: F⁻ ions)

In the unit cell which is also a cube, there are six faces, twelve edges and eight corners. A count of the ions in the unit cell reveals that there are 14 calcium ions and 8 fluoride ions at least partly within the unit cell. What is the cell occupancy of the unit cell of fluorite (CaF_2)? Eight calcium ions are at the corners ($8 \times \frac{1}{8} = 1$) and there are six calcium ions at the centre of each face ($6 \times \frac{1}{2} = 3$) in the unit cell giving a total of 4 calcium ions. There are eight fluoride ions completely within the unit cell so there are 8 fluoride ions. The cell occupancy is $4 + 8 = 12$. The ratio of ions is 4:8 which cancels down to give a stoichiometry of 1:2. Hence the formula is CaF_2.

Questions 12.3

1. What is a unit cell?

2. What information is given by the unit cell for halite?

3. How many atoms are there in the unit cell for this body centred cubic arrangement of sodium?

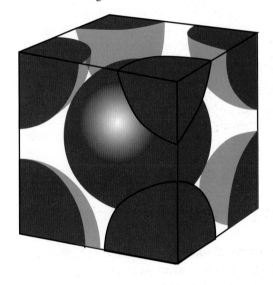

4. Which option shows the correct fractions for the different positions that atoms/ions can adopt in unit cells?

	Centre of edge	Corner	Centre of face
A	$\frac{1}{4}$	$\frac{1}{8}$	$\frac{1}{2}$
B	$\frac{1}{8}$	$\frac{1}{4}$	$\frac{1}{4}$
C	$\frac{1}{4}$	$\frac{1}{4}$	$\frac{1}{2}$
D	$\frac{1}{2}$	$\frac{1}{8}$	$\frac{1}{4}$

B2.5 (c) Lattices (geometry and coordination number)

Shapes and geometry were discussed for simple molecules and hypervalent species in A1.2g. In terms of lattices, we will only consider the geometry for tetrahedral and octahedral atoms/ions. A particle with four nearest neighbours is said to have a coordination number of four and is described as having a **tetrahedral geometry**. A particle with six nearest neighbours is said to have a coordination number of six and is described as having an **octahedral geometry**. Coordination number is defined as the number of nearest neighbouring atoms or ions touching or surrounding a central atom or ions within a three dimensional lattice structure. It is sometimes overlooked that the ratio of coordination numbers is the same as the stoichiometric ratio found in the formula for the compound.

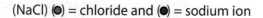

(NaCl) (◉) = chloride and (◉) = sodium ion

CN = 6

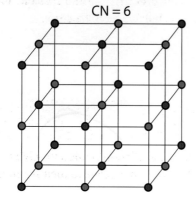

Ball-and-stick model of sodium chloride

Sodium chloride

In the diagram ● represents a sodium ion and ● represents a chloride ion. It should be easy to spot that the central sodium ion has a coordination number of six in this cubic-close packed arrangement. If this is not apparent, then there is no substitute for holding a plastic model of the sodium chloride crystal lattice in your hand and looking at it more closely. The next three diagrams show the coordination number, geometry and shape by focussing on the central sodium ion of the unit cell. The blue lines show how the coordination number (CN) of six is arrived at for the central sodium ion. This coordination number gives rise to an octahedral geometry.

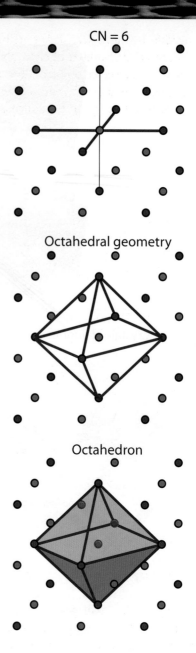

CN = 6

Octahedral geometry

Octahedron

You can see that the six nearest neighbours of the sodium in the body centre of the unit cell are the chloride ions in the centre of the six faces of the cube. It is important to realise that the nearest neighbours of an ion can only be the counter ions of opposite charge. This is how the structure maximises the attractive ionic forces between ions of opposite charge. The coordination number of chloride is also six. This is less easy to observe in the unit cell drawing but, using the same arguments and making ● represent a chloride ion and ● represent a sodium ion would work.

Calcium fluoride

Calcium fluoride has twice as many fluoride ions as calcium ions because it has a 1:2 stoichiometry. The calcium ions are found in the corners and the centres of the faces of the unit cell whilst the fluoride ions occupy the tetrahedral sites.

By stitching together two unit cells, it is possible to see that calcium has a coordination number of eight. By looking at a calcium ion that is on the centre of a face, it is apparent that there are four fluoride ions above the edge of the unit cell and four fluoride ions below the edge of the unit cell.

Ion	Ionic radius / nm
Na$^+$	0.102
Cl$^-$	0.180
Ca^{2+}	0.100
F$^-$	0.133

For sodium chloride:

the radius ratio $= \dfrac{0.102 \text{ nm}}{0.180 \text{ nm}} = 0.57$

and for calcium fluoride:

the radius ratio $= \dfrac{0.100 \text{ nm}}{0.133 \text{ nm}} = 0.75$

The larger radius ratio for calcium fluoride compared with sodium chloride offers an explanation as to why Ca^{2+} ions have a larger coordination number of eight compared with that for Na$^+$, which is six. It has been found that ionic substances with radius ratios between 0.41 and 0.73 and 1:1 stoichiometry tend to have the sodium chloride type structure.

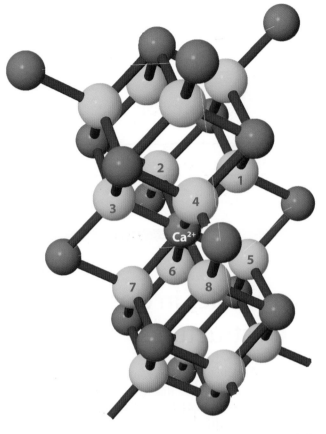

Diagram to show that calcium has a CN = 8 in CaF$_2$

It is a little easier to look at a diagram of a calcium fluoride lattice and spot that each fluoride ion has a coordination number of four and therefore a tetrahedral geometry. A simplified diagram to show that the fluoride ions have tetrahedral geometry can be drawn by placing a calcium ion at four alternate corners of a cube and placing a fluoride ion at the centre of the cube. What is worth remembering here is that, for CaF$_2$, it is the ion with the smallest number in the formula that has the largest coordination number and, by inference, it is the ion with the largest number in the formula that has the smallest coordination number.

The coordination number for an ion depends on the relative sizes of the ions contained within the lattice. It is common sense to realise that a larger ion can accommodate more counter ions around it than a smaller ion. The coordination number has been found to relate to the ratio of the radii of the cations and anions. When the cation radius is divided by the anion radius, the number arrived at is called the **radius ratio**.

Questions 12.4

1. What is the ratio of coordination numbers in NaCl and CaF$_2$ and how do they relate to their formulae?

2. Which option shows the correct coordination numbers for the cations in CaF$_2$ and NaCl?

	Coordination number of Ca^{2+}	Coordination number of Na$^+$
A	6	8
B	8	6
C	6	4
D	4	6

3. Which option shows the correct coordination numbers for the anions in CaF_2 and NaCl?

	Coordination number of Cl⁻	Coordination number of F⁻
A	4	6
B	6	8
C	6	4
D	8	6

4. Label the diagram which shows one chloride ion in place for part of a sodium chloride crystal.

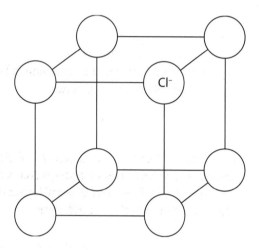

Cl⁻

5. What information is obtained from the coordination numbers for the ions in fluorite?

6. A student drew a diagram to represent part of a lattice and later could not remember whether it was for NaCl or CaF_2. Describe their lattice and assign the ions in this lattice.

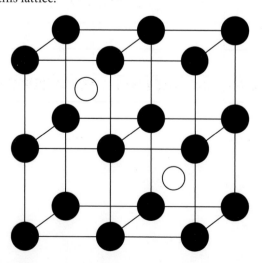

7. What affects the geometry in a crystal lattice?

8. Complete the following table by giving the coordination numbers of the ions in the crystals of sodium chloride and calcium fluoride, where C.N. = coordination number.

Crystal	C.N. of Cation	C.N. of Anion
NaCl		
CaF_2		

B2.5 (d) Holes in close-packed structures

In close-packed structures, there are two types of hole (octahedral and tetrahedral) that counter ions can occupy within the three dimensional lattice. Ions occupying octahedral holes will have a coordination number of six. Ions occupying tetrahedral holes will have a coordination number of four. With a little experience, you should be able to locate and identify the different types of holes in close-packed structures. The diagrams show how a tetrahedral site fits into a cube and how an octahedral site cuts into eight different cubes. A particle set in a tetrahedral hole will have four nearest neighbours and a particle set in an octahedral hole will have six nearest neighbours.

Tetrahedral site

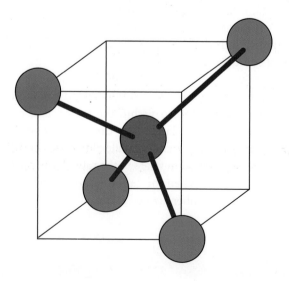

Part of an octahedral site

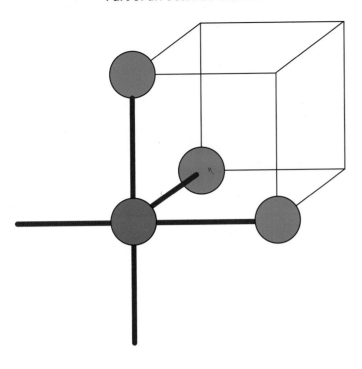

By examining crystal structures, it has been found that both structures have three times as many holes as atoms/ions. They each have one octahedral hole per atom, and two tetrahedral holes per atom. It has also been shown that octahedral holes are larger than tetrahedral holes. In close-packed structures, the 3rd layer of particles fit above the tetrahedral holes (●) in HCP crystals and above the octahedral holes (●) in CCP crystals. The tetrahedral holes are directly above the centre of the spheres in the first layer, which is why you get an ABAB arrangement with HCP crystals. The octahedral holes are above the hollows in the first layer, which is why you get an ABC arrangement with CCP crystals.

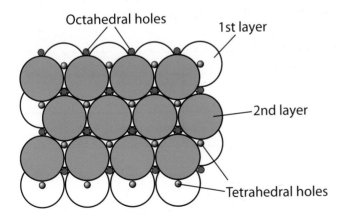

The position of octahedral and tetrahedral holes in the second layer of close packed spheres

Questions 12.5

1. Which option shows the correct ratio of holes to ions in close-packed structures?

	Ratio of holes : ions	
	CCP	HCP
A	1:3	3:1
B	1:1	2:1
C	1:1	1:2
D	2:1	1:1

2. Explain in words how you can distinguish between the two types of hole in a crystal lattice.

3. The diagram shows the arrangement of close-packed spheres. If a second layer of close-packed spheres rests directly on top of **B**, which holes will be tetrahedral and which octahedral in this second layer?

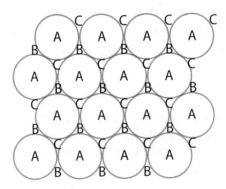

B2.5 (e) Lattice structures of sodium chloride and calcium fluoride

In crystal lattices of compounds such as sodium chloride and calcium fluoride a cation is always surrounded by anions and an anion is always surrounded by cations. Oppositely charged ions are sometimes described as counter ions. The counter ion to an anion is a cation and the counter ion to an anion is a cation. How ionic substances are held together by electrostatic forces results from the arrangement of their constituent ions.

Another way to describe the lattice of sodium chloride is that it is two interlocking cubic-close packed lattices one of Na^+ ions and the other of Cl^- ions. The Na^+ ions rest in all the octahedral holes in the Cl^- lattice. The Cl^- ions rest in all the octahedral holes in the Na^+ lattice.

Another way to describe the lattice of calcium fluoride is that it consists of cubic close-packed Ca^{2+} ions with F^- ions in the tetrahedral holes in the Ca^{2+} lattice. The calcium ions are situated at alternate corners of a cube with the fluoride ion in its centre. The diagram has red lines joining the calcium ions to show how the fluoride ion is at the centre of a tetrahedron. The size of the fluoride ions keeps the calcium ions further apart than in CCP, but in the same geometric arrangement. There are twice as many tetrahedral holes as octahedral holes which also fits with the stoichiometry for CaF_2 and NaCl.

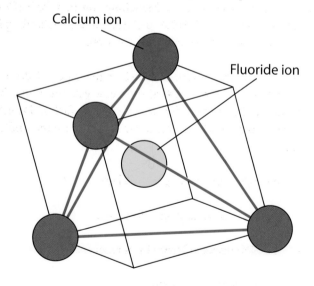

How to draw a tetrahedral fluoride ion in calcium fluoride

Questions 12.6

1. Complete the following table to show which factors are maximised and which factors are minimised when ions arrange themselves as a crystal grows in a saturated solution of a salt.

Property	Minimised	Maximized
Contact between oppositely charged ions		
Contact between ions of the same charge		
Repulsive forces		
Attractive forces		
Stability in terms of energy		
Lattice enthalpies		
Lattice entropies		

2. Complete the table for the two minerals: fluorite and halite.

Mineral	Formula	Crystal type	Position of six consecutive layers	Geometry of occupied holes
Fluorite				
Halite				

3. Why does the fluoride ion adopt its geometry in the fluorite lattice?

B2.5 (f) Determination of lattice energies

In a stable lattice, the repulsion energy between similarly charged ions is outweighed by the coulombic attractive energy between oppositely charge ions. The forces holding oppositely charged ions in a crystal lattice are electrostatic in nature. Lattice energies are exothermic, meaning that energy is released when gaseous ions come together to form a crystalline lattice when the ionic bonds form. Lattice energies are a measure of ionic bond strength. Ionic compounds have stable lattices as their lower energy means greater stability than if the ions existed in the gas phase. The lattice energy for sodium chloride has been determined experimentally from Born-Haber cycles (A1.3e) to be -787 kJ mol^{-1}. The formation of ionic compounds is favoured with high electron affinities for the anions and low ionisation energies for the cations.

Lattice energies can also be determined from crystal structure data and are thought of as being theoretical values. Lattice energies determined in this way are based on the geometry of the crystal lattice and assume the ions to be point charges and not vibrating, *i.e.* static. Lattice energies are shown in the table. To calculate lattice energies theoretical chemists need to know what is in the unit cell, the ion charges and the distance between the ions. When there is ~5% difference between the two lattice energies for a compound, the ionic model (B1.7d) works well. When there are large differences between the two lattice energies for a compound, it is due to there being considerable covalent character.

	Lattice energies $\left(\Delta H_{\text{latt}}^{\ominus} \right)$	
Ionic Compound	Experimental value (Born-Haber) kJ mol^{-1}	Theoretical value (Crystal data) kJ mol^{-1}
NaCl	-776	-766
NaBr	-719	-731
NaI	-670	-686
KI	-632	-631
ZnS	-3615	-3427
AgCl	-921	-769
AgBr	-876	-759
AgI	-862	-736

How does the electronegativity of the halogen affect the size of the lattice energy? The values tell us that sodium chloride has stronger ionic bonds than sodium bromide which in turn has stronger bonds than sodium iodide. In almost 'completely' ionic crystals, such as the Group 1 halides, where the ions are 'perfect' spheres, there is a strong agreement between the theoretical lattice energies and the experimental values. This is not the case where there is a small electronegativity difference between the elements making up the crystalline solid. When there are large differences between theoretical and experimental lattice energies, it provides evidence for some electron sharing between ions, indicating a partly covalent nature to the structure. The position of such compounds is worth plotting on the van Arkel triangle (A2.1d).

When calculating lattice energies using a simple electrostatic model, about 90% of the bonding energies are accounted for. In a crystal lattice, there are more interactions than just a simple ion pair. Other interactions include dispersion forces (van der Waals) and the repulsion of closed shells. The ionic model assumes that crystal lattices are made up of spherical ions and it is important to realise that ions are not point charges but can be considered to be electron clouds that repel each other at very close distances. The electron clouds can be visualised using electron density maps (B1.7d). In the case of sodium chloride, each sodium ion is attracted to its six nearest neighbours of opposite charge, but is also repelled by its twelve nearest neighbours of the same charge. Ions within a lattice are not motionless. Even at absolute zero there would have to be some vibration.

At university, the Born-Landé equation is used to determine lattice energies and the Madelung constant (summation of all the geometrical interactions) is used to determine the energy of a single ion in a crystal. The Madelung constant for NaCl is 1.74756 and for CaF$_2$ is 2.51939. This level of understanding is not required at high school/ sixth form level.

It is an interesting exercise to consider the types of defects that might occur in crystals. Since there will inevitably be imperfections in crystals due to an entropy factor. Defects which have been identified from x-ray crystallographic studies include:

- a single atom missing from a lattice

- an electron occupying anionic site

- a cation displaced from its normal site

- impurity of a higher charge.

The latter defect is the basis of doping in the semi-conductor industry.

Question 12.7

1.　What are the two lattice energies for any ionic compound and how may they be determined?

13 Organic Chemistry: Preliminaries

Organic Chemistry

Organic chemistry is the study of the compounds of carbon. As the name implies, organic compounds are integral to life. Organic chemistry is also of great importance in the modern technological world.

Organic chemist, Professor George Pettit of Arizona State University, who isolated the anti-cancer drug combrestatin in 1987.

Formulae

Chemists are very fortunate that they can communicate successfully with any chemist in the world using the subject's universal language of formulae.

There are several types of formula that chemists use depending on the complexity of the process or substances they are communicating to others. The types of formula are: molecular, empirical, structural, displayed, skeletal and partial skeletal. Drawing skeletal formulae can really save you time and is certainly worth practising early on in any chemistry course.

Formula	Definition	Example (butanoic acid)
molecular	Number and type of atoms grouped together.	$C_4H_8O_2$
empirical	Simplest whole number ratio of atoms.	C_2H_4O
structural	Groups of atoms, including functional group to give an unambiguous structure.	$CH_3CH_2CH_2COOH$
displayed	Shows all the bonds in a molecule.	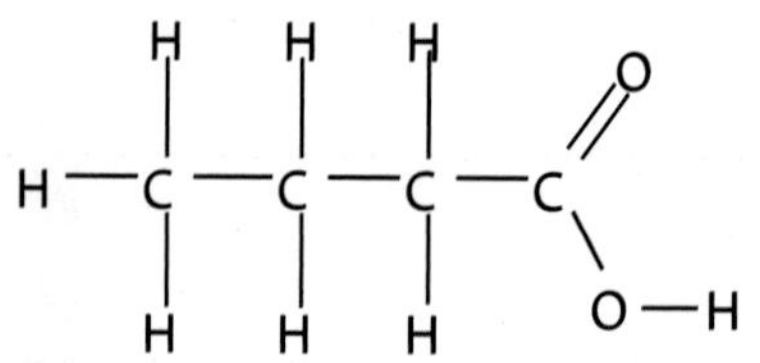
skeletal	Simplest organic formula. No need to show carbon or hydrogen atoms directly. Hydrocarbon parts are shown as zig-zags with functional groups drawn.	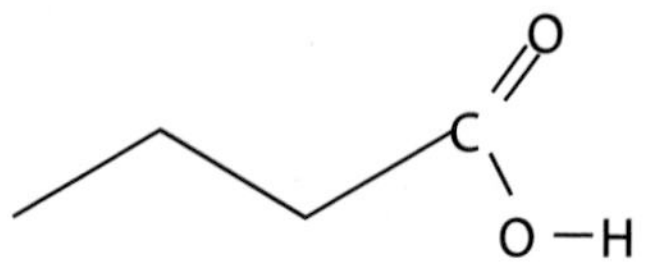
partial skeletal	A group or groups other than the functional group are shown. This is often helpful with stereoisomers.	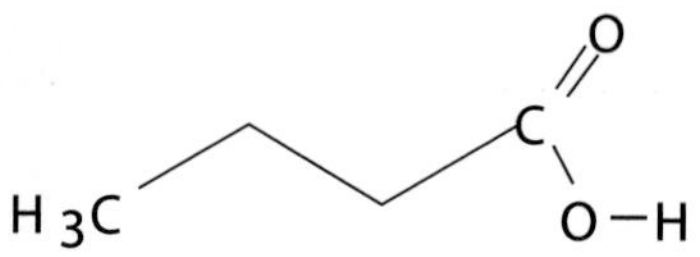
3-dimensional	The shape of a molecule shown in 3D. Groups are either in the plane of the page (shown as lines), out of the page (filled wedges) or into the page (dashed wedges).	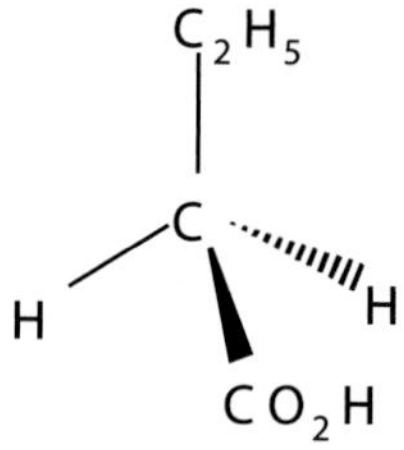

A3.1 (a) Tetrahedral carbon

Chemists need to think of organic molecules in 3 dimensions and to do this they need to appreciate that carbon is tetravalent, *i.e.* it forms four bonds in organic molecules.

Carbon with its atomic number of 6 has six electrons and an electron configuration $1s^2 2s^2 2p^2$. By promoting one of the 2s electrons to the vacant $2p_z$ orbital it has four unpaired electrons available for bonding which is why it has a valency of four.

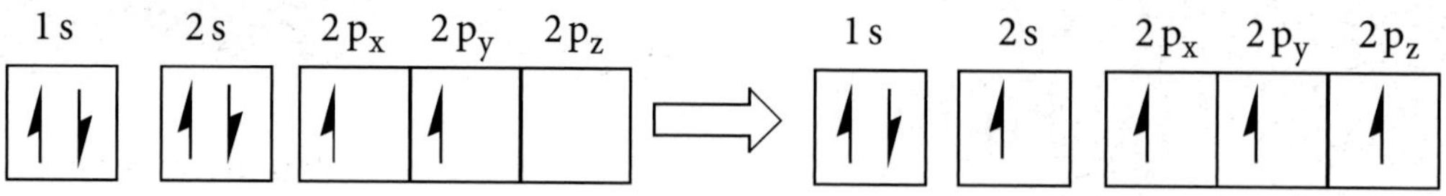

The energy needed to promote the 2s electron is more than 'paid back' when carbon forms covalent bonds. When drawing displayed, skeletal or 3D diagrams it is important to check the structure by ensuring that each carbon atom has four bonds.

Double and triple bonds have restricted rotation and they result in parts of a molecule being planar.

Molecular formula	Substance	3D structure
C_2H_6	ethane	
C_2H_4	ethene	
C_2H_2	ethyne	H—C≡C—H
C_2H_3N	ethanenitrile	
C_6H_6	benzene	

A3.1 (b) Skeletal formula

Realistic geometry essentially means drawing the carbon backbone (the skeleton of the molecule) as a zig-zag which it would adopt according to the VSEPR theory. X-ray crystallography has confirmed that simple structures do mostly adopt zig-zag conformations (shapes) in the solid state.

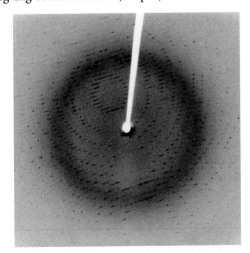

An x-ray diffraction photograph of a component of the SARS virus (GNU licensed photograph)

Zigzag road sign

Alkanes are hydrocarbons (compounds containing only hydrogen and carbon atoms) with the general formula C_nH_{2n+2} where n is the number of carbon atoms, and they are the simplest molecules to begin drawing as skeletal formulae.

Alkane	Displayed formula with zigzags	Skeletal formula
propane	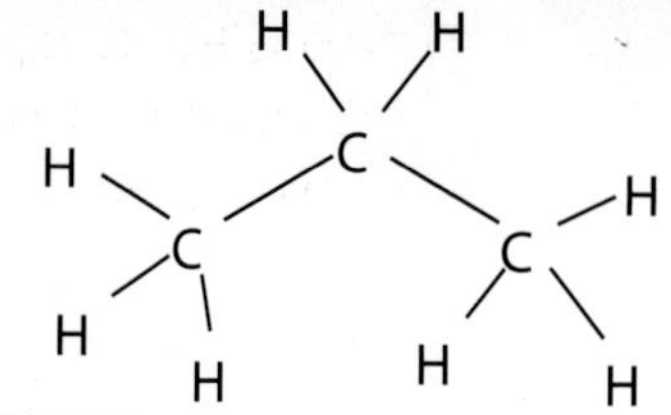	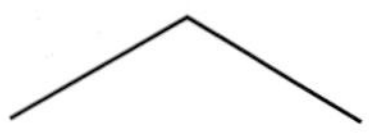
butane	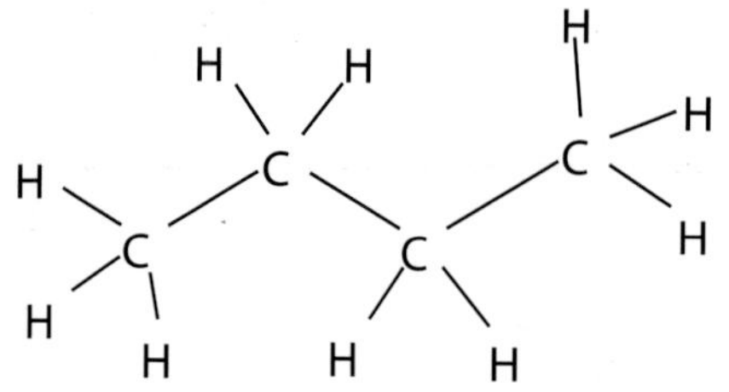	
pentane	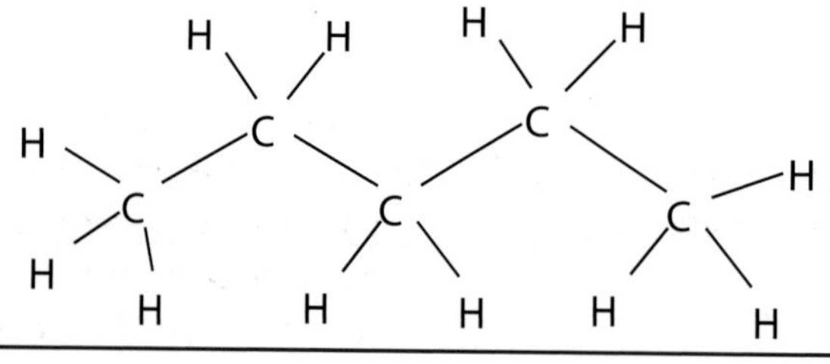	

Next follow some examples of skeletal formulae of interesting biological molecules.

Skeletal formula	Example
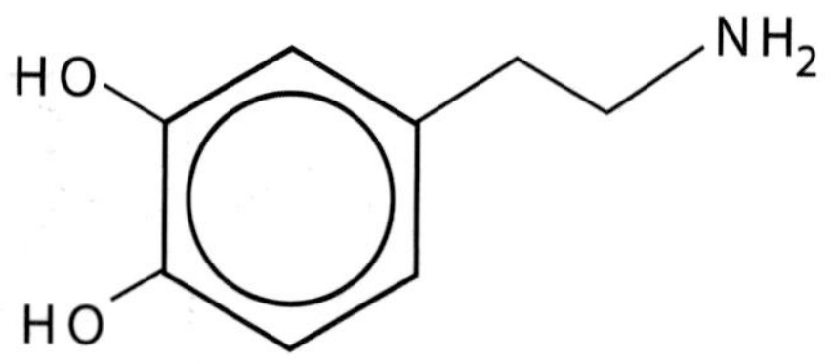	**Dopamine** is a neurotransmitter produced in the brain and low levels of it have been implicated with Parkinson's disease.
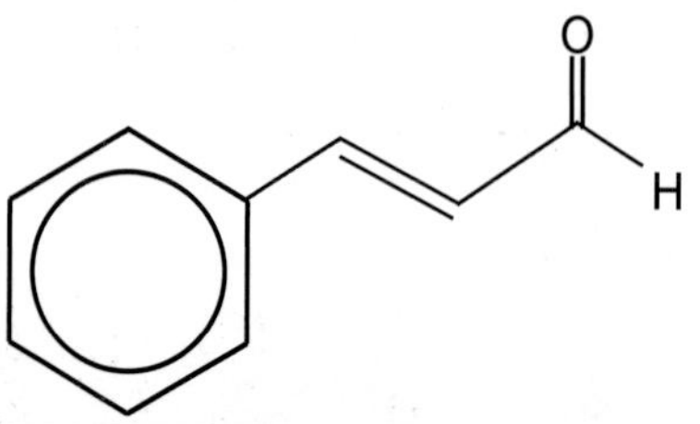	**Cinnamaldehyde** (or more precisely the *trans* isomer) is found in cinnamon and was the only spice to come out of the 'New World'.
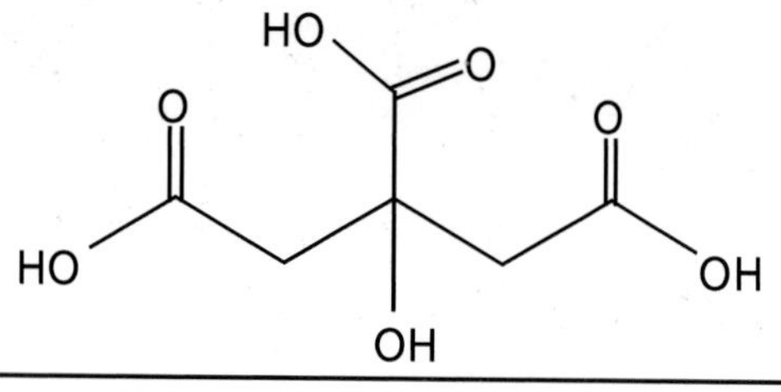	**Citric acid** is the chemical that gives citrus fruits their sour taste and is a natural preservative.
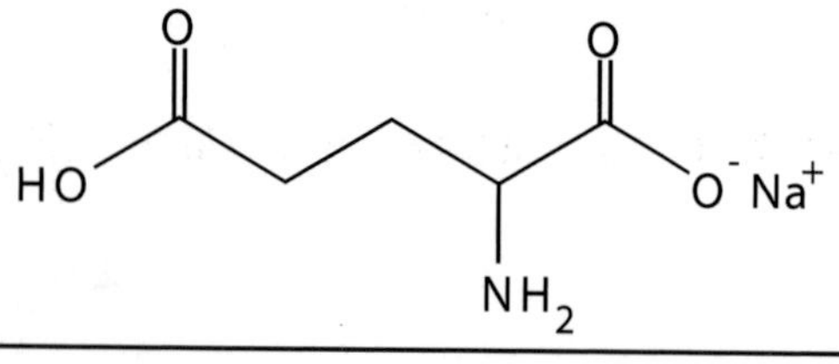	**Monosodium glutamate (MSG)** is a flavour enhancer. It is the sodium salt of a non-essential amino acid and has the code E612. Only the L-enantiomer is used in foods.

Skeletal formula	Example
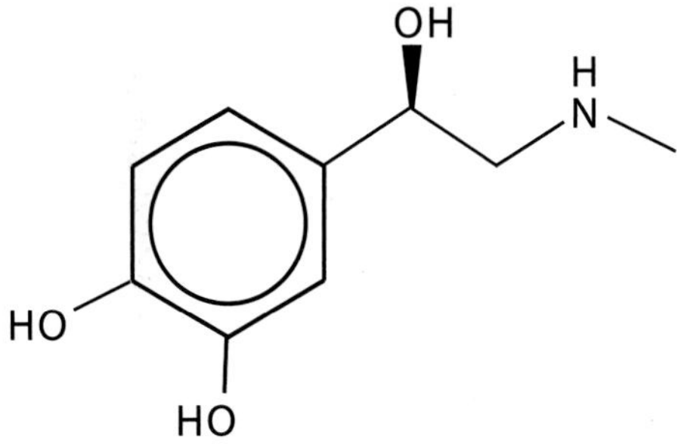	**Adrenaline** is the 'fight or flight' hormone is also called epinephrine. It is the active ingredient in Epi Pens used by people with allergies to prevent anaphylactic shock. 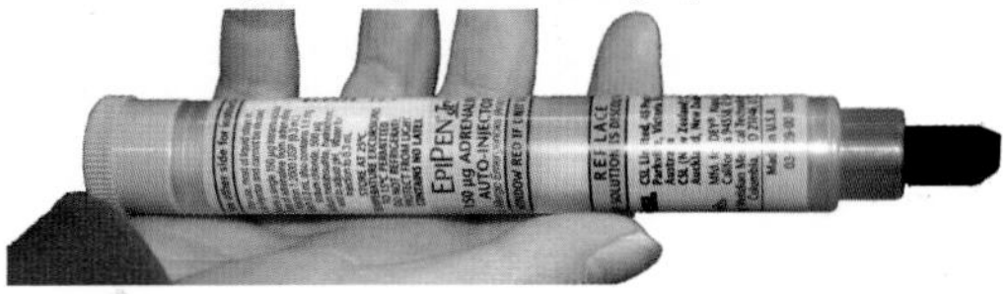 Epi Pen

A3.1 (c) Molecular formulae from structures

In a molecular formula it is conventional to write the number of carbons first, followed by the number of hydrogen atoms, and finally the other atoms (**heteroatoms**) in ascending atomic number order.

So for ethanol the correct order is carbon, then hydrogen and lastly oxygen, *i.e.* C_2H_6O. In the case of ethanol the heteroatom is oxygen.

For nitrobenzene there are two heteroatoms, nitrogen and oxygen and they are written in atomic order number, so the molecular formula is $C_6H_5NO_2$.

It is important that chemists can derive molecular formulae from structures as it allows them to calculate molar masses and to correctly predict the molecular ion in a mass spectrum. It is also an important part of calculating atom economy in reactions as well as calculating the correct proportion of reactants and reagents.

Care is needed when working out molecular formulae and it is often helpful to cross off atoms as they are counted or to draw out the displayed formula. Dettol is a versatile substance with many commercial uses as an anti-bacterial agent. Its IUPAC (International Union of Pure and Applied Chemists) name is 4-chloro-3,5-dimethylphenol.

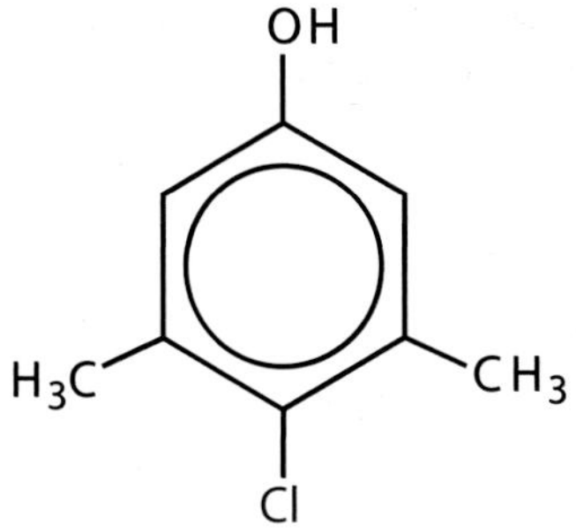

Dettol's molecular formula is C_8H_9OCl

Testosterone is the primary male sex hormone produced in the testes. It is also produced in the ovaries of females but in much smaller amounts. Testosterone belongs to a class of compounds called **anabolic steroids** which have been used by those athletes who are 'drug cheats' to enhance their performance through greater muscle building and increased red blood cell production. The structure of testosterone is shown, and next to it the atoms added in to make it easier to count and find the correct molecular formula.

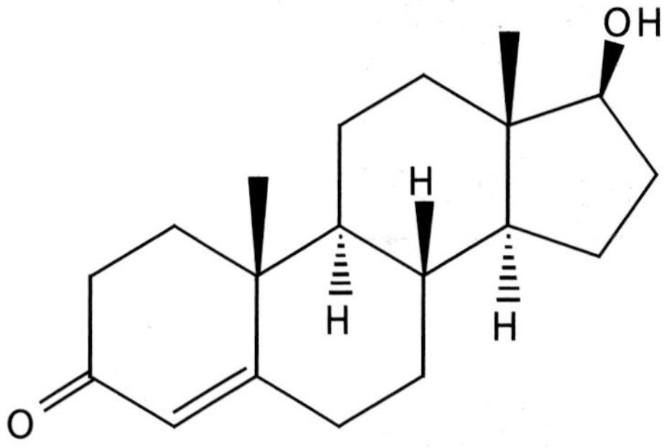

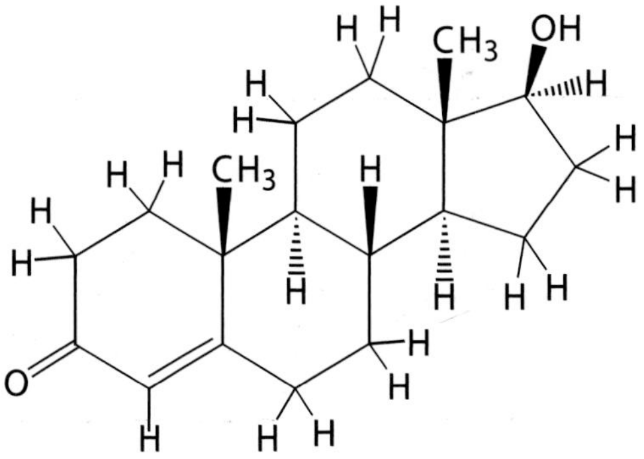

Testosterone's molecular formula is $C_{19}H_{28}O_2$

Question 13.1

Work out the molecular formulae and molar masses of the following compounds and complete the table.

Skeletal formula	Molecular formula	Molar mass (g mol⁻¹)
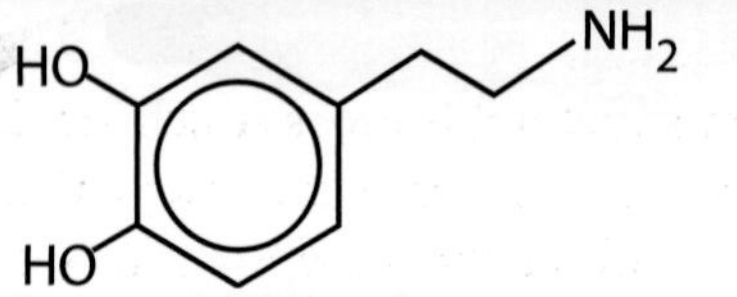 Dopamine		
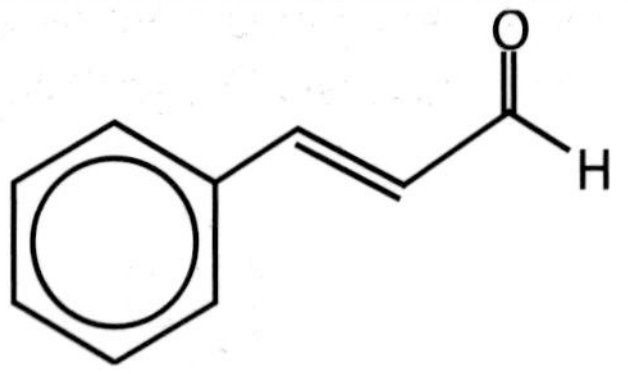 Cinnamaldehyde		
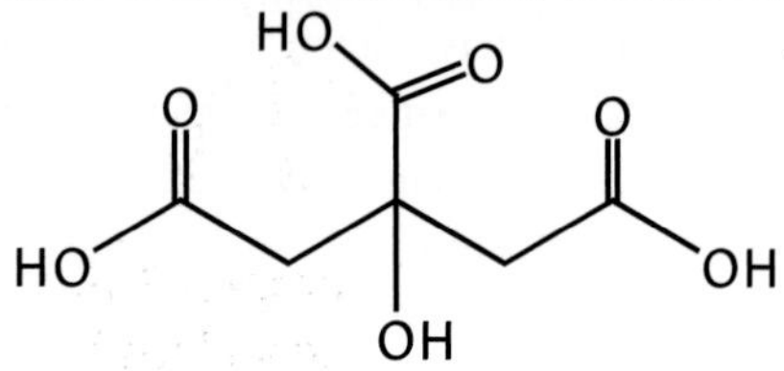 Citric acid		
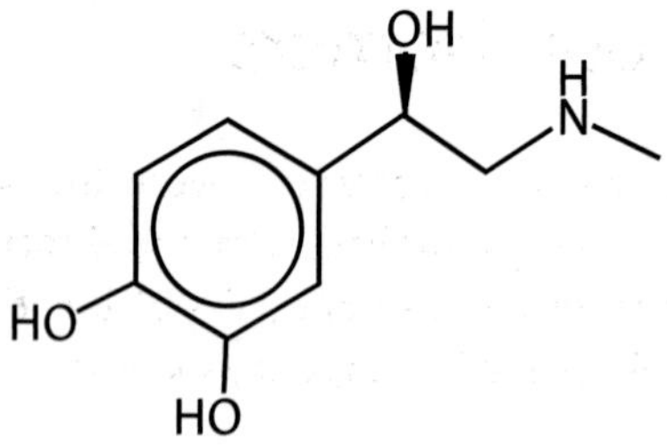 Adrenaline		

A3.1 (d) Structural isomerism

Isomers are not the same as isotopes. Isotopes are different versions of an element with different masses. Structural isomers are substances with the same type and number of atoms but with a different arrangement of those atoms. This means that structural isomers are substances with the same molecular formula, but having a different structural formula. The four types of structural isomers are: positional isomers, chain isomers, tautomers and functional group isomers. To be correctly classified as isomers both versions need to be isolated. Pairs of isomers will have distinctive physical and/or chemical properties.

Positional isomers

Positional isomers can be compounds that are either acyclic or cyclic. If the position of a functional group is different for the same carbon skeleton then it is a positional isomer. Acyclic examples shown as skeletal formulae are:

propan-1-ol:

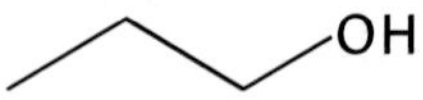

& propan-2-ol:

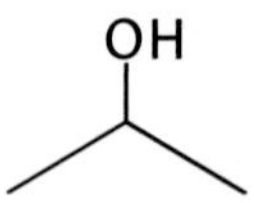

and pent-1-ene:

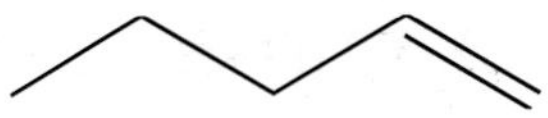

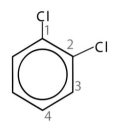

& pent-2-ene:

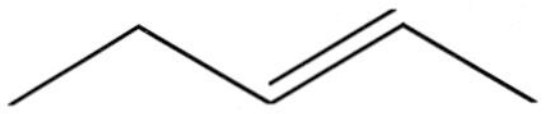

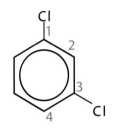

There are three isomers of dichlorobenzene (a cyclic compound) known historically as *ortho*, *meta* and *para*.

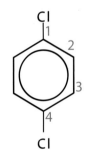

1,2-dichlorobenzene
ortho isomer

1,3-dichlorobenzene
meta isomer

1,4-dichlorobenzene
para isomer

Chain isomers

Chain isomers have different skeletons which differ because of varying amounts of branching. The chain isomers shown are butane (b.p. = -0.5°C) and 2-methylpropane (b.p. = -11.7°C) which have quite different physical properties. Butane which is often used as a fuel in caravans is not suitable in temperatures below the freezing point of water.

butane   2-methylpropane

Chain isomers have proved to be of great interest to the petroleum industry as the more branched isomers of octane, such as 2,2,4-trimethylpentane (octane rating 100%) burn more efficiently at lower temperatures and are less prone to pre-ignition in petrol engines.

Tautomers

Tautomers are pairs of structural isomers which are directly interconvertible and are in dynamic equilibrium with each other. Tautomers can exist in the solid state (crystals) as well as in aqueous solutions. Tautomers exist for carbonyl (C=O) compounds with hydrogen atoms on adjacent carbon atoms, *e.g.* keto ⇌ enol. These hydrogen atoms are often described as alpha (α). Propanone exists in equilibrium with its tautomer propen-2-ol.

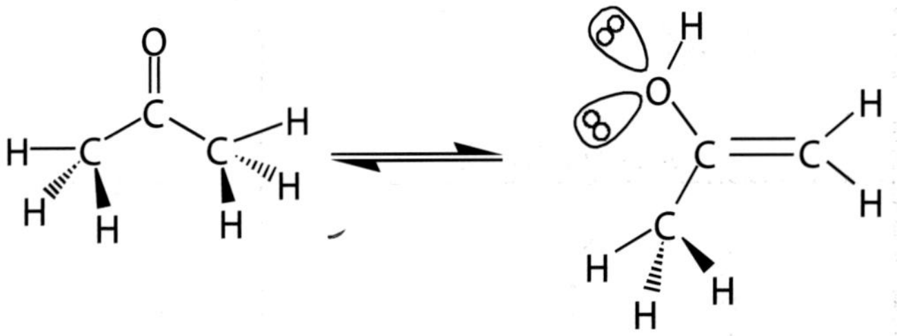

propanone
(*keto* form)

propen-2-ol
(*enol* form)

Functional group isomers

Functional group isomers are substances with the same molecular formula, but having a different structural formula and a different functional group. Certain pairs of functional groups have corresponding functional group isomer(s).

- aldehydes and ketones

- alcohols and ethers

- carboxylic acids and esters

- cycloalkanes and alkenes

- ketones and enols

It is relatively straightforward to remember that aldehydes and ketones can be functional group isomers, as both functional groups share the same general formula, $C_nH_{2n}O$, where n = number of carbon atoms. The first example of such a pair is propanal (CH_3CH_2CHO) and propanone (CH_3COCH_3) where n =3.

Alcohols and ethers are another example of functional group isomers. The simplest example is ethanol (C_2H_5OH) and methoxymethane (CH_3OCH_3) which both have the molecular formula C_2H_6O.

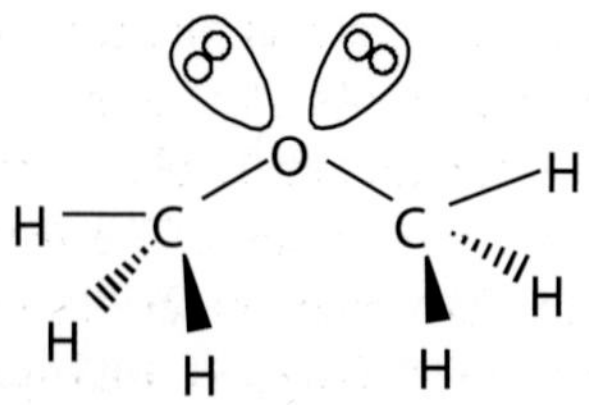

methoxymethane
C_2H_6O

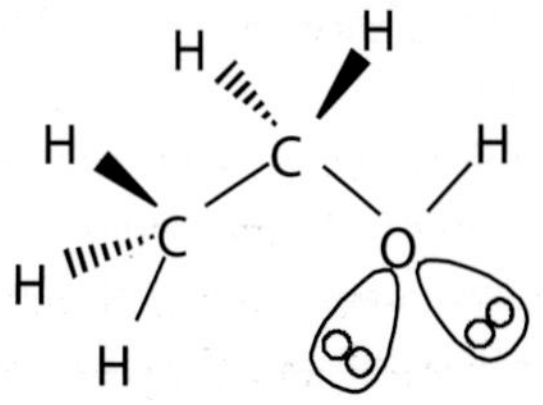

ethanol
C_2H_6O

Carboxylic acids and esters are another example of functional group isomers. An example is methyl ethanoate (CH_3OCOCH_3) and propanoic acid (CH_3CH_2COOH) which both have the molecular formula $C_3H_6O_2$.

A less obvious example of functional group isomers are cycloalkanes and alkenes. An example is cyclobutane ($CH_2)_4$ and but-1-ene ($CH_3CH_2CH=CH_2$) which share the same molecular formula C_4H_8.

Stereoisomers

Stereoisomers are two molecules which have the same molecular formula and their atoms are bonded in the same order. They have the same structural formula but are still non-identical. They are different because they have a different arrangement of bonds in space. The two types of stereoisomers are **geometric isomers**, also known as *cis-trans*, and **optical isomers**. It is helpful to think of stereoisomers as space isomers.

A3.1 (d)
Geometric isomerism

Geometric isomerism occurs because of restricted rotation about double bonds (C=C, N=N). What is needed for geometric isomerism is for each carbon in the C=C double bond to be bonded to two different groups. The prefix *cis* is given when two identical groups on the C=C bond are on the same side of the molecule. The prefix *trans* is given when two identical groups on the C=C bond are on opposite sides of the molecule. With carbon-carbon double bonds, there is restricted rotation because of the π-orbital overlap.

Alkene examples

For the geometric isomers of but-2-ene we will consider the methyl groups (CH_3) as the identical groups attached to the different carbons of the C=C bond. We could easily have considered the hydrogen atoms.

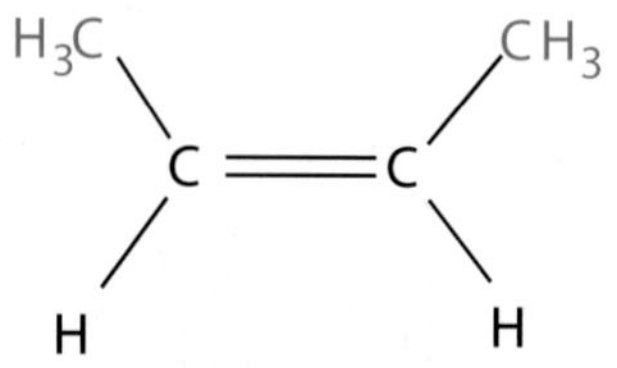

cis but-2-ene

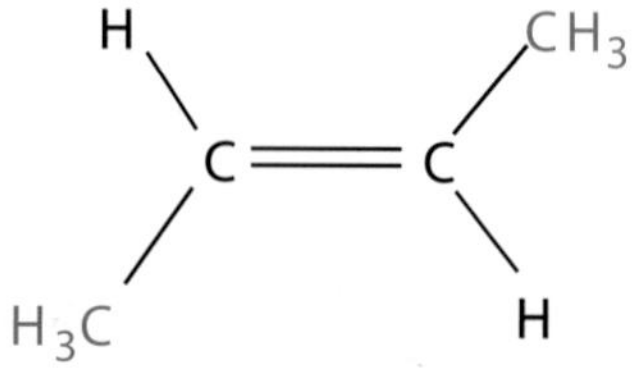

trans but-2-ene

Geometric isomers have different physical properties. For example maleic acid (*cis*-butenedioic acid) has a m.p. of 135°C whereas fumaric acid (*trans*-butenedioic acid) has a m.p. of 287°C. The *cis* isomer is also much more soluble (×100) in water than the *trans* isomer.

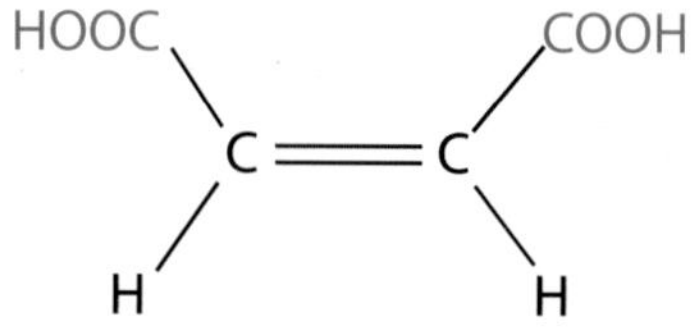

maleic acid
cis isomer

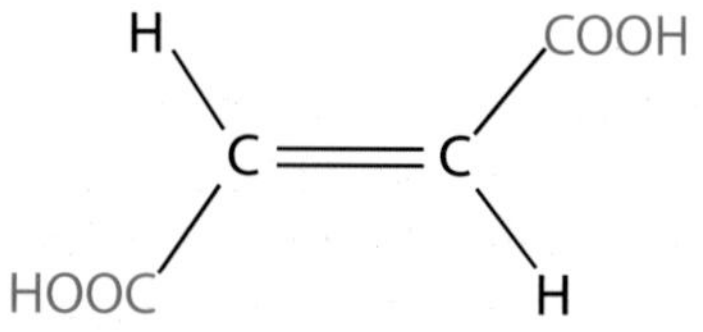

fumaric acid
trans isomer

Cycloalkane example

It is also possible to get geometric isomers with saturated ring structures. There is some rotation of the carbon-carbon bonds but it is restricted by the small 'ring size.' The example shown is 1,2-dibromocyclopropane. The *cis* isomer has the two bromine atoms above the plane of the ring. The *trans* isomer has one bromine atom above the plane of the ring and the other bromine atom below the plane of the ring.

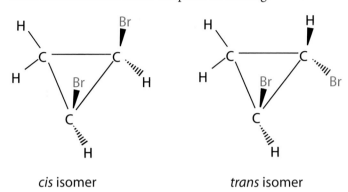

cis isomer   *trans* isomer

Transition metal complexes examples

Geometric isomerism also occurs with square planar transition metal complexes where the coordination number to the metal atom, or ion, is four.

The anti-cancer drug *cis*-platin $[Pt^{2+}Cl^-_2(NH_3)_2]$ used to 'cure' the *Tour de France* (cycling) champion Lance Armstrong is a geometric isomer. Geometric isomers are also possible with octahedral transition metal complexes with a coordination number of six.

A3.1 (e) Optical isomerism

Optical isomerism exists in substances with asymmetric (unsymmetrical) carbon atoms. Optical isomers are easy to recognise from their skeletal or displayed formulae because the simplest type have four different groups attached to one carbon atom. Optical isomers have the same molecular formula, the same structural formula and the same chemical properties. Optical isomers have a different arrangement in space and show a marked difference in their physiological activity. This phenomenon of different chemical reactivity in biochemical reactions is a result of the importance of the substrate's geometry and the shape of the active site of the enzyme. This is often called the 'lock and key' theory. One optical isomer fits into the active site much as the left hand fits into the left hand of a pair of gloves.

Chirality is a term applied to any asymmetric molecule which does not match its mirror image. Asymmetric molecules do not possess a centre of symmetry, a plane of symmetry or an axis of symmetry so are essentially unsymmetrical.

In humans about 10% of the population are left-handed, but all biomolecules which can exist as optical isomers are 'left-handed.' It is helpful to imagine molecules as having handedness. There are two versions of chiral molecules which cannot be superimposed on their mirror images. The pairs of versions are called **enantiomers**. Each enantiomer has the ability to rotate the plane of polarisation of plane polarised light (ppl) in different directions by the same number of degrees (°). Rotation of ppl can be either in a clockwise direction (+°) or in an anticlockwise direction (-°). If you have a 50:50 (equimolar) mixture of both enantiomers it is called a **racemic mixture**.

As with all repeatable experiments, comparisons are needed. The standard against which all other optically active isomers are compared is 2,3-dihydroxypropanal (glyceraldehyde).

$$ HO - \overset{\overset{\displaystyle H}{|}}{C} \cdots CHO $$
$$ CH_2OH $$

glyceraldehyde

The specific rotation of ppl by optically active isomers depends upon concentration of the substance (mol dm^{-3}), path length, and the substance itself. Plane polarised light is 'made' when white light is passed through a calcite ($CaCO_3$) nicol prism. Plane polarised light is light which vibrates in a single plane. The angle of rotation of ppl caused by optically active isomers is measured in a polarimeter.

Amino acids are as good a place as any to begin to explore the differences between a pair of enantiomers. The simplest amino acid is glycine, NH_2CH_2COOH which is 2-aminoethanoic acid. It does not form optical isomers as there are not four different groups attached to the central carbon atom. The mirror plane is indicated by the dashed vertical line between the stereoisomers.

glycine   glycine

But the next simplest amino acid, $NH_2CH(CH_3)(COOH)$, (alanine) 2-aminopropanoic acid does have four different groups attached to the central carbon atom and therefore has optical isomers. Glycine has superimposable mirror images, but alanine does not have superimposable mirror images.

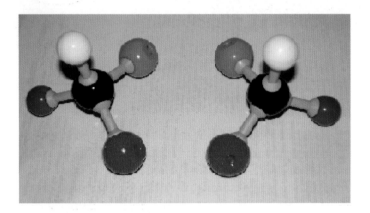

alanine | alanine

When playing with **molymods** it is very easy to switch from one enantiomer to the other. All you have to do is to swap any two of the groups attached to the chiral carbon atom. When you have models of enantiomers it is possible to line up any two of the groups attached to the chiral carbon atom, but the other two groups are always a mismatch.

Lactic acid, 2-hydroxypropanoic acid is a product of the anaerobic respiration of glucose. It is also found in milk which has been left to be turned sour by bacteria. Lactic acid has two forms as it has four different groups attached to the middle carbon atom. The four groups are a hydrogen atom, methyl, hydroxyl and carboxyl groups.

lactic acid | lactic acid

A common misconception

Don't fall into the common mistake of thinking that there is a connection between the letter assigned to an enantiomer (R or S) and the direction of rotation of ppl. The following examples illustrate there is no relationship or clear cut pattern between the two. The direction of rotation cannot be accurately predicted and needs to be determined experimentally. R-glyceraldehye rotates ppl to the right +° but R-phenylsuccinic acid rotates ppl to the left -°. The structural formula for phenylsuccinic acid is $C_6H_5CH(COOH)CH_2COOH$

Molecules with several chiral centres

Many of the six million known organic compounds contain more than one asymmetric carbon atom. The simple formula used to calculate the possible number of stereoisomers for molecules containing one or more chiral carbons is 2^n where n = number of chiral centres. So for a substance with four chiral centres $2^n = 2^4 = 16$ stereoisomers. This means that there will be eight pairs of enantiomers. There are three stereoisomers of 2,3-dibromobutane, a pair of enantiomers (+) 2,3-dibromobutane, (-) 2,3-dibromobutane and the diastereoisomer *meso*-2,3-dibromobutane which despite the two asymmetric (chiral) carbon atoms has a plane of symmetry. In order to have a *meso* compound the molecule must have two chiral centres which have identical substituents. The RS notation will be explained in a later chapter discussing the Cahn-Ingold-Prelog selection rules.

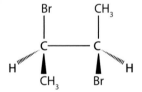

(RR) 2,3-dibromobutane | (SS) 2,3-dibromobutane

meso (RS) 2,3-dibromobutane | *meso* (SR) 2,3-dibromobutane

Other types of optical isomers

There are examples of some crystals, such as quartz, which have chirality within their crystal structures. Quartz (SiO_2) is the low temperature form of silicon(IV) oxide. It is also possible to get optical isomers with transition metal complexes, which are discussed elsewhere.

Summary of isomerism

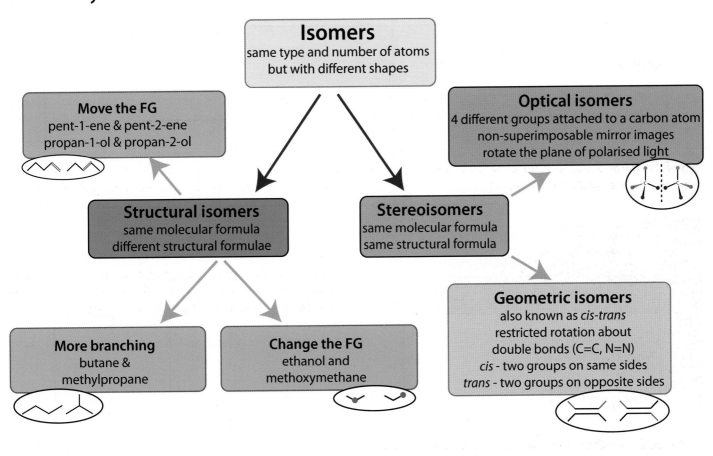

Isomers
same type and number of atoms but with different shapes

Move the FG
pent-1-ene & pent-2-ene
propan-1-ol & propan-2-ol

Optical isomers
4 different groups attached to a carbon atom
non-superimposable mirror images
rotate the plane of polarised light

Structural isomers
same molecular formula
different structural formulae

Stereoisomers
same molecular formula
same structural formula

More branching
butane &
methylpropane

Change the FG
ethanol and
methoxymethane

Geometric isomers
also known as *cis-trans*
restricted rotation about
double bonds (C=C, N=N)
cis - two groups on same sides
trans - two groups on opposite sides

A3.1 (f) 3D Structures

When drawing structures in three dimensions, it takes practice to make them look realistic. Some guidance on the stages needed to draw successfully follows. Start off by drawing the framework tetrahedral arrangement and then add in the atoms or groups of atoms. There are three dimensions: the first two dimensions are in the plane of the paper shown as plain lines, the third dimension is towards the reader shown as wedged bonds and away from the reader shown as dashed bonds.

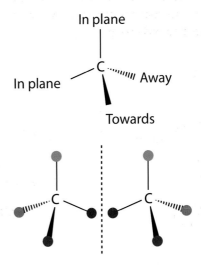

Questions 13.2

1. Complete the table to show the similarities and differences between the different types of isomers from structural to stereoisomers.

Isomers	Chemical properties	Physical properties	Effect on ppl
structural			
geometric			
optical			

2. Complete the table by placing a tick (√) in the boxes that correspond to each pair of molecules. Leave blank boxes where there is no tick required.

Pair of molecules	Structural isomers	Geometric isomers	Not isomers
but-1-ene & but-2-ene			
cis but-2-ene & trans but-2-ene			
propan-1-ol & propan-2-ol			
propanal & propanone			
1,1-dichloroethene & 1,2-dichloroethane			

A3.1 (g) Nomenclature

Nomenclature is the unambiguous naming of compounds to give their exact structures. There are over six million known organic compounds and an organisation called IUPAC (International Union of Pure and Applied Chemists) was formed in 1919 to agree the rules for chemists to name new organic compounds. It takes plenty of practice to be able to name organic molecules and eventually you should be able to name a molecule from its structure and also draw the structure from a name. As all other functional groups (FG) have their names referenced to an alkane, the simplest type of hydrocarbon, it is a good place to begin to learn the naming rules. Alkyl groups are the alkane minus one hydrogen atom to which a functional group (FG) or side chain is attached.

Main chain			Branch (side chains)	
Alkane name	Alkane formula	Number of carbons	Alkyl group	Alkyl formula
Methane	CH_4	1	Methyl	CH_3—
Ethane	C_2H_6	2	Ethyl	C_2H_5—
Propane	C_3H_8	3	Propyl	C_3H_7—
Butane	C_4H_{10}	4	Butyl	C_4H_9—
Pentane	C_5H_{12}	5	Pentyl	C_5H_{11}—
Hexane	C_6H_{14}	6	Hexyl	C_6H_{13}—
Heptane	C_7H_{16}	7	Heptyl	C_7H_{15}—
Octane	C_8H_{18}	8	Octyl	C_8H_{17}—
Nonane	C_9H_{20}	9	Nonyl	C_9H_{19}—
Decane	$C_{10}H_{22}$	10	Decyl	$C_{10}H_{21}$—

The ending of a name (suffix) tells you which FG is present. The rest of the name tells you the number of carbon atoms in the molecule.

Number of groups	Prefix (before the name)
1	mono
2	di
3	tri
4	tetra
5	penta

The prefix tells you how many of a particular group are present, for example the prefix di means two. When naming compounds the logical order is;

- identify the functional group(s)

- look for the longest chain of carbon atoms

- give the lowest possible number for the functional group(s)

- give the lowest possible number for the substituents

- place different FG or substituents in alphabetical order

- use the correct suffix and prefix.

Name of FG	Atoms of FG	Suffix	Example	Structure of example
alkane	C-C	ane	ethane	H_3C—CH_3
alkene	C=C	ene	ethene	H_2C=CH_2
alkyne	C≡C	yne	ethyne	HC≡CH
alcohol	OH	ol	ethanol	H_3C—CH_2—OH
aldehyde	CHO	al	ethanal	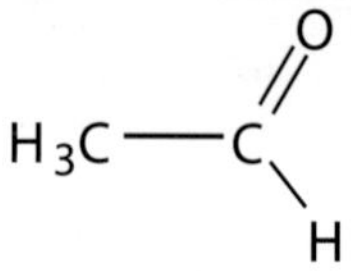
ketone	C(C=O)C	one	propanone	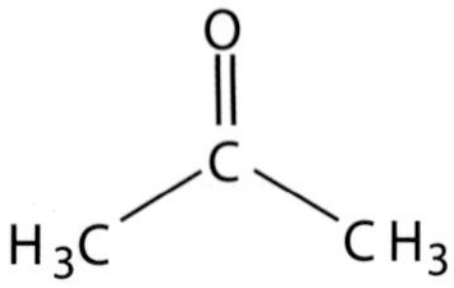
carboxylic acid	(C=O)OH	oic acid	ethanoic acid	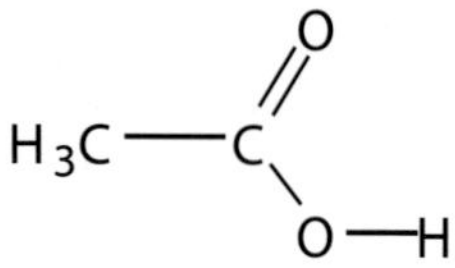
ester	(C=O)OC	oate	methyl methanoate	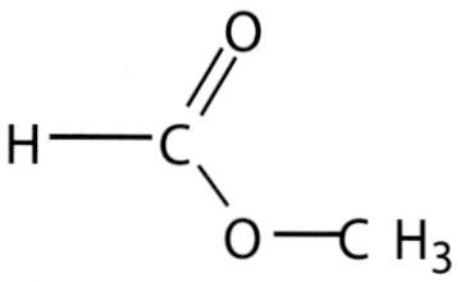
acid chloride	COCl	oyl chloride	ethanoyl chloride	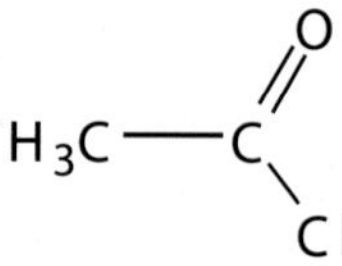
halogenoalkane	-Cl, -Br, -I	chloro ane	chloroethane	H_3C—CH_2Cl
ether	C-O-C	oxy ane	methoxymethane	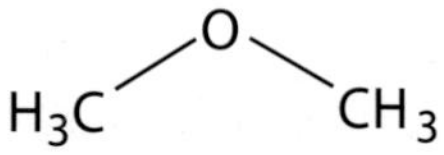
amide	-(C=O)NH-	amide	ethanamide	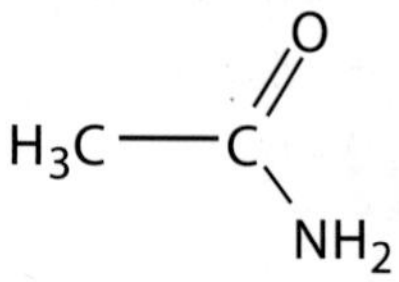
sulfonic acid	$-SO_3H$	sulfonic acid	methanesulfonic acid	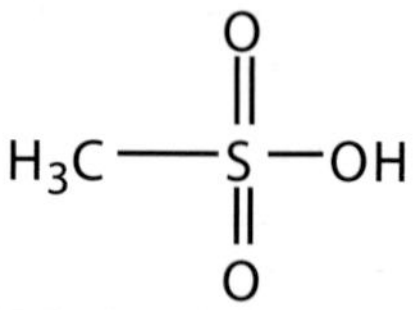
amine	NH_2	amine	methanamine	H_3C—NH_2
nitrile (cyanide)	C≡N	nitrile	ethanenitrile	H_3C—C≡N

Example 13.1

Propan-1-ol is a name that provides three pieces of information. The first part of the name is *propan* and this gives the length of the carbon chain, *i.e.* three carbon atoms joined with single covalent (C-C) bonds. The suffix *ol* which is the end of the name gives the functional group which is an alcohol. The number gives the position of the functional group on the first carbon atom. Both structures below are propan-1-ol as the numbering begins from the end of the chain that gives the lowest possible number. Note how the number of the substituent is separated from the letters in the name by hyphens.

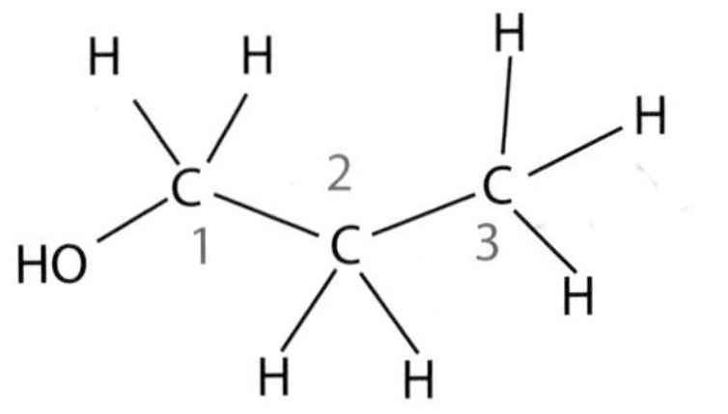

propan-1-ol

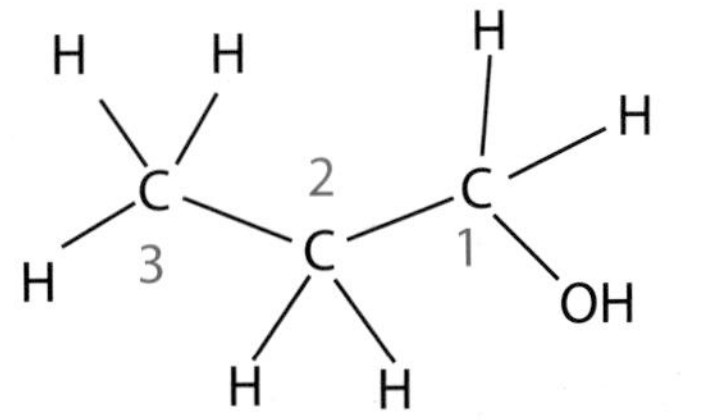

propan-1-ol

Example 13.2

Buta-1,3-diene is a name that provides four pieces of information. The first part of the name *buta* gives the length of the carbon chain, *i.e.* four carbon atoms. The suffix *ene* informs you that it is an alkene with a C=C bond. The *di* tells you there are two C=C double bonds. The numbers tell you that the C=C bonds start on the first and third carbons of the chain. Note how the numbers for the substituents are separated by a comma in the name.

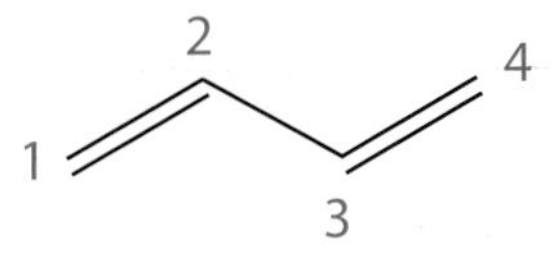

Example 13.3

Pentan-2-one and pentan-3-one are both ketones. The suffix *one* tells you that the carbonyl (C=O) is attached to a carbon atom on both sides. The stem of the name *pent* tells you that there are five carbon atoms. The numbers tell you on which carbon atom the carbonyl is attached.

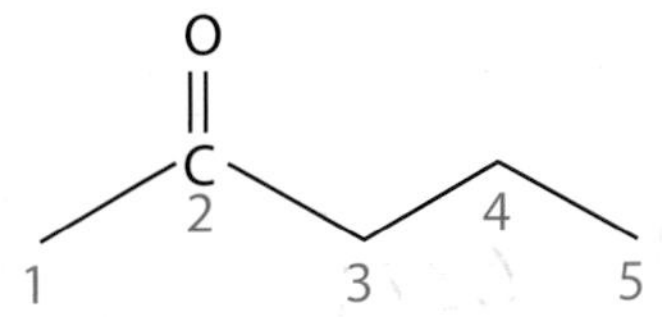

pentan-2-one

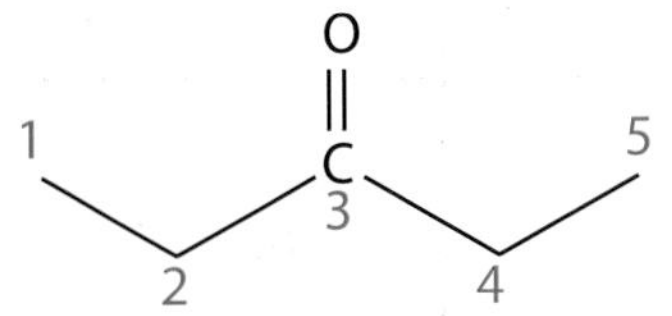

pentan-3-one

Example 13.4

Drawing the skeletal formula of 3-ethylpentane. The longest chain contains five carbon atoms which are linked by saturated C-C bonds. On the third carbon is an ethyl group (C_2H_5). Remember to try to draw the structure with a realistic zigzag.

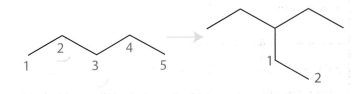

Example 13.5

Drawing a 3D formula of 2-chloro-2-methylpropane. The longest chain contains three carbon atoms which are linked by saturated C-C bonds. On the second carbon is a methyl group (CH_3) and a chlorine (Cl) atom. Remember that substituents joined to the main carbon chain are listed alphabetically.

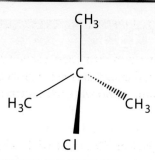

Example 13.6

Naming a chlorofluorocarbon (CFC) from its structure. The alphabetical rule makes the carbon on the left-hand side carbon number 1 as it has two chlorine atoms compared with the carbon on the right-hand side with one chlorine atom which becomes carbon number 2. The prefix *tri*, meaning three, is needed to describe the number of each type of halogen. So the name is 1,1,2-trichloro-1,2,2-trifluoroethane.

Example 13.7

Esters are one of the most difficult functional groups to name. The key is to remember that the portion joined to the oxygen in the C-O bond came from the alcohol and the portion joined to the carbon of the carbonyl came from the carboxylic acid. The alcohol part is written before the carboxylic acid part which is a convenient alphabetical order for these functional groups. The simplest ester is methyl methanoate which might look like an aldehyde to an inexperienced chemist. Remember the ester functional group is like that of a carboxylic acid (COOH) where the acidic proton has been replaced by a carbon atom to give COOC. As esters are used in flavourings it is not too difficult to remember cooc as a mispronunciation of cook.

carboxylic acid part   alcohol part

A3.1 (h) Terms and Reactions

Like all subjects, chemistry has an abundance of terms, and words, specific to the subject. Some of the key words which form the 'language' of organic chemists are explained followed by a few examples. More detail will be given in the discussion of the different functional groups. Chemists often have a number of models and definitions which they select depending on the chemical reaction being discussed. It is no different from a golfer picking out a sand wedge when caught in a bunker and reverting to a putter on the green.

It is important to understand the different types of reactions and to be able to use the correct vocabulary.

Oxidation

Addition of oxygen is a familiar definition of oxidation, *e.g.* the complete or partial combustion of a hydrocarbon like methane.

$$CH_4 (g) + 2 O_2 (g) \rightarrow CO_2 (g) + 2 H_2O (l)$$
complete combustion

$$CH_4 (g) + 1\frac{1}{2} O_2 (g) \rightarrow CO (g) + 2 H_2O (l)$$
incomplete combustion

$$CH_4 (g) + O_2 (g) \rightarrow C (s) + 2H_2O (l)$$
incomplete combustion

A less familiar definition of oxidation is an increase in the functional group level (FGL) *e.g.* the oxidation of ethanol to ethanal and/or ethanoic acid using acidified sodium dichromate solution. The oxidising agent is indicated by the symbol for oxygen in square brackets [O].

$$CH_3CH_2OH + [O] \rightarrow CH_3CHO + H_2O$$

$$CH_3CH_2OH + 2[O] \rightarrow CH_3COOH + H_2O$$

In terms of inorganic substances an oxidation is accompanied by an increase in oxidation number, due to a loss of electrons, *e.g.* $Fe^{2+} - e^- \rightarrow Fe^{3+}$ which happens when green iron(II) hydroxide is left exposed to the oxygen in air and turns rusty in colour.

Reduction

Reduction is the opposite reaction to oxidation. Reduction often accompanies an oxidation reaction. Reduction is loss of oxygen or gain of hydrogen as in the hydrogenation of an alkene, *e.g.* the reduction of cyclohexene to cyclohexane.

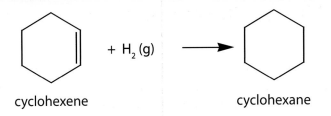

cyclohexene   cyclohexane

A less familiar definition of reduction is a decrease in the functional group level (FGL) *e.g.* the reduction of propanone to propan-2-ol using sodium borohydride ($NaBH_4$) or lithium aluminium hydride ($LiAlH_4$). The reducing agent is indicated by the symbol for hydrogen in square brackets [H].

$$CH_3COCH_3 + 2\,[H] \rightarrow CH_3CHOHCH_3$$

In terms of inorganic substances a reduction is accompanied by a decrease in oxidation number, due to a gain of electrons, *e.g.* $Cr^{6+} + 3e^- \rightarrow Cr^{3+}$ which is why orange dichromate changes colour to blue-green in the oxidation of alcohols.

Hydrolysis

Hydrolysis is the splitting of covalent bonds using water (H_2O) and can be carried out in either the presence of acid (H^+) or the presence of hydroxide (OH^-). Hydrolysis of any FG leads to the named FG of that level.

Hydrolysis of a halogenoalkane leads to an alcohol. This reaction takes place in water and in the presence of aqueous hydroxide, *e.g.* the hydrolysis of 1-chloropropane to propan-1-ol

$$CH_3CH_2CH_2Cl + H_2O \rightarrow CH_3CH_2CH_2OH + HCl$$

$$CH_3CH_2CH_2Cl + OH^- \rightarrow CH_3CH_2CH_2OH + Cl^-$$

Hydrolysis of esters can take place in the presence of acid (H^+) or the presence of a hydroxide such as sodium hydroxide, *e.g.* the hydrolysis of methyl ethanoate to methanol and ethanoic acid or sodium ethanoate. Don't forget that acid hydrolysis, like esterification, is reversible.

$$CH_3CO_2CH_3 + H_2O \rightleftharpoons CH_3CO_2H + CH_3OH$$

$$CH_3CO_2CH_3 + NaOH \rightarrow CH_3CO_2Na + CH_3OH$$

Condensation

Condensation is when two molecules react with the elimination of a small molecule. An **esterification reaction** is a condensation as a small molecule of water is eliminated, *e.g.* the condensation of ethanoic acid and ethanol to form ethyl ethanoate and water.

$$CH_3CO_2H + CH_3CH_2OH \rightleftharpoons CH_3CO_2CH_2CH_3 + H_2O$$

Amides can be prepared *via* a condensation reaction between an acid chloride and an amine, *e.g.* ethanoyl chloride reacting with methylamine to form N-methylethanamide and hydrogen chloride.

$$CH_3COCl + CH_3NH_2 \rightarrow CH_3CONHCH_3 + HCl$$

Condensation reactions are very important in living systems as polyamides such as proteins are made *via* multiple condensations of amino acids. Complex carbohydrates, such as starch and cellulose, are made by condensation of glucose molecules.

University level condensations include:

- Claisen condensation (ester + ester $\rightarrow$ β-ketonic ester + alcohol)

- Aldol condensation ($CH_3CHO + CH_3CHO \rightarrow CH_3CH=CHCHO + H_2O$)

Isomerisation

Isomerisation is the conversion of a compound to an isomer of that compound. Isomerisation of straight chain alkanes to branched alkanes using a platinum catalyst by the petrochemical industry has led to more efficient fuels being prepared for use in motor vehicles. The fuels are assigned an octane rating from 0 (heptane) to 100 (2,2,4-trimethylpentane).

Isomerisation reactions are very important in living systems and are carried out by enzymes called **isomerases**. A liver enzyme (fumarase) converts fumaric acid into maleic acid, *i.e.* the *trans* isomer to the *cis* isomer of butenedioic acid.

Substitution

Substitution reactions are where one atom or group is replaced by another atom or group.

The test for phenol is a good example of an (electrophilic) substitution reaction where three hydrogen atoms in the 2, 4, 6- positions are substituted (swapped) for bromine atoms when a phenolic solution reacts with bromine water.

The preparation of an alcohol from a halogenoalkane is a good example of a (nucleophilic) substitution reaction where the halogen group is substituted by an OH group. Care is needed with the reaction conditions as the substitution reaction competes with an elimination reaction. Ethanol can be made from chloroethane in a substitution reaction with hydroxide.

$$CH_3CH_2Cl + NaOH \rightarrow CH_3CH_2OH + NaCl$$

The halogen can also be substituted by other groups and chloroethane reacts with ammonia to form ethylamine and hydrogen chloride.

$$CH_3CH_2Cl + NH_3 \rightarrow CH_3CH_2NH_2 + HCl$$

Addition

Addition reactions are where one molecule adds onto another molecule with the formation of a single product. Alkene reactions are characterised by (electrophilic) addition reactions, *e.g.* the addition of hydrogen (H_2), bromine (Br_2), hydrogen bromide (HBr), or hydrogen oxide (H_2O) to ethene.

$$CH_2=CH_2 \quad + \quad H_2 \rightarrow \quad CH_3CH_3$$

$$CH_2=CH_2 \quad + \quad Br_2 \rightarrow \quad CH_2BrCH_2Br$$

$$CH_2=CH_2 \quad + \quad HBr \rightarrow CH_3CH_2Br$$

$$CH_2=CH_2 \quad + \quad H_2O \rightarrow CH_3CH_2OH$$

Carbonyls are susceptible to (nucleophilic) addition reactions, *e.g.* the addition of hydrogen cyanide (HCN) to propanone to form 2-hydroxy-2-methylpropanenitrile, which can be hydrolysed to the corresponding carboxylic acid.

$$CH_3COCH_3 + HCN \rightarrow CH_3C(OH)(CH_3)CN$$

Elimination

Elimination is the opposite of addition. Elimination reactions are where one or more groups are removed (eliminated) from a molecule. One molecule results in two products.

$$CH_3CH_2Br \rightarrow CH_2=CH_2 + HBr$$

Dehydration of an alcohol is an elimination reaction where an alkene is formed and a molecule of water is removed (eliminated). This reaction happens when propanol is passed over a catalyst (Al_2O_3) at 400°C.

$$CH_3CH_2CH_2OH \rightarrow CH_3CH=CH_2 + H_2O$$

Electrophile

Electrophiles are lone pair acceptors (**Lewis acids**) and have a vacancy for a pair of electrons and are often positively charged. Examples include; bromonium ion (Br^+), nitronium ion (NO_2^+), proton (H^+), sulfur trioxide (SO_3) and boron trifluoride (BF_3).

Electrophilic

Electrophilic reactions can be addition or substitution reactions.

Nucleophile

Nucleophiles are lone pair donors (**Lewis bases**) and have a lone pair of electrons available to form a new covalent bond and they are negatively charged or neutral.

Examples include hydroxide (OH^-), ammonia (NH_3), water (H_2O), cyanide (CN^-).

Nucleophilic

Nucleophilic reactions can be addition or substitution reactions.

Questions 13.3

1. Name the following four halogenoalkanes; **A**, **B**, **C**, and **D**.

A   **B**

C   **D**

2. Name the following esters; **E, F, G, H, I** and **J**.

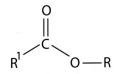

Esters		
R¹	R	IUPAC name for ester
E CH_3	CH_3	
F H	CH_3	
G CH_3	CH_3CH_2	
H H	CH_3CH_2	
I CH_3CH_2	CH_3	
J CH_3CH_2	CH_3CH_2	

3. Which of the following is **not** a heteroatom?

A   N

B   O

C   H

D   S

4. Which of the following is **not** a heteroatom?

A   Cl

B   P

C   C

D   Br

5. Which of the following pairs of compounds are **not** functional group isomers?

A   butanal and butanone

B   ethoxyethane and 2-methylpropan-2-ol

C   ethyl ethanoate and methyl propanoate

D   cyclopropane and propene

6. Which of the following pairs of compounds are functional group isomers?

A   propan-1-ol and propan-2-ol

B   ethanol and methoxymethane

C   2-methylpropan-2-ol and 2-methylpropan-1-ol

D   cyclopropene and propene

7. Describe and explain the possible isomers of the simplest alkane that has them.

8. Name and draw the skeletal formulae of the isomers with molecular formula C_5H_{12}.

9. Name and draw the unsaturated structural isomers (without branching) containing four carbons.

10. Which of these compounds has optical isomers?

A   3-hydroxypropanoic acid

B   2-aminoethanoic acid

C   2-hydroxypropanoic acid

D   3-aminopropanoic acid

11. Which alkene will form when HCl is eliminated from 2-chloro-2-methylpropane?

12. How many straight chain isomers are there with molecular formula $C_4H_8Cl_2$?

Give their names and their structural formulae.

13. Explain what type of isomerism is shown by the following dicarboxylic acid.

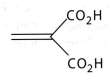

14. How could you show that three flasks contained the +, - and ± isomers of the same molecule? What results might you expect?

15. Adrenaline is a hormone which can be synthesized in the laboratory. It is the main drug used during resuscitation following a cardiac arrest and anaphylactic shock. A structure of adrenaline was drawn by a student as shown.

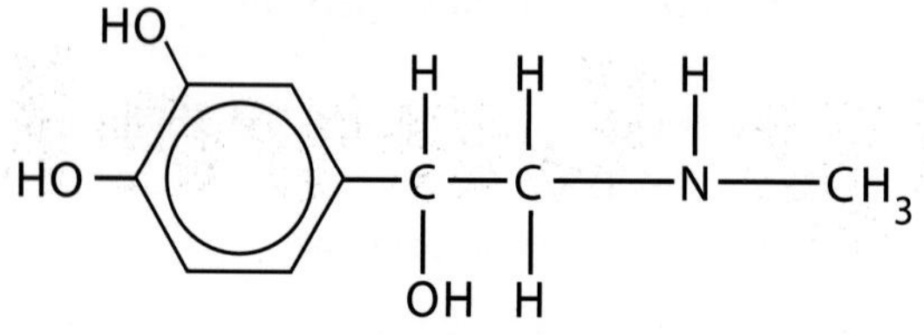

adrenaline

Re-draw this diagram showing both optical isomers, and a mirror plane, with the chiral carbon atom at the centre of the tetrahedral arrangement.

16. Which of the following could be a racemic mixture?

    A   butan-2-ol

    B   propan-1-ol

    C   butan-1-ol

    D   pentan-3-ol

17. How many forms of 2-hydroxypropanoic acid (lactic acid) are there?

    A   4

    B   3

    C   2

    D   1

14 Functional Group Level

Contents

A3.2 (a) Inactivity of C-H & C-C bonds

When organic molecules are undergoing chemical reaction, energy is needed to break the bonds in the reactant molecules. Energy is subsequently released when new bonds form in products. When molecules collide the most likely outcome of the collision is repulsion of their electron clouds and no reaction. The reason alkanes are relatively unreactive compared to the other functional groups is because they only possess single carbon-carbon bonds (C–C) and single carbon-hydrogen bonds (C–H). The combustion (A1.3a) of alkanes is the major reaction of this functional group, *e.g.* the complete combustion of methane.

$$CH_4 \, (g) + 2 \, O_2 \, (g) \rightarrow CO_2 \, (g) + 2 \, H_2O \, (l)$$

Carbon and hydrogen have similar electronegativities (A1.2i) which is why alkanes are non-polar. As alkanes have no 'weak' spots in the molecule; they resist 'attack' by electrophiles (A3.1h) and nucleophiles (A3.1h). The carbonyl (C=O) bond is polarised because the oxygen atom gets a greater share of the bonding electrons because oxygen has a higher electronegativity (A1.2i) than carbon.

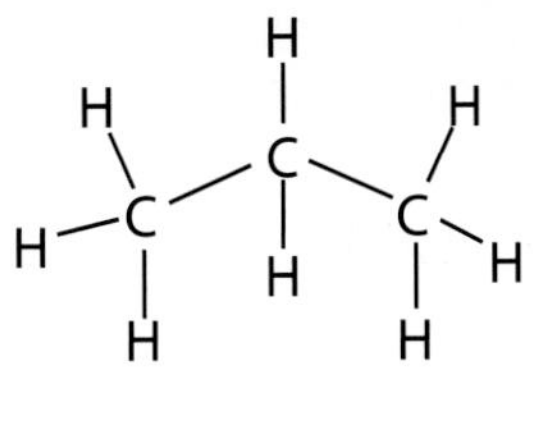

propane 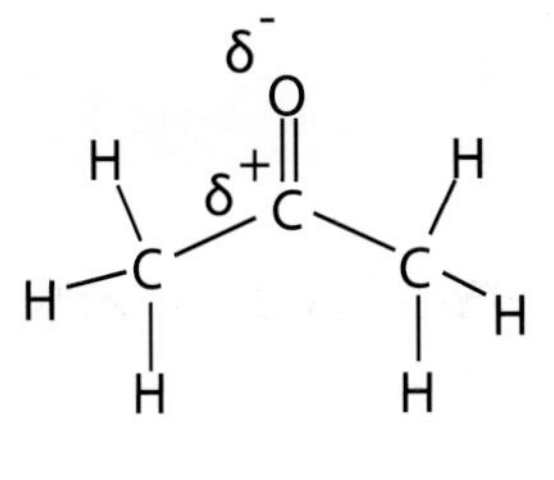   propanone

During a chemical reaction there is a movement of electrons. Molecules that possess lone pairs and dipole moments (A3.2b) such as propanone are much more reactive than the alkanes as they have centres which can donate or accept electrons. Alkenes are more reactive than alkanes because they have a region of high electron density (C=C) and a weaker π-bond.

A3.2 (b) Heteroatoms increase reactivity

Heteroatoms are atoms other than carbon or hydrogen covalently bonded within a molecule. Examples of heteroatoms are: O, N, F, Cl, Br, I, S, & P. The introduction of heteroatoms into the hydrocarbon skeleton leads to more diverse and interesting chemistry. The increased reactivity due to the presence of heteroatoms is because of the presence of high energy lone pairs and dipole moments. The dipoles and lone pairs are shown for propan-2-ol and 2-aminopropane.

propane

propan-2-ol   2-aminopropane

Propane is inert to oxidising agents such as acidified dichromate(VI). The introduction of an oxygen atom onto the second carbon of propane gives propan-2-ol which is oxidised to propanone by acidified dichromate(VI). Propane is inert to acids such as hydrochloric acid whereas 2-aminopropane, being basic, forms the hydrochloride salt.

Questions 14.1

1. Draw displayed formulae for propanal, butanone and chloroethane (ethyl chloride) and add the relevant dipoles.

2. Draw skeletal formulae for phenol, ethane-1,2-diol and phenylamine and add the relevant lone pairs.

Benzene does not react with bromine at room temperature whereas phenol (B3.10c) does because the lone pair on the oxygen atom activates the ring by overlapping with the π electrons. The formation of the white precipitate

2,4,6-tribromophenol is a qualitative test for phenol.

Butane does not react with hydroxide whereas 1-chlorobutane does react with aqueous hydroxide solution in a substitution reaction (B3.9d). The nucleophilic hydroxide ion ($:OH^-$) is attracted electrostatically to the positive end of the dipole on the carbon atom adjacent to the chlorine atom. If the orbitals are correctly aligned then electronic repulsions can be overcome.

A dipole in a molecule is indicated by δ^+ and δ^- and it shows how the electron distribution is imbalanced. A dipole is a partial charge separation caused by differences in electronegativity. Molecules with dipoles are likely to react with charged reagents. Nucleophiles can be neutral or negative but all have high energy lone pairs which are attracted to positive atoms in a dipole. Nucleophiles supply the electrons for the new bond by reacting with empty orbitals. The relative energy of a lone pair depends on the electronegativity of the atom. The larger the electronegativity of the heteroatom the lower will be the energy (greater stability) of its lone pair. An oxygen atom has a stronger nuclear attraction on its outer electrons than a nitrogen atom which lowers the energy of its lone pair relative to nitrogen's lone pair. Distortion of the electron cloud leads to charge separation and a dipole.

Electrophiles can accept electrons into empty orbitals or antibonding orbitals and are attracted to atoms with negative dipoles. Full orbitals are of lower energy than empty orbitals. An example is the reaction between ammonia and boron trifluoride. Ammonia donates its high energy lone pair (non-bonding) electrons into the vacant (atomic) orbital of boron in boron trifluoride.

The dipole moment of a molecule can be determined using spectroscopic techniques and from dielectric constants. Dipole moment = size of charges × distance between two charges. The unit of dipole moment is the **debye (D)** where $1D = 3.34 \times 10^{-30}$ C m. The size of a dipole moment gives a measure of the polarization of a molecule. Diatomic elements such as H_2, N_2, O_2, X_2 (where X = halogen) do not have dipole moments as they are symmetrical. Carbon dioxide (CO_2) and carbon tetrachloride (CCl_4) have no dipole moment as their bond dipoles cancel. A dipole moment of ~2 D is considered to be fairly large.

Molecule	Dipole moment (D)
CH_3CH_3	0
HI	0.4
HBr	0.8
HCl	1.0
NH_3	1.5
C_6H_5Cl	1.7
H_2O	1.8
HF	1.9
C_2H_5Cl	2.0

The dipole moment is the sum of all the bond polarities. Molecules with a permanent dipole are called **polar molecules**. In polar molecules, where the dipoles do not cancel, the electron density in covalent bonds is drawn towards the more electronegative atom. Organic liquids can be identified as being polar by running them through a burette and observing whether the stream is deflected by a charged material such as a polythene rod (A1.2i). It is traditional to show a dipole as an arrow with a cross ($+\!\!\longrightarrow$). The arrow points in the direction of the negative end of the dipole (δ^-), and the end that looks like a plus sign is towards the end of the positive dipole (δ^+).

Questions 14.2

1. Complete the table to indicate which liquids have their streams deflected when they pass near a charged insulator.

Molecule	Deflected	Undeflected
trichloromethane		
tetrachloromethane		
cyclohexane		

2. Explain why carbon dioxide has a dipole moment of zero (0 D) but sulfur dioxide has a dipole moment of 1.6 D.

3. Put the three alkyl halides in order of most polar to least polar based on their dipole moments. On the basis of their dipoles give examples of reagents which might attack them.

Alkyl halide	Dipole moment (D)
CH_3CH_2Cl	2.16
CH_3CH_2I	1.81
CH_3CH_2Br	1.93

4. Which molecule has **no** dipole moment?

A3.2 (c) Functional group recognition and naming simple molecules

The recognition of functional groups is very important as it is often necessary to carry out a reaction on one functional group whilst leaving others alone within the same molecule. The correct choice of reducing reagent allows such a transformation, *e.g.* the selective reduction of the carbon-carbon double bond (C=C) and the aldehyde group (CHO) in a bifunctional molecule such as pent-3-enal. Reduction using hydrogen and a platinum catalyst reduces the alkene whilst leaving the aldehyde group. Reduction using sodium borohydride ($NaBH_4$) reduces the aldehyde (CHO) whilst leaving the alkene group

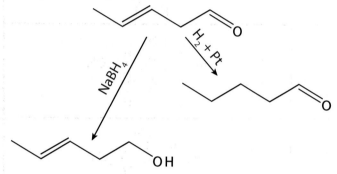

At times it is necessary to protect a functional group by temporarily converting it into another functional group. The protection of functional groups is mostly beyond the scope of this course and is an important aspect of the work of scientists trying to synthesise complex natural products in research laboratories.

Once the functional group has been identified using the rules for nomenclature (A3.1g), the naming of simple molecules can soon become routine. Next follow the names and formulae of simple examples from each of the functional group levels.

Hydrocarbon level

The naming of the first ten straight chain alkanes has been covered in the organic preliminaries (A3.1g). The names of the more reactive alkenes are tabulated along with some cyclic examples. In the laboratory, cyclohexene is often used to illustrate the reactions of alkenes as it is convenient to use a liquid rather than an invisible gas like ethene. Alkenes contain carbon-carbon double bonds consisting of a sigma (σ) bond and a pi (π) bond.

Acyclic alkenes (C_nH_{2n})			Cyclic alkenes	
Alkene name	Alkene formula	Number of carbons	Examples	
Ethene	C_2H_4	2	cyclo-propene	△
Propene	C_3H_6	3		
Butene	C_4H_8	4	cyclo-butene	▢
Pentene	C_5H_{10}	5		
Hexene	C_6H_{12}	6	cyclo-pentene	⬠
Heptene	C_7H_{14}	7		
Octene	C_8H_{16}	8	cyclo-pentadiene	⬠
Nonene	C_9H_{18}	9		
Decene	$C_{10}H_{20}$	10	cyclo-hexene	⬡
Undecene	$C_{11}H_{22}$	11		

Alkynes contain carbon carbon triple bonds consisting of a sigma bond and two pi bonds.

Acyclic alkynes (C_nH_{2n-2})			
Alkyne name	Alkyne formula	Number of carbons	Structure
Ethyne	C_2H_2	2	H—C≡C—H
Propyne	C_3H_4	3	H—C≡C—C(H)(H)—H
But-1-yne	C_4H_6	4	H—C≡C—C(H)(H)—C(H)(H)—H

Alcohol level

Alcohols contain the hydroxyl group with the O–H atoms connected *via* the oxygen atom. Alcohols can be primary (RCH_2OH), secondary (R_2CHOH) or tertiary (R_3COH).

Acyclic alcohols ($C_nH_{2n+1}OH$)			
Alcohol name	Alcohol formula	Number of carbons	Structure
Methanol	CH_3OH	1	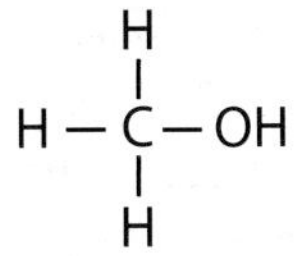
Ethanol	CH_3CH_2OH	2	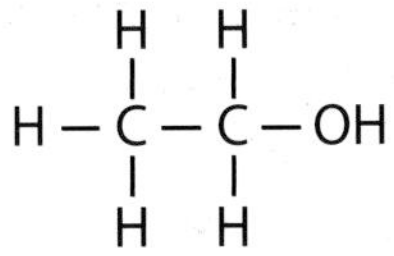
Propan-1-ol	$CH_3CH_2CH_2OH$	3	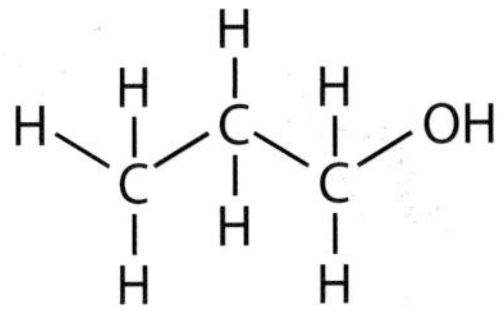
Propan-2-ol	$CH_3CH(OH)CH_3$	3	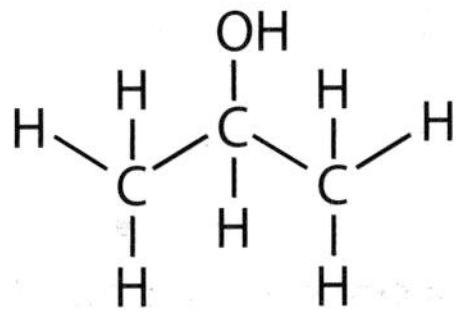
Butan-1-ol	$CH_3CH_2CH_2CH_2OH$	4	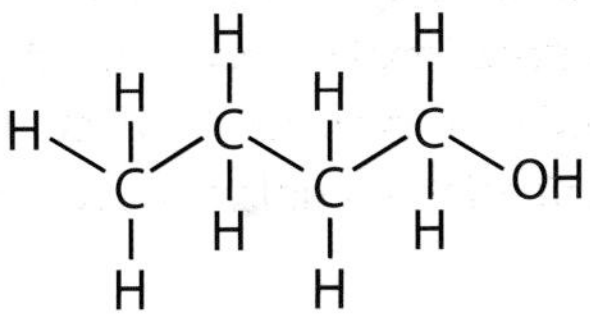
Butan-2-ol	$CH_3CH(OH)CH_2CH_3$	4	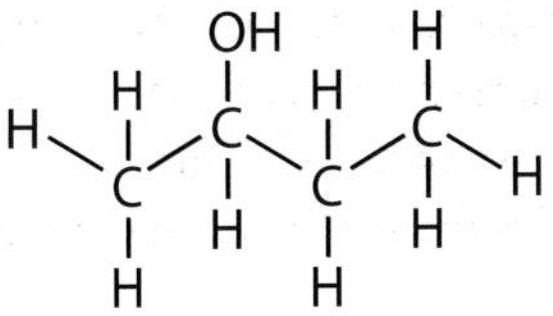
2-methylpropan-1-ol	$(CH_3)_2CHCH_2OH$	4	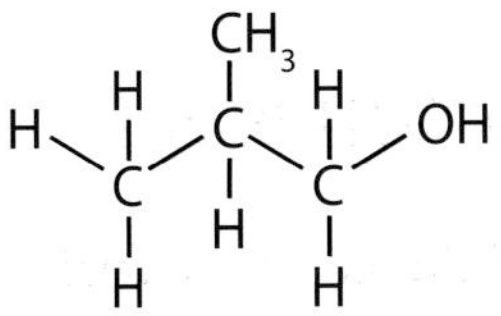
2-methylpropan-2-ol	$(CH_3)_3COH$	4	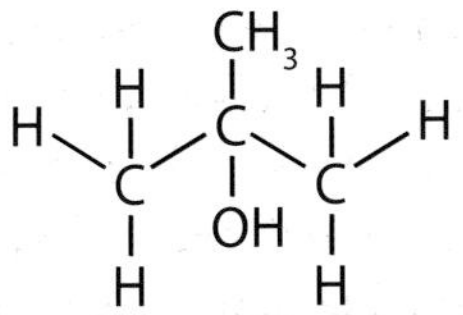

Alcohols can also be cyclic aliphatic as well as aromatic (B3.10).

Cyclic alcohols	
Examples	
Cyclopentanol	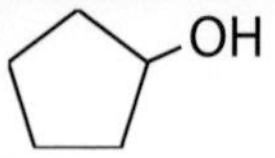
Cyclohexanol	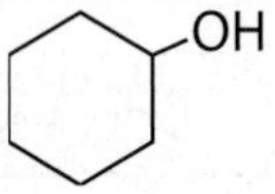
Phenol	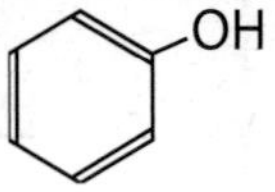

Cyclic alcohols	
Examples	
1,2-dihydroxybenzene (catechol)	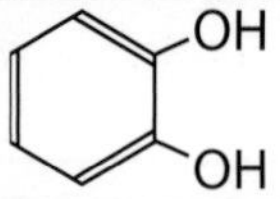
1-naphthol	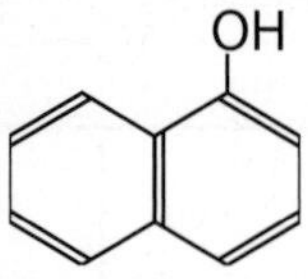
2-naphthol	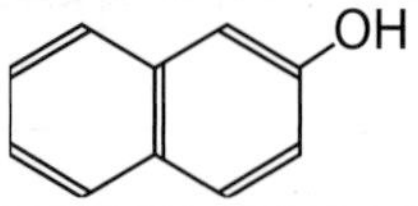

Alkyl halides are named after the corresponding alkane molecules where one or more hydrogen atoms have been replaced by a Group 17 halogen. Like alcohols, they can be primary, secondary or tertiary depending on the degree of branching.

Alkyl halides ($C_nH_{2n+1}X$) where X = F, Cl, Br, I			
Akyl halide name	Alkyl halide formula	Number of carbons	Structure
Methyl chloride (chloromethane)	CH_3Cl	1	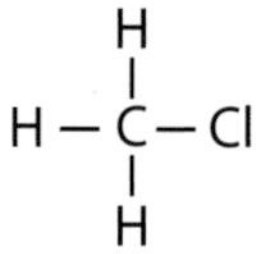
Ethyl bromide (bromoethane)	CH_3CH_2Br	2	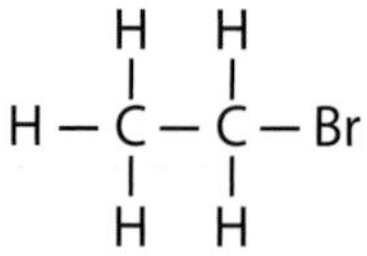
Propyl iodide (1-iodopropane)	$CH_3CH_2CH_2I$	3	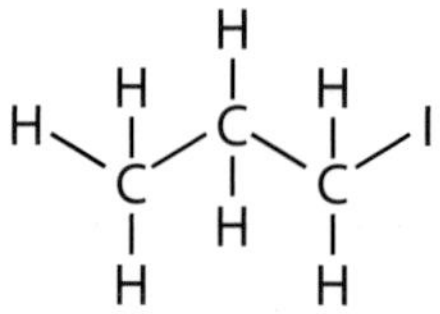
Isopropyl chloride (2-chloropropane)	$CH_3CH(Cl)CH_3$	3	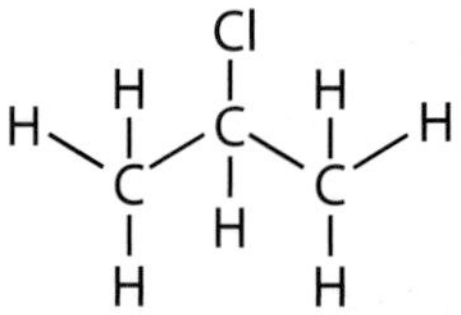
Butyl bromide (1-bromobutane)	$CH_3CH_2CH_2CH_2Br$	4	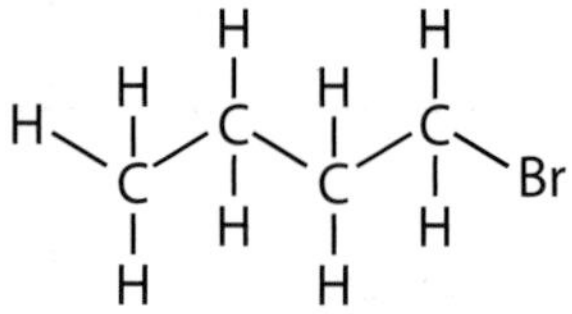
Chlorobenzene	C_6H_5Cl	6	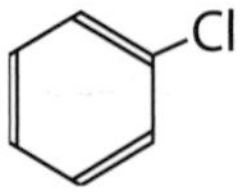
Benzyl chloride	$C_6H_5CH_2Cl$	7	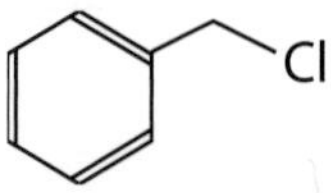

Like alcohols, amines can also be primary, secondary or tertiary depending on the degree of substitution at the nitrogen atom. Amines are named after the corresponding alkyl or aryl group. Where there are more than one alkyl or aryl group these substituents are named alphabetically. Remember when drawing amines that the nitrogen atom is generally trivalent, *i.e.* it forms three bonds.

Amines (1° amines = $C_nH_{2n+1}NH_2$)			
Amine name	Amine formula	Number of carbons	Structure
Methylamine (aminomethane)	CH_3NH_2	1	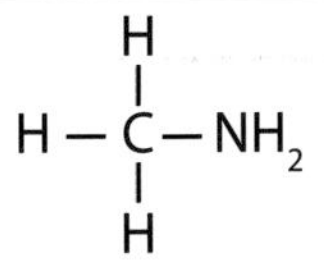
Ethylamine (aminoethane)	$CH_3CH_2NH_2$	2	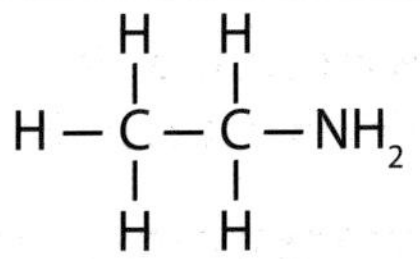
Propylamine (1-aminopropane)	$CH_3CH_2CH_2NH_2$	3	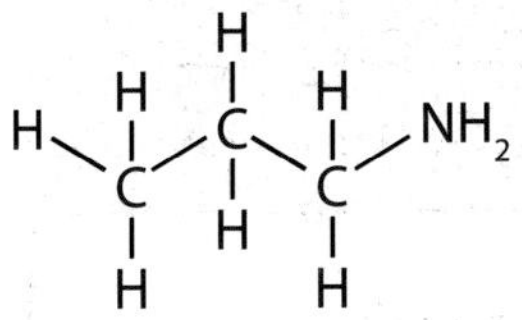
Isopropylamine (2-aminopropane)	$CH_3CH(NH_2)CH_3$	3	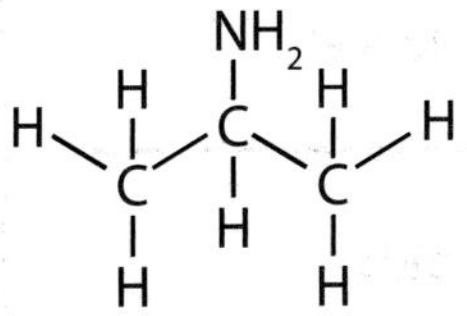
Butylamine (1-aminobutane)	$CH_3CH_2CH_2CH_2NH_2$	4	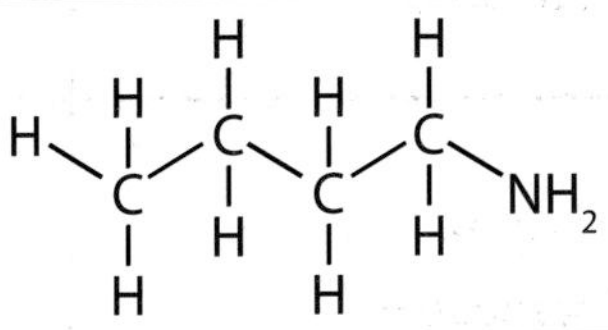
Phenylamine (aniline) or aminobenzene	$C_6H_5NH_2$	6	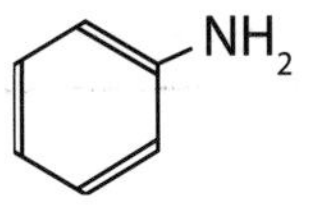
Dimethylamine	$(CH_3)_2NH$	2	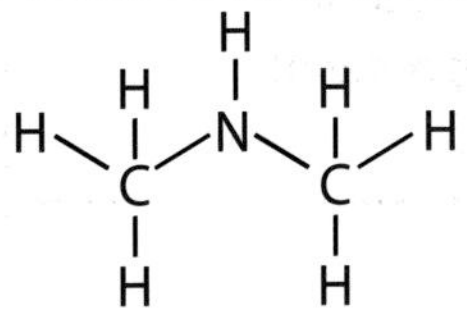
Ethylmethylamine	$C_2H_5NHCH_3$	3	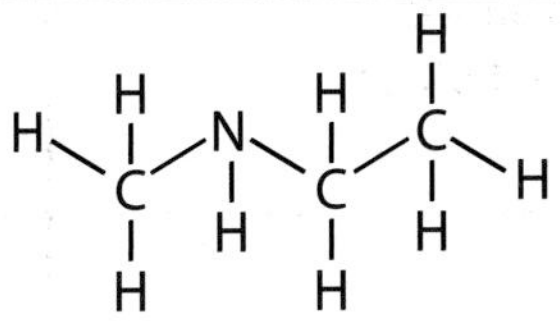

Like amines, ethers are named after the corresponding alkyl or aryl groups. Where there is more than one different alkyl or aryl group these substituents are named alphabetically.

Ethers ($C_nH_{2n+2}O$)			
Ether name	Ether formula	Number of carbons	Structure
Dimethyl ether (methoxymethane)	CH_3OCH_3	2	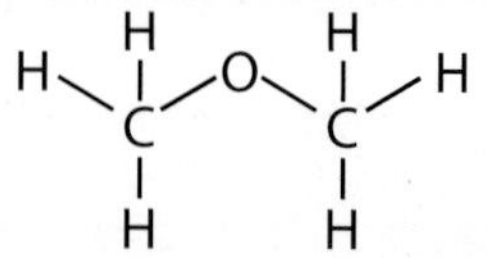
Diethyl ether (ethoxyethane)	$CH_3CH_2OCH_2CH_3$	4	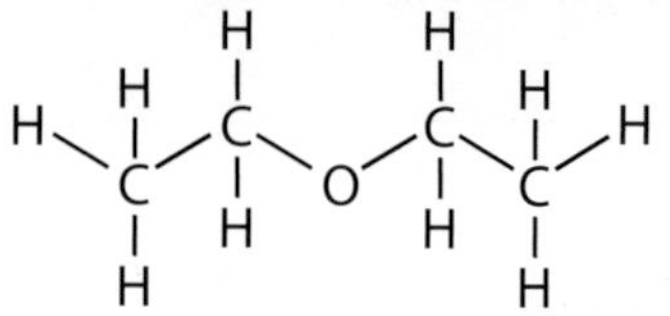
Ethyl methyl ether (ethoxymethane)	$CH_3CH_2OCH_3$	3	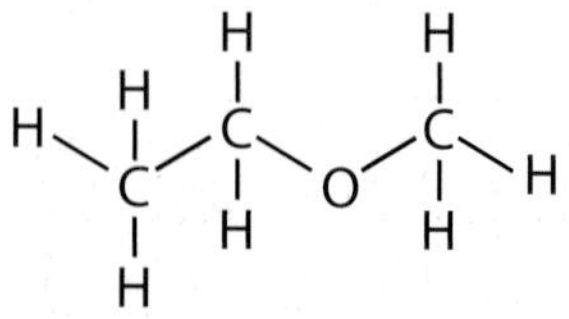

Carbonyl level

Aldehydes contain the carbonyl group (C=O) on the end of a chain and there is a hydrogen atom directly attached to this C=O group. The group is often represented as CHO. The simplest aldehyde HCHO (methanal) is often used to preserve biological specimens where it is known as formalin which is a 40% aqueous solution by mass.

Aldehydes ($C_nH_{2n}O$)			
Aldehyde name	Aldehyde formula	Number of carbons	Structure
Methanal (formaldehyde)	HCHO	1	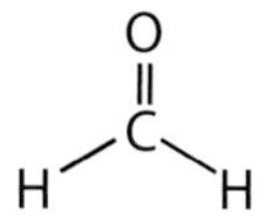
Ethanal (acetaldehyde)	CH_3CHO	2	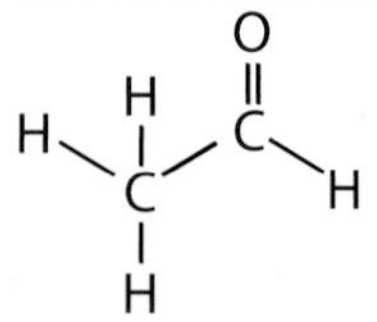
Propanal	CH_3CH_2CHO	3	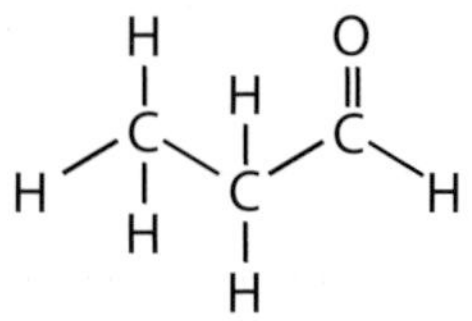
Butanal	$CH_3CH_2CH_2CHO$	4	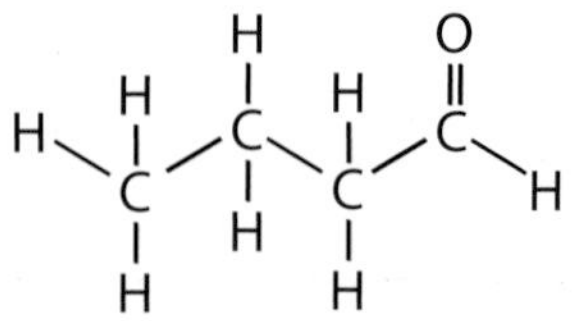

Aldehydes ($C_nH_{2n}O$)

Aldehyde name	Aldehyde formula	Number of carbons	Structure
Pentanal	$CH_3CH_2CH_2CH_2CHO$	5	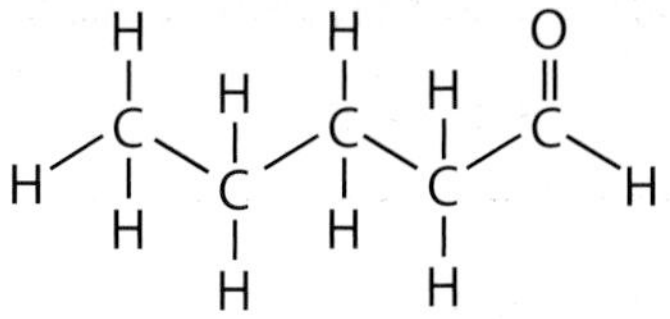
Benzaldehyde	C_6H_5CHO	7	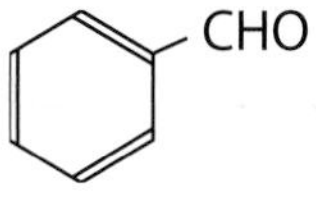

Ketones contain the carbonyl group (C=O) in the middle of a chain or ring directly attached to two carbon atoms. The simplest ketone is CH_3COCH_3 propanone (acetone) which is often used as a solvent.

Ketones ($C_nH_{2n}O$)

Ketone name	Ketone formula	Number of carbons	Structure
Propanone (acetone)	CH_3COCH_3	3	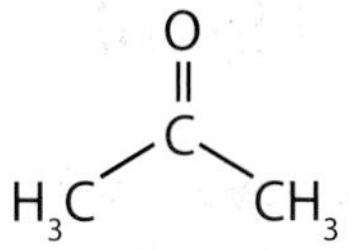
Butanone	$CH_3COCH_2CH_3$	4	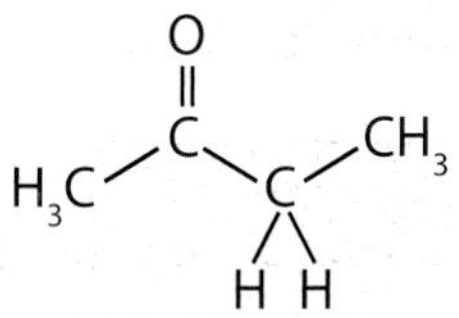
Pentan-2-one	$CH_3COCH_2CH_2CH_3$	5	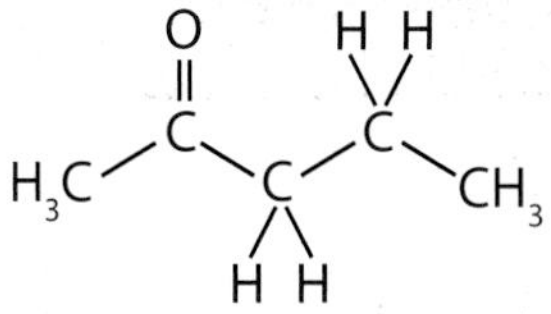
Pentan-3-one	$CH_3CH_2COCH_2CH_3$	5	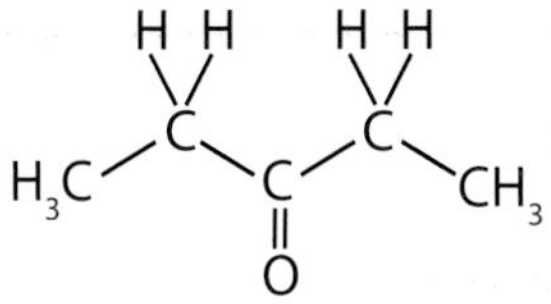
Cyclopentanone	$\left[CH_2CH_2CH_2CH_2\overset{O}{\overset{\|}{C}} \right]$	5	
Cyclohexanone	$\left[CH_2CH_2CH_2CH_2CH_2\overset{O}{\overset{\|}{C}} \right]$	6	

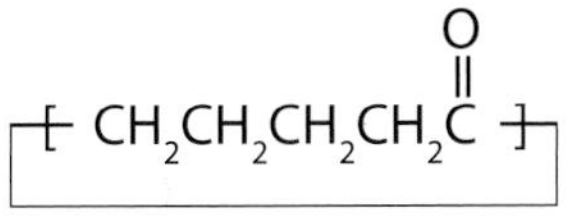

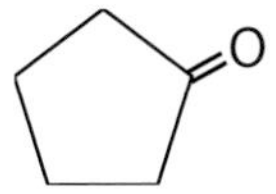

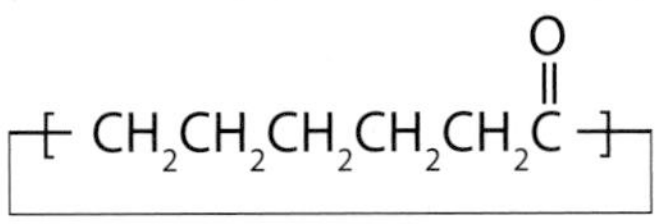

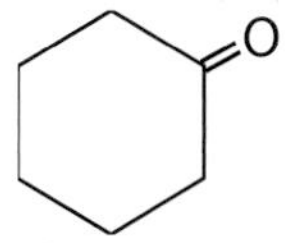

Carboxylic acid level

Carboxylic acids contain the COOH (CO_2H) group. The hydroxyl group is directly attached to the carbonyl group (C=O). The COOH group is at the end of a chain or directly attached to a ring. The simplest carboxylic acid is HCOOH methanoic acid (formic acid) which is found in nettle stings and ant bites. In the general formula, the carbon of COOH is not counted in the carbon count for the value of n.

Carboxylic acids ($C_nH_{2n+1}COOH$)			
Carboxylic acid name	Carboxylic acid formula	Number of carbons	Structure
Methanoic acid (formic acid)	HCOOH	1	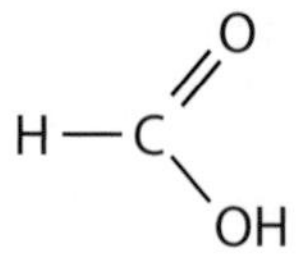
Ethanoic acid (acetic acid)	CH_3COOH	2	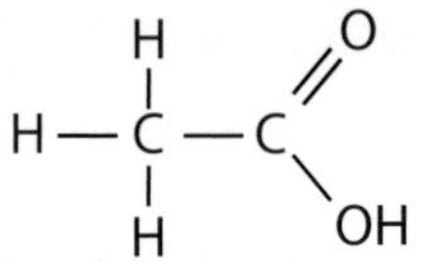
Propanoic acid (propionic acid)	CH_3CH_2COOH	3	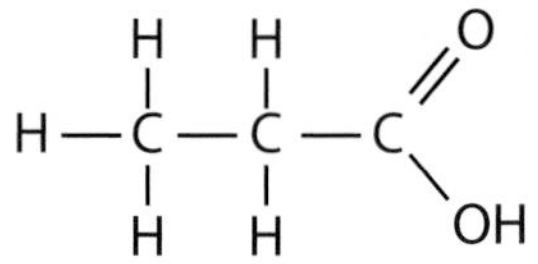
Butanoic acid (butyric acid)	$CH_3CH_2CH_2COOH$	4	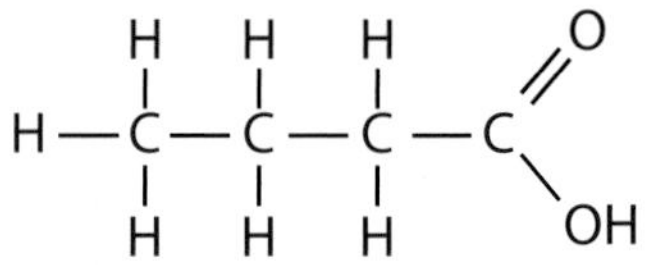
Pentanoic acid (valeric acid)	$CH_3CH_2CH_2CH_2COOH$	5	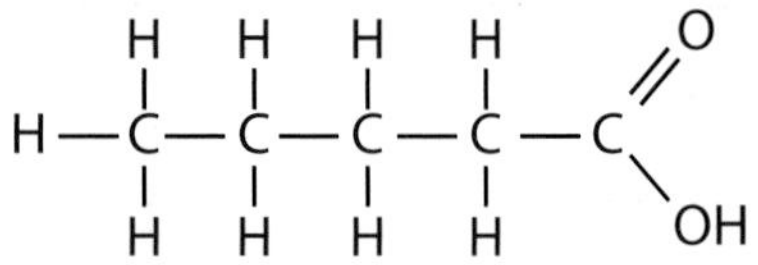
Benzoic acid	C_6H_5COOH	7	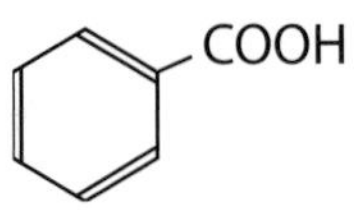

Esters are substituted carboxylic acids. The acid hydrogen atom of the O–H is replaced by a carbon atom and the ester group is COOR (CO_2R) where R = alkyl or aryl groups. Esters are sweet-smelling molecules often used in flavourings or perfumes. The simplest ester is $HCOOCH_3$ methyl methanoate which smells like glue. Cyclic esters are known as lactones.

Esters ($C_nH_{2n+1}COOH$)			
Ester name	Ester formula	Number of carbons	Structure
Methyl methanoate	$HCOOCH_3$	2	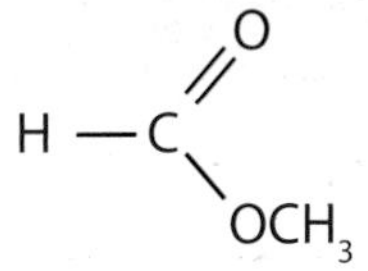
Methyl ethanoate	CH_3COOCH_3	3	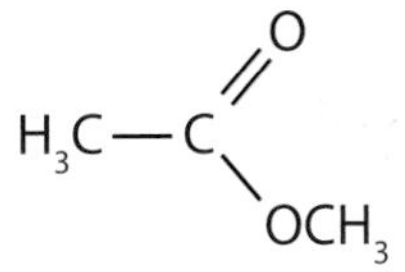
Ethyl methanoate	$HCOOCH_2CH_3$	3	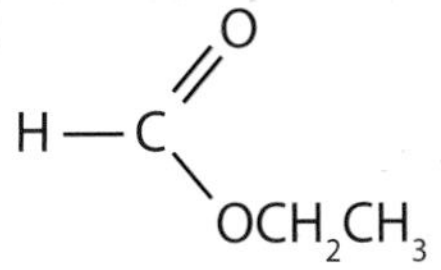
Ethyl ethanoate (ethyl acetate)	$CH_3COOCH_2CH_3$	4	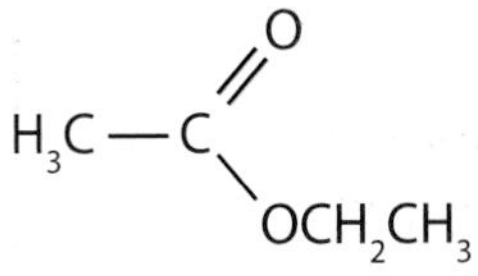
Phenyl ethanoate	$C_6H_5OCOCH_3$	8	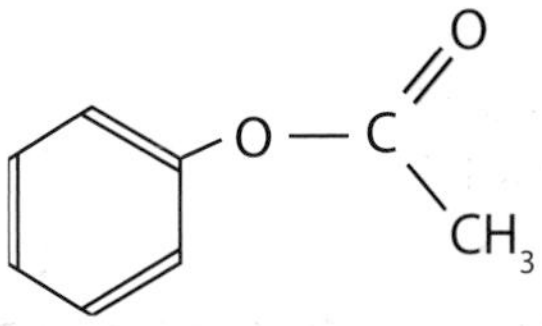
Methyl benzoate	$C_6H_5COOCH_3$	8	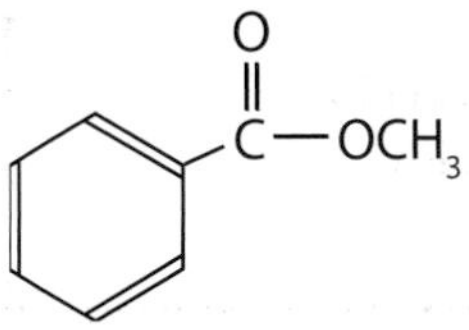
Propriolactone	$[CH_2OCOCH_2]$	3	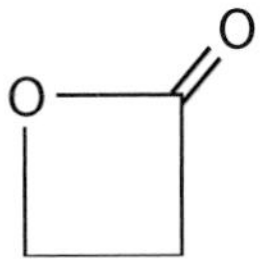

Amides can also be considered to be substituted carboxylic acids. The group OH is replaced by a nitrogen atom and the amide group is $RCONR^1R^2$ where R, R^1, R^2 = hydrogen, alkyl or aryl groups. Amides are recognised because the carbonyl (C=O) is attached to a nitrogen atom. Cyclic amides are known as lactams and caprolactam is the monomer used in the formation of nylon-6.

Amides			
Amide name	Amide formula	Number of carbons	Structure
Ethanamide (acetamide)	CH_3CONH_2	2	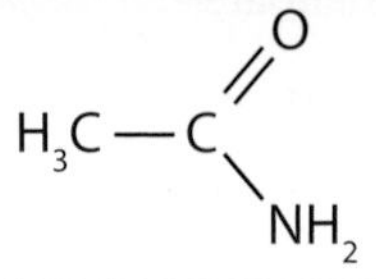
Propanamide	$CH_3CH_2CONH_2$	3	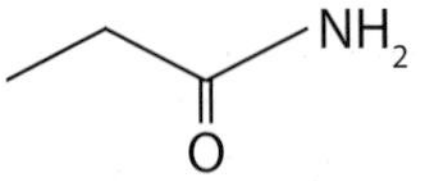
Butanamide	$CH_3CH_2CH_2CONH_2$	4	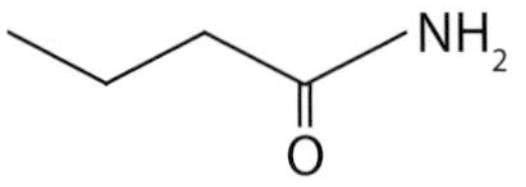
N-methylbenzamide	$C_6H_5CONHCH_3$	8	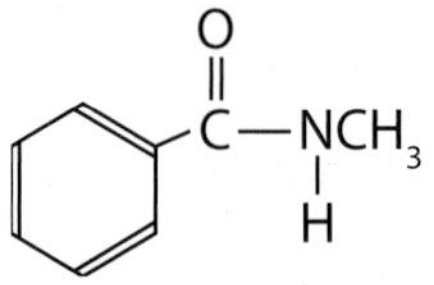
N-phenylethanamide (acetanilide)	$CH_3CONHC_6H_5$	8	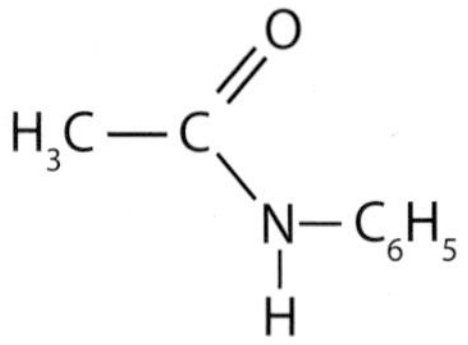
Caprolactam		6	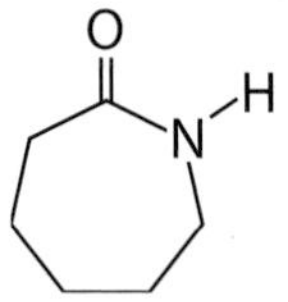

Acyl chlorides (acid chlorides) can also be considered to be substituted carboxylic acids. The OH group is replaced by a chlorine atom and the acyl chloride group is RCOCl where R = hydrogen, alkyl or aryl groups. Acyl chlorides are recognised because the carbonyl (C=O) is attached to a chlorine atom.

Acyl chlorides			
Acyl chloride name	Acyl chloride formula	Number of carbons	Structure
Ethanoyl chloride (acetyl chloride)	CH_3COCl	2	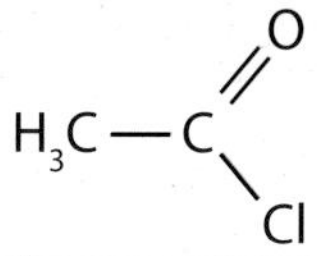
Propanoyl chloride	CH_3CH_2COCl	3	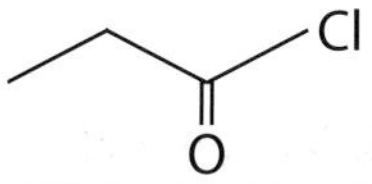
Butanoyl chloride	$CH_3CH_2CH_2COCl$	4	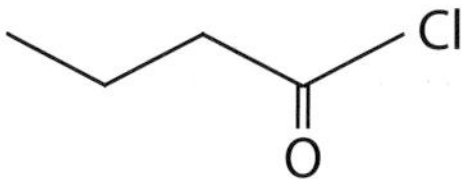
Benzoyl chloride (benzene carbanoyl chloride)	C_6H_5COCl	7	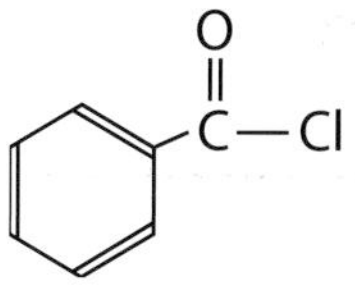

Nitriles (cyanides) contain the nitrile group (C≡N). The group is often represented as CN with the carbon atom of the nitrile group attached to a alkyl or aryl group. The simplest nitrile CH_3CN (ethanenitrile) is often used as a solvent.

Nitriles			
Nitrile name	Nitrile formula	Number of carbons	Structure
Ethanenitrile (acetonitrile) or methyl cyanide	CH_3CN	2	$H_3C-C{\equiv}N$
Propanenitrile (ethyl cyanide)	CH_3CH_2CN	3	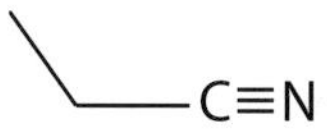
Butanenitrile (butyronitrile)	$CH_3CH_2CH_2CN$	4	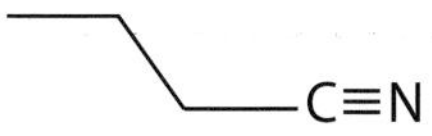
Benzenenitrile (benzonitrile) or phenyl cyanide	C_6H_5CN	7	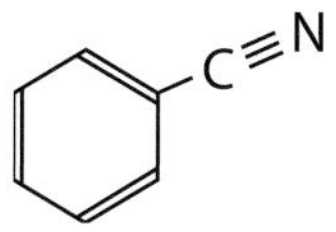
Benzyl cyanide	$C_6H_5CH_2CN$	8	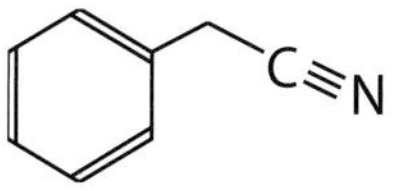

Carbon dioxide level

Urea (carbamide) has the formula H_2NCONH_2 and was first synthesized in 1828 by Wohler in a crucial experiment that started the field of organic chemistry. Urea is found in mammalian urine and makes a good fertiliser. It can be prepared by heating ammonium cyanate (NH_4OCN).

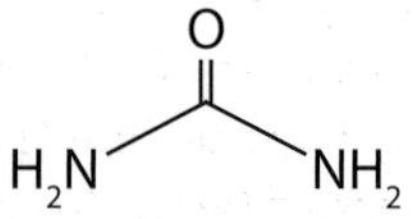

Example 14.1

Identify the functional groups present in 2,3-dihydroxy-propanal (glyceraldehyde) a triose monosaccharide which is an intermediate in the metabolism of carbohydrates.

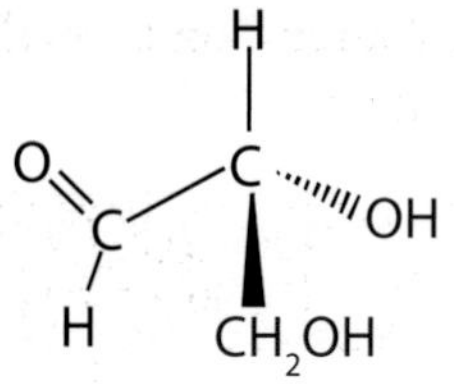

glyceraldehyde

Solution:

Aldehyde CHO, primary alcohol CH_2OH, and secondary alcohol CHOH.

Example 14.2

Identify the functional groups present in ethanedioic acid (oxalic acid) a toxin found in the leaves of rhubarb.

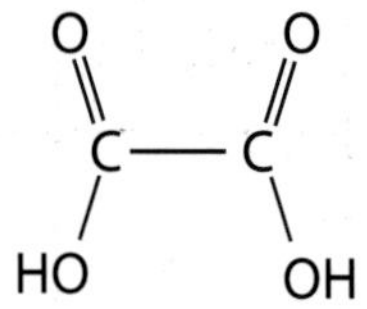

oxalic acid

Solution:

Carboxylic acid COOH (CO_2H)

Example 14.3

Identify the functional groups present in paracetamol (acetaminophen) which is a widely taken analgesic (painkiller).

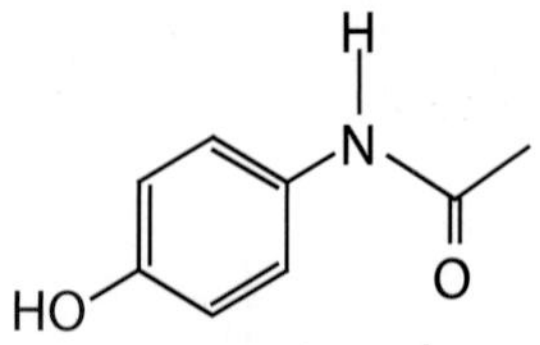

paracetamol

Solution:

Phenol RC_6H_4OH & amide -NHCO-

Example 14.4

Identify the functional groups present in the transparent thermoplastic perspex (poly-methyl methacrylate) which is a useful substitute for glass.

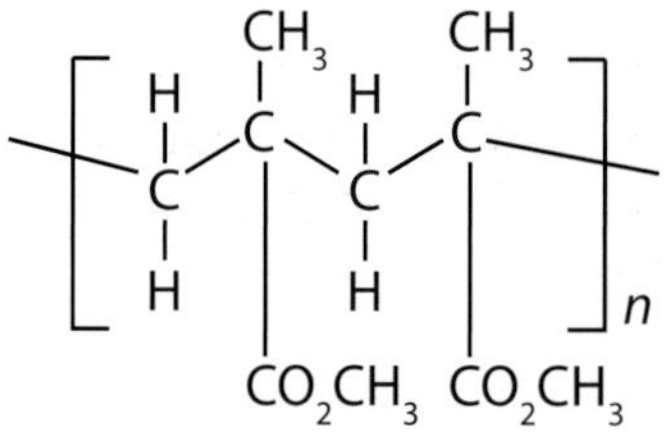

perspex

Solution:

Ester CO_2CH_3

Questions 14.3

1. Identify the functional groups present in aspirin (2-ethanoyloxybenzoic acid) which is a widely taken analgesic (painkiller) and antipyretic (reduces fevers). Aspirin is also prescribed for those at risk of strokes or heart attacks as it reduces the chance of clots forming.

Aspirin

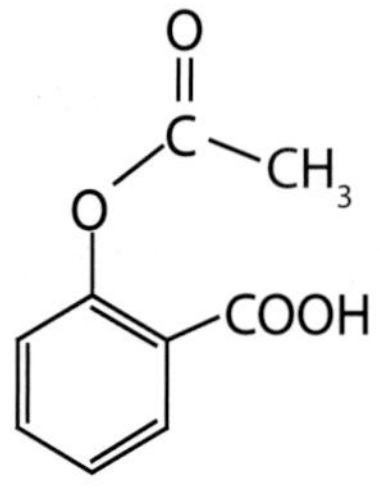

2. Identify the functional groups present in vanillin which is the flavouring extracted from the fermented seed pods of the vanilla orchid.

Vanillin

3. Give the molecular formula and identify the functional groups present in cinnamaldehyde which is a flavour extracted by steam distillation of the bark of the cinnamon tree.

Cinnamaldehyde

4. Identify the functional groups present in the vital antioxidant ascorbic acid (vitamin C) which is found in potatoes, green vegetables and citrus fruits such as lemons and oranges.

Vitamin C

5. Identify the functional groups present in the anti-ulcer drug Zantac® (Ranitidine) which inhibits acid production in the stomach.

Zantac®

A3.2 (d)
Functional group level (FGL)

The concept of **functional group level** (FGL) might still be unfamiliar to a large number of chemists at the start of the 21st century. It is a useful tool for organic chemists as it reduces the need for rote learning which may have been the common approach to organic chemistry in the past. To work out the FGL of a single carbon atom in a molecule it is just a matter of counting the number of bonds from the carbon atom to electronegative atoms. Recognising the FGL of a reactant and a product allows the correct choice of reagent for a chemical transformation. A chemist needs to be able to know which reagent to select, even with unfamiliar molecules, much as a professional golfer such as Tiger Woods knows when to pull a 5 iron out on a new course. FGL provides a framework to understand organic reactions. There are five Functional Group Levels [0, 1, 2, 3 & 4] and the table shows how the levels are derived using red coloured bonds to electronegative atoms from a single carbon atom.

FGL	FGL Name	Common examples	Examples
4	Carbon Dioxide	CO_2	$O = C = O$
3	Carboxylic Acid	RCO_2H, RCO_2R, $RCONH_2$, RCN, $RCOCl$	
2	Carbonyl	$RCHO$, $RCOR$	
1	Alcohol	ROH, RNH_2, RX	
0	Hydrocarbon	R-R	

The most frequently encountered heteroatoms in organic molecules are the highly electronegative elements nitrogen, oxygen and chlorine. FGL 3 consists of carboxylic acids, esters, amides, nitriles and acyl chlorides. It is helpful to remember the name of each FGL as this is the product of hydrolysis for all of its members. FGL 2 consists of aldehydes and ketones. FGL 1 consists of primary, secondary and tertiary: alcohols, alkyl

279

halides and amines. FGL 0 are the relatively unreactive non-polar hydrocarbons (A3.1a). There is no particular advantage of using the Functional Group Level approach to organic chemistry for the alkenes. It is more useful to remember that all their reactions are addition reactions.

A3.2 (e)
FGL of unfamiliar examples and changes in FGL
Natural products

Natural products are naturally occurring molecules which can be isolated from living organisms. Both plants and animals have yielded many important biomolecules. Some perhaps familiar examples from the seemingly endless list provided by nature include; glucose, caffeine, nicotine, adrenaline, DNA, amino acids, testosterone, lactic acid, insulin, menthol, citric acid, taxol, cholesterol, penicillin, and chlorophyll. Millions of natural products had been isolated and characterised by the start of the 21st century. It takes decades from initial discovery of a molecule to its isolation, characterisation and eventual use as a new medicine. Development of new medicines involves the collaboration of hundreds of dedicated researchers from the many different scientific branches. An invaluable starting point for many chemists in the search for useful natural products has been the plants and animal products used by indigenous people around the world. Examples are: the chemical defences found in animals such as the frog poison epibatidine and in plants such as the foxglove which contains digitalis. All these are useful compounds. The FGL of some natural products are given so that, with practice, any unfamiliar molecule can be looked at in terms of the FGL of individual carbon atoms.

Vitamin B$_2$

Example 14.6

Cholecalciferol (vitamin D$_3$) is added to milk for good health because of the vital role it plays in absorption of calcium ions. Vitamin D is produced by the skin when exposed to sunlight.

Vitamin D$_3$

Questions 14.4

1. Serotonin (5-hydroxytryptamine) is an important neurotransmitter that modulates mood, sleep and appetite and is synthesized in the body from tryptophan an essential amino acid. Give its molecular formula and assign FGL as a number for any carbon atoms attached to an electronegative element.

Example 14.5

Riboflavin (vitamin B$_2$) is added to breakfast cereals as it is essential for good health because of the vital role it plays in metabolism. Good sources of vitamin B$_2$ are liver, cheese and milk. The FGL of each carbon atom associated with a particular functional group is indicated with a red number. Remember that FGL refers only to individual carbon atoms, not molecules.

Serotonin

2. Saccharine is a substance where serendipity led to the discovery of a sweet tasting molecule without the calorific value of sugars because it is not metabolised. It is an important part in the battle against obesity in the US and Western Europe. Give its molecular formula and assign FGL as a number for any carbon atoms attached to an electronegative element.

Saccharine

3. It has been discovered that the bee sting releases a pheromone which alarms other members of the hive and causes them to attack! The pheromone in bee stings is 3-methylbutyl ethanoate. Write an equation to show how this ester can be formed from ethanoic acid and describe any changes in FGL.

H_3C—C $\begin{array}{c} O \\ \\ OCH_2CH_2CH(CH_3)_2 \end{array}$

4. Oil of wintergreen is a phenolic ester used in products, such as Deep Heat, which are used to relieve minor muscle pain. Its chemical name is methyl 2-hydroxybenzoate and more trivially it is known as methyl salicylate. Write an equation to show how this ester can be formed from methanol and describe any changes in FGL.

OH
COOCH$_3$

Oil of wintergreen

5. Identify the FGL for each carbon atom in caffeine. Caffeine is a xanthine alkaloid found in cocoa beans which increases the heart rate in humans and so is classified as a stimulant.

Caffeine

6. Identify the FGL for each carbon adjacent to a nitrogen atom in nicotine. Nicotine is the addictive alkaloid which is often found at about 3% by mass in tobacco leaves.

Nicotine

Synthetic products

Einstein said "imagination is more important than knowledge." It is in the area of science, often dubbed **nanotechnology** or **supramolecular chemistry**, that imagination is critical in the development of new materials. Scientists are building novel structures which are not found in nature, even after billions of years of evolutionary processes. Some important classes of synthetic products provided by chemists include: catenanes, rotaxanes, bucky balls, bucky tubes, calixarenes, crown ethers, carcerands, cryptands, dendrimers, and liquid crystals. Nature is often the inspiration for new molecules and, perhaps, increasingly familiar examples of synthetic products include: paracetamol, Viagra®, fluoxetine (Prozac®), nitroglycerine, benzocaine, porphyrins & morphine. The FGL of some synthetic products are given so that, with practice, any unfamiliar molecule can be looked at in terms of the FGL of individual carbon atoms.

Example 14.7

Prozac® (fluoxetine) is prescribed as an antidepressant and works as a serotonin re-uptake inhibitor. Depression is one unpleasant legacy of modern society where communities have become fragmented and people live in boxes not knowing their neighbours.

Fluoxetine

Example 14.8

Nitroglycerine is a colourless, oily, shock-sensitive liquid. It is one of those interesting molecules which serve a dual purpose. Alfred Nobel made nitroglycerine safe in dynamite by mixing it with *kieselguhr*, a soft chalk-like sedimentary rock. It is also used as a vasodilator for the heart condition angina, which it controls by releasing nitrogen monoxide (NO).

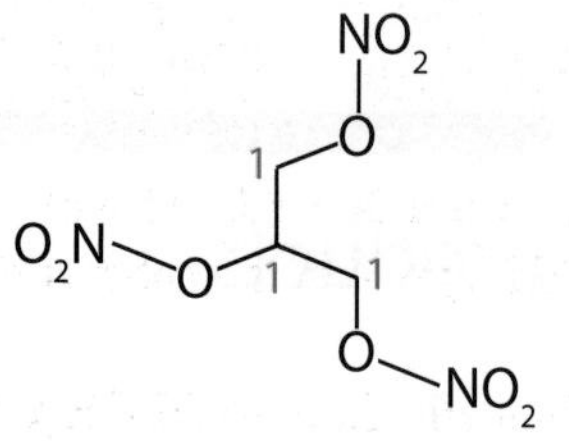

Nitroglycerine

Example 14.9

Porphyrins are **heterocyclic macrocycles**, *i.e.* large cyclic compounds containing the heteroatom nitrogen. They are named after a Greek word meaning purple. They are found in nature, in leaves, and form the central part of the haemoglobin molecule which is the red blood cell oxygen carrier.

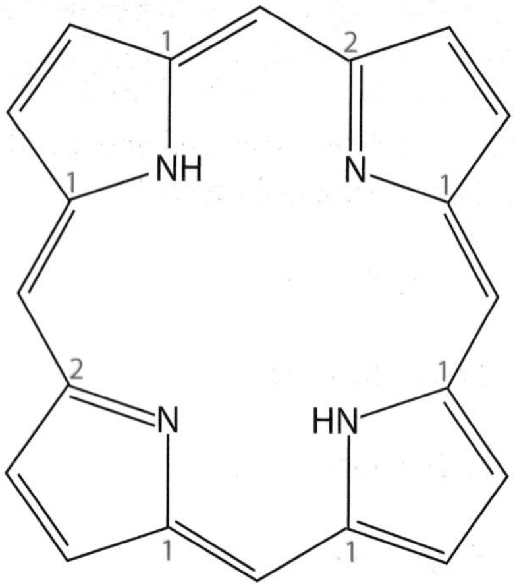

Porphyrin

Changes in FGL

Example 14.10

Benzocaine is a topical anaesthetic used by dentists prior to drilling and filling of damaged teeth. It has also been used in the relief of pain in patients with mouth ulcers. Benzocaine can be made by the simple esterifcation of *para*-aminobenzoic acid by reaction with ethanol in the presence of an acid catalyst, *e.g.* sulphuric acid (H_2SO_4).

Benzocaine

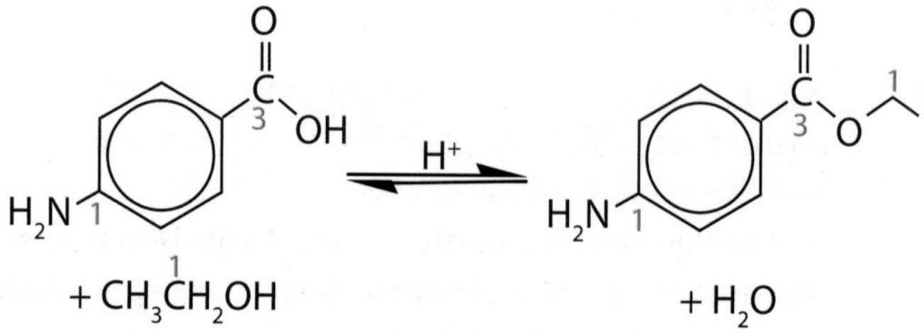

Esterifications like hydrolysis reactions do not change the FGL level. The carbon atom of the carboxylic acid is at FGL 3 as is the carbon of the ester group.

Example 14.11

Paracetamol can be prepared from phenol in three steps. Paracetamol is a widely prescribed painkiller and is useful for reducing fevers.

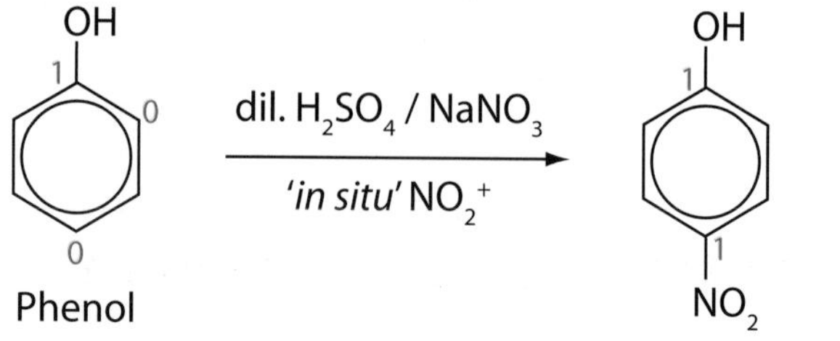

25%
m.p. = 113.8 °C
para

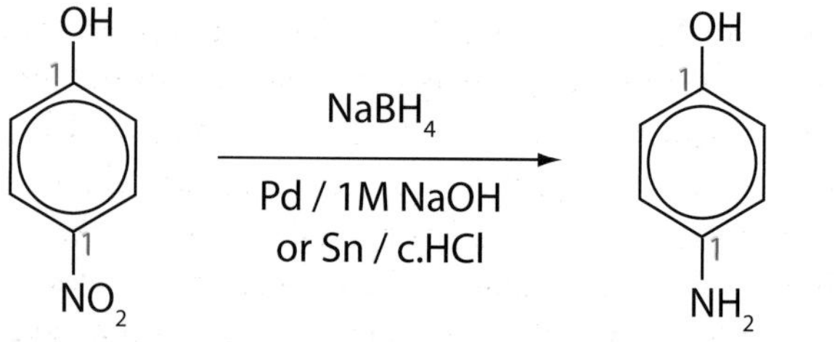

74%

4-nitrophenol

4-aminophenol

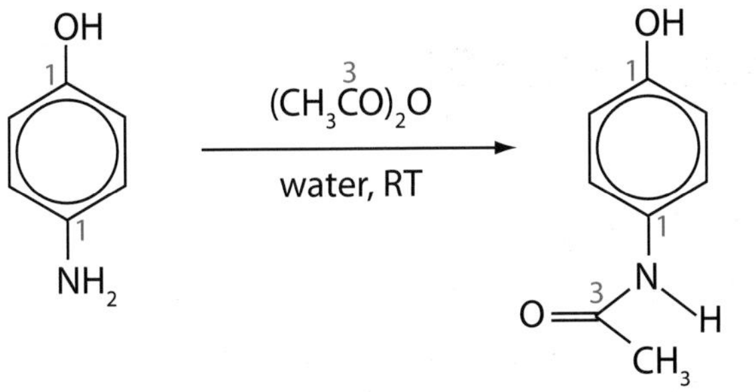

60%
Paracetamol

Amide formations, like hydrolysis reactions, do not change the FGL level. The carbon atom of the acid anhydride, $(CH_3CO)_2O$ is at FGL 3 as is the carbon of the amide group.

Question 14.5

1. Indigo was first synthesised in the 1880s by Adolf von Baeyer. It is made from the reaction between propanone (acetone), 2-nitrobenzaldehyde and water. It is still finding commercial use today as a dye for denim jeans. Describe any changes in FGL in this reaction scheme.

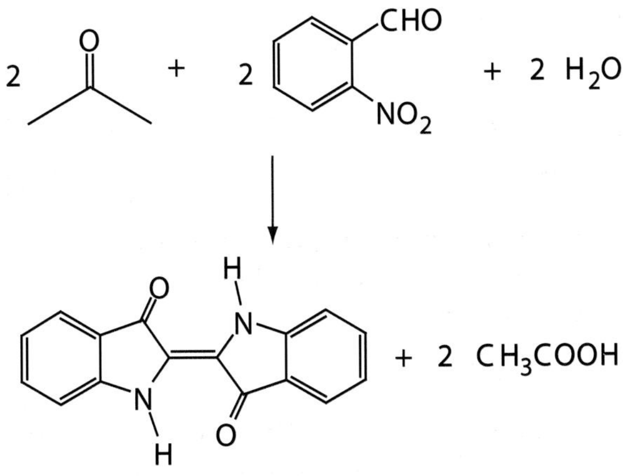

indigo

A3.2 (f) Choice of reagents guided by FGL

Reactions happen around the heteroatoms in molecules because they have high energy electrons and introduce dipoles into molecules which make them the targets of electrophiles (A3.1h) or nucleophiles (A3.1h). There are three types of possible movement with Functional Group Levels. Reactions where there is no change of FGL, when the reaction will be hydrolysis, substitution or condensation. In the case of any hydrolysis, the product will have the functional group after which the level is named.

Example 14.12

Hydrolysis of methyl ethanoate (FGL 3) yields ethanoic acid (FGL 3).

$$CH_3CO_2CH_3 + H_2O \rightarrow CH_3CO_2H + CH_3OH$$

Example 14.13

Reaction of ethyl bromide (FGL 1) with aqueous hydroxide yields ethanol (FGL 1) which is a substitution reaction.

$$CH_3CH_2Br + OH^-(aq) \rightarrow CH_3CH_2OH + Br^-(aq)$$

Example 14.14

Reaction of ethanoyl chloride (FGL 3) with ammonia yields ethanamide (FGL 3) which is a condensation reaction.

$$CH_3COCl + 2\,NH_3 \rightarrow CH_3CONH_2 + NH_4Cl$$

Questions 14.6

1. Which option does not give ethanoic acid as the organic product after being hydrolysed?

   A   Ethanoyl chloride.

   B   Ethyl ethanoate.

   C   Ethanamide.

   D   Ethylamine.

2. Complete the table and, using FGL, classify the type of reaction.

	Reactant	Reagent	Product
	CH_3CH_2OH	$SOCl_2$	CH_3CH_2Cl
FGL			

3. Complete the table and using FGL classify the type of reaction.

Reactant	Reagent	Product
CH_3COOH	$SOCl_2$	CH_3COCl
FGL		

4. Which of the following is **not** a sign of a reduction?

A   Decrease in FGL.

B   Loss of electrons.

C   Loss of oxygen.

D   Gain of hydrogen.

The second type of movement with Functional Group Levels is down FGL. A reduction in FGL is a reduction reaction. The list of reducing agents below shows a selection of a large number of reducing agents available to organic chemists which include both metallic and non-metallic elements as well as cations and anions. During reduction reactions new C–H bonds are formed and C–X bonds are broken [where X = heteroatom].

Reducing Agents

Metals (Zn, Sn), Fe^{2+}, I^- / H^+, H_2, $S_2O_3^{2-}$, $C_2O_4^{2-}$, S^{2-} (H_2S), Sn^{2+}, H_2O_2, $LiAlH_4$, $NaBH_4$.

Example 14.15

In the laboratory, carbonyl compounds (FGL 2) are reduced to alcohols (FGL 1) by hydrides, such as $LiAlH_4$ (lithium aluminium hydride) or $NaBH_4$ (sodium borohydride). On a larger scale, the reducing agent is hydrogen gas with a platinum catalyst under pressure and carried out at high temperatures.

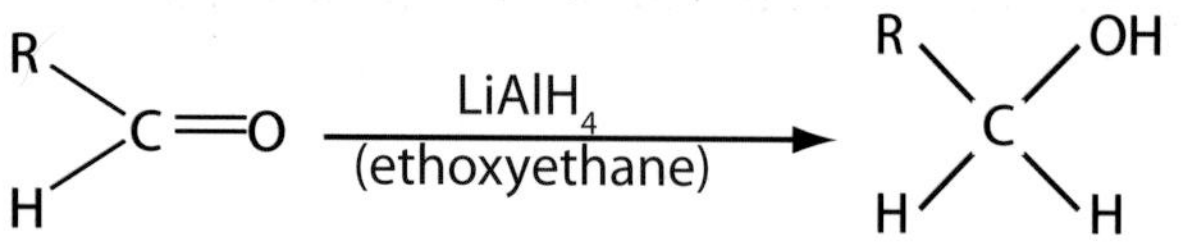

aldehyde → primary alcohol ($LiAlH_4$, ethoxyethane)

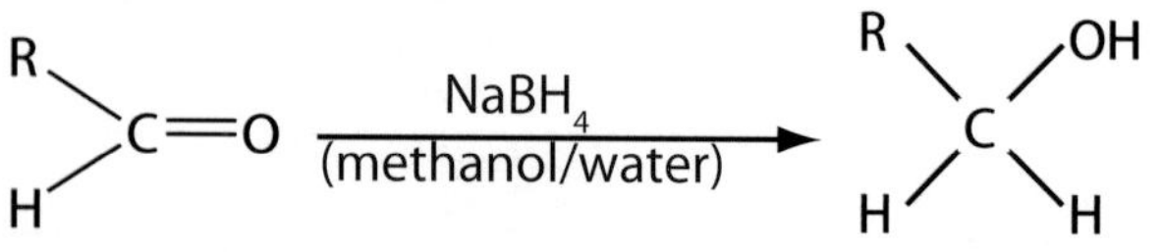

aldehyde → primary alcohol ($NaBH_4$, methanol/water)

ketone → secondary alcohol ($LiAlH_4$, ethoxyethane)

Example 14.16

Lithium aluminium hydride ($LiAlH_4$) also reduces nitriles (FGL 3) to primary amines (FGL 1).

$$CH_3CH_2CN \xrightarrow[\text{(ethoxyethane)}]{LiAlH_4} CH_3CH_2CH_2NH_2$$

propanenitrile → propylamine

Questions 14.7

1. Why can't you use FGL to explain the type of reaction when nitrobenzene reacts with Sn / c.HCl to form phenylamine?

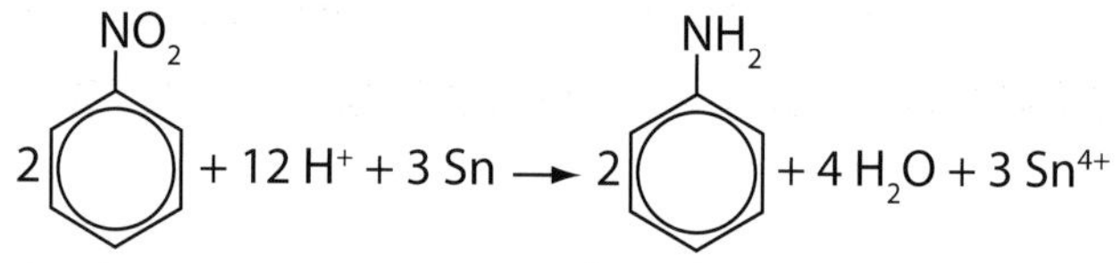

$$2\,(NO_2\text{-benzene}) + 12\,H^+ + 3\,Sn \longrightarrow 2\,(NH_2\text{-benzene}) + 4\,H_2O + 3\,Sn^{4+}$$

nitrobenzene → phenylamine

2. Complete the table to show the products when the powerful reducing agent $LiAlH_4$ is used on the reactants.

Reactant	Reducing agent	Product(s)	Change in FGL
CH_3COOH	$LiAlH_4$		
$CH_3COOC_2H_5$	$LiAlH_4$		
CH_3COOCH_3	$LiAlH_4$		
CH_3CONH_2	$LiAlH_4$		
CH_3CH_2CN	$LiAlH_4$		

The third type of movement with Functional Group Levels is up FGL. An increase in FGL is an oxidation reaction. The list of oxidising agents shows a selection of a large number of oxidising agents available to organic chemists which include non-metallic elements as well as anions and iron(III). During oxidation reactions new C–X bonds are formed where X = heteroatom.

Oxidising Agents

O_2, Cl_2, Br_2, I_2, MnO_4^- / H^+, Fe^{3+}, H^+, H_2O_2, MnO_2, H_2SO_4, $Cr_2O_7^{2-}$ / H^+.

Example 14.17

Propanone can be prepared by the oxidation of propan-2-ol using acidified potassium dichromate (with warming).

$$\text{Propan-2-ol} \xrightarrow[\text{warm}]{K_2Cr_2O_7 / H^+} \text{Propanone}$$

The reaction is an oxidation because there is an increase in FGL as propan-2-ol has a FGL = 1 and propanone has a FGL = 2.

Questions 14.8

1. The reaction of ethanol with acidified dichromate can be stopped at the aldehyde stage (step 1) if distillation apparatus is used. If the reaction mixture is heated under reflux the fully oxidised ethanoic acid (step 2) is the organic product. Describe what type of reactions are taking place for both steps in terms of FGL.

$$CH_3CH_2OH \xrightarrow[\text{step 1}]{Cr_2O_7^{2-} / H^+} CH_3CHO$$

$$CH_3CHO \xrightarrow[\text{step 2}]{Cr_2O_7^{2-} / H^+} CH_3COOH$$

2. Explain, using FGL, what type of reaction happens when methylbenzene (toluene) reacts with acidified potassium manganate(VII).

$$C_6H_5CH_3 \xrightarrow{KMnO_4 / H^+} C_6H_5COOH$$

3. Explain, using FGL, what type of reaction happens when but-2-ene reacts with hot concentrated potassium manganate(VII).

$$CH_3CH=CHCH_3 \xrightarrow{KMnO_4} 2\ CH_3CHO$$

4. Explain, using FGL, what type of reaction happens when toluene (methylbenzene) reacts with manganese(IV) oxide.

$$C_6H_5CH_3 \xrightarrow{MnO_2} C_6H_5CHO$$

5. The conversion of propanoic acid into pentan-2-one is achieved in 4 steps. Describe what type of reactions are taking place for all four steps in terms of FGL.

A3.2 (g) Common examples within FGL

Recognition of FGL (A3.2c) revealed that some functional groups are more difficult to name than others. In functional groups at the carboxylic acid level, e.g. carboxylic acids, esters, acid chlorides, amides and nitriles, the carbon of the functional group is counted in the naming of these compounds.

Example 14.18

Name the molecules belonging to the alcohol level (FGL 1) that have three carbon atoms.

Solution:

Alcohol level (Examples containing three carbon atoms)				
Alcohols	Propan-1-ol	Propan-2-ol		
Alkyl halides	1-chloropropane	1-bromopropane	1-iodopropane	
Amines	1-aminopropane	2-aminopropane	Trimethylamine	N-methylethanamine
Ethers	Ethoxymethane			

Questions 14.9

1. Name the three-carbon molecules belonging to the carbonyl level (FGL 2).

2. Name the two-carbon molecules belonging to the carboxylic acid level (FGL 3).

3. Complete the table by assigning the FGL for each reactant and product and, based on these FGL, describe the type of reaction that has taken place.

Reactant	Product	FGL → FGL	Reaction type
Ethanol	Ethanal		
Ethanal	Ethanoic acid		
Propanal	Propanoic acid		
Propanal	Propan-1-ol		
Bromoethane	Ethanol		
Ethanol	Bromoethane		
Ethanoyl chloride	Ethanoic acid		
Ethanenitrile	Ethylamine		

A3.2 (h) Unstable groups

The simplest aldehyde, formaldehyde (methanal), is commercially available as 40% aqueous solutions called **formalin**. This is a chemical familiar to biologists as it is often used for preserving biological specimens. Methanal is in equilibrium with methanediol which is a stable hydrate of methanal. Methanediol is described as a **gem diol** because both alcohol groups (OH) are attached to the same carbon atom. The value of the equilibrium constant $K = 2280$ (B1.5c). The equilibrium lies predominantly to the side of the hydrate.

Methanal + H_2O ⇌ Methanediol

Evidence for the existence of methane diol comes from its ^{13}C nmr spectrum (A4.5b). The carbon resonates at 83 ppm rather than the expected range (150-200 ppm). Other hydrates of aldehydes and ketones are found in much smaller amounts than methanediol which can be attributed to steric hindrance making the reaction with water less likely and their gem diols are less stable.

Ethanal 41% + H_2O ⇌ 1-hydroxyethanol 59%

Propanone 99.8% + H_2O ⇌ 2,2-dihydroxypropane 0.2%

The presence of more than one hydroxyl group on one carbon atom increases the instability of the molecule. When there are two OH groups on the same carbon atom, elimination of a water molecule leads to the formation of an aldehyde or a ketone.

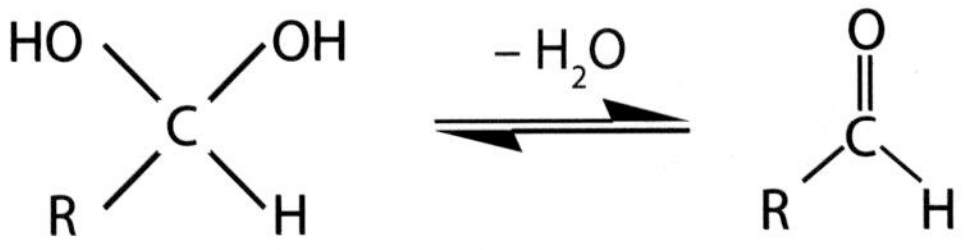

HO—C(OH)(R)(H) $-H_2O$ → R—C(=O)—H

Hydrate   Aldehyde

HO—C(OH)(R)(R) $-H_2O$ → R—C(=O)—R

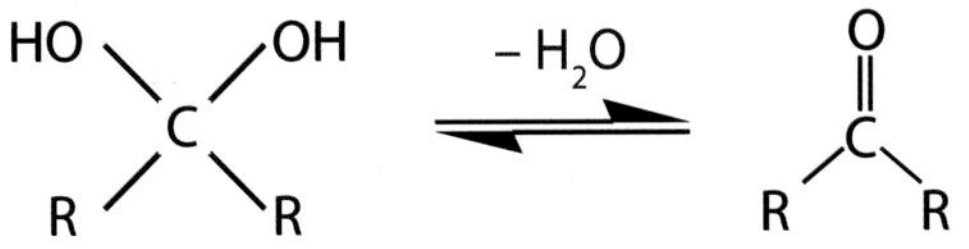

Hydrate   Ketone

When there are three OH groups on the same carbon atom elimination of a water molecule leads to the formation of a carboxylic acid.

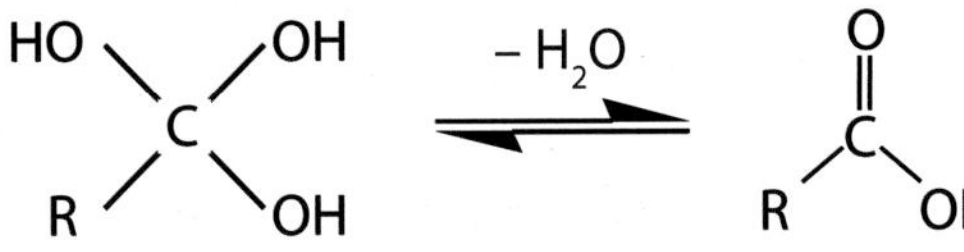

HO—C(OH)(R)(OH) $-H_2O$ → R—C(=O)—OH

Hydrate   Carboxylic acid

When there are four OH groups on the same carbon atom, elimination of one water molecule leads to the formation of carbonic acid (H_2CO_3) and elimination of two water molecules leads to carbon dioxide.

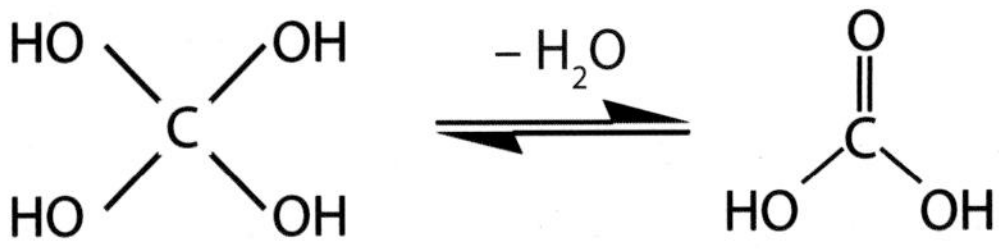

HO—C(OH)(HO)(OH) $-H_2O$ → HO—C(=O)—OH

Hydrate   Carbonic acid

HO—C(OH)(HO)(OH) $-2H_2O$ → $O=C=O$

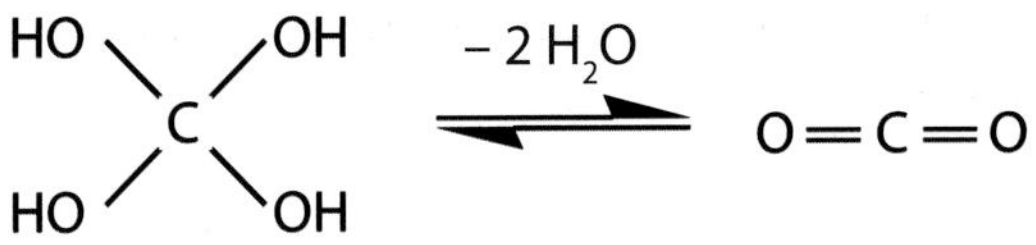

Hydrate   Carbon dioxide

Questions 14.10

1. Cyclopropanone reacts with water to form a hydrate. Show this equilibrium reaction.

2. Which unstable compound would eliminate water to form propanal?

3. What type of compound has the structural formula $CH_3CH(OH)_2$ and what would be formed if it underwent an elimination reaction?

4. Complete the table below by suggesting the final product of hydrolysis for the following molecules (FGL 4).

Name	Formula	Hydrolysis product
Phosgene	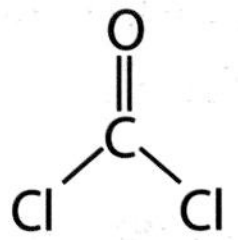 Cl—C(=O)—Cl	
Urea	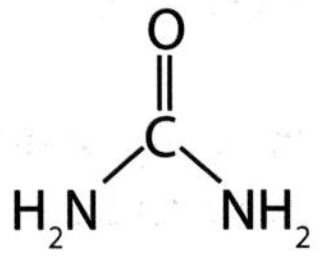 H_2N—C(=O)—NH_2	
Guanidine	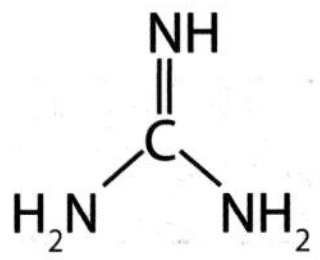 H_2N—C(=NH)—NH_2	

15 Alcohol Level

Contents

The members of the **Alcohol Level** (FGL 1) have one bond to an electronegative element from a particular carbon atom. Members include: alcohols (ROH), amines (R_3N), halogenoalkanes, which are also known as alkyl halides, (RX where X = F, Cl, Br, I) and ethers (ROR). Alcohols are a key functional group level as they are versatile and can move up and down FGL as well as within FGL.

There are many interesting molecules with alcohol groups as part of their structure, for example:

Adrenaline is the fight or flight hormone.

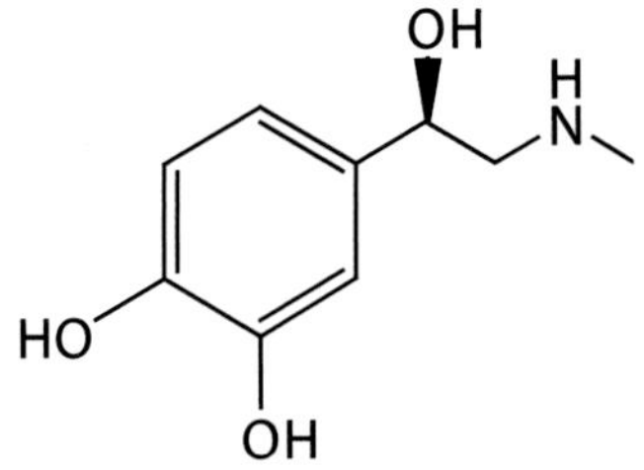

Salbutamol is the active ingredient of asthma inhalers.

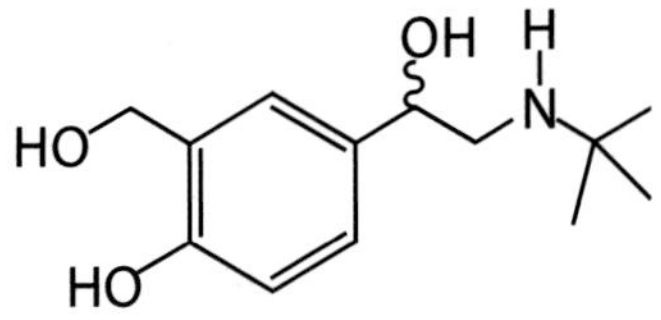

Menthol is found in peppermint and has local anaesthetic properties.

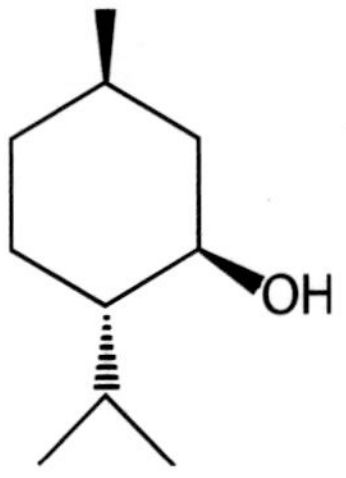

Some molecules contain more than one hydroxyl group, for example,

Ethylene glycol (ethane-1,2-diol) is used as an antifreeze:

$$CH_2OH$$
$$|$$
$$CH_2OH$$

Glycerol (propane-1,2,3-triol) $CH_2OHCHOHCH_2OH$ glycerin(e), which is central to many lipids and, when nitrated, forms the explosive nitroglycerine used in dynamite.

Within the alcohol level there are three possible FGL changes. These are moving within the level. Reactions include synthesis of alcohols and amines from halogenoalkanes and the synthesis of halogenoalkanes from alcohols. Moving down a level, reactions include the substitution of halogenoalkanes with cyanide. Moving up a level, reactions include the oxidation of alcohols to aldehydes and ketones. The 'spider diagram' below shows all the interconversions with the alcohol level towards the centre of the diagram. The diagram and the conditions (numbered 1-20) need to be reviewed periodically if this body of work is to be recalled for application at a later date.

Alcohol Level

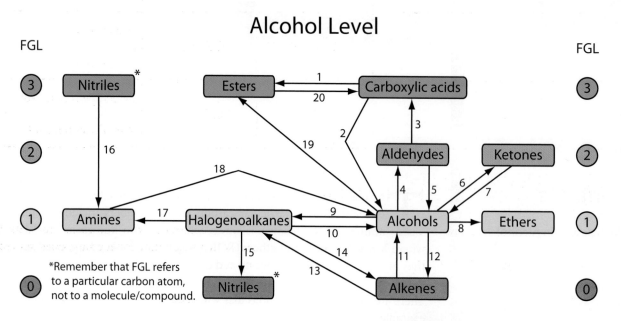

*Remember that FGL refers to a particular carbon atom, not to a molecule/compound.

Organic chemistry is the one branch of chemistry where everyone needs to spend time learning things by rote. It may not be educationally fashionable, but there is no substitute for spending time practising writing out equations until their recall becomes second nature. All students should be able to make use of the FGL concept to tackle questions with more confidence than previous generations of students. It is expected that by the end of the Pre-U course, a distinction level student will be able to look at a spider diagram for any FGL and describe the reactions and the conditions. For the alcohol level, this includes each of the chemical transformations 1-20.

#	Conditions
1	Alcohol / H+
2	LiAlH$_4$ / dry Et$_2$O
3	Cr$_2$O$_7$$^{2-}$ / H+ / heat
4	Cr$_2$O$_7$$^{2-}$ / H+
5	LiAlH$_4$ / dry Et$_2$O
6	Cr$_2$O$_7$$^{2-}$ / H+
7	LiAlH$_4$ / dry Et$_2$O
8	RX
9	HBr or PX$_3$ or PX$_5$ or SOCl$_2$
10	OH− (aq) / heat

#	Conditions
11	H$_2$O / H$_3$PO$_4$ / heat / pressure
12	Heat with Al$_2$O$_3$ or heat with c.H$_2$SO$_4$
13	HX or X$_2$
14	OH− (ethanolic) / heat
15	NaCN or KCN in ethanol / heat
16	LiAlH$_4$ / dry Et$_2$O or H$_2$ / Ni
17	NH$_3$ in ethanol / heat / pressure
18	HNO$_2$
19	RCO$_2$H / H+ or RCOCl
20	H+ or OH−

All alcohols contain the hydroxyl group (OH). When discussing alcohols in general terms it is convenient to refer to them as ROH where R = alkyl group. The general formula for an alcohol is C$_n$H$_{2n+1}$OH where n is the number of carbon atoms. Alcohols can be further classified into primary (1°), secondary (2°) or tertiary (3°). The type of alcohol describes the number of carbon atoms bonded to the carbon atom bearing the OH group. Thus primary alcohols have 1 carbon joined to the carbon of the C–OH. It is often quickest to recognise them as containing RCH$_2$OH where R = H, alkyl or aryl. The following table summarises the three types of alcohol.

Alcohol type		Carbons joined to C–OH	General	R	Example
Primary	1°	1	RCH$_2$OH	H, alkyl or aryl	Ethanol Propan-1-ol
Secondary	2°	2	R$_2$CHOH	Alkyl or aryl	Propan-2-ol Butan-2-ol
Tertiary	3°	3	R$_3$COH	Alkyl or aryl	2-methylpropan-2-ol 2-methylbutan-2-ol

Questions 15.1

1. Which of the options is a secondary (2°) alcohol?

   A   CH$_3$CH(CH$_3$)CH(OH)CH$_2$CH$_3$

   B   CH$_3$CH(CH$_3$)CH$_2$OH

   C   CH$_3$C(CH$_3$)$_2$CH$_2$OH

   D   CH$_3$C(OH)(CH$_3$)CH$_2$OH

2. Tertiary alcohols are not easily oxidised. Which of the options is a tertiary (3°) alcohol?

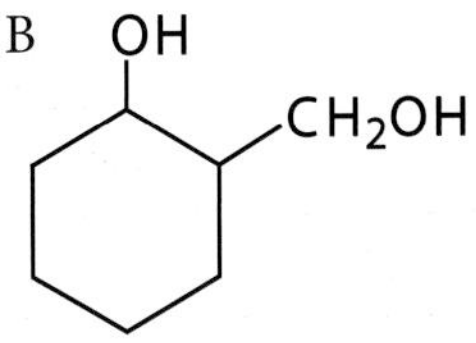

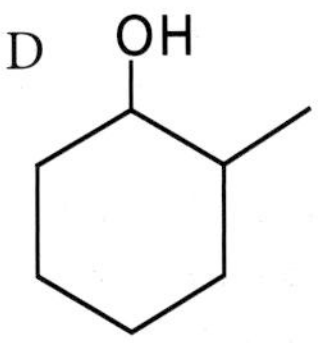

3. Classify each of these alcohols as 1°, 2° or 3° and name them.

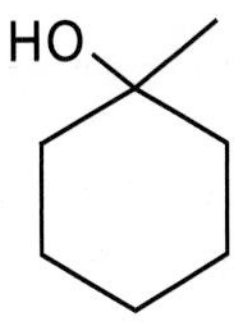

   CH$_3$CHOHCH$_3$ CH$_3$CH$_2$CH$_2$OH

   CH$_3$CH(CH$_3$)CH$_2$OH   (CH$_3$)$_3$COH

4. Which compound with molecular formula C$_4$H$_{10}$O and with a single functional group, does not react with sodium?

   A   1° alcohol

   B   3° alcohol

   C   ether

   D   2° alcohol

5. If one hydrogen atom was replaced by a hydroxyl (OH) group in 2-methylbutane, how many possible isomeric 1° alcohols would result?

   A   1

   B   3

   C   2

   D   0

A3.3 (a) Hydrolysis within alcohol level

In organic chemistry, a hydrolysis reaction involves the breaking of covalent bonds with water. Hydrolysis reactions can be acid and/or base catalysed. A common method for the preparation of alcohols is the hydrolysis of halogenoalkanes. The details of this nucleophilic substitution are found in section B3.9b. Halogenoalkanes have the general formula $C_nH_{2n+1}X$ where X = halogen (F, Cl, Br, I). Like alcohols, halogenoalkanes can also be 1°, 2° or 3° depending on the degree of branching.

1° halogenoalkane *e.g.* 1-chlorobutane ($CH_3CH_2CH_2CH_2Cl$)

2° halogenoalkane *e.g.* 2-chlorobutane ($CH_3CHClCH_2CH_3$)

3° halogenoalkane *e.g.* 2-chloro-2-methylpropane ($CH_3)_3CCl$)

Hydrolysis of halogenoalkanes is slow at room temperature in water and much more rapid if hydroxide ions are employed. In both cases, the water and hydroxide behave as nucleophiles (B3.9b). As both halogenoalkanes and alcohols have an FGL = 1, hydrolysis of halogenoalkanes is moving within the FGL. At all FGL, hydrolysis always leads to the formation of the functional group that gave rise to the name of the FGL.

$$RX + H_2O \rightarrow ROH + HX$$

$$RX + OH^- \rightarrow ROH + X^-$$

The rate of hydrolysis of halogenoalkanes can be followed in several ways, *e.g.* changes in conductivity, and is a reaction much used in studying reaction kinetics (B1.6i).

Example 15.1

Bromoethane can be hydrolysed by refluxing with an aqueous sodium hydroxide solution.

$$C_2H_5Br + NaOH \rightarrow C_2H_5OH + NaBr$$

As both products are colourless, the addition of aqueous silver nitrate (1cm³) will allow this reaction to be followed using a colorimeter, as the by-product can be detected according to the ionic equation $Ag^+ (aq) + Br^- (aq) \rightarrow AgBr (s)$. Silver bromide is a cream coloured solid. The higher the rate of hydrolysis, the sooner the precipitate of silver halide will appear.

Example 15.2

Chloromethane and 1-bromopropane can both be hydrolysed by water.

$$CH_3Cl + H_2O \rightarrow CH_3OH + HCl$$

$$CH_3CH_2CH_2Br + H_2O \rightarrow CH_3CH_2CH_2OH + HBr$$

Hydrolysis experiment

The hydrolysis of halogenoalkanes works best when carried out at 50°C. This might be achieved by placing the test tubes into a beaker of water or, if available, a water bath. Ethanol (1 cm³) and silver nitrate solution (1 cm³) are placed into a test tube. A stop watch is started once 5 drops of liquid halogenoalkane have been added. The rate is taken as the reciprocal of the time for a precipitate to appear.

$$CH_3CH_2CH_2X + H_2O \rightarrow CH_3CH_2CH_2OH + HX$$

$$Ag^+ (aq) + X^- (aq) \rightarrow AgX (s)$$

AgI (s) is yellow, AgBr (s) is cream and AgCl (s) is white.

The rates of hydrolysis are:

$$CH_3CH_2CH_2Cl < CH_3CH_2CH_2Br < CH_3CH_2CH_2I$$

This order reflects the weaker C–I bond strength (A1.3d) rather than the polarity of the C–X bond. The values for bond enthalpies in kJ mol⁻¹ are; C–I (230), C–Br (280) and C–Cl (339).

The test tube on the left shows very little precipitate of AgCl. The middle test tube shows quite a lot of AgBr. The test tube on the right shows a lot of pale yellow AgI after 5 minutes.

Question 15.2

1. Using skeletal formulae, write an equation for the reaction between cyclohexanol and hydrogen bromide gas. How would this gas be prepared *in situ*? What type of reaction is this? Describe any changes in FGL.

Moving down a level

Halogenoalkanes react with ethanolic hydroxide by elimination of a hydrogen halide (HX) to produce an alkene. With dihalogenoalkanes, the product when two molecules of HX are eliminated will be an alkyne. 1,1-dichloroethane and 1,2-dibromoethane both react with ethanolic potassium hydroxide when heated under reflux to form ethyne (C_2H_2).

$$CH_3CHCl_2 + 2\ KOH \xrightarrow[\text{reflux}]{\text{ethanol/}} HC\equiv CH + 2\ KCl + 2\ H_2O$$

$$CH_2BrCH_2Br + 2\ KOH \xrightarrow[\text{reflux}]{\text{ethanol/}} HC\equiv CH + 2\ KBr + 2\ H_2O$$

Moving within a level

Ethers are inert compounds which are often used as solvents in reactions. They contain the C-O-C bonds and are functional group isomers (A3.1d) of alcohols. Ethers can be prepared by reaction of halogenoalkanes with the alcohol or the faster reaction where the sodium 'salt' of the alcohol is used as a reactant. When naming ethers, do not forget the alphabetical rule, e.g. $CH_3CH_2OCH_3$ is ethoxymethane rather than methoxyethane. When an alcohol is converted into an ether, there is no change in FGL as both reactant and product are FGL = 1.

$$CH_3CH_2Br + CH_3OH \rightarrow CH_3CH_2OCH_3 + HBr$$

$$CH_3CH_2Br + CH_3O^- \rightarrow CH_3CH_2OCH_3 + Br^-$$

In the world of research chemistry, there has been significant interest in ethers which form rings. This led to the award of a shared Nobel Prize in chemistry in 1987 to Charles Pedersen who 'discovered' **crown ethers**. 24–crown–8 is shown. The 24 represents the number of atoms in the cycle and the 8 is the number of oxygen atoms.

24–crown–8

A3.3 (b)
Synthesising functional groups with FGL = 1

Alcohols may be synthesized from halogenoalkanes using aqueous sodium hydroxide and this was detailed in A3.3a. As halogenoalkanes are generally very water insoluble, ethanol needs to be used as a solvent for the halogenoalkanes. The result is that two competing reactions take place: substitution to make the desired alcohol and elimination to make an alkene (by-product).

Synthesis of amines

Amines may be synthesized from halogenoalkanes using ethanolic ammonia. The mixtures are heated under pressure in sealed tubes. This is not to be recommended in a laboratory because of the inherent dangers in this type of experiment. This is moving within the alcohol level as both amines (product) and halogenoalkanes (reactant) are both at FGL = 1. Halogenoalkanes react with concentrated ammonia in a sealed tube to produce an amine. The problem with this synthetic route to amines is that you get a mixture of amines which can be avoided if excess ammonia is used.

$$C_2H_5I + c.NH_3 \rightarrow C_2H_5NH_2 + HI$$

Question 15.3

1. How can ethylamine be prepared from bromoethane and what conditions would help avoid further substitutions leading to the formation of 2° and 3° amines? How might the inorganic by-product be neutralised?

Synthesis of halogenoalkanes

Tertiary alcohols react rapidly with concentrated hydrohalic acids (HCl, HBr, HI) at room temperature to form the corresponding halogenoalkanes. 2-methylpropan-2-ol reacts with concentrated hydrochloric acid to form 2-chloro-2-methylpropane and water as shown in the equation, with a yield of 85%.

The order of hydrolysis is 3° > 2° > 1° and this is the basis of the **Lucas test** which is used to distinguish between the types of alcohol. As the halogenoalkane is insoluble in water its formation is indicated by cloudiness of the reaction mixture. The reaction mixture for 2° alcohols goes cloudy on warming after 5 minutes and for 1° alcohols there is no reaction observed. To make halogenoalkanes from 1° alcohols, a halide of phosphorus needs to be employed.

Alcohols (ROH) may also be halogenated using phosphorus(III) halides or phosphorus(V) halides , *e.g.* PBr_3 or PCl_5. If phosphorus tribromide is used as the halogenating agent, it is generated *in situ* by adding bromine to a mixture of red phosphorus and the alcohol is heated under reflux.

$$2\,P + 3\,Br_2 \rightarrow 2\,PBr_3$$

$$3\,ROH + PBr_3 \rightarrow 3\,R–Br + H_3PO_3$$

Alcohols can be halogenated using PCl_3, which is a liquid. It is important to ensure the alcohol is dried to remove any water that would react with PCl_3 (A2.1h).

$$3\,ROH + PCl_3 \rightarrow 3\,R–Cl + H_3PO_3$$

Question 15.4

1. Give a balanced formula equation for the reaction between ethanol and phosphorus(III) bromide. What type of reaction is this and what is the change in FGL?

Laboratory preparation of bromoethane

Ethanol (5 cm³) is placed in a round bottomed flask as part of a distillation set up. Concentrated sulfuric acid (6 cm³) is slowly added with swirling and cooling. Solid potassium bromide (6 g) is then added to the reaction mixture which is heated gently whilst the bromoethane distils into a test tube placed in ice in a beaker. The fraction which boils between 38-40°C is collected. To the distillate is added saturated sodium hydrogen carbonate solution (4 cm³). The mixture is transferred to a separating funnel and the lower organic layer is dried with anhydrous calcium chloride ($CaCl_2$) or magnesium sulfate ($MgSO_4$).

$$KBr + H_2SO_4 \rightarrow KHSO_4 + HBr$$

$$CH_3CH_2OH + HBr \rightarrow CH_3CH_2Br + H_2O$$

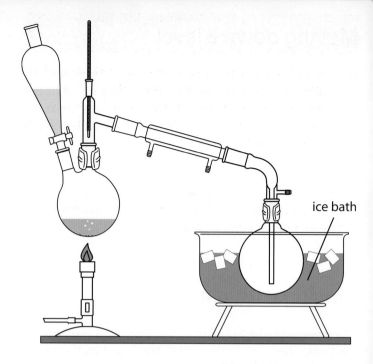

ice bath

Anhydrous alcohols (ROH) may also be halogenated using solid phosphorus(V) chloride (PCl_5) at room temperature. It is not the best choice of halogenating agent but it does make a good test for alcohols as it produces clouds of hydrogen chloride gas. The chloroethane can be distilled off from the inorganic product.

$$CH_3CH_2OH + PCl_5 \rightarrow CH_3CH_2Cl + POCl_3 + HCl$$

Halogenoalkanes may also be synthesized from alcohols using thionyl chloride ($SOCl_2$) which is also known as sulfur dichloride oxide. This latter method is very effective as it can be carried out at room temperature as the two unwanted products are acidic gases which can easily be removed or neutralised with an organic base such as pyridine (C_5H_5N).

$$CH_3CH_2OH + SOCl_2 \rightarrow CH_3CH_2Cl + SO_2 + HCl$$

Questions 15.5

1. Give the balanced equation for the reaction between propan-1-ol and thionyl chloride. Explain the advantages and disadvantages of this method for preparing a halogenoalkane compared with using a chloride of phosphorus.

2. Which of these alcohols reacts with acidified $K_2Cr_2O_7$ to give a ketone?

    A $(CH_3)_2CHCH_2OH$

    B $CH_3CH_2CH_2OH$

    C $CH_3CHOHCH_3$

    D $(CH_3)_3COH$

3. Which of these alcohols reacts with acidified $K_2Cr_2O_7$ to give a carboxylic acid?

    A $(CH_3)_2CHCH_2OH$

    B $CH_3CH_2CH_2OH$

    C $CH_3CHOHCH_3$

    D $(CH_3)_3COH$

4. When naming alcohols, the carbon bearing the OH (hydroxyl) group is given the lowest possible number, and substituents on the longest chain are included in the name as a prefix. Name the following alcohol from its structural formula, $CH_3CH_2CH(CH_3)CH(OH)CH_3$.

5. Draw 2,2-dimethylpropan-1-ol and show its reaction with sodium.

A3.3 (c) Halogenoalkanes reacting with cyanide

Refluxing an ethanolic solution of sodium cyanide (NaCN) with a halogenoalkane (R–X) leads to the formation of a nitrile (R–C≡N). Substitution of a halogenoalkane by cyanide (C≡N⁻) lowers the FGL from 1 to FGL 0, which is the hydrocarbon level. Reaction of bromoethane with sodium cyanide gives ethyl cyanide (C_2H_5CN), which is a colourless liquid having the IUPAC name propanenitrile.

$$C_2H_5Br + NaCN \rightarrow C_2H_5CN + NaBr$$

Care is needed when naming nitriles as the carbon of the nitrile group is included in the name. The change in FGL in this reaction might also cause confusion as the carbon of the nitrile group (C≡N) is at FGL = 3. Remember to look at the changes in FGL at a particular carbon during a reaction. The formation of nitriles is a very versatile reaction as it gives a controlled way of ascending a homologous series by adding one carbon at a time. Nitriles can also be reduced to give 1° amines (B3.7d) and hydrolysed *via* the amide to give carboxylic acids (B3.7a).

Questions 15.6

1. What is the organic product formed when 1-iodobutane reacts with potassium cyanide. How could the colourless inorganic product be detected using a qualitative test?

2. For the reaction scheme below, classify the type of reaction using FGLs taking place in steps 1, 2 & 3.

    $CH_3OH \xrightarrow{\text{step 1}} CH_3Br$

    $CH_3Br \xrightarrow{\text{step 2}} CH_3CN$

    $CH_3CN \xrightarrow{\text{step 3}} CH_3CH_2NH_2$

A3.3 (d) Oxidation of alcohols

Oxidation can be thought of as moving up one or more oxidation levels. The oxidation of primary (1°) and secondary (2°) alcohols is achieved using acidified sodium dichromate(VI). ($Na_2Cr_2O_7$). The acid used in the reactions is sulfuric acid (H_2SO_4). The oxidation state of the chromium is 6+ as indicated by the roman numerals. During the course of the reaction the orange solution of dichromate(VI) changes to blue-green as this species is reduced to the chromium(III) ion, Cr^{3+} (aq). Tertiary alcohols (3°) are far more resistant to oxidation and cannot readily be oxidised by acidified dichromate(VI). The half equation (B1.5j) for the oxidising agent is:

$$Cr_2O_7^{2-} + 14\ H^+ + 6e^- \rightarrow 2\ Cr^{3+} + 7\ H_2O$$

Oxidation of ethanol

The oxidation of ethanol, which is a primary alcohol, takes place in two steps. It is convenient to represent the oxidising agent as [O] to simplify the equation. Note how the alcohol, aldehyde and carboxylic acid all contain the same number of carbon atoms.

Step1: $CH_3CH_2OH + [O] \rightarrow CH_3CHO + H_2O$

Step 2: $CH_3CHO + [O] \rightarrow CH_3COOH$

Overall: $CH_3CH_2OH + 2[O] \rightarrow CH_3COOH + H_2O$

The full equation including the dichromate(VI) and the acid (H^+) is also shown.

Step 1:

$3CH_3CH_2OH + 8H^+ + Cr_2O_7^{2-} \rightarrow 3CH_3CHO + 7H_2O + 2Cr^{3+}$

Step 2:

$3CH_3CHO + 8\ H^+ + Cr_2O_7^{2-} \rightarrow 3CH_3COOH + 4H_2O + 2Cr^{3+}$

Overall:

$3CH_3CH_2OH + 16H^+ + 2Cr_2O_7^{2-} \rightarrow 3CH_3COOH + 11H_2O + 4Cr^{3+}$

To prevent the aldehyde being oxidised further to the carboxylic acid, the highly volatile product can be distilled off as soon as it forms. If the desired end product is the carboxylic acid then the reaction mixture is heated under reflux.

Oxidation of propan-2-ol

The oxidation of secondary alcohols with acidified dichromate(VI) is a one step reaction which stops at the ketone. Further oxidation of the ketone is not possible with acidified dichromate(VI). Propan-2-ol is oxidised to propanone. When writing these equations don't forget to include the inorganic product (water). A common mistake is to write the by-product as hydrogen.

Step1:

$CH_3CHOHCH_3 + [O] \rightarrow CH_3COCH_3 + H_2O$

The identification of the oxidation product (aldehyde, ketone or carboxylic acid) is one method for distinguishing between 1°, 2° and 3° alcohols. Aldehydes can be detected with **Tollens' reagent** (A3.4c) and carboxylic acids by their reaction with sodium carbonate (Na_2CO_3).

If alcohols are oxidised with alkaline potassium manganate(VII) $KMnO_4$ under reflux, the three types of alcohols can be distinguished.

Alcohol	Product with alkaline KMnO$_4$
1°	aldehyde
2°	ketone
3°	no reaction

FGL changes

The oxidation of alcohols with acidified dichromate(VI) can be explained in terms of FGL changes of the organic reactants and products. When there is an increase in FGL, this is termed an oxidation.

Substance	FGL
alcohol	1
aldehyde	2
ketone	2
carboxylic acid	3

Questions 15.7

1. Using FGL changes, describe what is happening in this two step reaction.

$$CH_3OH \rightarrow HCHO \rightarrow HCOOH$$

2. Using FGL changes, describe what is happening in the reaction.

$$CH_3CHO \rightarrow CH_3CH_2OH$$

3. Complete the table by identifying the organic reactant or product.

#	Reactant	Reagent	Product
1	1–bromopropane	OH^- (aq)	
2		HBr (g)	bromo-cyclohexane
3	1,1–dichloroethane	x.s. KOH (ethanolic)	
4	2-chloropropane	H_2O	
5		$SOCl_2$	1-chlorobutane
6	1-iodopropane	NaCN	
7	ethanol	Na	
8		$Cr_2O_7^{2-}/H^+$	ethanal
9		$Cr_2O_7^{2-}/H^+$	butanone
10	propan-1-ol	PCl_5	
11		PBr_3	1-bromopentane
12	1-iodopropane	NH_3	

4. How could a reaction be used to distinguish between 1°, 2° and 3° alcohols?

5. Put the three carbon compounds ethanol, ethane-1,2-diol and ethanal in order of decreasing volatility and explain the order you have chosen.

6. How can you convert ethanoic acid into the next member of its homologous series?

7. What is a halogenoalkane (alkyl halide)? Illustrate your answer with the simplest primary, secondary and tertiary chloroalkanes.

8. Name **all** the structural isomers of $C_5H_{11}Cl$. Identify each one as 1°, 2° or 3°.

9. Explain, using FGL, what type of reaction it is when iodine reacts with propan-2-ol.

10. Draw in 3D the two organic products formed when 2-bromobutane undergoes alkaline hydrolysis.

11. Primary amines react with nitrous acid (HNO_2) according to the equation below.

$$RNH_2 + HNO_2 \xrightarrow{30-50\,°C} ROH + N_2 + H_2O$$

What observations might you make and explain how would you classify this reaction?

How might the unstable nitrous acid be prepared *in situ*?

12. Three different 1° halogenoalkanes having the formula C_4H_9X (where X= Cl, Br & I) were hydrolysed with warm aqueous sodium hydroxide solution in the presence of $AgNO_3$. Explain the results and suggest the identity and colour of the precipitates.

Halogenoalkane	Time / sec	Precipitate (name & colour)
C_4H_9Cl	75	
C_4H_9Br	30	
C_4H_9I	15	

16 Carbonyl Level

Contents

The members of the Carbonyl level (FGL 2) have two bonds to electronegative element(s) from a carbon atom. Members include; aldehydes [RCHO], ketones [R_2CO], gem-diols [$RC(OH)_2$], gem-dihalides [$R_2C(X)_2$], hemiacetals [RCH(OH)OR], acetals [$RCH(OR)_2$], hemiketals [$R_2C(OH)OR$], ketals [$R_2C(OR)_2$], imines [$R_2C=NR$], oximes [$R_2C=NOH$], and hydrazones [$R_2C=N-NH_2$].

Carbonyls are versatile as they can move up FGL by oxidation reactions, down FGL by addition reactions as well as within FGL by hydrolysis and addition of bisulfite. Aldehydes and ketones both have the characteristic carbonyl (C=O) group. The differences in their chemical properties arise because aldehydes have a hydrogen atom directly attached to the carbon atom of the carbonyl group. At university, aldehydes are also known as alkanals and ketones are known as alkanones.

There are many interesting molecules with carbonyl groups as part of their structure. Examples of aldehydes include:

benzaldehyde (C_6H_5CHO) which smells of almonds,

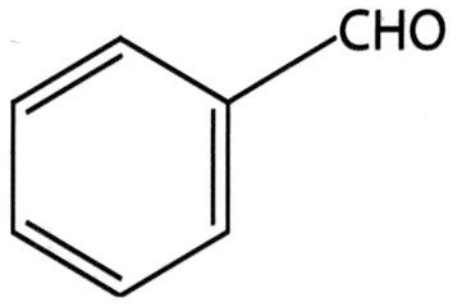

the open chain form of **glucose** ($C_6H_{12}O_6$) is an aldehyde,

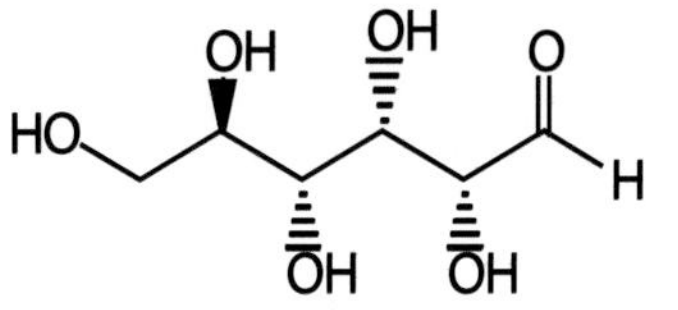

trans-**cinnamaldehyde** found in the bark of cinnamon trees,

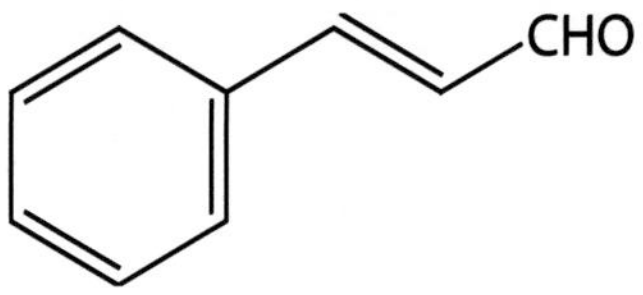

and

vanillin = 4-hydroxy-3-methoxybenzaldehyde has the flavour of vanilla.

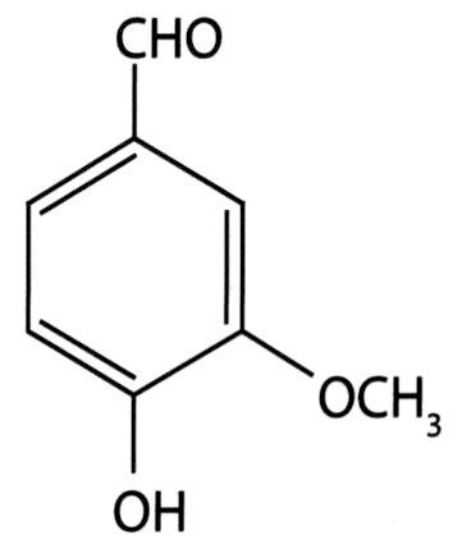

299

Examples of aldehydes and ketones include **benzaldehyde** (C_6H_5CHO) which smells of almonds and the enantiomers (B3.12d) of **carvone**, which have different smells; S-carvone (caraway) and R-carvone (spearmint).

S-carvone 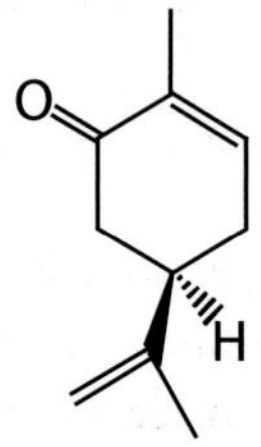   R-carvone

Within the first ten minutes of birth, new born babies are injected with the blood coagulant vitamin K, which is a ketone.

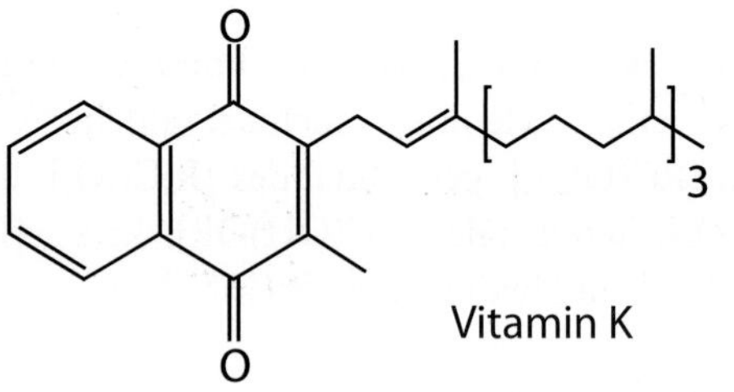

Vitamin K

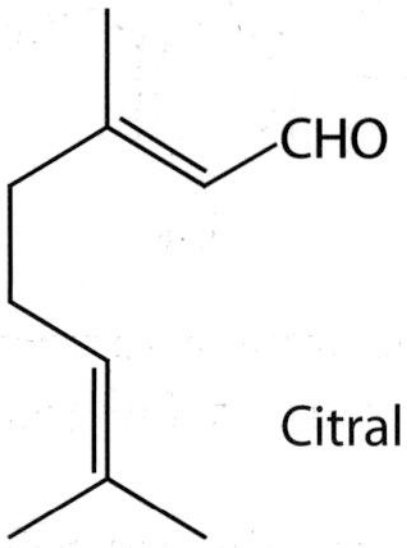

Citral (lemon grass)

Within the Carbonyl level there are three possible FGL changes. These are:

- Moving within the level: reactions include synthesis of hemiacetals & acetals from aldehydes, and hemiketals & ketals from ketones. Also, the synthesis of imines (**Schiff's bases**), oximes & hydrazones from aldehydes and ketones. Hydrolysis of most Carbonyl level compounds yields aldehydes or ketones.

- Moving down a level: reaction includes reduction of aldehydes to 1° alcohols and reduction of ketones to 2° alcohols. Preparation of hydroxynitriles (cyanohydrins) is possible from aldehydes and ketones and can also be considered to be a 'reduction' as it is moving down a level.

- Moving up a level: reactions include the oxidation of aldehydes to carboxylic acids. The spider diagram below shows all the interconversions with the Carbonyl level towards the centre of the diagram. The diagram and the conditions (numbered 1-19) need to be reviewed periodically if this body of work is to be recalled for application at a later date.

Carbonyl Level

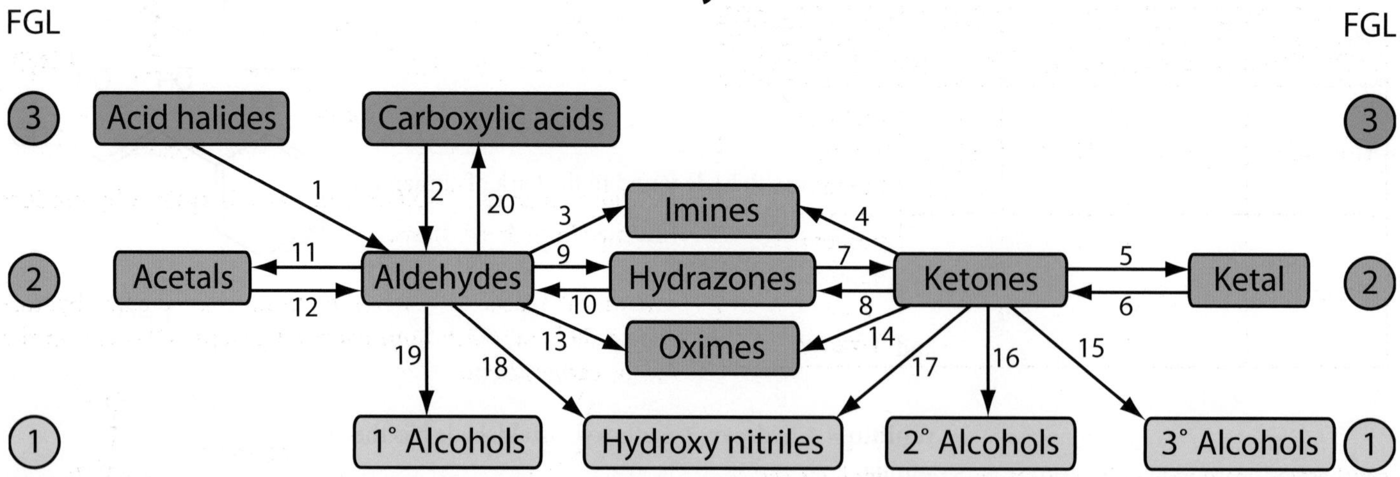

#	Conditions
1	LiAlH$_4$ / THF
2	LiAlH$_4$
3	RNH$_2$
4	RNH$_2$
5	ROH / TsOH (p-Toluenesulfonic acid)
6	H$_2$SO$_4$ (aq)
7	HCl (aq)
8	NH$_2$NH$_2$
9	NH$_2$NH$_2$
10	HCl (aq)
11	ROH / TsOH
12	H$_2$SO$_4$ (aq)
13	NH$_2$OH
14	NH$_2$OH
15	RMgX / (C$_2$H$_5$)$_2$O
16	LiAlH$_4$ or NaBH$_4$
17	HCN
18	HCN
19	LiAlH$_4$ or NaBH$_4$
20	Cr$_2$O$_7^{2-}$ / H$^+$ or Tollens (Ag$^+$)

All carbonyls contain the carbonyl group (C=O). When discussing aldehydes in general terms it is convenient to refer to them as RCHO where R = alkyl group or an aryl group and R$_2$CO is used for ketones. The general formula for both aldehydes and ketones is C$_n$H$_{2n}$O, where n = number of carbon atoms. When the carbonyl is at the end of a chain or ring you have an aldehyde and when the carbonyl is in middle of a chain you have a ketone. It is also possible to get cyclic ketones, *e.g.* cyclohexanone.

Carbonyls	General formula	General structure	R	Examples
aldehydes	C$_n$H$_{2n}$O	RCHO	H, alkyl or aryl	methanal, ethanal, benzaldehyde
ketones	C$_n$H$_{2n}$O	R$_2$CO	alkyl	propanone, butanone, cyclo-hexanone

The less familiar functional groups in the Carbonyl level are synthesized from aldehydes and/or ketones. Dihalides can be prepared by reacting aldehydes and ketones with phosphorus pentachloride (PCl$_5$). Ethanal reacts with PCl$_5$ to make

1,1-dichloroethane and propanone reacts with PCl$_5$ to make 2,2-dichloropropane. In these reactions there is movement within the carbonyl functional group level.

$$CH_3CHO + PCl_5 \rightarrow CH_3CHCl_2 + POCl_3$$

$$CH_3COCH_3 + PCl_5 \rightarrow CH_3CCl_2CH_3 + POCl_3$$

Imines can be prepared by reacting aldehydes and ketones with primary (1°) amines. In these reactions, there is no change in the FGL as both reactants and products are FGL = 2. Imines contain a C=N and water is the by-product formed from the oxygen atom of the carbonyl (C=O) and the two hydrogen atoms of the primary amine (RNH$_2$). Interestingly, ammonia does not form stable addition compounds with carbonyls but, instead, forms polymers.

Imine

+ H$_2$O

Imine

+ H$_2$O

The formation of an imine from a carbonyl can also be described as a condensation reaction. Can you explain why?

Oximes can be prepared by reacting aldehydes and ketones with hydroxylamine (NH$_2$OH). In these reactions there is no change in the FGL as both reactants and products are FGL = 2. Propanone reacts with hydroxylamine to make propanone oxime which is a stable compound.

Hydroxylamine

Oxime

+ H$_2$O

Oximes contain a C=NOH and water is again a by-product formed in their synthesis.

Methanal reacts with water to form a tetrahedral hydrate (gem-diol) in which both hydroxyl groups (OH) are on the same carbon atom.

Methanal

Gem-diol

The formation of the hydrate is movement within the Carbonyl level as both organic substances have FGL = 2. In this equilibrium mixture, the gem-diol is the major product (99%). The equivalent gem-diol formed from ethanal is 59% and that formed from propanone is 0.2%. The percentage of the gem-diol formed reduces as the size of the group(s) adjacent to the carbonyl increases.

Aldehydes can also react with alcohols under non-aqueous acidic conditions to form hemiacetals (generally unstable) and acetals. Hemiacetals are compounds where there is one ether group and an alcohol directly attached to the same carbon atom. Acetals are compounds where there are two ether groups directly attached to the same carbon atom. Acetals are also known at university as 1,1-geminal diethers. To promote the formation of the acetal, two equivalents of alcohol are used in the reaction (or one equivalent when dealing with a diol), *para*-toluene sulfonic acid ($CH_3C_6H_4SO_3H$) is added as catalyst and water is removed as it forms.

Aldehyde + Alcohol ⇌ Hemiacetal

R^1OH/H^+ ⇌ Acetal + H_2O

Interestingly, sugars such as glucose exist largely as cyclic hemiacetals, *e.g.* α-D-glucopyranose where there is an ether group (COC) and an alcohol group (OH) attached to the same carbon atom which is indicated by the red dot. Cyclic hemiacetals are much more stable than their open chain equivalents.

α-D-glucopyranose

Port wines mature and improve with age due to oxidative processes that lead to the presence of molecules (FGL 2) such as ethanal and a few of its isomeric acetals. These isomeric acetals (A3.1d) give port its characteristic bouquet and flavours. The flavour threshold for the mixture of isomers is approximately 100 mg dm^{-3}. These acetals are more concentrated in wines older than 30 years.

5-hydroxy-2-methyl-1,3-dioxane

cis-isomer   *trans*-isomer

4-hydroxymethyl-2-methyl-1,3-dioxolane

cis-isomer   *trans*-isomer

Ketones can also react with alcohols under acidic conditions to form hemiketals and ketals. They can be distinguished from the corresponding hemiacetals and acetals by the number of carbons attached to the carbon with the ether groups.

Ketone + Alcohol ⇌ Hemiketal

R^2OH/H^+ ⇌ Ketal + H_2O

Acetals and ketals provide a convenient way of protecting carbonyl groups in multistep syntheses as they are stable under basic conditions. Hydrolysis is achieved under aqueous acidic conditions (A3.4a).

Questions 16.1

1. Which of the following options is **not** an acetal?

   A $CH_3CH(OCH_3)_2$

   B $CH_3CH(OH)(OCH_3)$

   C $CH_2(OCH_3)_2$

   D $C_2H_5CH(OCH_3)(OC_2H_5)_2$

2. For the following reagents, complete the reaction and discuss in terms of Functional Group Levels.

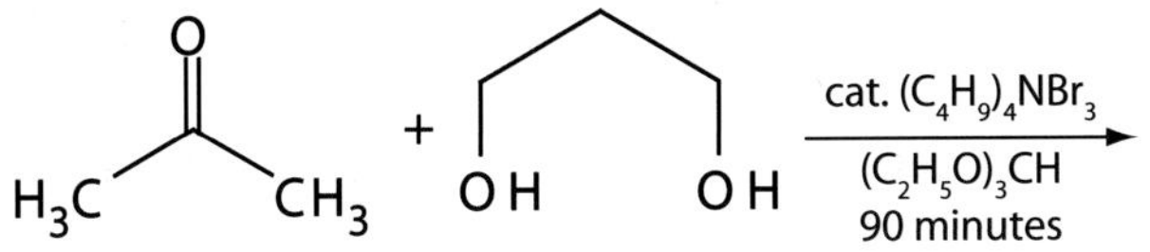

    + 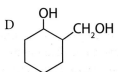 → (cat. $(C_4H_9)_4NBr_3$ / $(C_2H_5O)_3CH$ / 90 minutes)

3. Write an equation for the reaction between ethanal and hydroxylamine. Explain why this is neither a reduction nor an oxidation reaction.

4. Which of the options can have three positional isomers that are ketones?

   A   propanone

   B   heptanone

   C   hexanone

   D   pentanone

5. Which of the options will not oxidise to give a ketone?

   A HO (structure)   B OH (structure)

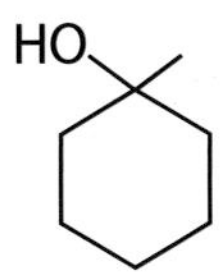

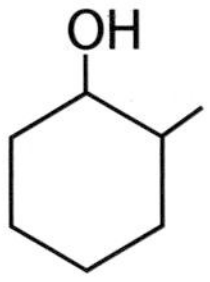

   C OH (structure)   D OH (structure) CH_2OH

6. Name the organic products when each of these alcohols are heated under reflux and oxidised by acidified dichromate(VI) .

   (i) $CH_3CHOHCH_3$

   (ii) $CH_3CH_2CH_2OH$

   (iii) $CH_3CH(CH_3)CH_2OH$

   (iv) $CH_3C(CH_3)_2OH$

7. Draw all the possible carbonyl compounds that have molecular formula C_4H_8O as skeletal formulae.

8. If you wanted the aldehyde as the product in the oxidation of a 1° alcohol, how would you stop further oxidation into the carboxylic acid?

9. Benzaldehyde reacts with chlorine in the absence of a catalyst to form benzoyl chloride. Write a balanced equation for the reaction and describe the changes in terms of Functional Group Level.

10. Why do the compounds methanone and ethanone not exist but methanal and ethanal do exist?

11. Industrially, ethanal is made from ethene according to the following equation.

    $$CH_2{=}CH_2 + \tfrac{1}{2}\,O_2 \xrightarrow{PdCl_2\,/\,CuCl_2} CH_3CHO$$

    Explain what type of reaction this is and suggest a role for the chlorides ($PdCl_2$ and $CuCl_2$).

A3.4 (a) Lower functional group level reactions – Carbonyl level

In organic chemistry, a hydrolysis reaction involves the breaking of covalent bonds with water. All hydrolysis reactions are catalysed by acid and/or base. Most FGL = 2 groups will hydrolyse to form aldehydes or ketones.

Both aldehydes and ketones are formed by the hydrolysis of gem-dichlorides, e.g.

$$CH_3CHCl_2 + H_2O \rightarrow CH_3CHO + 2\ HCl$$

$$(CH_3)_2CCl_2 + H_2O \rightarrow (CH_3)_2CO + 2\ HCl$$

$$C_6H_5CHCl_2 + H_2O \rightarrow C_6H_5CHO + 2\ HCl$$

Questions 16.2

1. Write an equation to show which dihalide would hydrolyse to form methanal.

    Suggest the identity of an unstable organic intermediate.

2. Write an equation to show which ketal would hydrolyse in aqueous acidic conditions to form butanone and two equivalents of ethanol.

A3.3 (b) Addition of bisulfite

Sodium sulfate (Na_2SO_4) is a familiar salt met early on in school chemistry courses. Sodium bisulfite might not have been met until advanced level courses. Sodium bisulfite has the formula $NaHSO_3$. To be able to write the correct formula for the bisulfite you need to substitute one sodium (Na^+) in the sulfate with hydrogen (H^+) and remove one oxygen atom to leave 3. The oxidation number on the sulfur in $NaHSO_3$ is 4+. It is for this reason that $NaHSO_3$ is also known as sodium hydrogensulfate(IV).

Addition of bisulfite to carbonyls is an example of reaction within the Carbonyl level. During reactions it is the π bond of the carbonyl that breaks. Sulfur is a heteroatom with a high electronegativity compared with most elements. It is the lone pair on the bisulfite ion that is attracted to the carbon of the carbonyl.

Element	C	O	S
Electronegativity	2.5	3.5	2.5

Addition of bisulfite to aldehydes works well. The reaction is less successful with ketones, where one of the hydrocarbon groups attached to the carbonyl group needs to be a methyl group (CH_3). Bulky groups attached to the carbonyl group of a ketone get in the way of the reaction happening. This shielding of a reactive centre by a bulky group is often referred to as **steric hindrance**. The carbonyl group is polarised because the oxygen of the carbonyl is more electronegative than the carbon. The $C^{\delta+}$ is attacked by the donation of a lone pair of electrons from the nucleophilic bisulfite ion. The reactions with ethanal and propanone are;

Ethanal → Bisulfite addition compound

Propanone → Bisulfite addition compound

There is no overall change in FGL as in both the reactant and product there are two bonds to heteroatoms which are indicated by single red lines for the covalent bonds.

It is worth distilling carbonyls prior to reaction as many are often sold as aqueous solutions. The aldehyde or methyl ketone is shaken with a saturated solution of sodium bisulfite in water. In reactions where the addition product is formed, it separates out as white crystals. These crystals can be collected by **buchner filtration**. It is worth noting that, in the reaction with bisulfite, the addition products of methanal and ethanal are reasonably water soluble. The addition products are usually called bisulfite addition compounds. The addition of bisulfite is a very useful method for the purification of aldehydes and methyl ketones. Alkaline or acidic hydrolysis of the bisulfite addition compound regenerates the aldehyde or methyl ketone respectively.

FGL 2   Hydrolysis (H^+ or OH^-)   FGL 2

Questions 16.3

1. How would you separate a pure aldehyde from excess acid and inorganics?

2. Which of the following alcohols reacts with acidified $K_2Cr_2O_7$ to give a ketone?

   A $(CH_3)_2CHCH_2OH$

   B $CH_3CH_2CH_2OH$

   C $CH_3CHOHCH_3$

   D $(CH_3)_3COH$

3. Which of the following alcohols react with acidified $K_2Cr_2O_7$ to give a carboxylic acid?

   A $(CH_3)_2CHCH_2OH$

   B $CH_3CH_2CH_2OH$

   C $CH_3CHOHCH_3$

   D $(CH_3)_3COH$

A3.4 (c)
Oxidation of aldehydes

Aldehydes are easily oxidised to carboxylic acids and this transformation is an example of moving up an oxidation level, *i.e.* from FGL 2 to FGL 3. Biologists test for reducing sugars such as glucose using **Benedict's solution** when the aqueous blue copper(II) ion, Cu^{2+} (aq) ion is reduced to the red copper(I) oxide Cu_2O (s). Chemists also carry out the oxidation of an aldehyde to a carboxylic acid using **Tollens' reagent** (ammoniacal silver nitrate) where silver(I) ions Ag^+ (aq) are reduced to metallic silver Ag^0 (s). Ketones are not as readily oxidised as aldehydes and give a negative test with Benedict's solution and Tollens' reagent. The oxidation of ketones requires drastic conditions and leads to mixtures of carboxylic acids and disruption to the ketone structure.

Oxidation of ethanal

The oxidation of ethanal is a straightforward reaction to carry out in the laboratory. The oxidising agent is orange acidified dichromate(VI) which gets reduced to the blue-green Cr^{3+}. The simplified equation is;
$CH_3CHO + [O] \rightarrow CH_3COOH$
and the overall equation including oxidising agent is:

$$3CH_3CHO + 8H^+ + Cr_2O_7^{2-} \rightarrow 3CH_3COOH + 4H_2O + 2Cr^{3+}$$

Tollens' Reagent

Tollens' reagent is ammoniacal silver nitrate and it is used in what is generally called the **Silver Mirror Test**. In the reaction Ag^+ oxidises aldehydes to carboxylic acids and is itself reduced to metallic silver. In order to keep the silver ion in solution it is combined with a pair of ammonia ligands (B2.4d). This complex $[Ag(NH_3)_2]^+$ (aq) is in equilibrium with a very low concentration of free Ag^+ (aq) ions. The reaction works very well with glucose, which is an aldehyde in its open chain form and when warmed in a test tube of Tollens' reagent, a silver mirror is deposited on the walls of the test tube.

To prepare Tollens' Reagent put 2 cm^3 of AgNO$_3$ (aq) into a test tube. Add 1 drop of dilute NaOH (aq). A brown precipitate of Ag$_2$O is observed. Add sufficient dilute aqueous NH$_3$ solution dropwise until all the precipitate just dissolves. It is usually about 10 drops. CARE is needed to destroy all the Tollens' reagent within 20 minutes as explosions have been known to occur! Ketones do not react with Tollens' reagent.

Questions 16.4

1. Which of the following options would not take place if butanone was given these tests?

    A   Formation of an orange precipitate on addition of 2,4-dinitrophenylhydrazine.

    B   Silver mirror on reaction with Tollens' reagent.

    C   Reduction with NaBH$_4$ to form butan-2-ol.

    D   Reaction with iodine in the presence of acid (H$^+$) catalyst.

2. Which option does not give an addition compound with ethanal?

    A   NaHSO$_3$

    B   HCN

    C   Cr$_2$O$_7$$^{2-}$/H$^+$

    D   NaBH$_4$

3. Which functional group does not contain a carbonyl compound?

    A   carboxylic acid

    B   aldehyde

    C   ketone

    D   acetal

4. Which reagent does not react with the CHO group?

    A   potassium cyanide

    B   sodium metal

    C   acidified sodium dichromate(VI)

    D   sodium borohydride

5. Which substance could be oxidised to an aldehyde?

    A   1° alcohol

    B   carboxylic acid

    C   3° alcohol

    D   2° alcohol

6. Name these carbonyl compounds;

    (i)   CH$_3$CH$_2$CH$_2$CH$_2$CHO

    (ii)   CH$_3$CH$_2$COCH$_2$CH$_3$

    (iii)   C$_6$H$_5$CHO

    (iv)   C$_6$H$_5$COCH$_3$

7. Give the structural formulae of;

    (i)   hexan-2-one

    (ii)   hexan-3-one

    (iii)   butanal

A3.4 (d)
Addition to carbonyls

In the addition reactions to carbonyls, it is the weaker π bond (A1.2e) of the carbonyl that breaks. In these addition reactions, new C-C or C-H bonds form and consequently these reactions are examples of carbon atoms moving down level(s).

Hydrogen cyanide

The reaction of hydrogen cyanide (HCN) with carbonyl compounds takes place more rapidly in the presence of a strong base. This is because, as hydrogen cyanide is a weak acid (B1.5f) with a K_a of 5×10^{-10}, there will only be a low concentration of cyanide (CN^-) ions, $HCN \rightleftharpoons H^+ + CN^-$. When hydrogen cyanide reacts with hydroxide ions it increases the concentration of cyanide ions according to the equation, $HCN + OH^- \rightleftharpoons CN^- + H_2O$. In the addition reaction, it is the cyanide ion that acts as a nucleophile (A3.1h). In step 1, the lone pair on the carbon of CN^- attacks the partially charged carbon atom of the polarised carbonyl bond. The mechanism shows that, as the nucleophile approaches the carbon of the carbonyl, the π electrons of the carbonyl are repelled towards the oxygen atom. Then in step 2, a proton is picked up from the HCN or the solvent to make the addition product - a hydroxynitrile, which is also known as a cyanohydrin. Hydroxynitriles have an OH and a CN group attached to the same carbon atom. Ethanal at FGL 2 has reacted with hydrogen cyanide to make 2–hydroxypropanenitrile, which is at FGL 1. As there is a decrease in FGL, the reaction can be thought of as a reduction. Synthetically this is a very important reaction as an extra carbon atom is added to the molecule.

2-hydroxypropanenitrile

Hydrolysis of this addition product will lead to a racemic mixture (B2.9i) of 2-hydroxypropanoic acid (lactic acid).

Metallic hydrides

The reduction of carbonyls can be carried out with metallic hydrides such as sodium borohydride ($NaBH_4$) or lithium aluminium hydride ($LiAlH_4$) which is often referred to as **lithal**.

One disadvantage of using lithal is that it reacts violently with water so it must be used in a solvent such as anhydrous diethyl ether $(CH_3CH_2)_2O$. This makes the reagent lithal impractical on the industrial scale but suitable for research scale reactions. In the reactions, the reducing agent is represented by [H]. Mechanistically, the hydrides are represented by H^- and it is worth spending time comparing the similarities between the different carbonyl addition reactions.

Ethanol

Aldehydes are reduced to primary (1°) alcohols by metallic hydrides and ketones are reduced to secondary (2°) alcohols by metallic hydrides. For example, sodium borohydride is composed of these two ions; Na^+ & BH_4^-. Lithium aluminium hydride consists of Li^+ & AlH_4^-. The order of reactivity for these hydride ions is $AlH_4^- > BH_4^-$. It is convenient to think of these anions as hydride (H^-) carriers. Methanal is reduced to methanol and propanone is reduced to propan-2-ol.

$$HCHO + H^- \xrightarrow{H^+} CH_3OH$$

$$CH_3COCH_3 + H^- \xrightarrow{H^+} (CH_3)_2CHOH$$

One of the advantages of using sodium borohydride as the metallic hydride is that aldehydes and ketones can be reduced to their corresponding alcohols in water. Using ethanal as the example, an intermediate boron complex is formed which is hydrolysed by water to give ethanol.

$$4\,CH_3CHO + NaBH_4 \rightarrow (CH_3CH_2O)_4B^-Na^+$$

$$(CH_3CH_2O)_4B^-Na^+ + 3\,H_2O \rightarrow 4\,CH_3CH_2OH + NaH_2BO_3$$

A similar intermediate aluminium complex is formed when carbonyls are reduced by the reducing agent lithium aluminium hydride. Using propanone as the example it is necessary to acidify the mixture during 'work up' to give propan-2-ol.

$$4\,(CH_3)_2CO + LiAlH_4 \rightarrow [(CH_3)_2CHO]_4Al^-Li^+$$

$$2\,[(CH_3)_2CHO]_4Al^-Li^+ + 4\,H_2SO_4$$
$$\rightarrow 8\,(CH_3)_2CHOH + Al_2(SO_4)_3 + Li_2SO_4$$

Questions 16.5

1. A reduction met at university is the Clemmensen reduction which reduces ketones to hydrocarbons. Using FGL, explain why this reaction can be described as a reduction.

Phenylethanone

Zn/HCl

Ethylbenzene

2. Using FGL changes, describe what is happening in the reaction.

Reaction: $CH_3CHO \rightarrow CH_3CH_2OH$

3. Give two examples of reducing agents that will reduce aldehydes. What will be the organic product of these reductions?

4. Write an equation for the reaction between cyclohexanone and lithium aluminium hydride using skeletal formula.

Grignard reagents

Victor Grignard was awarded the 1912 Nobel Prize in Chemistry for his discovery of Grignard reagents. These are organomagnesium reagents prepared by reacting magnesium turnings with a halogenoalkane under an inert atmosphere (nitrogen or argon) in anhydrous solvents such as ethers, *e.g.* ethoxyethane or tetrahydrofuran (THF).

Ethoxyethane
(diethyl ether)

Tetrahydrofuran

Grignard reagents are very versatile synthetic reagents because their use can result in the formation of carbon-carbon bonds. If magnesium reacts with chloromethane, the Grignard reagent that is prepared is methyl magnesium chloride;

$$Mg + CH_3Cl \rightarrow CH_3MgCl$$

The magnesium 'inserts' itself between the carbon atom and the chlorine (halogen). It is often convenient to refer to Grignard reagents by the generalised formula RMgX where R = alkyl or aryl and X = halogen (Group 17) Cl, Br or I. Grignard reagents are soluble in ethers. Iodine has been found to be a good initiator in their preparation. It is thought to help remove any magnesium oxide at the surface of the metal which prevents reaction.

The carbon-metal bond of Grignard reagents is highly polarised because of the difference in electronegativity between carbon (2.5) and magnesium (1.2). There is increased electron density on the carbon of the C-Mg bond.

$$\overset{\delta-}{C}\!-\!\overset{\delta+}{Mg}$$

The Grignard reagent is a highly nucleophilic ion and it is useful to think of RMgX as being essentially a carbanion, *i.e.* the nucleophile R⁻. The reduction of carbonyls can be carried out with Grignard reagents, *e.g.* RMgBr and in all cases the product is an alcohol. The intermediate is a halomagnesium alkoxide which hydrolyses in acid to release the desired alcohol product.

Secondary alcohol

Grignard reagents need to be prepared *in situ* as required and without being isolated because of their sensitivity to water and air. Grignard reagents react violently with water to give alkanes; *e.g.* $2\ C_2H_5MgBr + 2\ H_2O \rightarrow 2\ C_2H_6 + MgBr_2 + Mg(OH)_2$

Methanal forms primary (1°) alcohols, whilst other aldehydes form secondary (2°) alcohols and ketones form tertiary (3°) alcohols. In all cases the starting FGL is 2 and the alcohols have FGL 1. The Grignard reagents react *via* a nucleophilic addition reaction and once again it is the weaker π-bond of the carbonyl that breaks during reaction.

Example 16.1

What are the organic and inorganic products in the reaction between propanone and methylmagnesium bromide followed by the addition of water?

Solution:

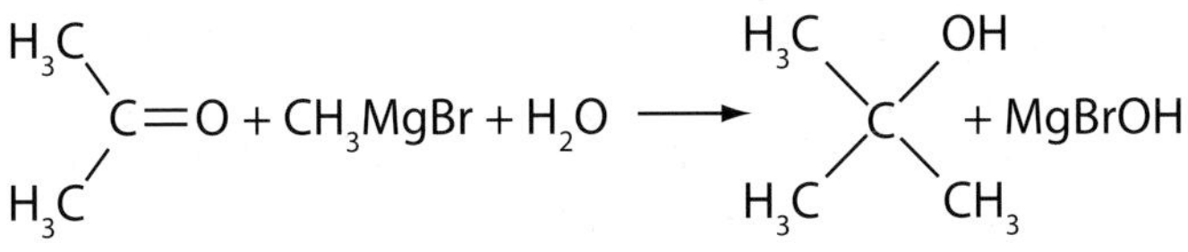

$$H_3C\!\!\diagdown\!\!C\!\!=\!\!O + CH_3MgBr + H_2O \longrightarrow \begin{array}{c} H_3C \quad OH \\ \diagdown \quad / \\ C \\ / \quad \diagdown \\ H_3C \quad CH_3 \end{array} + MgBrOH$$

Questions 16.6

1. Name the following Grignard reagents from their formulae:

   (a) $CH_3CH_2CH_2MgBr$

   (b) CH_3CH_2MgCl

   (c) C_6H_5MgBr

2. Give the names of the organic products when the following are treated with the Grignard reagent methylmagnesium bromide followed by the addition of water. Explain, using Functional Group Levels, how these reactions can be classified.

   (a) ethanal

   (b) methanal

   (c) butanone

3. Identify the reagent, solvent and organic product in the following reaction.

$$\begin{array}{c} O \\ \diagdown\diagup\diagdown\diagup\diagdown \end{array} \quad \begin{array}{c} 1)\ CH_3(CH_2)_4MgBr\ /\ Et_2O \\ \xrightarrow{\hspace{3cm}} \\ 2)\ H_3O^+ \end{array}$$

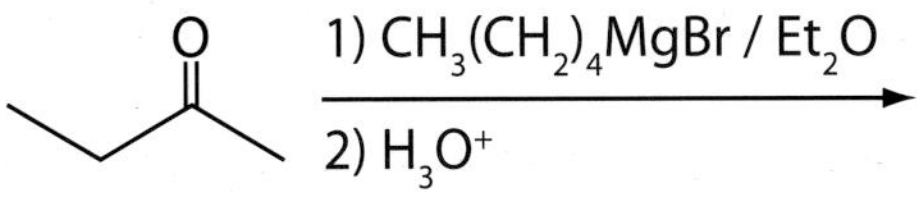

4. Identify the reactant in the following reaction.

$$?\ \begin{array}{c} 1)\ CH_3MgBr\ /\ Et_2O \\ \xrightarrow{\hspace{3cm}} \\ 2)\ H_3O^+ \end{array}$$

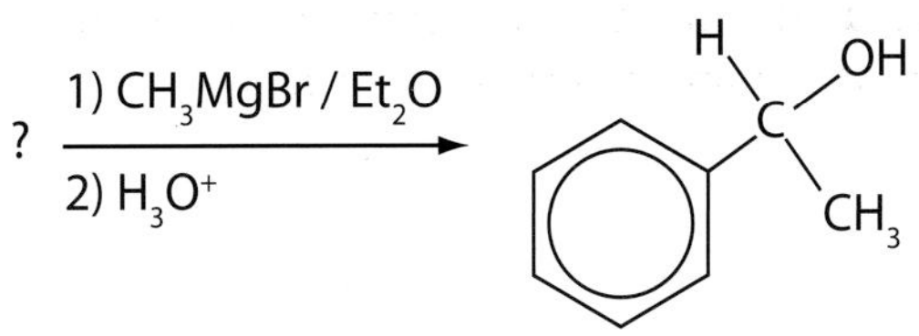

5. Identify the reagents and conditions needed to carry out the following reaction and describe how they can be achieved in the laboratory.

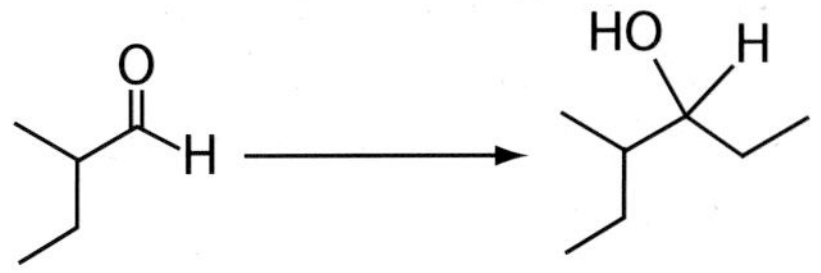

6. Complete the table, which summarises some of the most important reactions of ethanal and propanone.

Reagent	Product from ethanal	Product from propanone	Type of reaction
HCN			
NaHSO$_3$			
LiAlH$_4$			
Ag$^+$ (Tollens')			
Cu^{2+} (Benedict's)			
CH$_3$MgBr (Grignard)			
Cr$_2$O$_7^{2-}$ / H$^+$			

17

Addition and Elimination Reactions

Contents

Addition reactions can be spotted from their equations in which two things react to form just the one product. Addition reactions (A3.3b) generally take place across the carbon-carbon double bond (C=C) of alkenes. Depending on which reactant adds to the C=C bond, there is either no change in the FGL or an increase in the FGL. The opposite of an addition reaction is an elimination reaction (A3.3d) which results in the formation of an alkene. In these reactions, a small molecule is eliminated, either water (H_2O) from alcohols or hydrogen halides (HX) from alkyl halides. An industrially important series of addition reactions is the formation of addition polymers (A3.3c) from alkenes such as ethene, or substituted ethenes such as chloroethene.

As is the case with some of the most important discoveries in science, accident played a part in the discovery of the first industrially produced addition polymer, polyethene more usually known as polythene. Polythene was first synthesized industrially by Reginald Gibson & Eric Fawcett in 1933. They were trying to react ethene ($CH_2=CH_2$) with benzaldehyde (C_6H_5CHO) and accidentally produced a white waxy substance which later turned out to be polyethene. A trace of oxygen in their experiment was catalysing the polymerisation of ethene into polyethene. This reaction became a commercial success from 1939 onwards thanks to the work of the chemist Sir Michael Willcox Perrin who went to Twyford Preparatory School prior to attending Winchester College. In addition to his important work on addition polymerisations, Perrin also helped the famous scientist Niels Bohr escape war torn Europe to the scientific haven of the United States. He also led the allied intelligence effort to monitor Nazi atomic research and was instrumental in bringing Werner Heisenberg to England for interrogation at the end of the war.

A3.5 (a) π-bonds in double bonds (C=C and C=O)

Both alkenes (FGL = 0) and carbonyl compounds (FGL = 2) contain double bonds which consist of a σ-bond shown in red and a weaker π-bond shown in blue. The reactions of these two types of double bond containing molecules are quite different.

Alkene

$$\diagdown\!\!\diagup C = C \diagdown\!\!\diagup$$

vs.

Carbonyl

$$\diagdown\!\!\diagup \overset{\delta^+}{C} = \overset{\delta^-}{O}$$

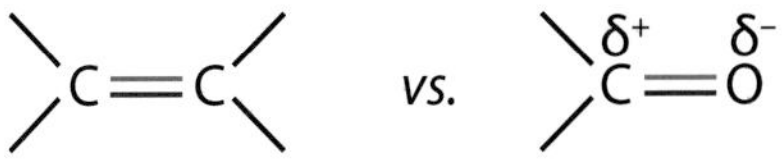

The C=C bond of alkenes is formed by two adjacent carbon atoms sharing four electrons. This gives an alkene a region (C=C) where there is a high electron density. The carbon atoms of the double bond are not polarised (no dipole) as both carbon atoms will have the same value for their electronegativities (2.5). Simple alkenes being electron rich are, therefore, not attacked by nucleophiles. In a later chapter (B3.9g) it will be shown how nucleophiles can affect the product formed with unsymmetrical alkenes. Alkenes, rather than be susceptible to attack by nucleophiles, are themselves nucleophilic and they will readily react with electrophiles (B3.9e). Alkenes react with electrophiles to form addition products, sometimes called **adducts**, in which the π-bond is replaced by two σ-bonds. In terms of orbital interactions (A1.2d), it is the filled π-orbital of the alkene which interacts with the empty σ^* orbital of, say, bromine.

Since the highest electron density is in the middle of the C=C bond, electrophiles will approach this bond end on with symmetric molecules such as H_2 being polarised. This is shown below for hydrogen, bromine and hydrogen bromide. It is important to remember that the molecules which add to the C=C bond do so across the double bond with each carbon receiving a new atom.

End on approach of electrophiles to an alkene

Covalent compounds such as carbonyls (aldehydes and ketones), which have adjacent atoms with differing electronegativities, will have unequal sharing of the bonding electrons. In the case of carbonyls (C=O), the oxygen atom, which has the higher electronegativity, will pull the bonding electrons in its direction. This displacement of the charge within the molecular orbital will give the bond some ionic character causing it to be polar. To indicate bond polarization the more electronegative atom (C=**O**) is assigned 'delta negative' (δ^-) and the more electropositive element (**C**=O) assigned 'delta positive' (δ^+). Since the carbon atom of the carbonyl is positive, it is attacked by nucleophiles. The dipole moment (A3.2b) is shown for a generalised carbonyl compound.

Understanding polarity in molecules is very important as it affects their physical and chemical properties and the mechanisms by which they react (B3.9).

Question 17.1

1. Explain why carbonyls react with nucleophiles such as cyanide (CN^-) but alkenes do not despite alkenes having lower bond enthalpies.

Double bond	Bond enthalpy / kJ mol^{-1}
C=C	612
C=O (aldehydes)	736
C=O (ketones)	749

A3.5 (b)
Addition Reactions to C=C

Alkenes are described as 'unsaturated' because they contain at least one C=C bond. When these carbon-carbon double bonds react, they do so by addition, to give a single saturated product. In these addition reactions, it is the weaker π-bond of the C=C bond which breaks. The details of how the reactants transform into products (mechanisms) can be found in B3.9e. Molecules which add to a C=C bond include: water (H_2O), hydrogen bromide (HBr), hydrogen (H_2) and bromine (Br_2). It is important to remember that one part of the molecule, which is adding to the alkene, adds to one of the carbons of the **C**=**C** and the other part of the molecule adds to the other carbon of the C=**C**.

Reaction with bromine

Bromine is a highly corrosive liquid which causes nasty burns, so it is seldom reacted without dilution. Bromine is a substance which dissolves in water and organic solvents so it is a solution of bromine (orange) that is used in reactions. The usual test for unsaturation (C=C) is to add a few drops of bromine water to an alkene. The positive result, which indicates unsaturation, is the rapid decolourisation of the bromine water. In the laboratory, cyclohexene is a convenient alkene to use in reactions, since it is a liquid under standard conditions. Using the molecular formulae for reactants and product shows clearly that the reaction is an addition reaction, as the single product's molecular formula is obtained by adding up all the atoms of the reactants.

$$C_6H_{10} + Br_2 \rightarrow C_6H_{10}Br_2$$

Cyclohexene   Bromine   1,2-dibromocyclohexane

When ethene gas is bubbled into bromine water, it changes colour from orange to colourless, *i.e.* it decolourises the bromine water.

$$CH_2=CH_2 + Br_2 \rightarrow CH_2BrCH_2Br$$

The addition across a C=C double bond leads to a freely rotating saturated C-C bond in the addition product. One consequence of this single bond rotation is that addition to geometric isomers (A3.1d) leads to the same product. Addition of bromine to *trans*-but-2-ene and *cis*-but-2-ene yields 2,3-dibromobutane.

but-2-ene   bromine   2,3-dibromobutane

Reaction with Hydrogen bromide

Alkenes react with hydrogen bromide gas or aqueous solutions of hydrogen bromide to form bromoalkanes. Hydrogen bromide gas (HBr) can be generated by reacting sodium bromide and concentrated sulfuric acid (A2.2l). The addition of hydrogen bromide to a symmetrical alkene gives only one possible addition product. The addition of hydrogen bromide to an unsymmetrical alkene can lead to a mixture of two products according to **Markovnikov's Rule** (B3.9f). The addition of hydrogen bromide to ethene gives bromoethane.

$$C_2H_4 \text{ (g)} + HBr \text{ (aq)} \rightarrow C_2H_5Br \text{ (l)}$$

Other hydrogen halides also react with alkenes. If ethene is bubbled through concentrated hydrochloric acid, liquid chloroethane is the addition product.

$$CH_2=CH_2 \text{ (g)} + c. \text{ HCl (aq)} \rightarrow CH_3CH_2Cl \text{ (l)}$$

The order of reactivity between alkenes and hydrogen halides is HI > HBr > HCl > HF which follows the hydrogen halide bond enthalpies (A2.2k). Hydrogen fluoride will only react with alkenes under pressure.

Reaction with Water

Alkenes react with water (steam) at high temperatures and pressures to form alcohols (A3.3). Industrially, ethanol is made by the hydration of ethene at 300°C and 60 atmospheres of pressure using phosphoric acid (H_3PO_4) as the catalyst. This catalyst is absorbed onto silica (SiO_2) pellets.

$$CH_2=CH_2 \text{ (g)} + H_2O \text{ (g)} \rightleftharpoons CH_3CH_2OH \text{ (g)}$$

When water adds across the double bond of an alkene, hydrogen (**H**) from water (**HOH**) adds to one carbon of the double bond and the remaining hydroxyl group (**OH**) of water adds to the other carbon of the double bond. When the alcohol is unsymmetrical, *e.g.* propene, it is possible to get two different alcohol products which are positional isomers (A3.1d). The relative proportion of the alcohols depends on the stability of the carbocation intermediate formed during the first step in the mechanism when the π-bond of C=C breaks to join to the proton (H^+).

$$CH_3CH=CH_2 + H_2O \rightleftharpoons CH_3CH_2CH_2OH + CH_3CH(OH)CH_3$$

propene   steam   propanol   propan-2-ol

Reaction with Hydrogen

Alkenes react with hydrogen in the presence of transition metal catalysts (A1.3f) such as nickel (Ni), platinum (Pt) or palladium (Pd). The addition of hydrogen to unsaturated C=C bonds is called **hydrogenation**. Hydrogenation has been used industrially to create alternatives to butter (margarine). The process results in fats that are still soft at refrigerator temperature and therefore more 'spreadable'. Ethene reacts with hydrogen to form ethane using nickel as the catalyst at a temperature of 150-300°C.

$$CH_2=CH_2 \text{ (g)} + H_2\text{(g)} \rightarrow CH_3CH_3 \text{ (g)}$$

The addition of hydrogen to an alkene (forming an alkane) is a **reduction**. Looking at this reaction in terms of functional group levels (A3.2) might cause confusion as it is an example of a reduction where there is not a reduction in functional group level. This is because both the reactant (alkene) and the product (alkane) are in the hydrocarbon FGL = 0.

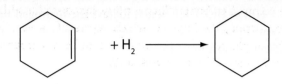

Cyclohexene   Hydrogen   Cyclohexane

Questions 17.2

1. Which option does not form an addition product with bromine at room temperature?

    A   cyclohexa-1,4-diene

    B   buta-1,3-diene

    C   benzene

    D   styrene

2. Which addition reaction is not classified as an oxidation in terms of change of FGL for at least one carbon of the C=C?

    A $CH_2=CH_2 + Br_2 \rightarrow CH_2BrCH_2Br$

    B $CH_2=CH_2 + HCl \rightarrow CH_3CH_2Cl$

    C $CH_2=CH_2 + HBr \rightarrow CH_3CH_2Br$

    D $CH_2=CH_2 + H_2 \rightarrow CH_3CH_3$

3. What is needed to turn ethene into ethanol?

4. Which option is not a correct description of the reaction between cyclohexene and hydrogen?

    A   reduction

    B   hydrogenation

    C   oxidation

    D   addition

5. Predict the addition products for the following reactions between alkenes and electrophiles.

	Reactants			Product
i.		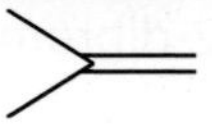 + HBr	→	
ii.		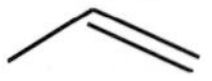 + HI	→	
iii.		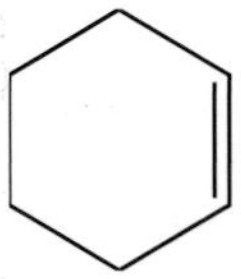 + HCl	→	
iv.		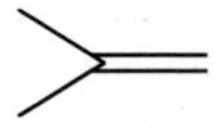 + Br$_2$	→	
v.		+ H$_2$O, H$^+$	→	
vi.		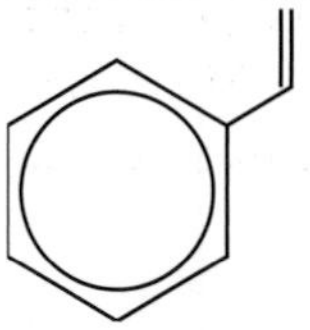 + HBr	→	

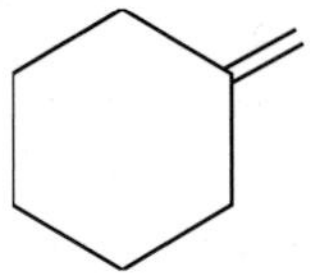

A3.5 (c)
Addition polymerisation

Alkenes are versatile chemicals because they are monomers which can undergo addition polymerisation. In **addition polymerisation**, unsaturated monomers add to each other to form saturated giant molecules called **polymers** with the same empirical formula. It is important to be able to suggest the polymer formed from a monomer and also to be able to suggest the monomer given the structure of an addition polymer. When alkenes add together to form polymers, the polymer formed contains saturated C-C bonds. Despite being saturated, the polymer is named after the monomer so it is known as a **poly**(alkene). The conditions under which the polymer is made affect the properties of the polymer. If a gas is blown into polystyrene, you end up with **expanded polystyrene**, which is used as packaging to protect electrical goods. There are a variety of addition polymers made from alkenes and substituted alkenes and they constitute an important industry that employs hundreds of thousands of people worldwide. Over 100 million tonnes of polymers are produced each year and, with the production of these chemicals, have come environmental issues (A3.6b).

Monomer	Addition polymer	Polymer uses
Ethene	Poly(ethene) = PE	Washing up bottles
Propene	Poly(propene) = PP	Carpets
Chloroethene (Vinylchloride)	Poly(chloroethene) (polyvinylchloride) = PVC	Vinyl records, window frames
Tetra-fluoroethene	Poly(tetrafluoroethene) = PTFE	Teflon® tape, non-stick pans, electrical insulation
Phenylethene (Styrene)	Poly(phenylethene) Polystyrene = PS	Insulation, packing, hot drinks cups

Until the advent of the compact disc (CD), music was recorded on records made from the addition polymer polyvinylchloride (PVC). As the former lead singer (Morrissey) of the band *The Smiths* turns fifty, it is interesting to note that vinyl records are making a come-back.

How Soon is Now by *The Smiths* on vinyl record (made from PVC)

During addition polymerisations two (usually) identical monomer units (alkenes) react together and addition takes place across the C=C double bond. When writing equations for addition polymerisation, it is often helpful to think of alkenes as being H-shaped. This way you get the four groups/atoms out of the way, leaving adjacent C=C double bonds to join up like the parts of a zipper. By making the C=C the horizontal line of the H-shape, you won't make the common mistake of drawing polyethene when you are attempting to draw polypropene. The polymer polypropene has one methyl group on alternating carbon atoms of the polymer chain,

unlike polyethene, which only has hydrogen atoms attached to the carbon backbone. When writing equations for addition polymerisation, the letter *n*, which represents a very large number, is placed before the monomer and again around the bracket that identifies the repeat unit.

Karl Ziegler won the 1963 Nobel Prize in Chemistry for his work on catalysts which allowed addition polymers, such as ethene, to be made at low temperatures (60°C) and atmospheric pressure. Previously higher temperatures (200°C) and higher pressures (1200 atmospheres) were needed.

Polypropene is a polymer that has found many uses from domestic kettles, to the lids on flip top bottles and the coloured squares on a Rubik's cube. Polypropene is a polymer that can be coloured and which has good heat resistance. It is also more resistant to fatigue than other addition polymers. It has the further advantage of being cheap to mould into complex shapes. Polypropene has the property of **tacticity**, where the relative orientation of the methyl group affects the property of the polymer.

Rubik's cube (coloured PP stickers)

Poly(chloroethene) was developed in Germany during World War II. It is a paradox that it seems to take a threat to the security and sovereignty of a nation before governments spend sufficient amounts of money on science for big advances in technology to be made. Advances that we now all take for granted. Plastics depend on chemicals from non-renewable fossil fuels such as oil. Since 56.8% by mass of polychloroethene is chlorine it therefore requires less petroleum for its production than many other addition polymers.

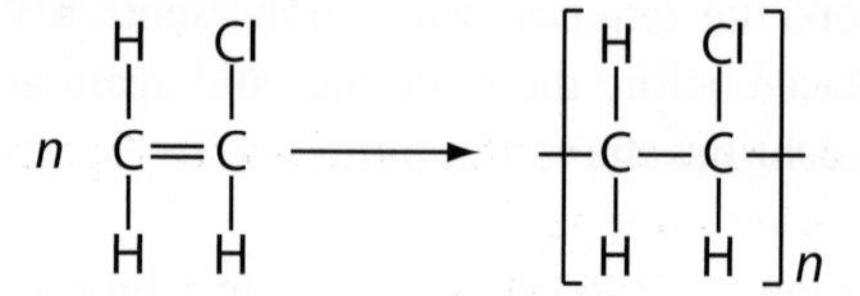

$$n \ \text{C=C} \longrightarrow \left[\text{C}-\text{C}\right]_n$$

Chloroethene   Poly(chloroethene)

Poly(**tetra**fluoro**ethene**), also known as PTFE or Teflon®, is a polymer which contains fluorine atoms at its surface. These repel all other molecules. It is for this reason that it is used as a coating on non-stick frying pans and as the lubricating tape for ground glass joints on laboratory apparatus. It is also the water-repellant substance found in Gortex®, the water-proof material on outdoor boots and water-proof clothing.

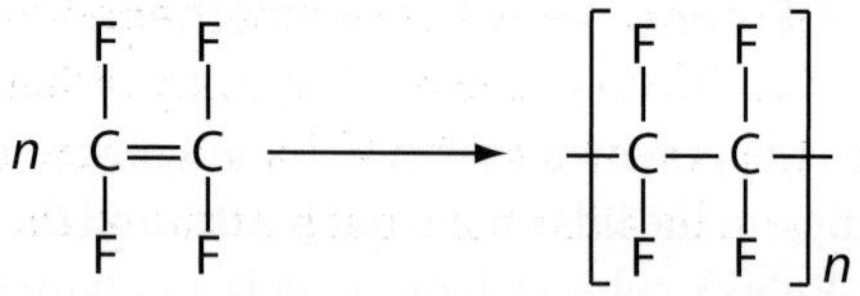

$$n \ \text{C=C} \longrightarrow \left[\text{C}-\text{C}\right]_n$$

Tetrafluoroethene   Poly(tetrafluoroethene)

Poly(phenylethene), more commonly known by the name polystyrene, is an aromatic addition polymer which as the chemical formula $(C_8H_8)_n$. The polymer consists of a long chain hydrocarbon with every other carbon connected to a phenyl group (C_6H_5). Like other aromatic compounds, polystyrene burns with an orange sooty flame.

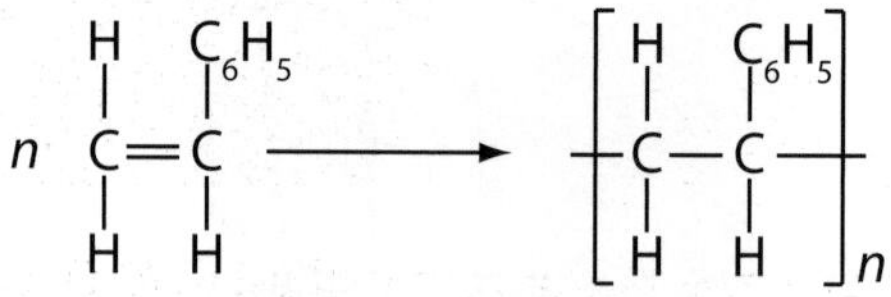

$$n \ \text{C=C} \longrightarrow \left[\text{C}-\text{C}\right]_n$$

Phenylethene   Poly(phenylethene)

Methyl-2-cyanoacrylate is a monomer that is used as glue in Superglue®. This polymerises when it is exposed to air and will subsequently stick to any surface, e.g. wood, plastic or metal. The analogue, 2-octylcyanoacrylate, is used medically as Dermabond® to rapidly close lacerations (cuts), without the need for stitches.

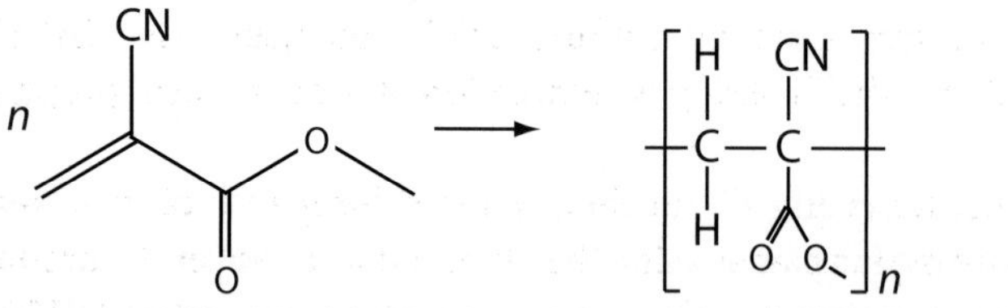

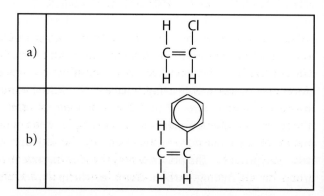

methyl 2-cyanoacrylate   Poly(methyl 2-cyanoacrylate)

Questions 17.3

1. Which option is not an addition polymer?

    A   polystyrene

    B   terylene

    C   polyvinylchloride

    D   polypropene

2. What is addition polymerisation?

3. Suggest the structure of the related monomers from the structures of these polymers

a)	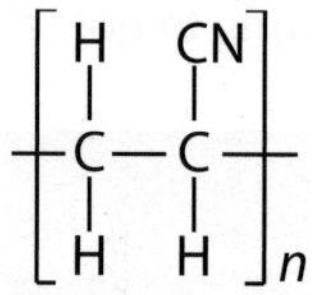 $\left[\text{C}(H)(CN)-\text{C}(H)(H)\right]_n$ Poly(propenenitrile)	Acrilan®
b)	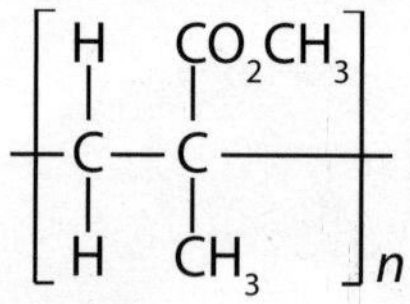 $\left[\text{C}(H)(CO_2CH_3)-\text{C}(H)(CH_3)\right]_n$ Poly(methyl methacrylate)	Perspex®
c)	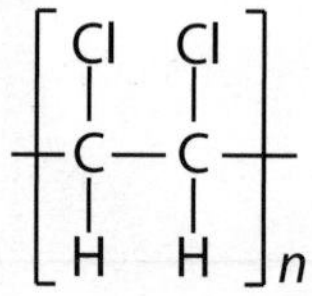 $\left[\text{C}(Cl)(Cl)-\text{C}(H)(H)\right]_n$ Poly(1,2-dichloroethene)	

4. Suggest the structure of the related polymer from the structure of these monomers

a)	$\text{C}(H)(H)=\text{C}(Cl)(H)$
b)	$\text{C}(H)(C_6H_5)=\text{C}(H)(H)$

316

c)	$\begin{array}{cc} H & CH_3 \\ | & | \\ C=C \\ | & | \\ H & H \end{array}$
d)	$\begin{array}{cc} H & OH \\ | & | \\ C=C \\ | & | \\ H & H \end{array}$

5. Poly(vinylalcohol) (PVA) is a water soluble polymer used in glue. The expected monomer, vinyl alcohol (CH$_2$=CHOH), is unstable so it is made from vinyl acetate in two steps. [Ac = CH$_3$CO].

$$\begin{array}{cc} H & OAc \\ | & | \\ C=C \\ | & | \\ H & H \end{array}$$

Vinyl acetate

Step 1

$$\begin{array}{cccc} OAc & OAc & OAc & OAc \end{array}$$

Poly(vinyl acetate)

Step 2

$$\begin{array}{cccc} OH & OH & OH & OH \end{array}$$

Poly(vinyl alcohol)

What type of reaction is taking place in **steps 1 & 2**?

A3.5 (d) Elimination from alcohols to make alkenes

When a small molecule is eliminated from a larger molecule, such as an alcohol or an alkyl halide, to produce an alkene (unsaturated), it is described as an **elimination reaction**. Alcohols eliminate water (H$_2$O) and alkyl halides eliminate hydrogen halides (HX). Elimination reactions are essentially the reverse of addition reactions. An example of the opposite nature of these reactions is illustrated by the fact that water adds to ethene to make ethanol and the elimination of water (dehydration) from ethanol makes ethene. Having a source of

ethene is important to importers of fruit as they add this gas to the atmosphere around their produce to speed up the ripening process.

Water is eliminated from ethanol when its vapour is passed over heated aluminium oxide.

$$CH_3CH_2OH \underset{Al_2O_3}{\overset{Al_2O_3}{\rightleftharpoons}} CH_2=CH_2 + H_2O$$

This experiment can be carried out in the laboratory by soaking mineral wool with ethanol in the end of a test tube. The test tube also contains the catalyst (Al$_2$O$_3$) and, as the hot ethanol vapour passes over the catalyst, water is eliminated. In this reaction it is possible to collect a few test tubes of ethene gas. The presence of this unsaturated gas (CH$_2$=CH$_2$) can be demonstrated as it will rapidly decolourise a few drops of bromine water. Care is needed once heat is removed from the test tube and the delivery tube needs quickly lifting out of the water trough to prevent 'suck back'. This is where cold water is drawn up the tube from the trough as the gases in the test tube cool.

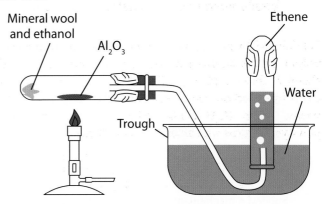

Elimination of water from ethanol using Al$_2$O$_3$ catalyst

Elimination of water from alcohols (1°, 2° and 3°) also happens in the presence of sulfuric acid. The secondary (2°) alcohol propan-2-ol will react with excess sulfuric acid when heated, with the elimination of water to produce propene.

$$CH_3CH(OH)CH_3 \underset{H_2SO_4}{\overset{H_2SO_4}{\rightleftharpoons}} CH_2=CHCH_3 + H_2O$$

It is believed that the first step in the reaction between sulfuric acid and propan-2-ol is the protonation of the alcohol (OH) group. This is followed by nucleophilic attack on a methyl hydrogen atom by sulfuric acid's conjugate base (B1.5b), HSO$_4^-$. The final step is elimination of water to form propene.

The tertiary (3°) alcohol, 2-methylpropan-2-ol will react with sulfuric acid, with the elimination of water, to produce 2-methylpropene. The mixture is heated under reflux to 170°C with excess of the dehydrating agent (c.H$_2$SO$_4$).

$$(CH_3)_3COH \xrightarrow{c. H_2SO_4} CH_2=C(CH_3)_2 + H_2O$$

317

Questions 17.4

1. A mixture of ethanol and excess concentrated sulfuric acid was heated to 170°C and the gas evolved was bubbled through a solution of bromine water.

   a) Give the type of reaction and equation for this reaction.

   b) Why was excess concentrated sulfuric acid used in this reaction?

   c) Explain the observations you would make in this experiment.

   d) How can 170°C be reached without heating the flask directly with a Bunsen burner?

2. Alcohols are an important functional group as a number of other functional groups can be made from them. What are the reaction conditions that favour *reaction A* and what conditions favour *reaction B*?

   $$CH_3CH_2OH \xrightarrow{\text{Reaction A}} CH_2=CH_2 + H_2O$$
   $$\xrightarrow{\text{Reaction B}} CH_3CH_2Br + H_2O$$

3. Suggest a mechanism for the elimination of water from 2-methylpropan-2-ol with sulfuric acid.

4. Predict the products when the following alcohols are treated with acid (H⁺).

   a) cyclohexanol

   b) cyclopropanol

   c) butan-2-ol

5. Draw the skeletal structure of the alcohol which will make a mixture of these regioisomers on elimination of water under acidic conditions.

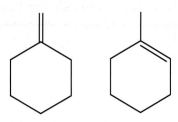

6. Heating 3-methylbutan-2-ol with phosphoric acid (H_3PO_4) leads to a mixture of unsaturated products. Write an equation for this reaction and suggest how the products might be separated.

7. Which option shows the most likely product when water is eliminated from 2-methylbutan-2-ol?

   A $CH_2=C(CH_3)CH_2CH_3$

   B $(CH_3)_2C=CHCH_3$

   C $CH_2=C(CH_2CH_3)CH_3$

   D $(CH_3)_2C=COH(CH_3)$

A3.5 (e) Elimination from alkyl halides to make alkenes

Alkenes are also formed when hydrogen halides (HX) are eliminated from alkyl halides (halogenoalkanes). Elimination is the opposite of addition as can be seen in the interconversions between alkenes and alkyl halides. The reversibility of this reaction illustrates the principle of **microscopic reversibility**, which recognises that there is a single lowest energy pathway for the interconversion of two states, independent of direction.

$$\boxed{\text{Alkene}} \underset{-\text{ HX (elimination)}}{\overset{+\text{ HX (addition)}}{\rightleftharpoons}} \boxed{\text{Alkyl halides}}$$

The elimination of HX from alkyl halides takes place in alkaline conditions. Careful choice of conditions is needed as elimination competes with substitution (B3.9d). Elimination reactions are favoured when the reaction conditions involve both a high temperature and a high pH, due to the presence of a strong base (B1.5b) such as ethoxide $C_2H_5O^-$ ($pK_a = 16$). Elimination of HX from alkyl halides is aided using ethanol as the solvent. One way to remember this is that **e**limination and **e**thanol both begin with the same letter. The ethanol is needed to solubilise alkyl halides which are not very miscible with water. It also acts as a base ($pK_a = -7$).

Example 17.1

Reaction:

$$CH_3CH_2Br + OH^- \rightarrow CH_2=CH_2 + H_2O + Br^-$$

Type of reaction: Elimination

Temperature: High

Base: Strong

Example 17.2

Reaction:

$$CH_3CH_2Br + OH^- \rightarrow CH_3CH_2OH + Br^-$$

Type of reaction: Substitution

Temperature: Low

Base: Weak

When hydrogen bromide is eliminated from 2-bromopropane to form propene, the hydroxide is acting as a base (proton acceptor), rather than as a nucleophile attacking $C^{\delta+}$. The hydroxide is able to attack a hydrogen atom on a carbon atom adjacent to the carbon that the bromine is on. This is because bromide is a good leaving group.

$$CH_3CHBrCH_3 + OH^- \rightarrow CH_3CH=CH_2 + H_2O + Br^-$$

For elimination of HX from alkyl halides, the hydroxide is in the rate determining step (B1.6g) and therefore appears in the rate equation, *e.g.* rate = k [$CH_3CHBrCH_3$][OH^-].

Questions 17.5

1. When 3-bromopentane is dissolved in ethanol and heated with a strong base, it undergoes an elimination reaction. Identify the organic and inorganic products and give tests that will confirm their presence.

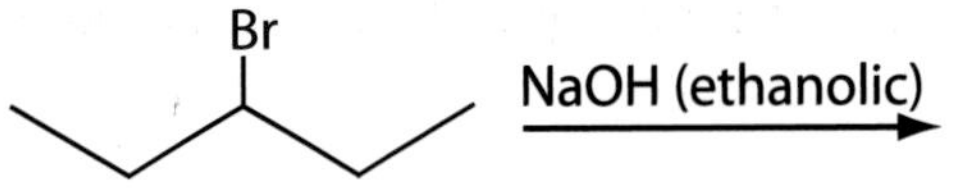

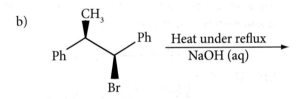

2. What are the two competing reactions when an aqueous solution of sodium hydroxide reacts with 2-methylpropyl bromide?

3. Predict the products in the following reactions.

a)

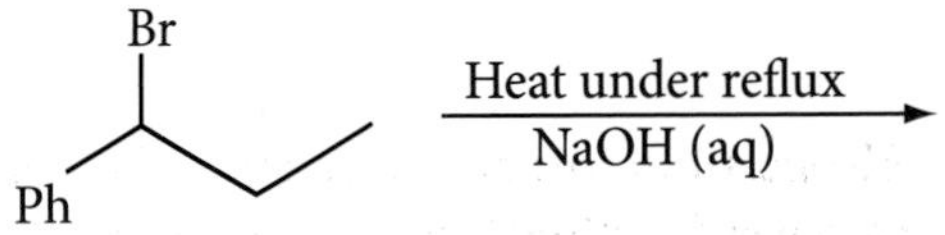

b)

4. Use the Gibbs energy equation ($\Delta G = \Delta H - T\Delta S$) to explain why elimination of HX from akyl halides (RX) is favoured at high temperatures, rather than substitution under alkaline conditions.

18 Green Chemistry

Contents

The work of chemists over the last few hundred years has led to dramatic improvements in living standards as new materials and improved medicines have been developed. At the start of the twenty-first century, the focus has shifted at times to the impact chemicals have on our environment. Most students are familiar with the replacement of CFCs (**chlorofluorocarbons**) used for refrigeration with safer alternatives that do not damage the Earth's ozone layer. It is such a pity that chemistry is at its most newsworthy following a disaster. Examples include oil leaking from tankers, mercury poisoning and pesticide residues in the food that we eat. Malaria is a disease carried by mosquitoes and is thought to have killed more humans than any other disease. An insecticide, DDT (**d**ichloro**d**iphenyl**t**richloroethane) was used extensively in the fight against biting insects. One consequence of its liberal use was the bioaccumulation of DDT in the fat tissues of top predators such as peregrine falcons. The dangers of this chemical were brought to the attention of the general public in 1962 when Rachel Carson published her book *Silent Spring*.

DDT

The danger to human health from contact with chemicals has long been known. Mercury was historically used in the making of felt hats. The inhalation of toxic mercury fumes by hatters was to give Lewis Carroll the idea for the 'Mad Hatter' in *Alice's Adventures in Wonderland*.

In 1976 at a chemical plant in Seveso in Northern Italy, TCDD (2,3,7,8-tetrachlorodibenzo-*para*-dioxin), a dioxin, was accidentally released into the atmosphere. Thousands of farm animals and pets were killed and locals suffered from a painful condition called chloracne. The same condition affected the 2004 Ukranian presidential candidate Viktor Yushchenko who was believed to have been poisoned by a dioxin during the *Orange Revolution*.

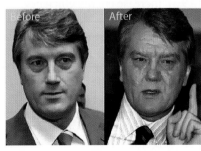

TCDD

Today chemists are looking to see which chemicals are finding their way into the water table and therefore into our water supply. They are also looking closely at chemicals found in foods. Each chemical is scrutinised and, if it is harmful, its source is identified and then removed. In many countries there are strict regulations in place about the use and disposal of chemicals. The spiralling cost of waste management has forced the chemical industry to look at its practices through 'green-tinted' spectacles. It is far better, and in the long term cheaper, to prevent pollution and the formation of hazardous materials than to invest time and money in cleaning them up. In 1998 Paul Anastas and John Warner published their twelve principles of Green Chemistry which are increasingly being applied around the world in the manufacture of chemicals. If chemists can clean up their act then this is a good thing for the industry and the environment. Principle number 6 is not always possible for organic chemists where protection of one or more functional groups is often necessary in a total synthesis of, for example, a complex natural product.

The 12 principles are;

	Principle	Description
1	Prevent waste.	Design chemical reactions to prevent waste which needs treating or cleaning up.
2	Design safer chemicals and products.	Design chemical products to be fully effective with little or no toxicity.
3	Design less hazardous chemical syntheses.	Design syntheses to use and generate substances with little or no toxicity to humans and the environment.
4	Use renewable feedstocks.	Use raw materials and feedstocks that are renewable (agricultural products or waste from other processes) rather than depleting feedstocks (fossil fuels, *e.g.* coal, oil, natural gas, and minerals).
5	Use catalysts, not stoichiometric reagents.	Minimize waste by using catalytic reactions. Catalysts are used in small amounts and can carry out a single reaction many times. Catalysts are preferable to stoichiometric reagents which only work once and are often used in excess.
6	Avoid chemical derivatives.	Avoid using protecting groups if possible. Derivatives use additional reagents and generate waste.
7	Maximize atom economy.	Design syntheses so that the final product contains the maximum proportion of the starting materials. There should be few, if any, wasted atoms.
8	Use safer solvents and reaction conditions.	Avoid using solvents, separation agents, or other auxiliary chemicals. If these chemicals are necessary, use innocuous chemicals.
9	Increase energy efficiency.	Run chemical reactions at ambient temperature and pressure whenever possible.
10	Design chemicals and products to degrade after use.	Design chemical products to break down to innocuous substances after use so that they do not accumulate in the environment.
11	Analyze in real time to prevent pollution.	Include in-process real-time monitoring and control during syntheses to minimize or eliminate the formation of unwanted by-products.
12	Minimize the potential for accidents.	Design chemicals and their forms (solid, liquid or gas) to minimize the potential for chemical accidents including explosions, fires and releases into the environment.

A3.6 (a) Atom economy

Chemists are always looking for ways to make products in fewer steps with higher yields. Another important consideration is called **atom economy**. Atom economy is a concept introduced by Barry Trost, a Professor at Stanford University (USA). In 1995 he wrote a seminal paper which went by the title; "*Atom Economy. A challenge for organic synthesis*". Atom economy for any reaction is straightforward to work out using this formula:

Atom Economy

$$= \frac{\text{formula weight of desired product}}{\text{sum of formula weights of all reactants}} \times 100\%$$

Atom economy is important as it will also help to conserve for longer our finite resources as well as making economic sense. Atom economy has also been called **atom utilisation** and is a measure of the percentage of starting materials that become a part of the final desired and useful product. Atom economy can be thought of as a measure of the efficiency of a synthesis. A low percentage for atom economy means that there is a lot of material to dispose of if other uses cannot be found for the by-product(s).

Steps to calculate atom economy from a balanced formula equation:

Step 1: Calculate M_r for each reactant.

Step 2: Calculate sum of M_r and/or A_r for all reactants.

Step 3: Calculate M_r and/or A_r of desired product.

Step 4: Account for the stoichiometry.

Step 5: Put the values into the % atom economy formula.

Example 18.1

Atom economy is not restricted to organic reactions. Iron ore is iron(III) oxide and, to obtain the iron for steel making, it can be reduced using coke. What is the % atom economy of the following reaction? [A_r: Fe = 55.8, C =12.0, O = 16.0].

$$2\ Fe_2O_3 + 3\ C \rightarrow 4\ Fe + 3\ CO_2$$

Solution:

$M_r\ (Fe_2O_3) = 2(55.8) + 3(16.0) = 159.6$

Reactants: $2\ Fe_2O_3 + 3\ C = 2(159.6) + 3(12.0) = 355.2$

Desired product: $4\ Fe = 4(55.8) = 223.2$

% atom economy $= \frac{223.2}{355.2} \times 100\% = 62.8\%$

Example 18.2

Cracking of hydrocarbons can result in the formation of shorter alkanes and alkenes. If the alkene is the only product which can be sold commercially after the cracking of octane, what is the % atom economy of the following reaction?

$$C_8H_{18} \rightarrow 3\ C_2H_4 + C_2H_6$$

[A_r: C =12.0, H = 1.0].

Solution:

Reactant: $M_r\ (C_8H_{18}) = 8(12.0) + 18(1.0) = 114$

$M_r\ (C_2H_4) = 2(12.0) + 4(1.0) = 28.0$

Desired product: $3\ C_2H_4 = 3(28) = 84.0$

% atom economy $= \frac{84.0}{114} \times 100\% = 73.7\%\ (74\%)$

Questions 18.1

1. Cyclohexene reacts with bromine in an electrophilic addition reaction to form 1,2-dibromocylcohexane. Write an equation for this reaction and calculate the % atom economy [A_r: Br = 79.9, C =12.0, H = 1.0].

2. The raspberry flavoured ester 2-methylpropyl methanoate can be formed by reacting 2-methylpropan-1-ol with methanoic acid in the presence of an acid catalyst. Write an equation for this reversible reaction and calculate the % atom economy [A_r: O = 16.0, C =12.0, H = 1.0].

3. The Wittig reaction is an important carbon-carbon bond forming reaction for the synthesis of alkenes. Cyclohexanone can be converted into methylene cyclohexane in 85% yield by reaction with a triphenyl phosphonium ylide. Calculate the % atom economy [A_r: P = 31.0, O = 16.0, C =12.0, H = 1.0] and explain why this is not a very 'green' reaction. How might this reaction be classified?

cyclohexanone

+ CH_2–PPh_3
ylide

methylene cyclohexane

+ O=PPh_3

Organic reactions are often classified by type (A3.1h), e.g. additions or substitutions. Each type of reaction, by its nature, has a higher or lower atom economy. In addition reactions there is 100% atom economy. As well as atom economy it is also important to consider the yield of a chemical reaction. There is little point in carrying out chemical reactions which, whilst they may be environmentally friendly, produce little chemical to sell at the end of the process. Conversely there is no point in making a chemical which has a high overall yield if the cost of the clean up exceeds the price that the market will sustain for the chemical. If all these factors were easy to manage then there would be many more profitable chemical firms in existence around the world! Atom economy is expressed as a percentage that tells us what percentage of the atoms in the reactants make their way into the desired product. Some reactions are more efficient than others in terms of atom economy.

Types of reaction	Atom economy	Examples
Addition	100%	$C_2H_4 + H_2O \rightarrow C_2H_5OH$ $C_2H_4 + HBr \rightarrow C_2H_5Br$ Diels-Alder
Elimination	poor (additional product formed)	$C_2H_5OH \rightarrow C_2H_4 + H_2O$ $CH_3CH_2CH_2Cl \rightarrow$ $CH_3CH=CH_2 + HCl$
Condensation	<100% (small molecules eliminated)	Esterification. Formation of condensation polymers (peptides, esters, ethers)

Types of reaction	Atom economy	Examples
Substitution	Poor to good	$CH_3CH_2Br + OH^- \rightarrow$ $CH_3CH_2OH + Br^-$ $C_6H_6 + NO_2^+ \rightarrow$ $C_6H_5NO_2 + H^+$
Isomerisation	100%	$CH_3(CH_2)_3CH_3 \rightarrow$ $CH_3CH_2CH(CH_3)_2$

Yield is not the same as atom economy and is a figure which seldom reaches 100%.

$$\% \text{ Yield} = \frac{\text{actual quantity of product obtained}}{\text{theoretical quantity of product obtained}} \times 100\%$$

During my PhD (Sheffield University) I only ever carried out one reaction which had an atom economy of 100% and a yield of 100%. This was the reaction between furan and maleic anhydride in the anhydrous solvent diethyl ether (ethoxyethane) to form a **Diels-Alder adduct**.

One of the other considerations in addition to yield and atom economy is the **stereoselectivity** of reactions that involve products with chiral centres (B3.12b). It is costly to separate a racemic mixture (B3.19i) and it is much better to predominantly make the biologically active enantiomer (B3.12d). The story of thalidomide highlights this point. Thalidomide was used for morning sickness and was withdrawn as it led to birth defects. It has since found use in the treatment of leprosy. Can you draw the three dimensional drawing (A3.1f) for the two enantiomers (B3.12d) of thalidomide?

Thalidomide

A3.6 (b) Chemicals and the Environment

One of the earliest and perhaps best known cases of chemicals affecting health is that of factory workers who developed **phossy jaw** from the white phosphorous used to make matches. Problems such as this have resulted in legislation (laws) that means that the chemical industry has to work hard to reduce its environmental impact. The high cost of meeting these stringent measures is also part of the impetus for chemical companies shifting production to countries like India and China. Reducing environmental impact takes many forms, *e.g.* finding alternative and less hazardous chemicals, using renewable feedstocks, reducing waste, recycling and using catalysts rather than stoichiometric reagents. In the UK there is a landfill tax which is making companies look closely at waste reduction. There will always be some waste in a chemical reaction and, rather than dumping toxic materials, the waste is now being treated before being buried. Degradation of waste products might involve neutralisations, oxidations or electrochemical reduction of metal ions. An infamous case of mercury poisoning was the result of a chemical factory in Japan dumping waste into the water supply in Minamata. Bioaccumulation of mercury in shell fish resulted in the tragic deaths of thousands of people.

Solvents

Alkali metals such as sodium are stored under oil to prevent their reaction with water and oxygen in the air. It was once common in school laboratories to use the solvents hexane or cyclohexane to wash the oil from the alkali metals prior to using them in reactions. A much more benign alternative to using (cyclo)hexane to remove the oil from sodium is to use the solvent Iotoxane. A substance which is 'environmentally benign' does not have any (known) damaging consequences to the environment. It is much better wherever possible to use benign alternatives. Finding alternative solvents can prove quite difficult. There has been a move away from chlorinated hydrocarbons which are linked to the hole in the ozone layer. Water is the ideal solvent as it is harmless but it is immiscible with most organic substrates. Chemists have devised some clever catalysts called **phase transfer catalysts (PTC)**, *e.g.* organometallic substances, which bring the reactants together at the water-organic interface. Propene, hydrogen and carbon monoxide can be made to react with 95% selectivity producing butanal using a phase transfer catalyst which is a rhodium(I) complex of trisulfonated triphenylphosphine.

It is important to remember that the choice of solvent can be critical to the yield and also the path taken. Chloroethane reacts with aqueous hydroxide (OH^-) to give ethanol as the main product and reacts with ethanolic hydroxide to give ethene as the main product. One way to remember which solvent gives which product is: you get **e**limination with **e**thanol and **s**ubstitution when aqueou**s**.

Chemists are working hard to improve the atom economy of reactions. Improvements can be made by careful selection of starting materials. It is far better to carry out a synthesis in as few steps as possible as this will generate less waste and is likely to give a better overall yield. If possible, catalysts are used as this makes for less waste. Increasing atom economy is going to help reduce energy consumption and reduce manufacturing costs as well as decreasing the amount of waste. There is some fascinating research taking place in laboratories around the world where **biotechnologists** (often chemists) are exploiting nature's catalysts, the enzymes.

The start of the 21st century has seen spiralling costs of crude oil partly because the oil is often in conflict zones (or conflicts move to oil zones). It is not surprising that chemists are looking for new feedstocks. It might be true that oil does not grow on trees. However, trees do contain valuable materials in their bark and wood. Digesting the lignin (fibrous part of wood) and the enzymatic hydrolysis of the cellulose is unlocking a valuable source of sugars for fermentation. This is one rapidly developing area of green chemistry where ethanol as a fuel for motor vehicles is becoming increasingly viable.

Renewable feedstocks

Paper mills use trees as their feedstock. A large component of wood is a substance called **lignin** which contains aromatic rings (B3.10) which stiffen the cell walls. Lignin is used to make the flavour vanillin which is used in food products. Wood is treated using the sulfite process and cellulose, another major component of wood, is used to make specialist papers. At one time the black liquor waste left behind was flushed into the local rivers. The waste is now treated and processed as it contains lignins, sugars and other valuable chemicals. The sugars are fermented. The lignin is broken down with alkalis and oxidising agents to give a mixture which contains vanillin. The vanillin is separated by solvent extraction and purified.

HO$_3$S–$\overset{\text{H}}{\underset{}{\text{C}}}$–CH$_2$CHO $\xrightarrow{\text{NaOH}}$ HO–$\overset{\text{H}}{\underset{}{\text{C}}}$–CH$_2$CHO

(benzene ring with OCH$_3$ and OH)

sulfonated fragment

$\xrightarrow{\text{[O]}}$ CHO (benzene ring with OCH$_3$ and OH)

vanillin

Other renewable feedstocks are sometimes called **bio-products**. In the near future it is highly likely there will be a conflict between our hunger for food and our hunger for chemicals. Sustainability of feedstocks in the 21st century is a serious issue facing the world. It is becoming increasingly common in the Summer across England to see yellow fields of oilseed rape which is grown for its oils. Flax and hemp are also grown as they can be used for fibres. The Royal Navy has been using hemp for ropes for hundreds of years. Flax and hemp are both being used in composites where they are mixed with polymeric matrices and are finding use in car door panels and boot linings. Diesel engines work perfectly well on vegetable oils and some entrepreneurs are using fat from restaurants to make biodiesel to run their cars.

New feedstocks are slow to enter the market place because initial costs are higher than existing materials being used in established industries. It is worth mentioning that three quarters of the active ingredients in medicines are based upon compounds (natural products) derived from plants. It is currently more economical to synthesise these active ingredients rather than to extract them from plants.

It is only multinational companies that can afford the huge budgets needed for the research and development that leads to new drug discoveries. It is at least seven years before a new drug discovery makes it to the market place and patients.

The following table shows recent examples of renewable feedstocks and their current uses. More will follow in the decades ahead as crude oil supplies are depleted.

Crop (feedstock)	Polymer	Use	Trademarks
Potatoes	Polylactic acid	Moulding	Natureworks™
Wheat	Starch based	Cellulose films	Materbi™
Corn	Polyesters	Resins, textiles	
Wood	Cellulose	Cellulose films	Natureflex™
Castor oil & soy	Polyurethane	Foams	
Sugar cane (bioethanol)	Poly(e)thene	Shopping bags	
Oilseed rape	Nylon from erucic acid	Clothing	

A 100% biodegradable plastic from corn starch is needed as supermarket plastic bags have found their way to the Antarctic on ocean currents. Every little bit of help individuals can give to recycling plastics or switching to biodegradable plastics is helpful. The Chinese philosopher Lao Tzu who was a contemporary of Confucius said, "a journey of a thousand miles begins with a single step." This quotation has impacted many events around the world over the centuries as it is applicable to any situation where something needs to be done such as improving the environment.

Questions 18.2

1. How does atom economy relate to waste in two processes which make the same product?

2. Natureflex™ films are manufactured by Innovia. At the time of writing, the company website contains product information sheets. How do these products differ from petroleum derived films?

3. Increased use of biofuels may have the effect of increasing food prices. Is there good evidence for this fear?

Catalysts

Catalysts will play a key part in the development of greener production methods for chemicals in industry and perhaps also in research. The search is now on for catalysts to be used rather than stoichiometric ratios. The main advantage of using catalysts is the reduction in energy demands for processes because of the lowering of activation energies (A1.3f). Catalysts will lead to better atom economies and the production of less waste. It is important that the catalysts have a high **turnover number (TON)** which is a measure of how long a catalyst can be used before it needs replacing. Waste includes inorganic salts formed in neutralisations (Na_2SO_4, $(NH_4)_2SO_4$, NaCl) or metallic reducing agents (Zn, Fe, Mg), metal hydrides ($NaBH_4$, $LiAlH_4$) or oxidants ($KMnO_4$, $K_2Cr_2O_7$). The advantage of catalytic methods over stoichiometric methods is illustrated in terms of atom economy, and therefore waste, which ultimately means a reduction in cost.

Example 18.3

The oxidation of a secondary alcohol can be carried out using **Jones reagent** (CrO_3/H_2SO_4) or using oxygen in the presence of a catalyst.

1-phenylethanol → 1-phenylethanone (acetophenone)

Method	Oxidant	Atom economy (%) accounting for waste
Stoichiometric	CrO_3 / H_2SO_4	42
Catalytic	O_2 / catalyst	87

Example 18.4

Friedel-Crafts acylation (B3.10b) of methoxybenzene can be carried out using a stoichiometric amount of ethanoyl chloride (CH_3COCl) or using acetic anhydride ($(CH_3CO)_2O$) and a catalyst. In both stoichiometric and catalytic methods the acetyl group (CH_3CO) attaches in the 4-position.

methoxybenzene (anisole)

Method	Stoichiometric	Catalytic
Solvent	√	x
Acylating reagent	CH_3COCl	$(CH_3CO)_2O$
Acylating agent	$AlCl_3$ (halogen carrier)	H-beta (catalyst)
Yield (%)	85	95
Other Product	HCl	CH_3CO_2H

In addition to a better yield, the catalytic method produces a benign by-product in ethanoic acid.

Questions 18.3

1. *p*-hydroxyacetophenone can be converted into an oxime which undergoes a Beckmann rearrangement. This is one industrial method for the production of the generic analgesic paracetamol. In step 1 the catalyst is titanium(IV) silicalite (Ts-1) and 2 moles of water are produced as a by-product. In step 2 the rearrangement is acid (H^+) catalysed.

   What is the atom economy for step 1 and step 2? Why can both steps be described as 'green' reactions?

paracetamol

2. Use the reaction scheme for the synthesis of the pain-relieving drug ibuprofen to complete the table. Explain what is meant by 'the final step is 96% selective'.

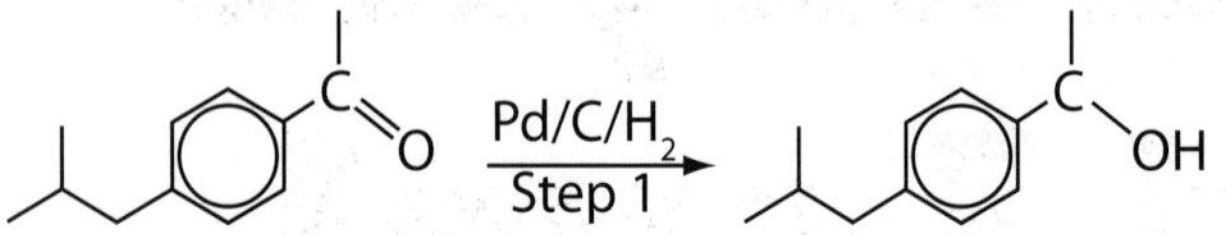

p-isobutylacetophenol

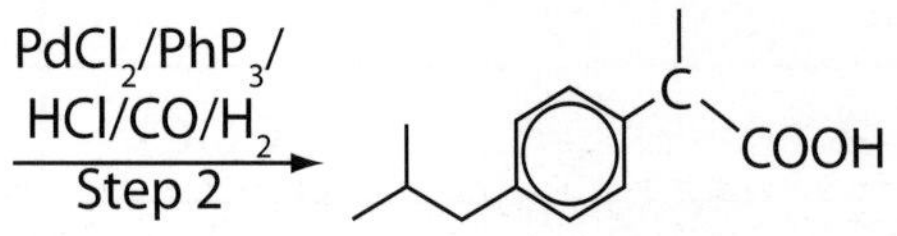

ibuprofen 99% yield

Step	Metal catalyst	Atom economy	reactant → product	Type of reaction
#1				
#2				

The need to clean up industries to improve the environment has been apparent since the smogs of the 1950s called 'pea-soupers' which resulted in my Mancunian grandmother getting emphysema (lung disease). Gas emissions are now passed through sprays of solutions (basic) that will absorb gases such as sulfur dioxide. The prevailing south westerly wind caused much of the UK's pollution to fall as acid in rain over Scandinavia (Sweden) and Germany (Black Forest).

The highly successful Beijing Olympics in the summer of 2008 was threatened by pollution caused by China's huge manufacturing industries. Politicians have an important part to play in passing laws to clean up the environment. The current focus is still on minimising waste, reducing energy consumption and preventing emissions whilst using petrochemical feedstocks. There will come a point in the near future when the shift will be more towards non-petrochemical feedstocks. One problem with the 'Atom Economy Calculation' is that it does not take into account the nature of the by-products and there will inevitably be a need to look at the benefits *versus* the cost with any new processes.

Nature has developed enzymes (proteins) with active sites that can catalyse specific reactions at rates with turnover numbers which chemists rarely match. The advantage of using biocatalysts in reactions is that they are generally carried out at atmospheric pressures and ambient temperatures without the need for solvents like dichloromethane (DCM) and they are stereoselective.

Work with enzymes is rightly blurring the boundaries between the sciences which are taught as discrete subjects in schools.

Question 18.4

1. Give five advantages of using an enzyme over a transition metal catalyst.

19 Carboxylic Acid Level

Contents

The members of the Carboxylic Acid level (FGL 3) have three bonds to an electronegative element (or elements) from a carbon atom. Members include; carboxylic acids (RCO_2H), esters (RCO_2R'), amides ($RCONH_2$), acyl chlorides ($RCOCl$), nitriles (RCN) and the condensation polymers: polyamides and polyesters. Most members of the Carboxylic Acid level have an electronegative atom joined to the carbonyl (C=O) group. The differences in their chemical properties arise from the other atoms or groups attached to this carbon atom.

There are many interesting molecules with carboxylic acid groups as part of their structure, *e.g.*

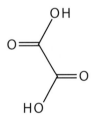

methanoic acid (formic acid) is the simplest carboxylic acid. It is used in the defence of nettles (stings) and by attacking ants (bites).

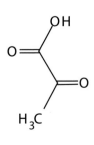

Oxalic acid (ethanedioic acid) is a dicarboxylic acid found in the leaves and roots of rhubarb. Its dianion is a reducing agent (B1.5j) and a ligand (B2.d)

Pyruvic acid is a colourless liquid which smells similar to vinegar. Two molecules if its anion (pyruvate) are produced by glycolysis (anaerobic metabolism of glucose). Energy is obtained from pyruvate and it takes part in the Krebs cycle (citric acid cycle) after being converted into acetyl-coenzyme A.

Sir Hans Krebs Nobel Prize: Medicine 1953

Many different natural carboxylic acids (fatty acids) come from vegetable oils and fats and are the plants' and animals' stores of energy, *e.g.* $CH_3(CH_2)_nCOOH$.

n	Trivial name
10	Lauric acid
14	Palmitic acid
16	Stearic acid

Other molecules in the Carboxylic Acid level are esters which can be recognised by their characteristic fruity smells.

3-methylbutyl ethanoate smells of bananas:

$CH_3COOCH_2CH_2CH(CH_3)_2$

Octyl ethanoate smells of oranges:

$CH_3COOC_8H_{17}$

Methyl 2-aminobenzoate smells of grapes:

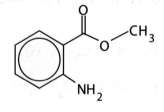

An example of an amide is aspartame.

Aspartame is a dipeptide methyl ester derivative made from aspartic acid and phenylalanine. It is used as a sweetener (sugar substitute) for those dieting.

Within the Carboxylic Acid level there are three possible FGL changes. The majority of reactions are substitutions which involve moving within the level.

Substitution reactions include: hydrolysis to carboxylic acids, making esters from carboxylic acids and acyl chlorides, synthesis of acyl chlorides from carboxylic acids, amides from acyl chlorides and carboxylic acids and condensation polymerisations.

Examples of moving down a level are reductions of FGL 3 compounds with metallic hydrides such as lithium aluminium hydride ($LiAlH_4$). Moving up a level to carbon dioxide is possible but is not included in the spider diagram. The spider diagram shows most of the interconversions leading to, or from, the Carboxylic Acid level. The diagram and the conditions (numbered 1-16) need to be given sufficient study time if this important information is to be used effectively. Reaction number 6 is the conversion from a carboxylic acid into acyl halide and the reverse reaction is numbered 7.

Carboxylic Acid Level

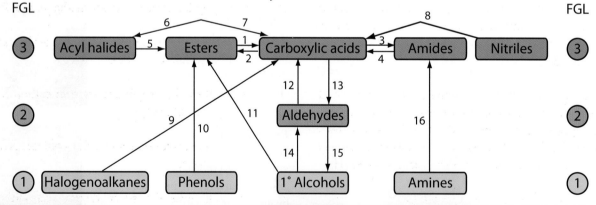

#	conditions	#	conditions	#	conditions	#	conditions
1	H_2O / H^+ or OH^-	5	ROH	9	Mg in Et_2O / CO_2 (s)	13	$LiAlH_4$
2	H^+ / ROH	6	PCl_5 or $SOCl_2$	10	RCOCl or H^+ / RCOOH	14	$Cr_2O_7^{2-}$ / H^+
3	NH_3 or RNH_2	7	H_2O or OH^-	11	H^+ / RCOOH	15	$LiAlH_4$ or $NaBH_4$
4	H_2O / H^+ or OH^-	8	H_2O / H^+	12	$Cr_2O_7^{2-}$ / H^+ or Tollens' (Ag^+)	16	RCOCl

All carboxylic acids contain the carbonyl group (C=O) and the hydroxyl group (OH) on the same carbon atom. When discussing carboxylic acids in general terms it is convenient to refer to them as RCO_2H or $RCOOH$ where R = alkyl group or an aryl group. There are two general formulae which work well for carboxylic acids and they are $C_nH_{2n+1}COOH$ where n = number of carbon atoms, or alternatively $C_nH_{2n}O_2$.

Of the carboxylic derivatives one functional group, the amides, can be further classified into primary (1°), secondary (2°) or tertiary (3°). The type of amide describes the number of carbon atoms bonded to the nitrogen atom of the amide group. Thus primary amides have one carbon attached directly to the nitrogen atom ($RCONH_2$). The table summarises the three types of amides.

Amide type		Hydrogen atoms joined to nitrogen	Carbon atoms joined to nitrogen	General	R (R¹) (R²)
primary	1°	2	1	$RCONH_2$	H, alkyl or aryl
secondary	2°	1	2	$RCONHR^1$	alkyl or aryl
tertiary	3°	0	3	$RCONR^1R^2$	alkyl or aryl

Carboxylic acids have characteristic odours with ethanoic acid having a vinegary smell. Butanoic acid has an extremely unpleasant smell like sweaty feet or rancid cheesy-vomit. Humans can detect butanoic acid to levels as low as 10^{-11} $moldm^{-3}$. Tracker dogs can detect this acid to levels as low as 10^{-17} $moldm^{-3}$.

The presence of a carboxylic acid group can be detected by the addition of an aqueous solution of sodium carbonate (Na_2CO_3) or sodium hydrogencarbonate ($NaHCO_3$). In both cases a colourless gas (CO_2) is evolved which gives a white precipitate with limewater. Ionic equations for these reactions are;

$$CO_3^{2-} + 2H^+ \rightarrow H_2O + CO_2$$

$$HCO_3^- + H^+ \rightarrow H_2O + CO_2$$

Carboxylic acids are weak acids so will give slower reactions than strong acids with the same concentration with alkalis (1), bases (2), metals (3), carbonates (4) and hydrogen carbonates (5).

#	Reactions of ethanoic acid to illustrate its reactions as an acid
1	CH_3COOH (aq) + KOH (aq) $\rightarrow CH_3COO^-K^+$ (aq) + H_2O (l)
2	2 CH_3COOH (aq) + MgO (s) $\rightarrow (CH_3COO^-)_2Mg^{2+}$ (aq) + H_2O (l)
3	2 CH_3COOH (aq) + Zn (s) $\rightarrow (CH_3COO^-)_2Zn^{2+}$ (aq) + H_2 (g)
4	$2CH_3COOH$ (aq) + Na_2CO_3 (aq) $\rightarrow 2CH_3COO^-Na^+$ (aq) + H_2O (l) + CO_2 (g)
5	CH_3COOH (aq) + $NaHCO_3$ (aq) $\rightarrow CH_3COO^-Na^+$ (aq) + H_2O (l) + CO_2 (g)

Questions 19.1

1. Which option is **not** a method for the preparation of carboxylic acids?

    A   Oxidation of 1° alcohol with $K_2Cr_2O_7$ in H_2SO_4.

    B   Hydrolysis of a nitrile with boiling dilute alkali or acid.

    C   Oxidation of 3° alcohol with $K_2Cr_2O_7$ in H_2SO_4.

    D   Oxidation of aldehydes with $K_2Cr_2O_7$ in H_2SO_4.

2. Which option is **incorrect** for methanoic acid?

    A   It is a strong acid with an acid dissociation constant of $K_a = 2.4 \times 10^{-4}$.

    B   It can be dehydrated to form carbon monoxide with c.H_2SO_4.

    C   It is a colourless liquid that contains an aldehyde group.

    D   It gives the silver mirror test with Tollens' reagent.

331

3. Which option is **not** isomeric with propanoic acid?

A   Ethyl methanoate

B   Propen-1-ol

C   Methyl ethanoate

D   1,1-dihydroxycyclopropane

4. Write down the structural formula and name of the acidic isomer having molecular formula $C_3H_6O_2$.

5. Explain why ethanoic acid has a higher boiling point (93°C) than its isomer methyl methanoate (b.p. = 6.6°C).

B3.7 (a) Hydrolysis (moving within the level)

Substances which are members of the Carboxylic Acid level, *e.g.* nitriles, amides, esters and acyl chlorides all hydrolyse with acids to give carboxylic acids. There is no change in FGL in these substitution reactions because after breaking the C-X bond there is formation of a C-OH to this carbon atom. When hydrolysis takes place under alkaline conditions it is the salt of the carboxylic acid that is formed. Neutralisation of the reaction mixture with acid will release the carboxylic acid.

Hydrolysis of nitriles

Nitriles are hydrolysed by heating under reflux with a strong acid such as hydrochloric acid. Propanenitrile is hydrolysed with hydrochloric acid to give propanoic acid. The organic hydrolysis product is sodium propanoate if carried out with sodium hydroxide (alkali).

CH_3CH_2CN (l) + 2 H_2O (l) + HCl (aq)

$\rightarrow CH_3CH_2COOH$ (aq) + NH_4Cl (aq)

CH_3CH_2CN (l) + H_2O (l) + NaOH (aq)

$\rightarrow CH_3CH_2COO^-Na^+$ (aq) + NH_3 (aq)

The hydrolysis of nitriles is thought to go *via* the corresponding amide and ammonium intermediates.

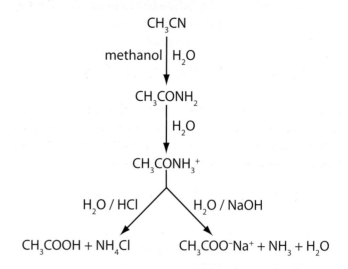

Hydrolysis of amides

Amides are hydrolysed by water, acids and alkalis. Ethanamide (CH_3CONH_2) is hydrolysed by water in the presence of hydrochloric acid to give ethanoic acid and ammonium chloride. In this hydrolysis of amides it is the C-N bond that breaks and is replaced by a C-O bond.

CH_3CONH_2 (aq) + H_2O (l) + HCl (aq)

$\rightarrow CH_3COOH$ (aq) + NH_4Cl (aq)

Once again, if alkaline conditions are chosen for the hydrolysis, it is the sodium salt of the carboxylic acid that is formed.

CH_3CONH_2 (aq) + NaOH (aq)

$\rightarrow CH_3COO^-Na^+$ (aq) + NH_3 (aq)

Hydrolysis of esters

Esters are rapidly hydrolysed by the addition of acid or alkali and heating in the presence of water. Ethyl ethanoate is hydrolysed by water to give ethanoic acid and ethanol. This hydrolysis is the reverse reaction to the original esterification to make the ester. Notice how the acidic hydrolysis is also an equilibrium reaction. If the ester undergoes alkaline hydrolysis with the sodium hydroxide, it is the sodium salt (sodium ethanoate) that is obtained and the hydrolysis is irreversible.

$CH_3COOCH_2CH_3$ (aq) + H_2O (l)

$\rightleftharpoons CH_3COOH$ (aq) + CH_3CH_2OH (aq)

$CH_3COOCH_2CH_3$ (aq) + NaOH (aq)

$$\rightarrow CH_3COO^-Na^+ \text{ (aq)} + CH_3CH_2OH \text{ (aq)}$$

Hydrolysis of acyl chlorides

Small aliphatic acyl chlorides are hydrolysed rapidly in cold water. Ethanoyl chloride hydrolyses to give ethanoic acid and hydrogen chloride which is seen as white fumes which will dissolve in water to form hydrochloric acid.

$$CH_3COCl \text{ (l)} + H_2O \text{ (l)} \rightarrow CH_3COOH \text{ (aq)} + HCl \text{ (g)}$$

Aromatic acyl chlorides such as benzoyl chloride (C_6H_5COCl) hydrolyse more slowly than aliphatic acyl chlorides due to their lower water-solubility..

$$C_6H_5COCl \text{ (l)} + H_2O \text{ (l)} \rightarrow C_6H_5COOH \text{ (aq)} + HCl \text{ (g)}$$

Acyl chlorides are also hydrolysed in alkaline conditions and it is the salt of the carboxylic acid which is formed.

CH_3COCl (l) + 2 KOH (aq)

$$\rightarrow CH_3COO^-K^+ \text{ (aq)} + H_2O \text{ (l)} + KCl \text{ (aq)}$$

Questions 19.2

1. (a) Identify the amino acids that form when the dipeptides **L** and **M** are hydrolysed.

   $L = H_2NCH_2CONHCH(CH_2OH)COOH$

   and $M = H_2NCH(CH_2OH)CONHCH(CH_3)COOH$

   (b) How could these amino acids be separated and identified without using spectroscopic techniques?

2. Complete the table by naming the esters which hydrolyse to give these alcohols and carboxylic acids.

Ester	Carboxylic acid	Alcohol
	propanoic acid	methanol
	butanoic acid	propan-1-ol
	methanoic acid	ethanol
	benzoic acid	phenol

3. Write equations for the acidic hydrolysis of the following carboxylic acid derivatives.

   (a) Propanamide

   (b) Benzonitrile

   (c) Propanoyl chloride

   (d) Propyl pentanoate

4. (a) Suggest a mechanism for the hydrolysis of ethanoyl chloride.

   (b) How could the presence of chloride ions be detected?

5. Which option shows the correct products for the hydrolysis of methyl methanoate?

	Acid hydrolysis	Alkaline hydrolysis
A	ethanal and methanoic acid	methanol and ethanoic acid
B	methanol and methanoic acid	methanol and sodium methanoate
C	methanal and methanoic acid	methanol and methanoic acid
D	methanol and ethanoic acid	methanol and sodium methanoate

6. What is the white precipitate formed when ethyl benzoate is firstly hydrolysed with sodium hydroxide and then acidified with hydrochloric acid?

7. What is produced when natural fats are hydrolysed with sodium hydroxide?

B3.7 (b) Substitution (moving within the level)

The preparation of esters, amides and acyl chlorides from carboxylic acids are all examples of substitution reactions within the Functional Group Level. In the synthesis of esters the hydroxyl group (RCOOH) is replaced by an alkoxy (OR) or phenoxy group (OC$_6$H$_5$). In the synthesis of amides the hydroxyl group (RCO**OH**) is replaced by NR$_2$ (where R = H, alkyl or aryl) and in the synthesis of acyl chlorides the hydroxyl group is replaced by a chlorine atom (Cl).

Synthesis of esters

Esterification reactions are reactions which produce esters. Esters are synthesized in reactions between alcohols/phenols and carboxylic acids or acyl chlorides.

It is important to be able to look at esters written in the two directions: RCOOR' and R'OCOR and identify which part of the molecule has come from the alcohol and which part has come from the carboxylic acid or acyl chloride.

Esters are named (A3.2d) with the alcohol/phenol part coming first in the name followed by the carboxylic acid part and ending with the suffix *oate*. Thus *methyl* propanoate can be made in a reversible reaction from *methanol* and propanoic acid.

$$CH_3OH\ (l) \quad + \quad CH_3CH_2COOH\ (l)$$
$$\text{Methanol} \qquad\qquad \text{Propanoic acid}$$

$$\Big\updownarrow\ H^+\ \text{cat.}$$

$$CH_3OCOCH_2CH_3\ (l) \quad + \quad H_2O\ (l)$$
$$\text{Methyl propanoate} \qquad \text{Water}$$

Esterification reactions without an acid catalyst and at room temperature can take up to a week to go to completion. With a catalyst (c.H$_2$SO$_4$) and heating under reflux, an equilibrium mixture can be reached in about an hour.

A more efficient method for the preparation of esters, because they go to completion, is the reaction between acyl chlorides and alcohols which form esters and hydrogen chloride. *Ethyl ethanoate can be made in a reaction from *ethanol* and ethanoyl chloride.

$$CH_3CH_2OH\ (l) + CH_3COCl\ (l)$$
$$\rightarrow CH_3COOCH_2CH_3\ (l) + HCl\ (g)$$

Phenols do not react readily with carboxylic acids to form esters, but they do react readily with acyl chlorides to form esters. If the reactions are carried out under alkaline conditions, the hydrogen chloride gas formed will be neutralised, thus allowing the esterification reaction to go to completion.

Synthesis of acyl chlorides

Acyl chlorides are colourless liquids with pungent smells which are prepared from carboxylic acids. This conversion is achieved by some Period 3 chlorinating agents. Acyl chlorides are formed when the hydroxy group in a carboxylic acid is replaced by a chlorine atom. Ethanoyl chloride is prepared by the reaction of ethanoic acid with phosphorus(V) chloride. The pure acyl chloride can be obtained by distillation from the reaction mixture as the acyl chloride and phosphorus oxychloride ($POCl_3$) are both liquids. The other product in the reaction is hydrogen chloride gas.

$$CH_3COOH \text{ (l)} + PCl_5 \text{ (s)}$$

$$\rightarrow CH_3COCl \text{ (l)} + POCl_3 \text{ (l)} + HCl \text{ (g)}$$

Acyl chlorides are useful intermediates because they are much more reactive than carboxylic acids. Ethanoyl chloride can also be prepared by the reaction of ethanoic acid with thionyl chloride ($SOCl_2$), also known as sulfur dichloride oxide.

$$CH_3COOH \text{ (l)} + SOCl_2 \text{ (l)}$$

$$\rightarrow CH_3COCl \text{ (l)} + SO_2 \text{ (g)} + HCl \text{ (g)}$$

In this method, the pure acyl chloride can be obtained much more easily as the undesired products are both gases.

Synthesis of amides

The simplest amide, methanamide ($HCONH_2$), is a liquid at room temperature whilst the other amides are white crystalline solids. Primary amides ($RCONH_2$) can be prepared by the reaction between acyl chlorides and ammonia. Ethanamide is made when excess ammonia is reacted with ethanoyl chloride. The excess ammonia neutralises the hydrogen chloride gas formed in this reaction.

$$CH_3COCl + \text{x.s. } NH_3 \rightarrow CH_3CONH_2 + NH_4Cl$$

Secondary amides ($RCONHR'$), also referred to as N-substituted amides, can be prepared by the reaction between acyl chlorides and primary amines. N-methyl ethanamide is made when methylamine is reacted with ethanoyl chloride.

$$CH_3COCl + CH_3NH_2 \rightarrow CH_3CONHCH_3 + HCl$$

The painkiller (analgesic) paracetamol contains a phenol residue as well as an amide group. It gets its generic drug name from one name *para*-**acet**yl**am**inophen**ol**. It can be prepared by the reaction between 4-hydroxyphenylamine and ethanoyl chloride.

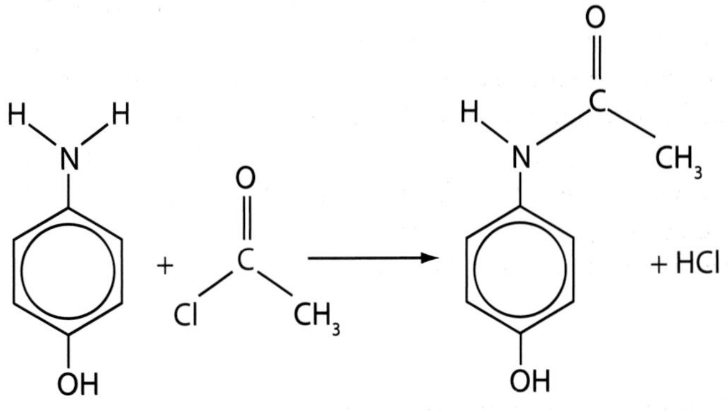

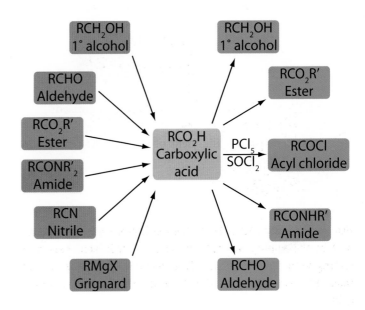

Paracetamol

Synthesis of carboxylic acids

When building up your knowledge of chemical reactions it is a very useful exercise to write down a functional group in a box in the middle of a blank page. The next thing to do is to draw arrows into the box on the left hand side and arrows out of the box on the opposite side. Then try to recall which functional groups can be turned into the central functional group and which functional groups can be made from the central functional group. As hydrolysis reactions lead to the functional group that gives its name to the FGL, a lot of material can be worked out rather than just learned by rote. The diagram shows how this works for the carboxylic acid functional group.

Questions 19.3

1. Match the reagents to the reactions shown:

$A = LiAlH_4$ $B = PCl_5$
$C = KMnO_4$ $D = NaOH$

(a) $CH_3CO_2H \rightarrow CH_3CO_2Na$

(b) $CH_3CH_2OH \rightarrow CH_3CO_2H$

(c) $CH_3CO_2H \rightarrow CH_3CH_2OH$

(d) $CH_3CO_2H \rightarrow CH_3COCl$

2. In the reaction between ethanol and ethanoic acid which option is **incorrect**?

A   The rate of reaction can be followed by titration.

B   The uncatalysed reaction is slow under standard conditions.

C   Removal of water from the reaction mixture increases the yield of ester.

D   The hydroxyl group of the alcohol is lost as water.

3.

(a)   Write an equation for the reaction between methanol and butanoic acid.

(b)   What type of reaction is this?

(c)   How can the rate of reaction be increased?

(d)   How can the yield of the organic product be increased?

4. Describe how the next member of the homologous series can be obtained from $C_{11}H_{23}COOH$.

5. Suggest the identity of the acyl chloride or carboxylic acid which reacts with ethanol to form the local anaesthetic benzocaine. Which will give the fastest reaction?

Benzocaine

6. Use the seven structures **A**-**G** to answer the questions in parts (a) to (f).

CH_3CONH_2
A

CH_3CH_2COCl
B

$CH_3CO_2CH_2CH_3$
C

COOCH_3
D

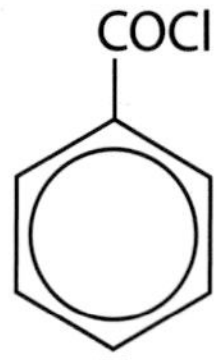

COCl
E

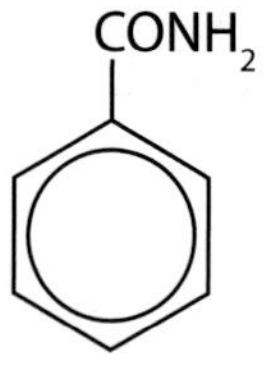

CONH_2
F

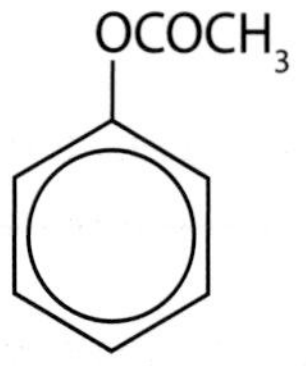

OCOCH_3
G

(a)   Which compounds are esters?

(b)   Which compounds are amides?

(c)   Which compounds are acyl chlorides?

(d)   Which compounds would produce benzoic acid on acidic hydrolysis?

(e)   Which compounds hydrolyse to give ethanoic acid?

(f)   Which compounds are isomeric?

7. Calculate the atom economy for the synthesis of ethanoyl chloride from ethanoic acid using the chlorinating agents, phosphorus pentachloride (PCl_5) and thionyl chloride ($SOCl_2$).

8. How would you prepare a sample of N,N-dimethylethanamide?

9. Describe, using equations, how ethanedioic acid (oxalic acid) could be synthesized from ethene.

10. Draw and label the geometric isomers for butenedioic acid.

11. What were the reactants in a condensation reaction that led to the formation of N-phenyl propanamide and hydrogen chloride gas?

12. Which option shows the correct products in the esterification reaction between a carboxylic acid and an isotopically labelled alcohol?

$$RCOOH + R'^{18}OH \underset{}{\overset{H^+ \text{ cat.}}{\rightleftharpoons}} \text{?}$$

	ester	water
A	$RC(O)OR'$	$H_2^{18}O$
B	$RC(O)^{18}OR'$	H_2O
C	$RC(O)^{18}OR'$	$H_2^{18}O$
D	$RC(^{18}O)OR'$	H_2O

13. Why are acyl chlorides more reactive than their parent carboxylic acids?

14. Explain why amides are all water soluble and crystalline solids at 298K, except methanamide, which is a liquid.

15. Suggest a mechanism for the acid catalysed reaction between ethanoic acid and ethanol.

What evidence is there for this mechanism?

16. Using the spider diagram, which option shows the correct general formulae for the structures **A**, **B**, **C** or **D**?

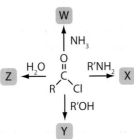

	1° amide	2° amide	Ester	Carboxylic acid
A	X	W	Y	Z
B	W	X	Z	Y
C	X	W	Z	Y
D	W	X	Y	Z

B3.7 (c)
Condensation polymerisation

Condensation polymers are usually formed when two different monomers which both have two functional groups react. When these bifunctional monomers react it is a condensation polymerisation in which a small molecule is eliminated, such as hydrogen chloride or water. Condensation polymers include: polyesters, polyamides, polyethers and polyurethanes. Condensation polymers can be natural (keratin, silk, wool, leather, hair, starch) or synthetic (nylon, polyesters). The different types of condensation polymers can be identified by how the monomers are linked once the polymer is formed, *e.g.* ester, amide or ether links.

Ester Link

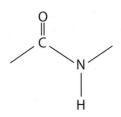

Amide Link

Ether Link

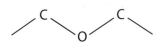

There are lots of examples of condensation polymers and they are growing in importance because they are recyclable and often biodegradable.

Condensation Polymers			
Name	Type	Link	Use
Terylene Polyethylene terephthalate	polyester	ester	Clothing, drinks bottles, sails, fishing lines. Drinks bottles, clothing, video tapes, food trays.
Keratin	polyamide	amide	Wool, hooves, horns, beaks, feathers and hair.
Nylon	polyamide	amide	Carpets, rope, hair combs, stockings, toothbrushes.
Kevlar®	polyamide	amide	Motorcycle helmets, bullet-proof vests, bicycle tyres, racing sails, lightweight skis.
Starch	polyether	ether	Energy store in plants, biodegradable plastics, bio-ethanol, paper making, test for iodine.
Cellulose	polyether	ether	Cell walls in plants, paper and cardboard, cellophane, rayon, dietary fibre.

Polyamides

Polyamides are formed in condensation reactions between carboxylic acids and amines with the elimination of water. Polyamides are also formed in the reaction between acyl chlorides and amines with the elimination of hydrogen chloride. Wallace Carothers was the scientist who discovered how to make the polyamide nylon whilst working for Dupont. Nylon is one of those acronyms that people often seem to know and is derived from the names of two important industrial cities, namely **N**ew **Y**ork and **Lon**don. The different types of nylon are numbered according to the number of carbon atoms in the reactant molecules.

Nylon-6,6

The reaction between 1,6-diaminohexane (H_2N-$(CH_2)_6$-NH_2) and hexanedioic acid leads to the formation of nylon-6,6. The first number in the name of nylon indicates the number of carbon atoms in the dicarboxylic acid monomer and the second number indicates the number of carbon atoms in the diamine monomer. The letter **n** represents a very large number (up to 100,000). For pairs of **n** monomers, **2n** molecules of water will be produced which are eliminated. The new bond that is formed in these condensations is the C-N bond of the amide link. At each end of the polymer chain will be either a carboxylic acid or an amine depending on when the supply of monomers was exhausted in the reaction.

1,6-diaminohexane

hexanedioic acid (adipic acid)

Nylon 6,6

A convenient laboratory method to make nylon-6,6 is to place 20 cm³ of a 5% solution of hexanedioyl chloride in the 'green solvent' lotoxane in a small beaker. Add the aqueous amine first, then the acyl chloride in lotoxane, because lotoxane is less dense than water, and floats on top. Then carefully add 20 cm³ of a 5% aqueous solution of hexanediamine. The two solutions do not mix (immiscible) and will only react where they meet (interface). Using a pair of tweezers it is possible to pull a fibre of nylon from the solution and by carefully wrapping it round a glass rod an impressive length of nylon can be produced.

Nylon 'rope' wrapped around a glass rod

The acidic hydrogen chloride gas eliminated during the condensations can be tested by using moist blue litmus paper which will turn red.

Nylon-6

It is possible to produce the polyamide nylon-6 using a single monomer, caprolactam, which is a cyclic amide (lactam). Caprolactam polymerises to form nylon-6 when heated to 260°C. This is not an example of a condensation polymerisation as no small molecule is eliminated, but it is a polyamide.

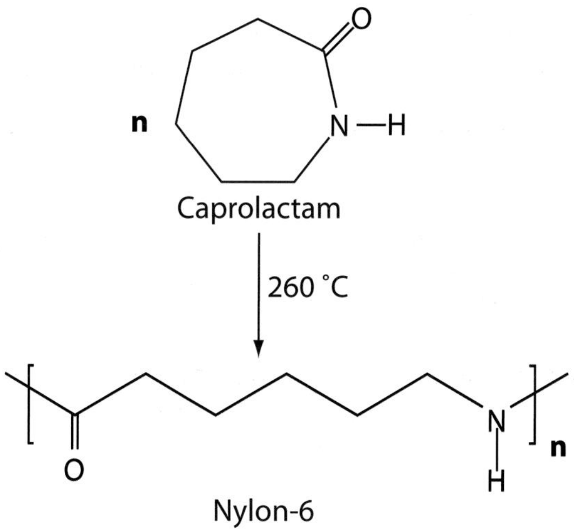

Caprolactam

260 °C

Nylon-6

Kevlar®

Kevlar is a polyamide developed by Stephanie Kwolek whilst working for Dupont and is formed in the reaction between benzene-1,4-dicarboxylic acid ($HO_2CC_6H_4CO_2H$) and benzene-1,4-diamine ($H_2NC_6H_4NH_2$). The aromatic rings provide stiffness to the polymer's structure and allow polymer chains to pack closely giving it its unique properties. These have been exploited by the police and the military in their protective clothing. Kevlar is a particularly useful polymer as it is five times stronger than steel.

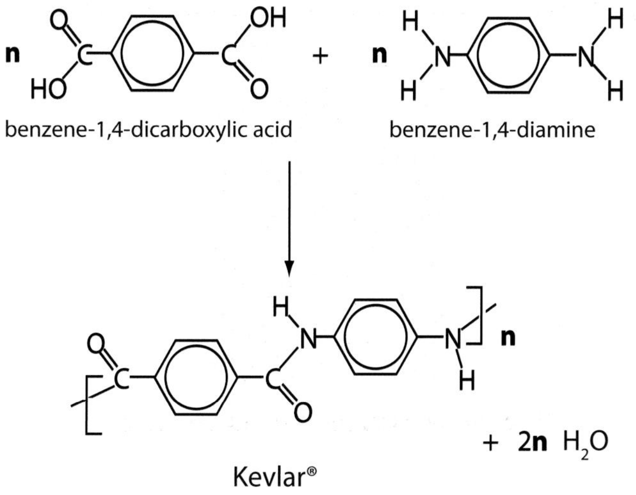

benzene-1,4-dicarboxylic acid   benzene-1,4-diamine

Kevlar®

$+ 2n\ H_2O$

Proteins

Polypeptides and proteins are natural macromolecules that are polyamides which can be described as condensation polymers where the monomers are amino acids. The amine group from one amino acid reacts with the carboxylic acid of another amino acid with elimination of one molecule of water. Polypeptides are made up of 2-50 amino acids, and proteins are built up from more than 50 amino acids. When two amino acids react, a dipeptide is formed. As the dipeptide is bifunctional at either end it can continue to grow into a protein *via* additional condensation reactions.

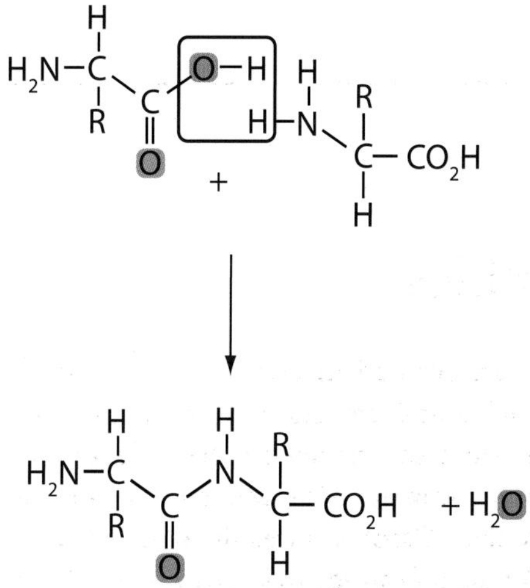

When R = H the amino acid is glycine and when R = CH_3 the amino acid is alanine.

Examples of proteins are enzymes which are biological catalysts vital to the success of reactions in living systems. Biologists often call the amide link in polypeptides and proteins a peptide link. The 1962 Nobel Prize in Chemistry was awarded to Max Perutz and John Kendrew for their work in solving the 3D structures of proteins by x-ray diffraction. The primary, secondary and tertiary structures of proteins are covered elsewhere in biochemistry textbooks.

Polyesters

Polyesters are formed in condensation reactions between carboxylic acids and alcohols with the elimination of water. Polyesters are also formed in the reaction between acyl chlorides and alcohols with the elimination of hydrogen chloride.

339

Terylene

The polyester terylene (Dacron in the USA) is formed in the reaction between benzene-1,4-dicarboxylic acid ($HO_2CC_6H_4CO_2H$), also known as terephthalic acid, and ethane-1,2-diol ($HOCH_2CH_2OH$) with the elimination of water. The polymer has a relative molecular mass of about 15 kDa.

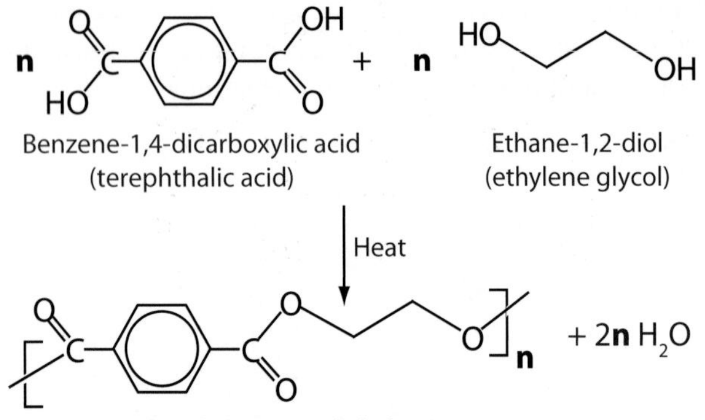

Benzene-1,4-dicarboxylic acid
(terephthalic acid)

Ethane-1,2-diol
(ethylene glycol)

Heat

Poly(ethyleneterephthalate)
Terylene

As a molten polymer, terylene is extruded (squeezed out) through holes to form fibres which can be used for making materials for the manufacture of clothes, car seat covers, sport sweatbands etc. A fibre is a solid material whose length is more than one thousand times longer than its width, whilst possessing the properties of strength and flexibility.

Terylene wrist band

Natural polyester (cutin) water-proofs leaves

Polyethers

Polyethers are formed in condensation reactions between the alcohol groups on sugars with elimination of molecules of water. Examples of natural macromolecules that are polyethers include the carbohydrates cellulose, starch and glycogen. Carbohydrates are compounds containing; carbon, hydrogen and oxygen fitting the general formula $C_xH_{2y}O_y$, e.g. glucose.

Starch

Starch is a condensation polymer built up from α-glucose units. Starch has the formula $(C_6H_{10}O_5)_n$ where n can be as much as 300 giving it a relative formula mass of 486 kDa. Starch is the main carbohydrate energy reserve (fuel) of plants and is found in foods such as cereals, rice and potatoes. The digestion of starch (hydrolysis) in the mouth, stomach and the small intestine leads to the formation of glucose.

$$(C_6H_{10}O_5)_n + n\,H_2O \rightarrow (n+1)\,C_6H_{12}O_6$$
$$\text{starch} \qquad\qquad\qquad \text{glucose}$$

The hydrolysis of starch is believed to go *via* the disaccharide maltose which is made up of two glucose units. Both the sugars maltose and glucose are water soluble and can pass into the blood stream for transport around the body. It is interesting to note the shape the six-membered rings take, which at University is described as a 'chair', is an energy minimised conformation (shape).

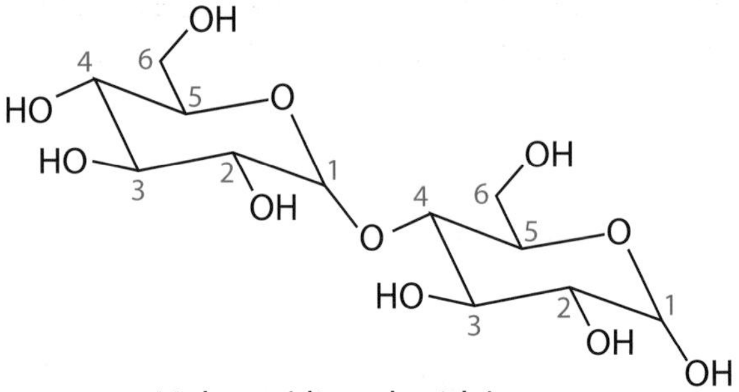

Maltose (disaccharide)

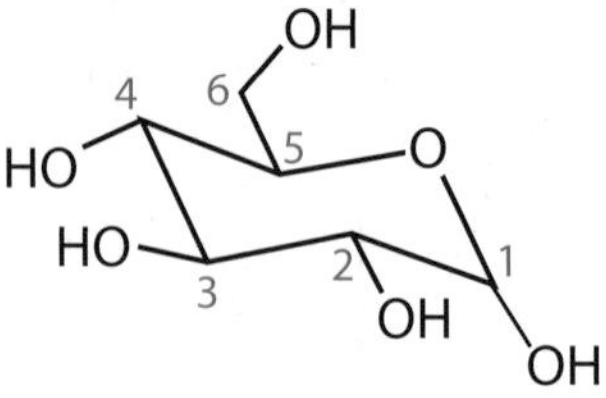

α-D-glucose (monosaccharide)

The test for starch is familiar to biologists - it turns blue-black with iodine solution. The colour is due to the iodine residing within the helix of one portion of the starch molecule. Starch has a complicated structure and is composed of two parts (α-amylose and β-amylose) which are both made up of long chains of α-glucose units. The α-amylose portion is helical in shape and water soluble. A portion of a starch molecule is shown with an unrealistic shape to make it easier to observe the α(1→4) ether linkages.

Starch molecule

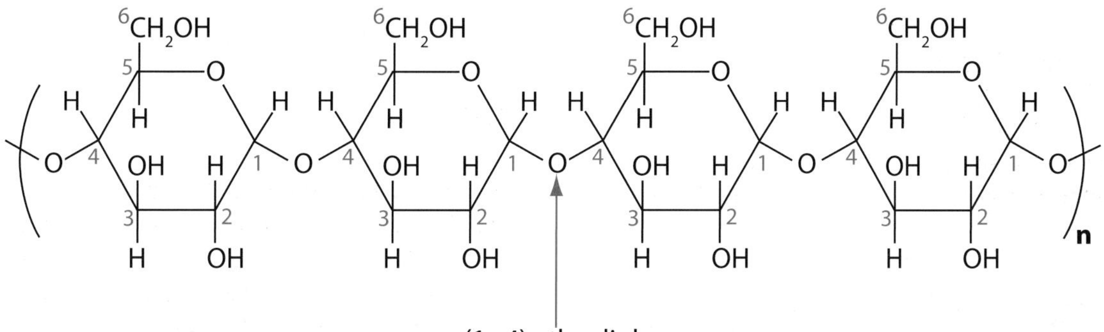

α(1→4) ether links

The β-amylose portion of starch (amylopectin) is made up of long chains of glucose with other glucose units joined at points along the chain. This branching results in a complex three dimensional network. This part of starch is insoluble in water.

In the laboratory, starch can be hydrolysed by boiling it with dilute hydrochloric acid for about five minutes followed by neutralisation of the excess acid with an aqueous alkali (NaOH). The product, glucose, will give a negative test with iodine and a positive test (silver mirror) with Tollens' reagent (A3.4c).

Cellulose

Glucose molecules can link up in a slightly different way with the loss (elimination) of water to make the condensation polymer cellulose, which is a three dimensional network of glucose chains. Cellulose is built up from β-glucose units and is the main component in cell walls, which are needed to support plants. Cellulose does not give a blue-black colour with iodine, unlike starch, which does. A portion of a cellulose molecule is shown with an unrealistic shape to make it easier to observe the β(1→4) ether linkages.

Cellulose molecule

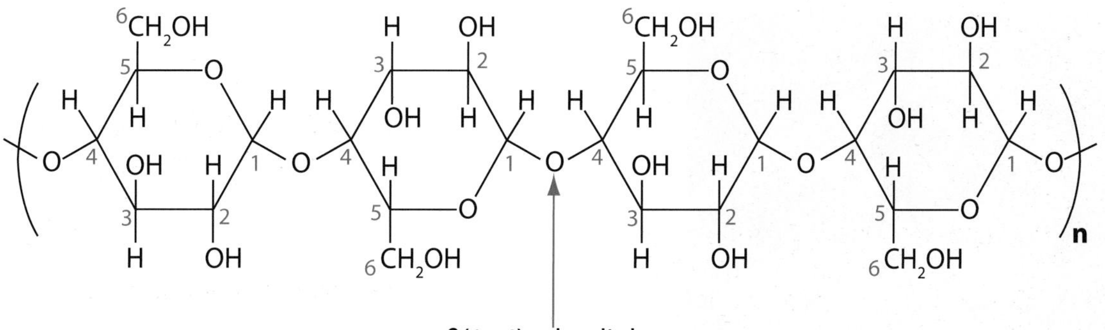

β(1→4) ether links

Cotton is almost pure cellulose and is associated with mills in my home county of Lancashire and the tragedy of a different kind of slavery in the New World (USA).

Cotton grows on bushes

A major component of wood is cellulose. Wood also contains about 30% lignin which is a phenyl propene polymer. Cellulose is believed to be the world's most abundant natural carbohydrate. It is the hydrogen bonds in cellulose that give cellulose its great strength. In cellulose, there are hydrogen bonds between hydrogen and oxygen atoms in adjacent glucose units. The hydrogen bonds occur within layers, *e.g.* **OH** on carbon 3 and the **O** in the pyranose ring, and also between CH$_2$**OH** attached to carbon 6 and **OH** on carbon 2. The hydrogen bonds that occur between layers are between CH$_2$**OH** attached to carbon 6 and the **OH** on carbon 3.

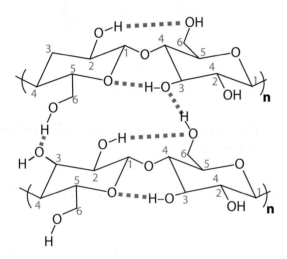

Hydrogen bonding in cellulose

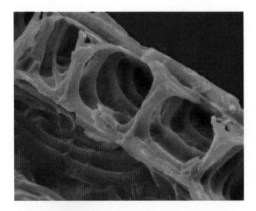

A cell wall is made from cellulose

Cellulose is not readily hydrolysed and cannot be digested by humans. Only grazing animals such as sheep, cows, rabbits and deer have a digestive system equipped to use cellulose as a food. For over one hundred years cellulose ethanoate has been the material on which to record films (movies) by reacting cellulose with ethanoic anhydride.

Questions 19.4

1. What technique can be used to identify the hydrolysis products of proteins?

2. What are the hydrolysis products for the following condensation polymers: polysaccharides, proteins and fats?

3. Which option correctly describes a condensation polymerisation?

	Monomer A	Monomer B	Polymer	Small molecule eliminated
A	diol	diacyl chloride	polyester	water
B	diol	diol	polyester	water
C	diamine	diol	polyamide	water
D	diamine	dioic acid	polyamide	water

4. Which option is not an example of a condensation polymer?

   A   Terylene

   B   Nylon-6

   C   Polystyrene

   D   Nylon-6,6

5. Which named reaction is the opposite of a condensation polymerisation?

   A   Elimination.

   B   Decomposition.

   C   Hydrolysis.

   D   Hydrogenolysis.

6. When the monomers **1a** and **1b** react:

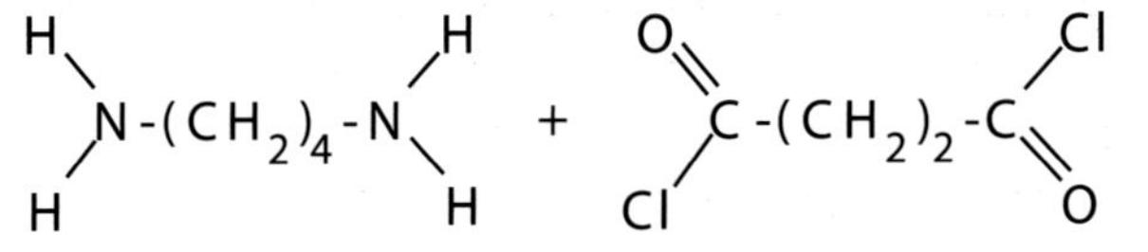

1a   **1b**

(a) Name the monomers.

(b) Name the type of polymerisation.

(c) What is the small molecule eliminated and how can it be tested?

(d) What type of polymer is formed?

(e) Draw one repeat unit for this polymer and name it.

7.

(a) What are the products when sucrose is hydrolysed by dilute HCl (aq)?

(b) What type of molecule is sucrose?

(c) What is the molecular formula of sucrose?

(d) Write an equation for the formation of sucrose.

(e) What type of link connects the two sugars in sucrose?

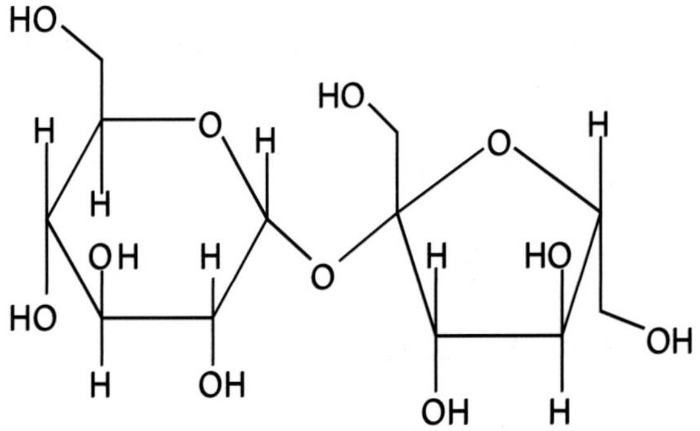

Sucrose

8. From the following structures identify the functional group present in the condensation polymers, polycarbonate and the biodegradable polylactic acid.

(a) Condensation polymer: Polycarbonate (bullet proof windows)

Skeletal formula:

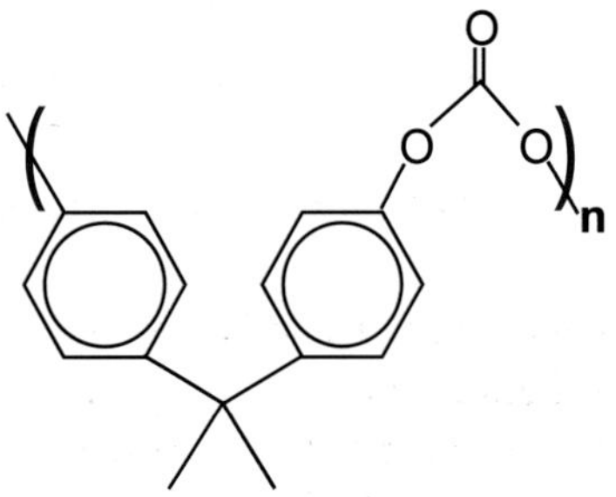

(b) Condensation polymer: Polylactic acid (sutures and bags)

Skeletal formula:

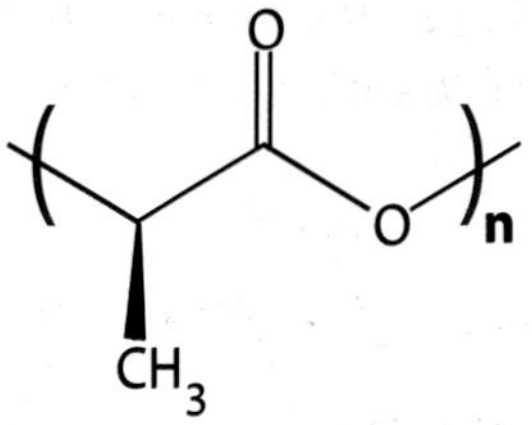

9. Why can starch and cellulose be considered to be ethers and acetals?

B3.7 (d) Reduction with metallic hydrides (moving down a level)

Two metallic hydrides which have been used in reductions of organic compounds are sodium borohydride ($NaBH_4$) and lithium aluminium hydride ($LiAlH_4$). The oxidation number (A2.1e) of hydrogen in these hydrides is -1. Lithium aluminium hydride is the more powerful of these two reducing agents. Sodium borohydride will reduce aldehydes and ketones to 1° and 2° alcohols respectively, and lithium aluminium hydride will also reduce esters to alcohols, and amides and nitriles to amines. Reduction with metallic hydrides of all these functional groups are examples of moving down a functional group level.

Reduction of carboxylic acids

The opposite reaction to oxidation is reduction. Therefore, since primary alcohols oxidise into carboxylic acids, it follows that the reduction of carboxylic acids gives primary alcohols. The reduction of carboxylic acids with lithium aluminium hydride is selective and any C=C bonds present in the rest of the molecule are not reduced by this metallic hydride. In equations, the reducing agent is represented by [H] which symbolises the hydrogen obtained from the reducing agent. Carboxylic acids are reduced by heating with lithium aluminium hydride under reflux in an anhydrous solvent such as ethoxyethane, according to this general equation:

$$RCOOH \, (l) + 4 \, [H] \rightarrow RCH_2OH \, (l) + H_2O \, (l)$$

Carboxylic acid	Product of LiAlH$_4$ reduction
Ethanoic acid	Ethanol
Propanoic acid	Propan-1-ol
Butanoic acid	Butan-1-ol
Benzoic acid	Benzyl alcohol

The reduction of a carboxylic acid with $LiAlH_4$ moves it from FGL 3 (carboxylic acid) to FGL 1 (1° alcohol).

Reduction of nitriles

Nitriles are reduced by lithium aluminium hydride (and also hydrogen gas) to give primary amines. This reaction is a particularly useful way to prepare amines. Nitriles are reduced by heating with lithium aluminium hydride under reflux in an anhydrous solvent such as ethoxyethane, according to this general equation:

$$RCN + 4 \, [H] \rightarrow RCH_2NH_2$$

Nitriles are also reduced by sodium in ethanol. In both cases these reductions are moving down from FGL 3 (nitrile) to FGL 1 (1° amine). Ethanenitrile is reduced by lithium aluminium hydride into ethylamine.

$$CH_3C{\equiv}N + 4 \, [H] \rightarrow CH_3CH_2NH_2$$

Reduction of esters

Esters are reduced by lithium aluminium hydride *via* aldehydes to give primary alcohols (RCH_2OH). The desired reduction product (alcohol) is the one where you keep the R group adjacent to the carbonyl group in the final product. This is a reaction which is not often met as esters find many uses as flavourings and perfumes owing to their pleasant smells and high volatility.

$$RCO_2R' + 4 \, [H] \rightarrow RCH_2OH + R'OH$$

The metallic hydride reduction of esters is another example of moving down from FGL 3 (ester) to FGL 1 (primary alcohol). The reduction of esters goes *via* the sequence;

$$RCO_2R' \rightarrow RCHO^-(OR') \rightarrow RCHO \rightarrow RCH_2OH.$$

Reduction of amides

Amides are reduced by lithium aluminium hydride to give amines. The type of amine (1°, 2° or 3°) depends on the degree of N-substitution on the amide. Amides are reduced by heating with lithium aluminium hydride under reflux in an anhydrous solvent such as ethoxyethane, according to this general equation:

$$RCONH_2 + 4 \, [H] \rightarrow RCH_2NH_2 + H_2O$$

Propanamide ($CH_3CH_2CONH_2$) is reduced by $LiAlH_4$ to give propylamine ($CH_3CH_2CH_2NH_2$). The reduction of amides is believed to go *via* an imine ($R_2C{=}NHR$) intermediate. The metallic hydride reduction of amides is another example of moving down from FGL 3 (amide) to FGL 1 (amine).

Secondary (2°) and tertiary (3°) amines are prepared in the laboratory by the reduction of N-substituted amides. N-methylethanamide is reduced by LiAlH$_4$ into methylethylamine.

N-methylethanamide   N-methylethylamine

Questions 19.5

1. Which option shows the correct products when excess quantities of the reducing agents H$_2$, Ni and LiAlH$_4$ are reacted separately with samples of fumaric acid?

Fumaric acid

	LiAlH$_4$ / anhydrous Et$_2$O	H$_2$ (nickel catalyst)
A	CH$_2$(COOH)CH$_2$(COOH)	CH$_2$(COOH)CH$_2$(COOH)
B	CH(CH$_2$OH)CH(CH$_2$OH)	CH(CH$_2$OH)CH(CH$_2$OH)
C	CH(CH$_2$OH)CH(CH$_2$OH)	CH$_2$(COOH)CH$_2$(COOH)
D	CH$_2$(COOH)CH$_2$(COOH)	CH(CH$_2$OH)CH(CH$_2$OH)

2. The ester methylethanoate can be converted into an amide by its reaction with concentrated aqueous ammonia solution. Explain why this reaction is **not** a reduction.

20

Carbon Dioxide Level

Contents

The members of the Carbon Dioxide level (FGL 4) have four bonds to electronegative elements from a carbon atom. There are few members of this Functional Group Level (FGL) which include; carbon dioxide (CO_2), isocyanates (RN=C=O), substituted ureas ($R_2N(C=O)NR_2$), carbonates (RO(C=O)OR) and carbamates (RNH(C=O)OR) which are also known as urethanes. The Carbon Dioxide level is the highest functional group level and movement can only take place within the FGL and down a FGL.

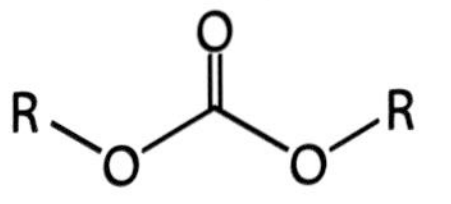

Carbonate 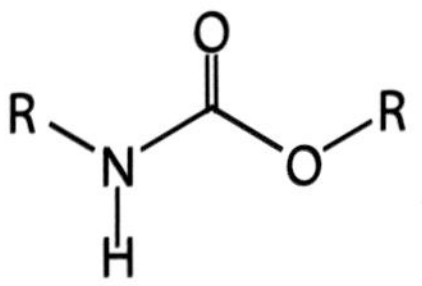   Carbamate (urethanes) 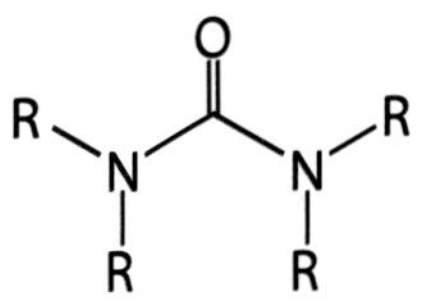   Substituted urea 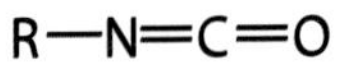   Isocyanate

There are some important molecules in the Carbon Dioxide level including four of the five nucleotide bases incorporated in the structures of DNA (**d**eoxyribo**n**ucleic **a**cid) and RNA (**r**ibo**n**ucleic **a**cid). The level four carbons are to be found in the six membered rings of the bases, at a carbon in the middle of two nitrogen atoms which is also attached to an amino group (NH_2) or a carbonyl group (C=O).

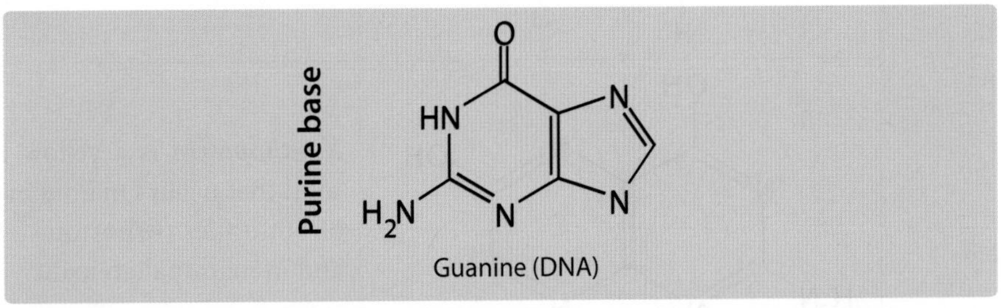

Purine base

Guanine (DNA)

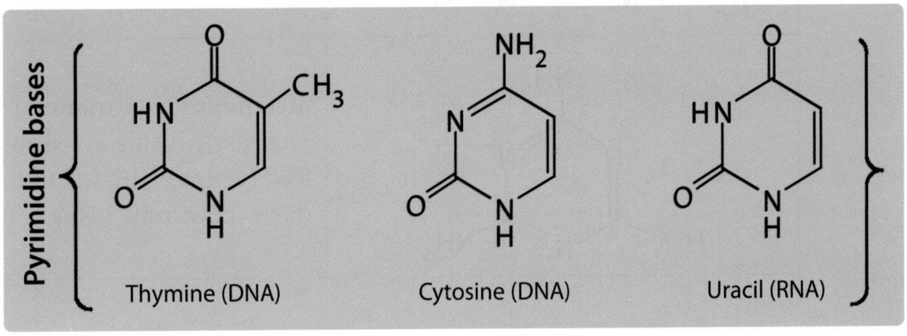

Pyrimidine bases

Thymine (DNA)   Cytosine (DNA)   Uracil (RNA)

347

There are some interesting molecules with a carbon atom at FGL = 4 in their structure, *e.g.*

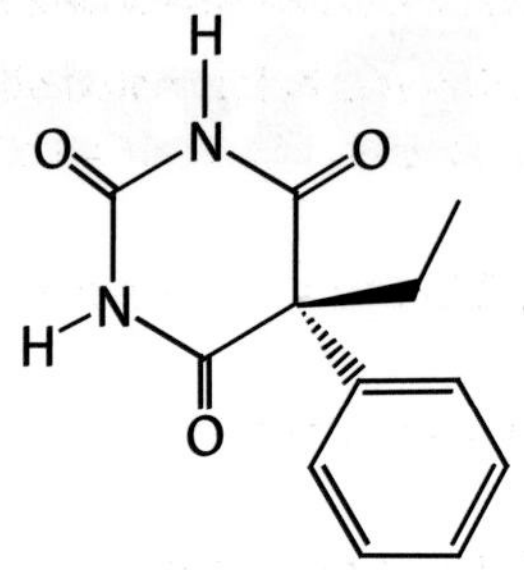	***Phenobarbitone*** is an anticonvulsant used to treat epileptic seizures.
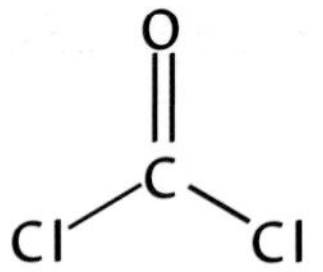	***Phosgene*** is a toxic gas that smells of freshly mown hay and has been used as a chemical weapon (WWI) and more recently as a monomer used to make polyesters (polycarbonates) for bullet-proof windows.
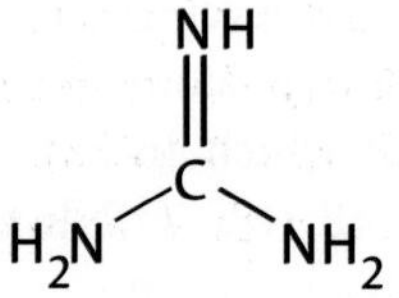	***Guanidine*** is found as a product of protein metabolism in urine and has been used to make plastics and a solid fuel for model aircraft and rockets.
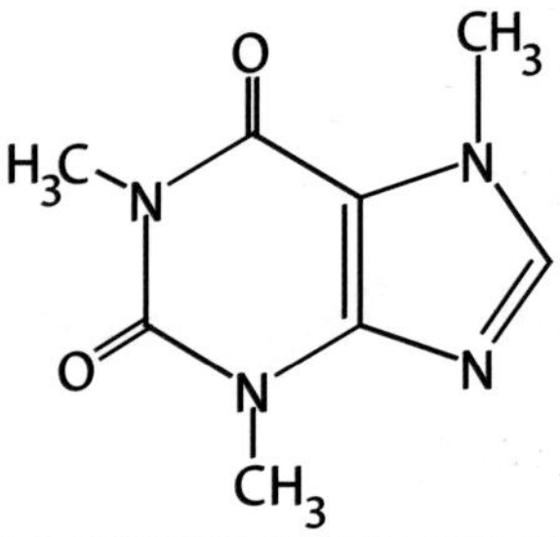	***Caffeine*** is found in cocoa beans where it acts as a natural insecticide, but in humans it can raise levels of alertness as it is a central nervous system stimulant.
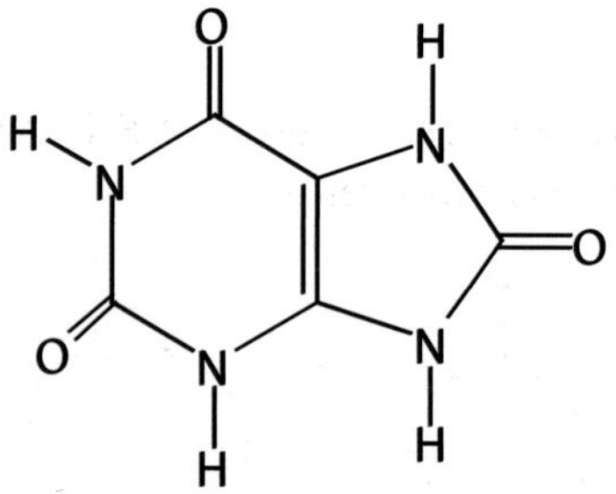	***Uric acid*** is the final breakdown product of purine metabolism and it is excreted in urine. In humans, about half of the blood's anti-oxidative capacity is believed to be due to uric acid. High levels of uric acid have been associated with gout, a painful arthritic condition that causes inflammation of the joints.
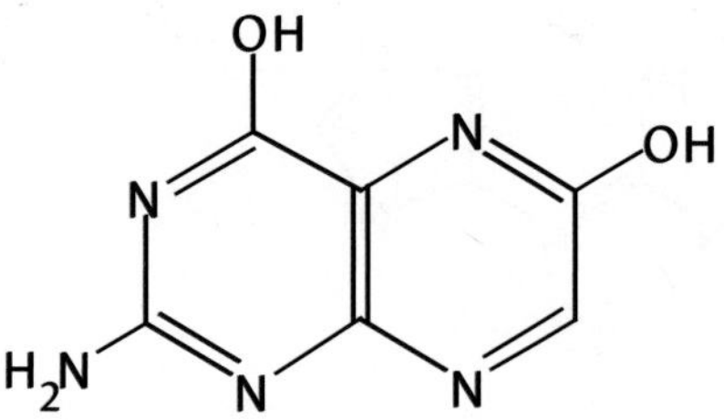	***Xanthopterin*** is a yellow crystalline solid that occurs mainly in the wings of butterflies (brimstone -see photo) and in mammalian urine. 
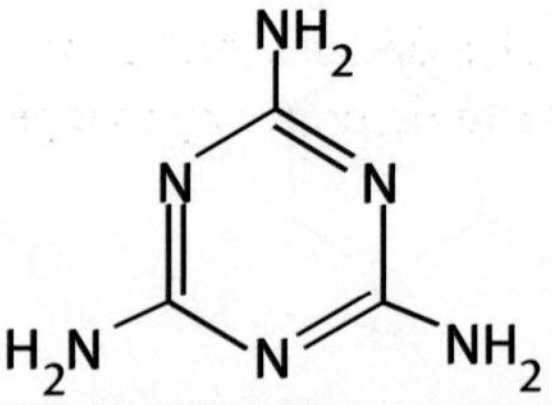	***Melamine*** (2,4,6-triamino-1,3,5-triazine) is a rich source of nitrogen which has led to its use as an additive in animal feed (China). This led to the tragic deaths of babies in 2008 due to cows milk being contaminated with melamine.

Barbituric acid (malonyl urea) is a cyclic ureide which can be synthesized by refluxing the diethyl malonic ester with urea in an ethanolic solution containing the base sodium ethoxide.

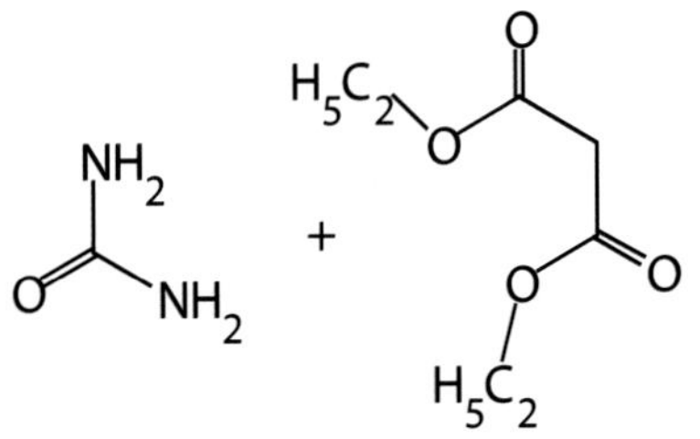

Urea   Malonic ester

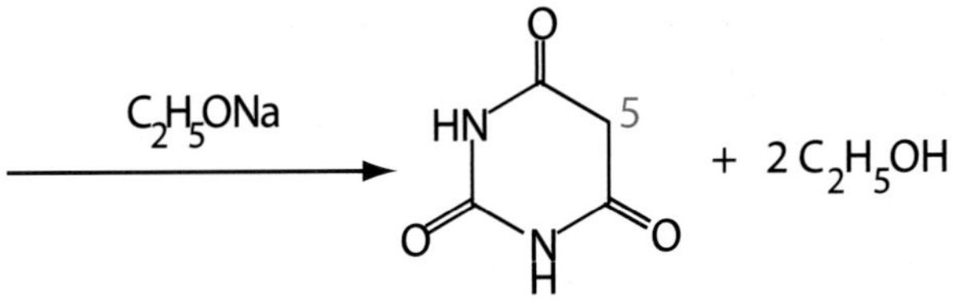

75%

Barbituric acid

Barbituric acids substituted at carbon atom numbered 5 have been shown to have useful medical properties, *e.g.* barbitone (5,5-diethylbarbituric acid) a hypnotic, and phenobarbitone (5-ethyl-5-phenylbarbituric acid) a sedative and anticonvulsant.

Parabanic acid (oxylurea) a cyclic ureide, which is an analogue of barbituric acid, can be prepared by the condensation of urea with oxalic acid (ethanedioic acid) in the presence of phosphoryl chloride ($POCl_3$).

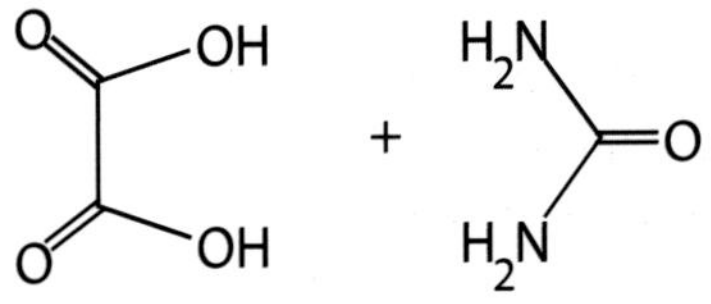

Oxalic acid   Urea

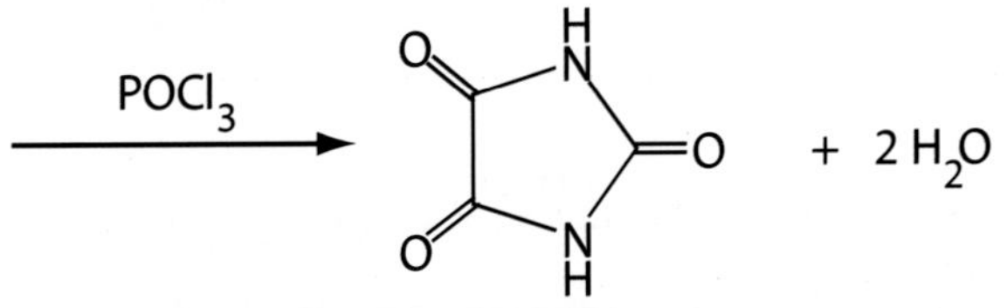

Parabanic acid

Within the Carbon Dioxide level there are two possible FGL changes. The FGL changes are moving within the level and moving down a level. Reactions within FGL 4 include: condensation reactions with urea and hydrolysis of members to give carbon dioxide. A useful reaction for moving down a level is the reaction of Grignard reagents with carbon dioxide for the preparation of carboxylic acids. Moving up a level is not possible because carbon is tetravalent (A3.1a) and forms stable compounds with four covalent bonds in order to fill its 2p sub-shells.

Questions 20.1

1. Which option is a halogenated alkane with one carbon atom in the Carbon Dioxide level?

    A   1,1,2,2-tetrachloroethane

    B   tetrachloromethane

    C   1,2,3,4-tetrachlorobutane

    D   dichlorofluoromethane

2. Chlorofluorocarbons (CFCs) were once used as aerosol propellants and refrigerants until it was discovered that they damage the protective ozone layer found in the stratosphere (10-50km). Which option does **not** contain a CFC with a carbon in the Carbon Dioxide level?

    A CF_2Cl_2

    B CF_3Cl

    C $CFCl_3$

    D $CHFCl_2$

3. Identify any carbon atoms at FGL 4 in the orange-red pigment erythropterin.

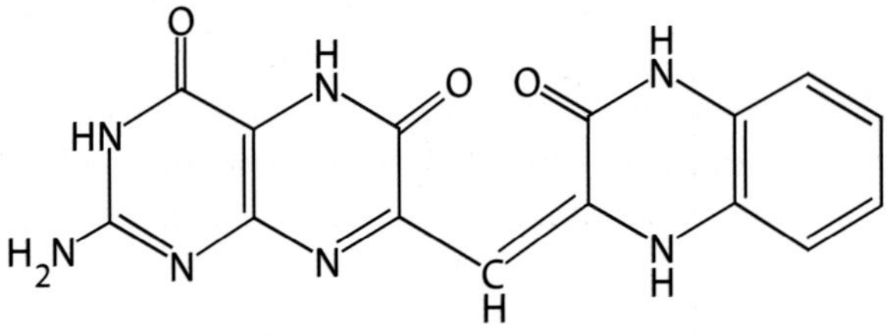

4. Write an equation for the equilibrium reaction between carbon dioxide and water to form carbonic acid (H_2CO_3) and describe any changes in FGL.

5. Identify the FGL of the carbon atoms in melamine $(C_3H_6N_6)$ which forms the condensation polymer with formaldehyde (HCHO) known as **formica**.

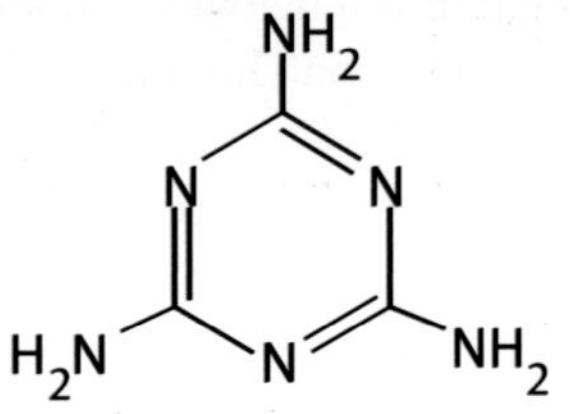

6. Assign the FGL of all the carbon atoms in the carbamate insecticide **methomyl** and give its molecular formula.

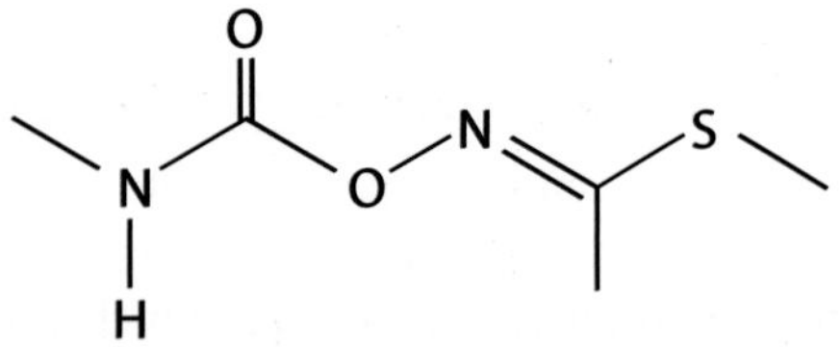

B3.8

(a) Hydrolysis (moving within the Carbon Dioxide level)

With all functional group levels, including the Carbon Dioxide level, hydrolysis leads to formation of the functional group that gives its name to this level. This means that hydrolysis of any member within FGL 4 leads to carbon dioxide and movement is within the level.

The body uses the carbons of amino acids as an energy source but it is unable to extract energy from amino acids' nitrogen atoms, which need to be removed. The simplest waste product from amino acid breakdown would be ammonia but this is too toxic to cells. Instead the body makes urea which is a stable nitrogen rich waste product which is excreted in adults *via* urine at a rate of ~30g per day.

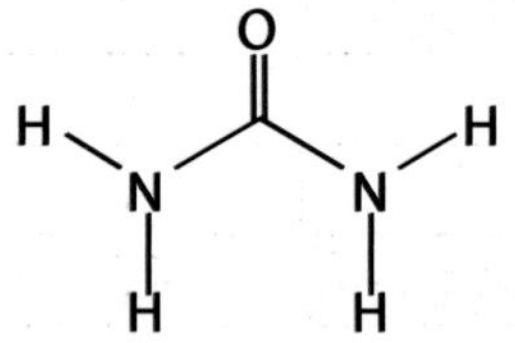

Urea

Example 20.1

Urea can be hydrolysed by boiling with aqueous solutions of acids or alkalis.

$$CO(NH_2)_2 + H_2O \rightarrow CO_2 + 2\,NH_3$$

Example 20.2

Chloropicrin is a highly toxic colourless liquid that was used in WW1 to make soldiers' eyes water (lachrymator) so they would remove their gas masks. It has since found use as a soil fumigant as it kills nematodes (round worms).

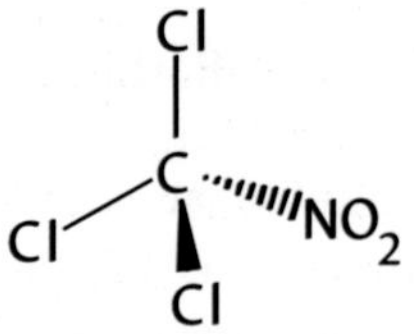

Chloropicrin

Chloropicrin is hydrolysed to give carbon dioxide, hydrogen chloride and nitrous acid.

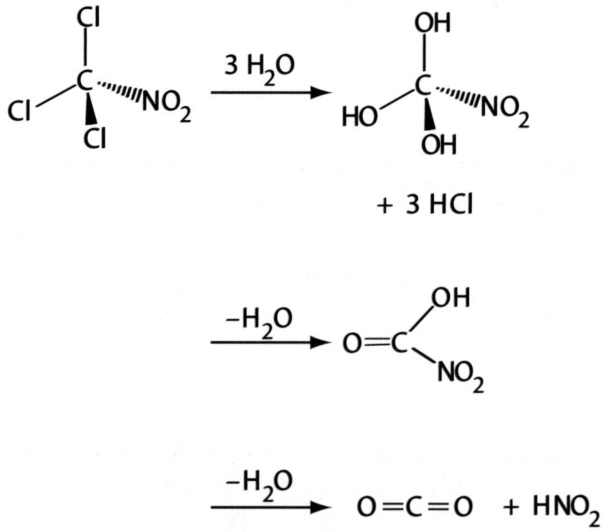

+ 3 HCl

Example 20.3

Phosgene reacts with water to release hydrogen chloride gas and carbon dioxide gas.

$$COCl_2 + H_2O \rightarrow 2HCl + CO_2$$

The hydrolysis of phosgene can be thought of as going *via* the intermediate, carbonic acid.

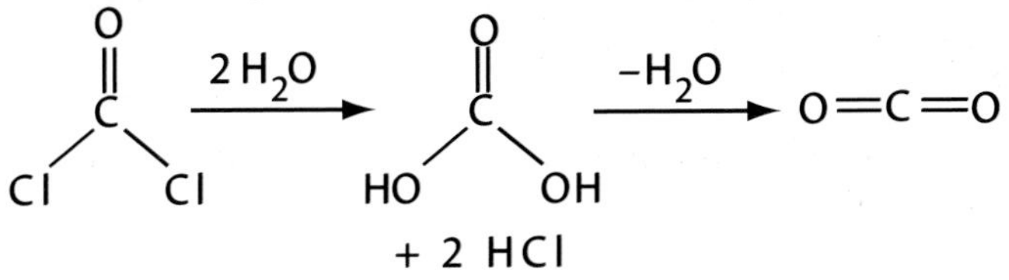

$$\overset{O}{\underset{Cl}{\overset{\|}{C}}}\overset{}{\underset{Cl}{}} \xrightarrow{2\,H_2O} \overset{O}{\underset{HO}{\overset{\|}{C}}}\overset{}{\underset{OH}{}} \xrightarrow{-H_2O} O{=}C{=}O$$

$$+\ 2\ HCl$$

Name	Formula	CO_2	HCl	NH_3
Guanidine	$\underset{H_2N}{}\overset{NH}{\underset{}{\overset{\|}{C}}}\underset{NH_2}{}$			

Example 20.4

Hydrolysis of isocyanates gives primary amines and carbon dioxide.

$$RN{=}C{=}O + H_2O \rightarrow RNH_2 + CO_2$$

The carbon dioxide produced can be made use of as a blowing agent to produce polyurethane foams which are made by the condensation of diisocyanates with diamines or diisocyanates with diols. The resulting polyurethane foam is rigid when it sets and is many times larger than the original volume of reactants. These foams have been used to insulate cavity walls in the gaps between the bricks and breeze blocks in modern houses.

Questions 20.2

1. What is produced when urea is hydrolysed and how could these products be tested for qualitatively?

2. Complete the table by placing a tick in the box that corresponds to their hydrolysis products.

Name	Formula	CO_2	HCl	NH_3
Phosgene	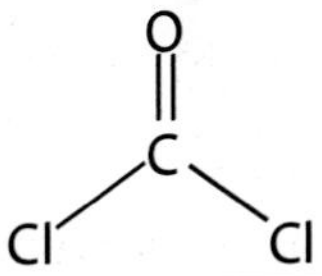 			
Urea	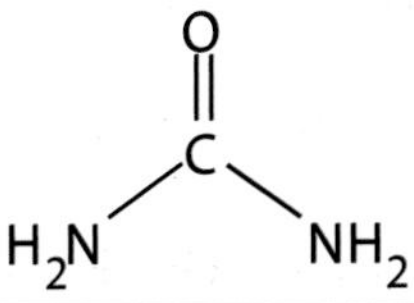			

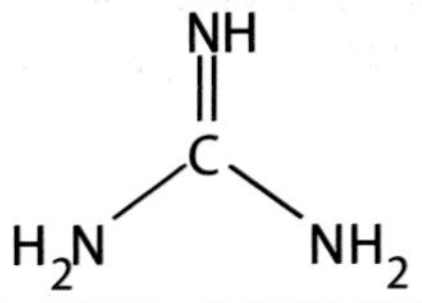

3. Draw the structures for the hydrolysis products for the carbamate shown below.

Carbamate

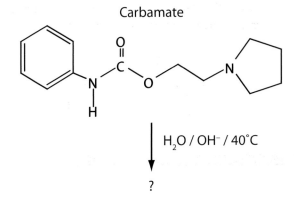

H_2O / OH^- / 40°C

?

4. Write a balanced equation for the alkaline hydrolysis of thiourea $S{=}C(NH_2)_2$.

5. Which option gives the best description for the muscle relaxant chlorphenesin, which is used to treat muscle pain and spasms?

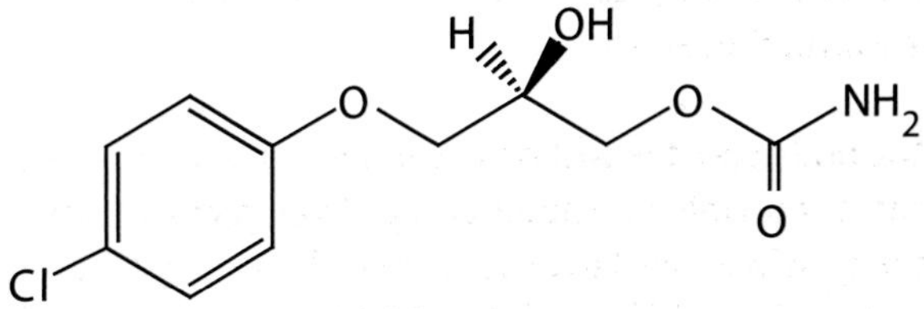

Chlorphenesin

	Ester	Carbamate	Alcohol
A		√	2°
B	√	√	1°
C	√	√	2°
D		√	1°

6. Which option does **not** hydrolyse to form carbon dioxide?

	Name	Formula
A	Methyl N-phenylcarbamate	$C_6H_5NHCO_2CH_3$
B	Carbamic acid	$HO(CO)NH_2$
C	Phenyl isocyanate	C_6H_5NCO
D	Phenylalanine	$C_6H_5CH_2CH(NH_2)CO_2H$

7. A very good reagent for adding ester groups is diethylcarbonate.

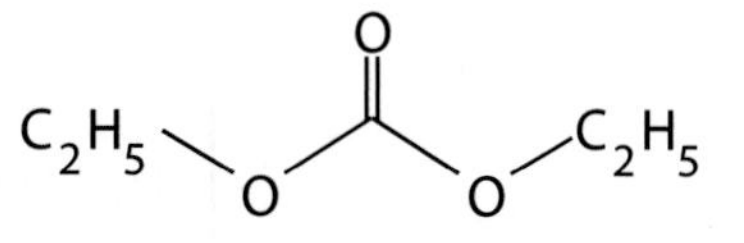

Diethylcarbonate

Explain why its reactions must be carried out in anhydrous solvents.

B3.8 (b) Carboxylic acids from Grignard reagents

The Grignard reagent (RMgX) is prepared *in situ* (A3.4d) by reacting a halogenoalkane with magnesium turnings in an anhydrous inert solvent such as diethyl ether $(C_2H_5)_2O$. The reaction is often carried out by adding two equivalents of the Grignard reagent to solid carbon dioxide (dry ice). Alternatively dry carbon dioxide can be generated from marble chips and dilute acid (in Kipp's apparatus) and blown into an ethereal solution of the Grignard reagent.

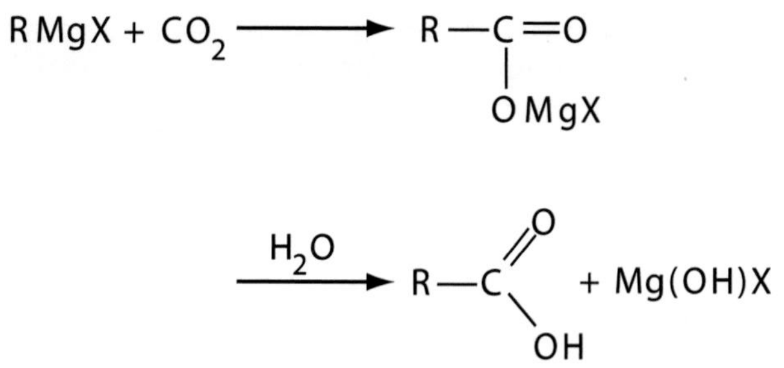

The reaction between carbon dioxide and Grignard reagents is a very important method of increasing a carbon chain by one carbon. Since radio-labelled dry ice is commercially available $(^{14}CO_2)$ this method is a good way to introduce isotopically labelled carboxylic acid groups into a molecule for mechanistic studies. The Grignard reagent (R^-) reacts *via* a nucleophilic addition reaction and adds to the weaker π-bond of one of the C=O in carbon dioxide in much the same way that it would react with a carbonyl in an aldehyde or ketone (A3.4d).

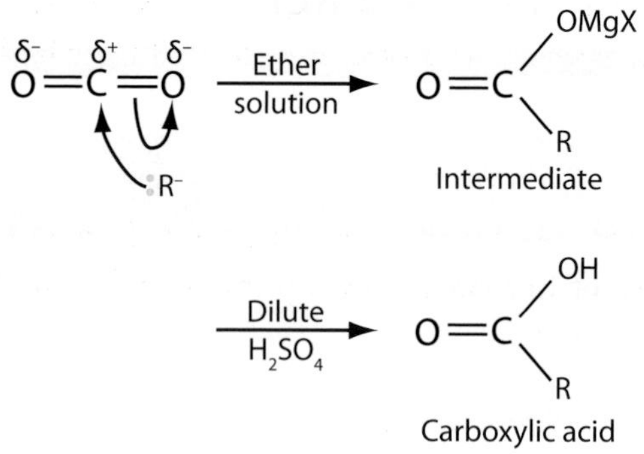

Synthesis of carboxylic acids (FGL 3) from Grignard reagents and carbon dioxide (FGL 4) is an example of moving down a Level. Preparing carboxylic acids by this method effectively converts a halogenoalkane (RX) into a carboxylic acid (RCO_2H) with an additional carbon on the chain. In essence, what is happening is that the halogen group is replaced by a carboxylic acid group.

Example 20.5

Propanoic acid can be prepared by reacting carbon dioxide with ethylmagnesium bromide followed by acid hydrolysis.

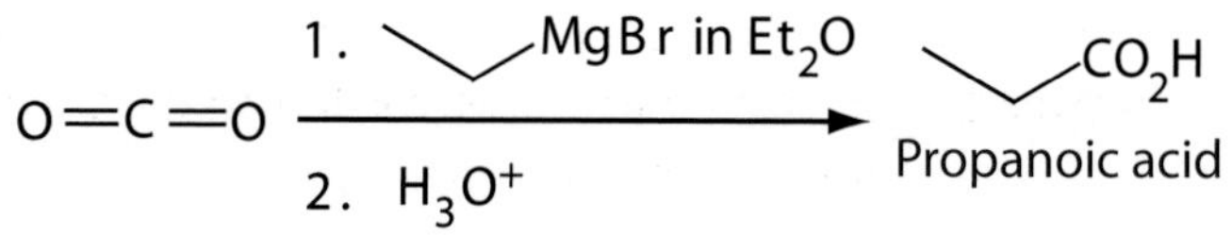

Example 20.6

2-methylbutanoic acid can be prepared in 78% yield by reacting carbon dioxide with 2-butylmagnesium chloride followed by acid hydrolysis.

2-methylbutanoic acid

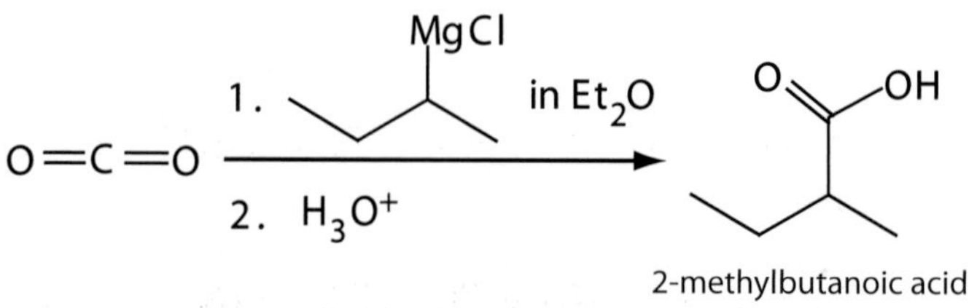

Questions 20.3

1. What organic product is formed when a stream of carbon dioxide gas is bubbled into phenylmagnesium bromide for 15 minutes and then slowly acidified with concentrated hydrochloric acid whilst cooling?

2. Give the names and structural formulae of the iodoalkanes that react with Mg and CO_2 to form the following carboxylic acids.

    (a)   Ethanoic acid.

    (b)   Butanoic acid.

    (c)   Heptanoic acid.

    (d)   Benzoic acid.

3. Name three halogenoalkanes which can be used to make propanoic acid on reaction with carbon dioxide. Describe how this synthesis of propanoic acid is achieved.

4. Draw the structure of an amino acid with a carbon atom at the Carbon Dioxide level. Identify the group where it is most likely to accept a proton.

5. Describe any changes in FGL when urea reacts with phosphorous pentachloride (PCl_5) to form carbodiimide.

$$H_2N \overset{\displaystyle O}{\underset{\displaystyle }{||}} NH_2 \xrightarrow{\ PCl_5\ } H-N=C=N-H$$

      Urea   Carbodiimide

6. What type of reaction is it when nitrous acid reacts with urea?

$$CO(NH_2)_2 + 2\ HNO_2 \rightarrow CO_2 + 3H_2O + 2N_2$$

21 | Mechanisms

Contents

What is a mechanism?

A mechanism is an organic chemist's way of explaining stepwise how the reactants are transformed into the products. Mechanisms are best illustrated with diagrams that make use of displayed formulae with curly arrows used to show the movement of electron pairs. The 'arrow head' shows you where the electron pair ends up after it has moved. The direction of the curly arrow is important and, in order to get it right, it is helpful to think of the arrow hitting the positive target in reactions. There are many different types of mechanism but we will learn the principles by looking in detail at three types of mechanisms: nucleophilic substitution, nucleophilic addition and electrophilic addition.

Mechanisms

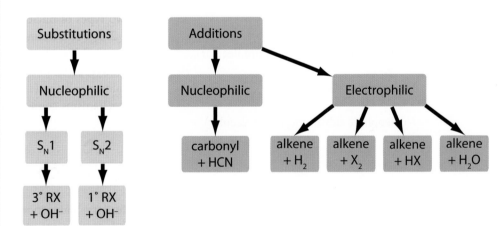

Questions 21.1

1. Which option gives the correct type of mechanism when hydrogen halides react with alkenes?

A   Nucleophilic addition.

B   Electrophilic substitution.

C   Electrophilic addition.

D   Nucleophilic substitution.

2. Which type of mechanism is it when nucleophiles react with 1° halogenoalkanes?

A   Nucleophilic addition.

B   Nucleophilic substitution (unimolecular).

C   Electrophilic addition.

D   Nucleophilic substitution (bimolecular).

3. Which type of mechanism is it when nucleophiles react with 3° halogenoalkanes?

A   Nucleophilic addition.

B   Nucleophilic substitution (unimolecular).

C   Electrophilic addition.

D   Nucleophilic substitution (bimolecular).

4. Which type of reaction is the opposite of an elimination reaction?

A   Displacement.

B   Substitution.

C   Addition.

D   Polymerisation.

5. What is the change in Functional Group Level in the following reaction?

$$(CH_3)_3CBr + OH^- \rightarrow (CH_3)_3COH + Br^-$$

A   0

B   +1

C   2

D   −1

B3.9 (a)
S_N1 and S_N2 mechanisms

A **substitution reaction** is when one atom or group of atoms in a reactant is exchanged (substituted) for another atom or group of atoms.

$$A–B + C–D \rightarrow A–D + B–C$$

In the above reaction, group B is replaced by group D. When the incoming group can donate a lone pair, *i.e.* it is a nucleophile, the reaction is described as a **nucleophilic substitution reaction**. A good example of a nucleophilic substitution reaction is when a halogenoalkane (RX) reacts with a hydroxide ion (OH⁻) to form an alcohol (ROH) and halide ion (X⁻) in a hydrolysis reaction (A3.3a). There are two types of nucleophilic substitutions and they are S_N1 and S_N2. S_N1 is a unimolecular reaction and S_N2 is a bimolecular reaction. The mechanism which predominates (S_N1 *vs.* S_N2) in the hydrolysis of a halogenoalkane depends on the type of the halogenoalkane (1°, 2° or 3°). Evidence for the two types of mechanisms comes from kinetic studies.

S_N1 mechanism

Tertiary halogenoalkanes react with nucleophiles *via* an S_N1 mechanism. A simple example is the reaction between 2-bromo-2-methylpropane and an aqueous solution of hydroxide. When balancing these equations, a useful tip is to remember to balance atoms as well as charges.

$$(CH_3)_3CBr + OH^- \rightarrow (CH_3)_3COH + Br^-$$

There are two steps in an S_N1 mechanism. In the first step, which is highly endothermic, heterolytic fission of the C-Br bond leads to the formation of a carbocation. A carbocation is a reactive species (intermediate) which possesses a positive charge on a carbon atom. The carbocation intermediate is trigonal planar. This ionization of the tertiary halogenoalkane is aided by using a polar solvent such as water. This first step is the slow step which is called the **rate determining step** (B1.6g). In the fast second step, which is fast, the nucleophile (OH^-) combines with the carbocation forming the alcohol product. Kinetics experiments show that when the reaction undergoes an S_N1 mechanism, the rate = k [RX]. This means that the rate is independent of the concentration of the nucleophile, e.g. [OH^-].

S_N1 mechanism

When the nucleophile is water, the reaction, in addition to hydrolysis, can also be described as a **solvolysis**,

e.g. $(CH_3)_3CBr + H_2O \rightarrow (CH_3)_3COH + HBr$

S_N2 mechanism

Primary halogenoalkanes react with nucleophiles *via* an S_N2 mechanism. A simple example is the reaction between bromomethane and an aqueous solution of hydroxide.

$$CH_3Br + OH^- \rightarrow CH_3OH + Br^-$$

There is one reaction step in an S_N2 mechanism. This is possible because a bond forms between the nucleophile and a carbon atom at the same time that the bond breaks between the same carbon atom and the halogen. The transition state is trigonal bipyramidal and is not isolated. In the proposed transition state, the C-Br bond is half broken as the C-OH bond is half formed.

Kinetics experiments show that when the reaction undergoes an S_N2 mechanism the rate = k [RX] [OH^-]. In other words the rate is dependent on the concentration of both the halogenoalkane and the nucleophile. The approach of the nucleophile along the central axis of the carbon-halogen atoms is the one requiring minimum energy.

When the halogenoalkane is secondary (2°) both S_N1 and S_N2 mechanisms are taking place. The result is the same product but it is obtained by a slightly different transition state and/or intermediate. The reaction of 1°, 2° and 3° halogenoalkanes with aqueous hydroxide can all be described as hydrolysis reactions as the alcohol products are at the same level as the halogenoalkanes (FGL = 1).

Kinetics experiments

In a series of kinetics experiments (B1.6f) it is possible to determine the rate equation by finding out how the concentration of the different reactants affects the reaction's rate. By plotting graphs of rate against concentration (B1.6i) for the individual reactants, you can determine the power to which their concentration is raised (order) in the rate equation. Then from this rate equation it is possible to suggest a mechanism for a reaction (B1.6h). In the reaction between a primary (1°) halogenoalkane and hydroxide, the rate is first order with respect to both reactants. Therefore, this reaction is biomolecular (S_N2) as two species come together in the transition state (B3.9b). In the reaction between a tertiary (3°) halogenoalkane and hydroxide the rate is first order with respect to the halogenoalkane and zero order with respect to the hydroxide (nucleophile). Therefore this reaction is unimolecular (S_N1) as one species, the carbocation, is involved in the rate determining step. This is also true if the nucleophile is water or an alcohol.

S_N2 mechanism

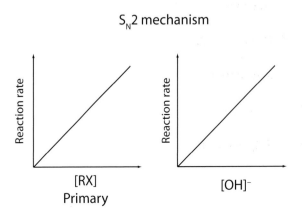

357

S_N1 mechanism

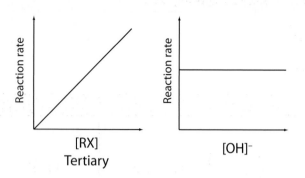

[RX]
Tertiary

[OH]⁻

A species whose concentration appears in the experimentally determined rate equation must be involved in the reaction up to and including the rate determining step (slowest step). Any species involved after the rate determining step does not appear in the rate equation. The two types of nucleophilic reactions illustrate these points.

Mechanism	Rate equation	Overall order	RX
S_N1	rate = k [RX]	1	3°
S_N2	rate = k [RX] [OH⁻]	2	1°

Question 21.2

1. Which option correctly shows the type of mechanism when a secondary halogenoalkane undergoes hydrolysis with aqueous hydroxide ions?

    A S_N1 or S_N2

    B S_N2

    C S_N1 and S_N2

    D S_N1

B3.9 (b) Transition states and intermediates

The important stages of a mechanism and the relative energies of the species involved can be shown using an **energy profile diagram** (A1.3g). In energy profile diagrams, the *x*-axis gives the extent of the reaction (reaction coordinate) and the *y*-axis is energy.

S_N2 mechanism

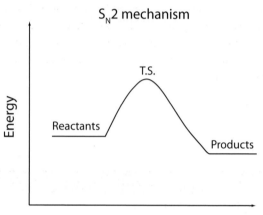

S_N1 mechanism

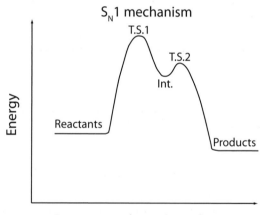

Between the reactants and products are substances with fleeting existences known as transition states (T.S.) which are found at the *maxima* on energy profile diagrams. The difference in energy between the transition state and reactants is the **activation energy** (A1.3f). There are also **intermediates** (Int.) formed after the reactants and before the products. Intermediates are molecules which are found at the *minima* (energy wells) on energy profile diagrams. Some reaction intermediates have been isolated. More often than not, intermediates only exist for brief periods of time because they are very reactive species. It is important to realise that intermediates are not the same as transition states. The upper diagram would look like this for S_N2 reactions which have a transition state but no intermediate. The lower diagram would look like this for S_N1 reactions with two transition states and an intermediate, *e.g.* carbocation. At university, the **Hammond**

postulate is taught which suggests that, in highly exothermic reactions, the transition state will more closely resemble the reactants and in highly endothermic reactions the transition state will more closely resemble the products.

During chemical reactions, as the atoms rearrange, there will inevitably be changes in geometry and bond angles for both the fleeting transition states and the reactive intermediates. This can be illustrated using the extensively studied S_N1 and S_N2 reactions. In the reaction between tertiary 2-bromo-2-methylpropane and the nucleophile OH⁻ (aq), the changes in bond angles and geometry are tabulated. Where there are three different groups attached to the intermediate carbocation there is **racemisation** (B3.9c) and the result is an **equimolar mixture** of the two enantiomers (B3.12d).

S_N1

Reactant:

3D structure	Geometry	Bond angle(s)
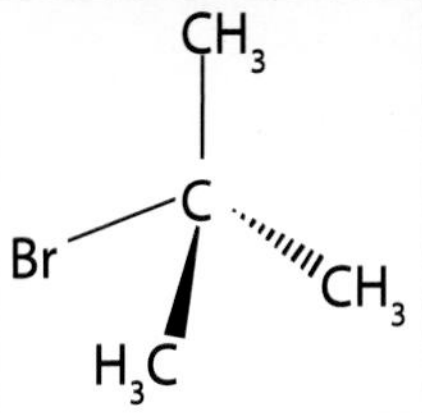	tetrahedral	109.5°

Intermediate:

3D structure	Geometry	Bond angle(s)
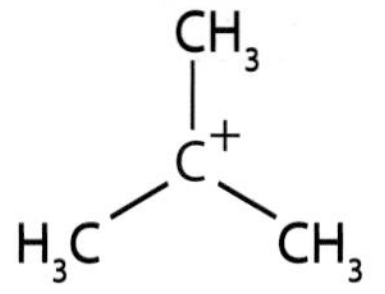	trigonal planar	120°

Product:

3D structure	Geometry	Bond angle(s)
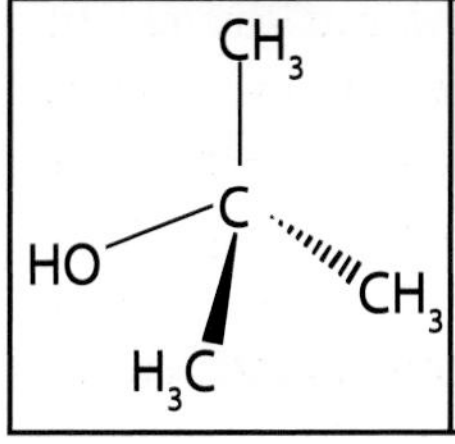	tetrahedral	109.5°

In the reaction between primary bromomethane and the nucleophile OH⁻ (aq) the changes are tabulated. In this particular S_N2 reaction there is only one product. In more complex reactions, where there is a measurable inversion of configuration (B3.12b), there is still only one product (B3.9c). In the transition state the Br and OH groups are at 90° to the

CH₃ portion of the molecule. The CH₃ portion is planar with the bond angle HCH being 120°.

S_N2

Reactant:

3D structure	Geometry	Bond angle(s)
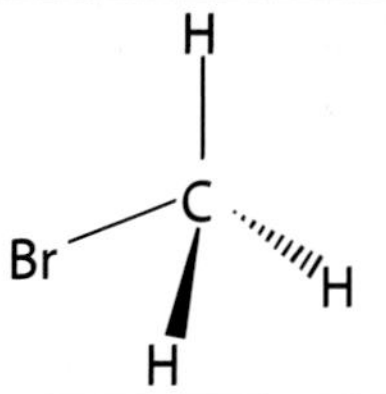	tetrahedral	109.5°

Transition state:

3D structure	Geometry	Bond angle(s)
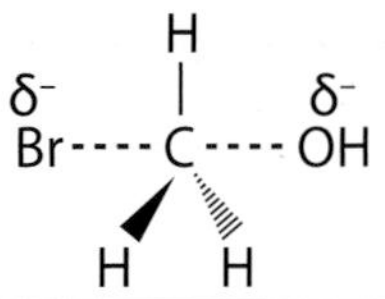	trigonal bipyramidal	120° & 90°

Product:

3D structure	Geometry	Bond angle(s)
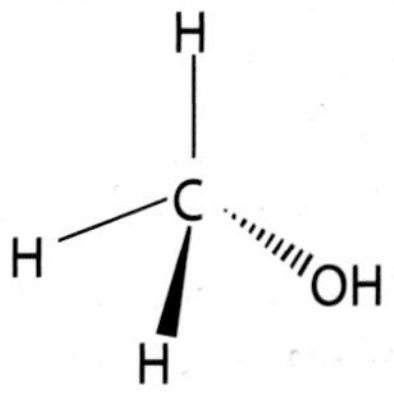	tetrahedral	109.5°

Questions 21.3

1. Which option best describes what happens when 2-bromo-2-methylpropane reacts with aqueous sodium hydroxide?

	Mechanism	Result
A	S_N1	Racemisation
B	S_N2	Inversion of configuration
C	S_N2	Racemisation
D	S_N1	Inversion of configuration

2. Which option best describes what happens when 1-bromopropane reacts with aqueous sodium hydroxide?

	Mechanism	Result
A	S_N1	Racemisation
B	S_N2	Inversion of configuration
C	S_N2	Racemisation
D	S_N1	Inversion of configuration

B3.9 (c) Inversion of configuration (S_N2) and racemisation (S_N1)

Configuration changes

When optically pure halogenoalkanes undergo S_N2 mechanisms with nucleophiles, there is inversion of configuration at the chiral carbon. This is illustrated by looking at the two versions of 2-bromobutane, which are assigned the prefix (R) from the Latin for right (*rectus*) and (S) from the Latin for left (*sinister*). The detailed rules concerning these prefixes are dealt with elsewhere (B3.12a). It is not possible to predict the direction of rotation (of plane polarised light) of the optical isomers (B3.12b) from the prefix. So despite the change in configuration, plane polarised light might still rotate in the same direction.

Inversion of configuration

(R) reactant → (S) product

(S) reactant → (R) product

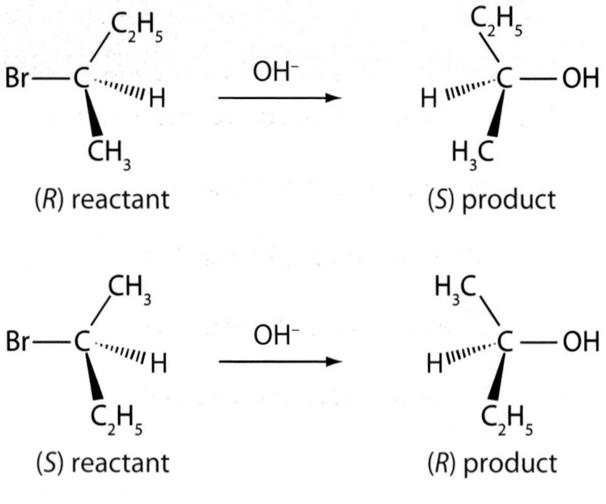

At university, this inversion of configuration is called **Walden Inversion**. In practice, this means that the configuration at the stereogenic (chiral) centre is inverted because the nucleophile approaches the chiral carbon from the opposite side to the leaving group (X⁻ = halide).

Evidence for inversion of configuration comes from kinetic studies using radioactive isotopes. Optically active (−)2-iodooctane was reacted with radio labelled sodium iodide. The radioactive isotope of iodine used is iodine-128. What do you think would be observed if the reaction was monitored using a polarimeter?

Isotopically labelled iodide ion

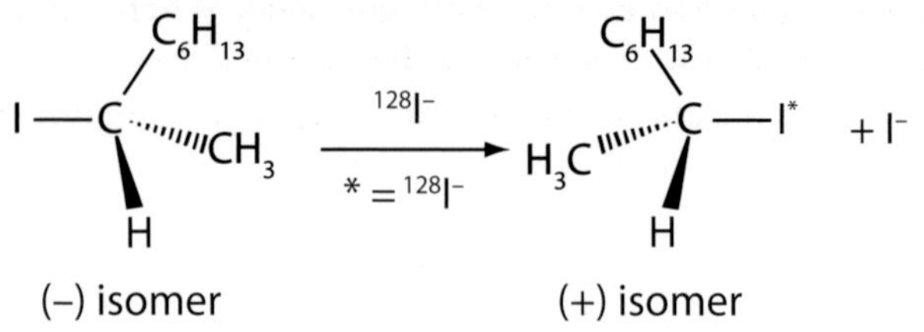

(−) isomer → (+) isomer

Questions 21.4

1. Which option best describes the organic product(s) when (R)-2-chlorobutane reacts with aqueous sodium hydroxide.

   A   (S)-butan-1-ol.

   B   (R)-butan-2-ol.

   C   (S)-butan-2-ol.

   D   (R)-butan-1-ol.

2. Draw the transition state in the reaction between the nucleophilic iodide-128 and (-)2-iodoctane.

   As the experiment proceeds, how can the reaction be monitored? How will the rates of inversion and displacement compare?

Racemisation

A **racemic mixture**, also called a **racemate**, contains equimolar amounts of a pair of enantiomers. When optically pure tertiary (3°) halogenoalkanes undergo S_N1 mechanisms with nucleophiles, there is racemisation at the chiral carbon. This happens because there is a planar carbocation intermediate which can be attacked evenly from either side by the nucleophile.

3-bromo-3-methylhexane reacts with aqueous hydroxide to form a racemic mixture of ($\pm$)3-methylhexan-3-ol. The mechanism shows that it is equally likely for the hydroxide nucleophile to attack the planar intermediate from either side.

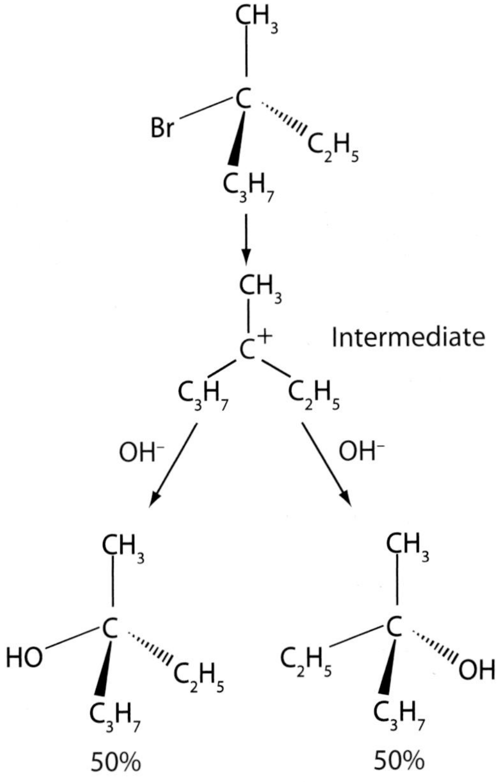

Intermediate

50% 50%

Racemic mixture

Forensic scientists make use of aspartic acid racemisation to age an adult body (cadaver). Racemisation of naturally occurring L-aspartic acid $(HO_2CCH(NH_2)CH_2CO_2H)$ happens in the dentine inside the teeth after death. The age can be estimated to within three years from the D:L ratio.

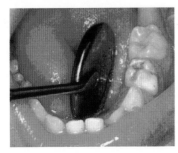

Using racemisation for aging purposes.

The amino acid isoleucine $(HO_2CCH(NH_2)CH(CH_3)CH_2CH_3)$ racemises more slowly than aspartic acid and has been used to date materials from 5×10^3 to 2×10^6 years.

The problem of thalidomide's racemisation at body temperature (37°C) and blood pH (7.4) is now well documented and has been found to occur at a rate of 0.3 h^{-1}. In some animals (humans) the S-enantiomer has been found to be teratogenic (causing birth defects) whilst the R-enantiomer is an effective sedative.

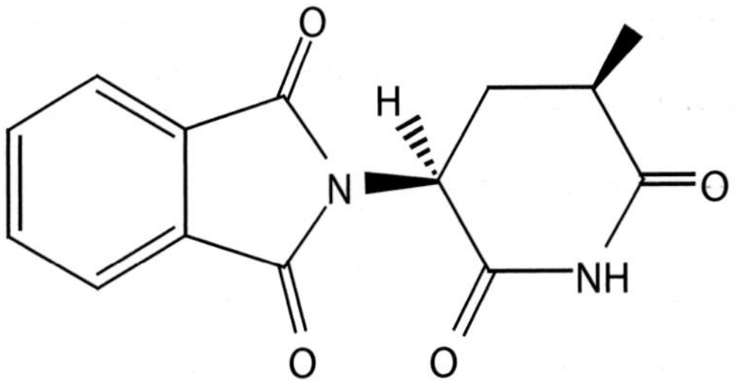

(−)-S-thalidomide

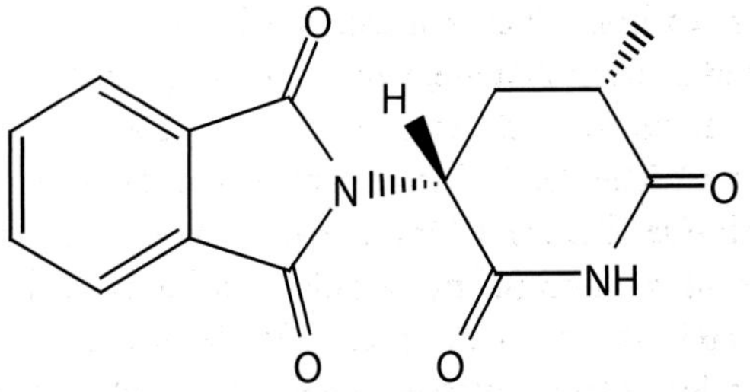

(+)-R-thalidomide

Questions 21.5

1. Which equimolar mixture is a racemic mixture?

    A   (S)-butan-1-ol & (S)-butan-2-ol

    B   (R)-butan-2-ol & (S)-butan-1-ol

    C   (S)-butan-1-ol & (R)-butan-2-ol

    D   (R)-butan-2-ol & (S)-butan-2-ol

2. What is meant by a racemic mixture and how do the components of this mixture differ from one another?

B3.9 (d) Effect of type of halogenoalkanes and C-X bond strength on mechanisms

The carbon-halogen bond strength is an important factor which affects the rate of hydrolysis of halogenoalkanes (A3.3a). The order of bond enthalpy is; C-F > C-Cl > C-Br > C-I.

Carbon-halogen	C-F	C-Cl	C-Br	C-I
Bond enthalpy kJ mol^{-1}	485	338	285	213

The carbon-halogen bond strength does not affect the type of nucleophilic substitution mechanism (B3.9a) but it does affect the reaction rate. The weaker the C-X bond the faster the rate of substitution. This makes iodide the best leaving group. This bond strength is a far more important consideration than the relative size of C-X polarities which is often a point of confusion for inexperienced students of chemistry. Fluoroalkanes are extremely unreactive, which is part of the problem of the very long half-lives of CFCs (chlorofluorocarbons) in the atmosphere.

Bromoalkanes are most often used in the laboratory simply because the iodoalkanes are expensive and the chloroalkanes are too slow in their reactions. The relative rates of hydrolysis of halogenoalkanes can be studied by dissolving the halogenoalkane in ethanol and adding an aqueous solution of silver nitrate. The formation of the silver halide (AgX) can be monitored using a colorimeter. This makes an ideal experiment for datalogging. The equation for this reaction is essentially; $RX + H_2O + Ag^+ \rightarrow ROH + H^+ + AgX$.

The type of halogenoalkane can be classified as 1° RCH_2X, 2° $(R)_2CHX$ or 3° $(R)_3CX$ and this does affect the type of nucleophilic substitution mechanism. Primary halogenoalkanes have one R group (hydrogen, alkyl or aryl), secondary halogenoalkanes have two R groups (alkyl or aryl) and tertiary halogenoalkanes have three R groups (alkyl or aryl).

The S_N1 mechanism is fastest with 3° halogenoalkanes and the S_N2 mechanism is fastest with 1° halogenoalkanes. The more crowded 3° halogenoalkanes have a higher activation energy for the transition state (B3.9b) because the carbon where the halogen is attached is **sterically hindered**. This factor coupled with the positive inductive effect of the R groups is why 3° halogenoalkanes undergo the S_N1 mechanism. It is possible for both S_N1 and S_N2 mechanisms to be taking place with different molecules in the same reaction mixture. This is what happens when the halogenoalkane is 2°. It has been found that both mechanisms are favoured by a good leaving group (I$^-$). Not surprisingly the S_N1 mechanism which leads to the formation of a carbocation intermediate (B3.9b) is strongly favoured by use of an ionising solvent (water and methanoic acid).

Questions 21.6

1. Give the structural formulae of the products or reactants for each of the following reactions;

    i. $CH_3CH_2Br + NaCN \rightarrow I + II$

    ii. $CH_3CH_2Br + (CH_3CH_2)_3N \rightarrow III$

    iii. $IV + V \rightarrow CH_3OH + Br^-$

    iv. $VI + VII \rightarrow$
            $CH_3CH_2NHCH_2CH_3 + (CH_3CH_2)_2NH_2^+ Br^-$

    v. $(CH_3)_3CBr + OH^- \rightarrow VIII + IX$

2. Which option gives the correct order for the halides as leaving groups in the nucleophilic substitution of halogenoalkanes?

    A $I_2 > Br_2 > Cl_2 > F_2$

    B $I^- < Br^- < Cl^- < F^-$

    C $I^- > Br^- > Cl^- > F^-$

    D $I^- > Cl^- > Br^- > F^-$

3. Which option shows an alkyl halide which reacts with hydroxide *via* S_N1 & S_N2 mechanisms?

    A $(CH_3)_3Cl$

    B $CH_3CH_2CH_2Br$

    C CH_3Br

    D $(CH_3)_2CHCl$

4. Complete the table for the reactions of bromoethane with different nucleophiles

Name of nucleophile	Formula of nucleophile	Products with bromoethane
water		
	OH⁻	
cyanide		
	NH₃	

5. Which option gives the fastest rate of reaction and an S_N1 mechanism?

A $(CH_3)_3Br$

B $(CH_3)_2CHBr$

C $CH_3CH_2CH_2I$

D $(CH_3)_3Cl$

B3.9 (e) Electrophilic addition mechanism

Alkenes behave as Lewis bases (electron pair donors) because of the π bond with its electron rich areas above and below their carbon-carbon double bonds (C=C). Alkenes react with Lewis acids (electron pair acceptors) such as all the hydrogen halides (HF, HCl, HBr, HI). The reaction of hydrogen halides with symmetrical alkenes (ethene, but-2-ene, cyclohexene) leads to one product (halogenoalkane). This is because both carbon atoms of the C=C have the same reactivity with the electrophilic end of the hydrogen halide and addition of H to either end of C=C results in the same product. The usual method for preparing halogenoalkanes is from alkanes (free radical substitution) or alcohols (nucleophilic substitution).

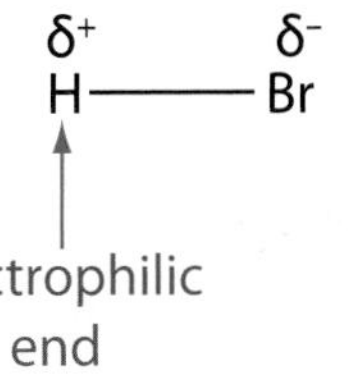

$$\overset{\delta^+}{H}\rule{2cm}{0.4pt}\overset{\delta^-}{Br}$$

Electrophilic end

The reaction of hydrogen halides with unsymmetrical (asymmetric) alkenes can lead to two products which are isomeric halogenoalkanes. The conditions of the reaction determine which product is formed as the major product. An empirical rule based entirely on observations was developed by Vladimir Markovnikov (B3.9f) to predict the likely outcome of the addition of hydrogen halides to alkenes.

Mechanism (Electrophilic Addition)

To illustrate the electrophilic addition (Markovnikov addition) of a hydrogen halide to an unsymmetrical alkene, let us consider the reaction between 2-methylpropene and hydrogen chloride. This reaction takes place in two steps.

Step 1: C=C double bond reacts with the H atom in HCl to give the more stable 3° carbocation.

Step 2: Carbocation combines with the chloride ion to produce 2-chloro-2-methylpropane.

Overall Equation:

$$(CH_3)_2C=CH_2 + HCl \rightarrow (CH_3)_2CCl-CH_3$$

Mechanism:

The electrophile is the polar molecule HCl. As chlorine is more E_{neg} than hydrogen it is the H atom of HCl which is electrophilic ($^{\delta+}$). Note that the movement of a pair of electrons in a mechanism is shown by a curly arrow. Step 1 is the slow (rate determining) step and step 2 is the fast step.

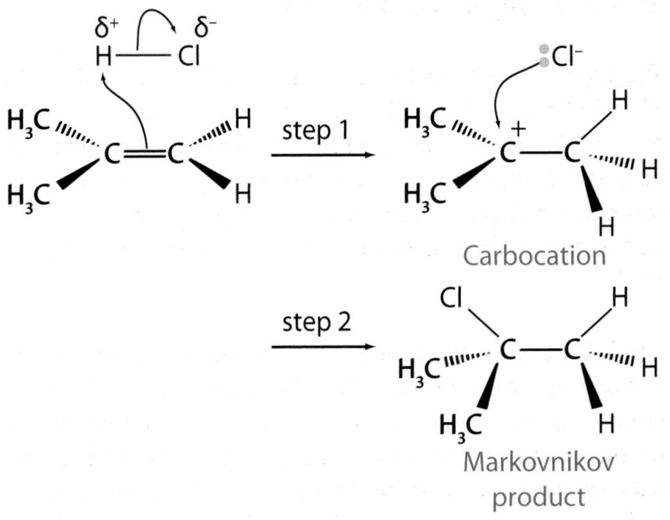

Questions 21.7

1. The geometric isomers *cis*-pent-2-ene and *trans*-pent-2-ene react with hydrogen bromide to produce identical mixtures of 2-bromopentane and 3-bromopentane. Suggest, with reasons, which halogenoalkane is the most favoured product and explain why both isomers produce the same products.

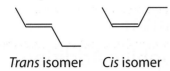

Trans isomer   *Cis* isomer

2. C_3H_6 reacts with hydrogen iodide to produce a mixture of isomers with molecular formula C_3H_7I. What type of reaction is this? Name the two isomers and state which one will form in the greatest amount.

3. Alkynes like alkenes are unsaturated and will react with hydrogen halides to give fully saturated compounds. The difference is that alkynes will react with two molecules of hydrogen halide. The addition of the first hydrogen halide is fast whereas the addition of the second hydrogen halide is much slower. Give the products for the addition of HBr to ethyne (C_2H_2) given that Markovnikov's rule is followed.

$$HC \equiv CH + 2\,HBr \longrightarrow \ ?$$

4. How does the rate of addition of HX (hydrogen halide) to an alkene vary with acid strength?

5. Which is the correct order for the rate of reaction of hydrogen halides adding to ethene?

   A   HF < HCl < HBr > HI

   B   HI < HBr < HCl < HF

   C   HI > HBr < HCl < HF

   D   HF < HCl < HBr < HI

B3.9 (f) Stability of carbocation (Markovnikov's Rule)

Markovnikov's Rule

Markovnikov's Rule predicts the:

- most likely product when HX (hydrogen halide) adds to an alkene.

- H atom attaches to the carbon of the C=C with the greatest number of H atoms.

- X atom attaches to the carbon of the C=C with the smallest number of H atoms.

Markovnikov additions

The electrophilic addition of hydrogen bromide (HBr) to a symmetrical alkene such as ethene leads to only one product. It does not matter which carbon of the C=C double bond the halogen adds to, the same product (bromoethane) will result.

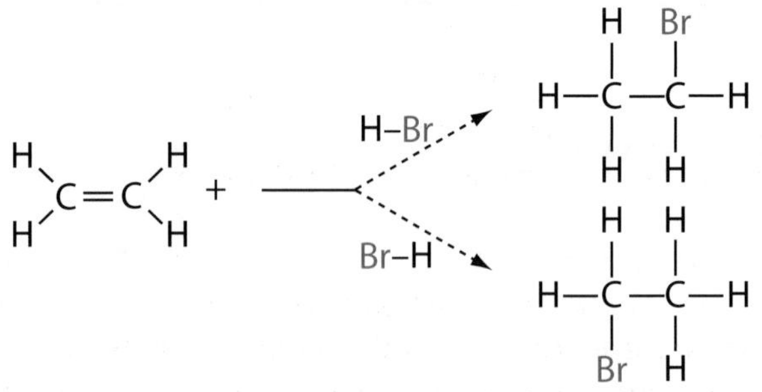

With unsymmetrical alkenes (propene $CH_3CH=CH_2$) there are two possible products when hydrogen bromine adds across the C=C double bond. Which of the addition products is formed in the greatest amount depends on the reaction conditions, and depends upon the relative rates of the addition of the hydrogen atom to each carbon atom of the C=C bond. The acidic hydrogen of the hydrogen halide goes to the carbon atom of the double bond with the most hydrogen atoms. One way to remember this is the old English saying of '*birds of a feather flock together*'.

Propene + hydrogen bromide

The electrophilic addition of hydrogen bromide (HBr) to propene can result in two products. The diagram shows how the different orientation of the hydrogen bromide might lead one to imagine that, statistically, the isomers might be formed in equimolar amounts. Under normal laboratory conditions the favoured product is 2-bromopropane, the Markovnikov product. The hydrogen bromide acts as an electrophile forming the intermediate $CH_3C^+HCH_3$ with positive charge on the $-CH-$ group. In sunlight, or in the presence of a suitable catalyst (peroxide), the alternative *anti*-Markovnikov product, 1-bromopropane, is formed. This alternative outcome (*anti*-Markovnikov) only holds true for HBr, but not for HCl or HI.

1-bromopropane

2-bromopropane

Explaining Markovnikov addition

Two things need considering when explaining the Markovnikov addition to alkenes: the inductive effect and the stability of carbocations. A carbocation is a carbon atom carrying a positive charge. The inductive effect is shown with red arrows from the methyl groups with the arrow points in the direction in which electrons are attracted.

| 3° carbocation | 2° carbocation | 1° carbocation | methyl cation |

Inductive Effect: All alkyl groups have a small positive inductive effect. This means that groups such as methyl are more electron donating than a hydrogen atom attached to carbon atoms in a C=C bond. The inductive effect changes the electron density around the carbon atoms.

Carbocation Stability: The electrons in the C-H bonds of a methyl group are attracted to the positive charge in the carbocation. This electron releasing from the alkyl group has the effect of lowering the size of the positive charge and thus stabilising the carbocation, making it more likely to be formed and go on to react with the halide ion.

The order of stability of carbocations is that tertiary is the most stable as it has three methyl groups 'leaking' electron density. Next comes secondary, then primary and finally the methyl cation is the least stable carbocation.

Markovnikov's Rule (H$_2$O)

This predicts the:

- most likely product when HOH (water) adds to an alkene.

- H atom attaches to the carbon of the C=C with the greatest number of H atoms.

- O atom of OH attaches to the carbon of the C=C with the smallest number of H atoms.

- most E_{neg} atom always adds to the carbon of C=C with the smallest number of H atoms attached.

- most stable carbocation has the greatest number of alkyl groups.

- most E_{neg} atom always adds to the more highly substituted carbon of C=C.

Propene reacts with steam to produce propan-2-ol, the Markovnikov product.

Questions 21.8

1. Which Markovnikov product is formed when hydrogen bromide reacts with propene?

    A   1-bromopropene

    B   2-bromopropane

    C   1-bromopropane

    D   2-bromopropene

2. 1-methylcyclcohexene is dissolved in dichloromethane (CH$_2$Cl$_2$) and the solution is cooled to 0°C. Hydrogen chloride gas is bubbled into the solution until the reaction has gone to completion (finished). The excess acid is removed by washing the reaction mixture with an aqueous solution of sodium hydrogencarbonate. The mixture is filtered and the organic layer obtained using a separating funnel. The organic layer is dried by the

addition of anhydrous sodium sulfate and once again filtered. The solvent is evaporated to leave the product which has a molecular formula of $C_7H_{13}Cl$.

i. How would the chemist know that the reaction had finished?

ii. What is the Markovnikov product in this reaction?

iii. Write a balanced formula equation for the reaction.

iv. Why is sodium sulfate a suitable drying agent?

v. Why was evaporation a suitable method to remove the solvent?

3. Write the Markovnikov products using skeletal formulae and realistic zigzag for the reactions of;

a. but-1-ene with hydrogen chloride

b. but-2-ene with hydrogen bromide

c. 2-methylpropene with hydrogen iodide

B3.9 (g) Evidence for carbocation intermediates

Evidence that electrophilic addition mechanisms proceed *via* carbocation intermediates comes from the formation of Markovknikov products (B3.9f) and the effect that the presence of nucleophiles has on the products formed in these reactions.

The simple test for alkenes is the decolorisation of bromine water. The addition product contains two bromine atoms which have added across the double bond. It might be assumed that both bromine atoms add simultaneously. In the case of ethene the product is 1,2-dibromoethane and not 1,1-dibromoethane.

$$CH_2=CH_2 + Br_2 \rightarrow CH_2BrCH_2Br$$

Evidence that the mechanism proceeds *via* a carbocation (B3.9e) comes from the addition of bromine to unsaturated compounds carried out in the presence of nucleophiles.

When ethene reacts with bromine in the presence of chloride ions, in addition to the expected product (1,2-dibromoethane) another product 1-bromo-2-chloroethane is formed. The carbocation intermediate ($CH_2BrCH_2^+$) can react with either the bromide formed during the reaction or with the chloride present in the reaction mixture.

$$CH_2=CH_2 + Br_2 + Cl^- \rightarrow CH_2BrCH_2Br + CH_2BrCH_2Cl$$

Questions 21.9

1. Which option shows a pair of compounds that could be formed in the reaction between ethene and chlorine water in the presence of fluoride ion?

	Product 1	Product 2
A	CH_2ClCH_2Cl	CH_2FCH_2F
B	CH_2FCH_2Cl	CH_2ClCH_2F
C	CH_2ClCH_2Cl	CH_2FCH_2Cl
D	CH_2ClCH_2Cl	$CHCl_2CH_2Cl$

2. Suggest the identity of the two organic products obtained from a sodium nitrate solution through which bromine and ethene were bubbled.

3. Complete the table by placing a tick ($\sqrt{}$) in one box for each row to indicate the most likely product in the reaction between propene and hydrogen bromide under different conditions.

Conditions	2-bromopropane	1-bromopropane
Polar and pure reactants		
Presence of sunlight		
Presence of hydrogen peroxide		

B3.9 (h) Nucleophilic addition mechanism

Both aldehydes and ketones react with hydrogen cyanide (HCN) to produce 2-hydroxynitriles, which are also known as cyanohydrins.

Hydrogen cyanide is a weak acid, $K_a = 5 \times 10^{-10}$ mol dm^{-3} (B1.5b), so at equilibrium there will be a low concentration of the nucleophile CN$^-$.

$$HCN \rightleftharpoons H^+ + CN^-$$

Two ways to increase the concentration of cyanide, to increase the rate of reaction, are the addition of potassium cyanide (KCN) or the addition of a base. They both serve to increase [CN$^-$].

$$HCN + OH^- \rightleftharpoons CN^- + H_2O$$

The first mechanism to be solved in 1902 was the alkali catalysed nucleophilic addition of hydrogen cyanide. The first step is the addition of the nucleophile to form an intermediate ion followed by addition of a proton to form the final product.

$$CH_3CHO + HCN \rightarrow CH_3CH(OH)(CN)$$

Front side attack

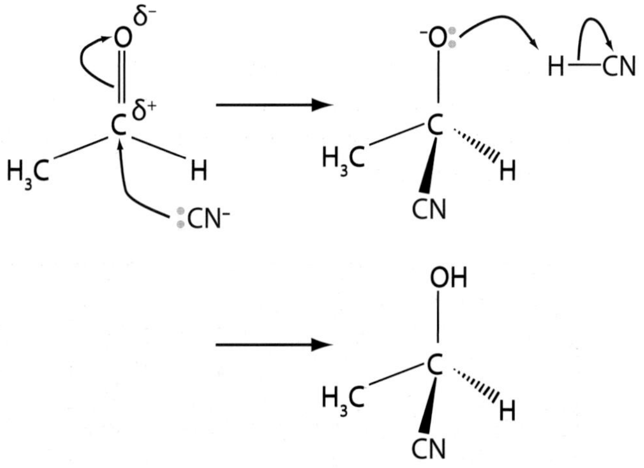

R-2-hydroxypropanenitrile

The different optical isomers result from the direction of attack by the nucleophile from the front or reverse side. The consequence of this attack for unsymmetrical carbonyl compounds is discussed further in B3.9i.

Reverse side attack

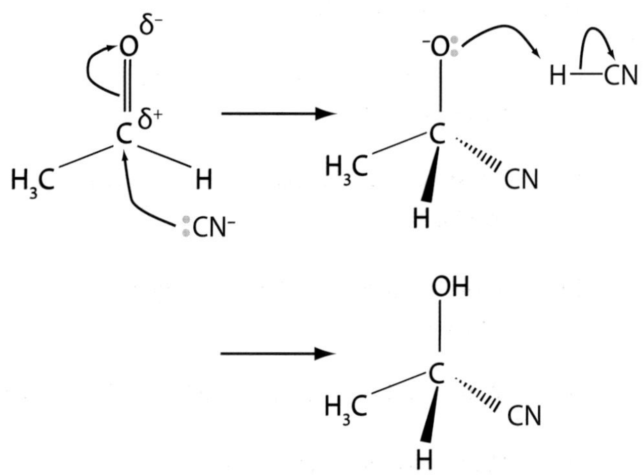

S-2-hydroxypropanenitrile

Questions 21.10

1. Which option gives the organic product when propanal reacts with hydrogen cyanide?

   A 2-hydroxypropanenitrile

   B 1-hydroxybutanenitrile

   C 2-hydroxybutanenitrile

   D 1-hydroxypropanenitrile

2. Which carbonyl reacts with hydrogen cyanide to give 2-hydroxy-2-methyl-2-propanenitrile?

   A butanone

   B propanal

   C butanal

   D propanone

B3.9 (i) Addition of HCN to unsymmetrical carbonyls (racemic products)

Addition of HCN to symmetrical carbonyl compounds leads to the formation of one product. The only symmetrical aldehyde is methanal (HCHO) which reacts with hydrogen cyanide to form 2-hydroxyethanenitrile.

$$HCHO + HCN \rightarrow HCH(OH)CN$$

Propanone reacts with hydrogen cyanide to form 2-hydroxy-2-methylpropanenitrile.

$$(CH_3)_2CO + HCN \rightarrow (CH_3)_2(CN)COH$$

When hydrogen cyanide (HCN) is added to an unsymmetrical carbonyl compound it leads to the formation of an equimolar mixture of enantiomers (racemate). This is because, during the nucleophilic addition (B3.9h), a chiral centre is formed and the nucleophile (CN^-) has no bias for which side of the plane containing the carbonyl bond it attacks. Statistically, attack of the nucleophile from the front or reverse side is equally likely.

All aldehydes, except the first member of the homologous series (methanal) are unsymmetrical and so react with hydrogen cyanide to form racemic mixtures.

Ethanal reacts with hydrogen cyanide to form ±2-hydroxypropanenitrile. Propanal reacts with hydrogen cyanide to form ±2-hydroxybutanenitrile.

$$CH_3CHO + HCN \rightarrow CH_3CHOH(CN)$$

$$CH_3CH_2CHO + HCN \rightarrow CH_3CH_2CHOH(CN)$$

Butan-2-one reacts with hydrogen cyanide to form ±2-hydroxy-2-methylbutanenitrile.

$$CH_3CH_2COCH_3 + HCN \rightarrow CH_3CH_2COH(CN)CH_3$$

Questions 21.11

1. Outline how the weak acid found in milk, lactic acid (2-hydroxypropanoic acid), can be prepared from ethanal. Give details of each stage and comment on the purity of the lactic acid.

2. Which carbonyl compound does **not** produce a racemate on the addition of HCN?

   A   heptanal

   B   heptan-4-one

   C   heptan-2-one

   D   heptan-3-one

22 Aromatic Chemistry

Aromatic compounds are hydrocarbons that contain at least one benzene ring. Benzene (C_6H_6) is a symmetrical molecule that consists of a planar ring made up of six carbon atoms. In benzene, each carbon atom is joined to two other carbon atoms and one hydrogen atom.

Molecular model of benzene (C_6H_6)

The systematic name for aromatic hydrocarbons is **arenes** of which the simplest example is benzene. Other examples include naphthalene ($C_{10}H_8$) as well as anthracene and phenanthrene, which are isomeric ($C_{14}H_{10}$). The numbering of the carbon atoms in arenes accounts for those carbons where electrophilic substitution can take place (B3.10b), namely those with a hydrogen atom attached.

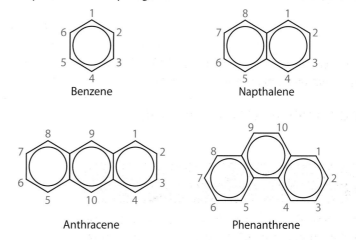

Benzene Napthalene

Anthracene Phenanthrene

Benzene was first isolated in 1825 by Michael Faraday. Benzene is a colourless liquid with a boiling point of 80°C. Benzene is a fuel additive which improves combustion and gives petrol its characteristic smell (aroma). It took another forty years before its structure was solved by Friedrich Kekulé. Like other chemists of his day, Kekulé knew that benzene had six carbons and six hydrogen atoms. He solved the structure by dreaming of whirling snakes where one snake bit its own tail.

This gave him the idea that benzene might have a hexagonal cyclic structure which has since been confirmed by x-ray crystallography.

B3.10 (a)
Aromatic stability of benzene

Benzene is resistant to addition reactions compared with alkenes despite being highly unsaturated. Given the usual test for unsaturation (A3.5b) benzene is found not to decolorise bromine water at room temperature. Benzene is often shown as containing three C=C double bonds and three C-C single bonds. If this was the case it could be thought of as cyclohexa-1,3,5-triene which is often described as a Kekulé structure.

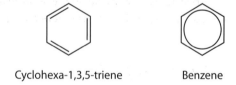

Cyclohexa-1,3,5-triene   Benzene

This is not the case as shown by carbon-carbon bond lengths which are 0.139 nm in benzene compared with 0.154 nm (C-C) and 0.134 nm (C=C). To show that some electrons in benzene are delocalised, we represent its structure as a hexagon with a circle inside. At university, benzene is also shown as a dotted circle inside a hexagon to indicate a bond order of 1.5 (A1.2f).

When two adjacent hydrogen atoms are replaced by other atoms, e.g. X & Y, only one product is formed (**I**) rather than two isomeric products (**II** & **III**). This is additional evidence for the modern representation of benzene.

Benzene is reluctant to form addition compounds as it destroys the stable aromatic system. This additional stability of benzene compared with the hypothetical cyclohexa-1,3,5-triene can be calculated by comparing the enthalpies of hydrogenation (A.13a) of cyclohexene (another hexagonal cyclic structure with six carbon atoms) and the value for benzene itself.

If benzene contained three carbon-carbon (C=C) double bonds it would be expected to have three times the enthalpy of hydrogenation of cyclohexene, *i.e.* $-120 \times 3 = -360$ kJ mol^{-1}. The experimental value for the enthalpy of hydrogenation of benzene is -208 kJ mol^{-1}. The additional stability is therefore $360 - 208 = 152$ kJ mol^{-1} and can be represented in an energy profile diagram (A1.3g).

Enthalpies of Hydrogenation

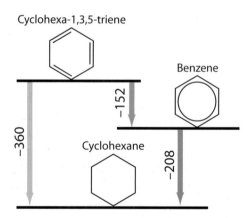

This delocalisation energy of benzene (152 kJ mol^{-1}) gives a measure of the size of the increased stability for benzene compared with the cyclic triene. Benzene has been shown to be a planar molecule as seen by its x-ray structure and when making its molecular model. Each carbon atom in benzene is joined to three other atoms, two carbons and one hydrogen. This leaves each carbon atom with a $2p_z$ atomic orbital which forms π-bonds (A1.2d) by sideways overlap. The net result of this overlap is the creation of three cyclic bonding π-orbitals which each hold two electrons and three cyclic antibonding π orbitals, which are vacant. It is convenient to think of the π-orbitals as being doughnut shaped molecular orbitals above and below the hexagonal ring of carbon atoms. It is the delocalised π-electrons which give the extra stability to benzene and help to explain why it undergoes electrophilic attack (B3.10b). For those who are partial to fast food, a molecule of benzene can be thought of as looking like a doughnut from above and like a burger from the side.

Electrophile (formula)	Electrophile (name)	Electrophilic substitution
NO_2^+	nitronium cation	nitration
Br^+	bromonium cation	bromination
$CH_3^+, C_2H_5^+$	alkyl cation	Friedel-Crafts alkylation
CH_3C^+O	acyl cation	Friedel-Crafts acylation

Nitration

Nitration is when a nitro group (NO_2) is introduced into the benzene ring. The success of these reactions is often indicated by a change from white or colourless to yellow.

Benzene + c. HNO_3 $\xrightarrow[<55°C]{c. H_2SO_4}$ Nitrobenzene + H_2O

The reaction between benzene and concentrated nitric acid to form the yellow oil nitrobenzene ($C_6H_5NO_2$) is slow. It is much faster when the reaction is carried out in the presence of concentrated sulphuric acid. In this case the temperature is kept below 55°C to avoid further substitution by the electrophile NO_2^+ (nitronium cation). The electrophile is generated by the reaction of the two acids. Nitric acid acts as a Brønsted-Lowry base (B1.5b) and sulfuric acid acts as a Brønsted-Lowry acid (B1.5b).

$c.HNO_3 + c.H_2SO_4 \rightarrow H_2NO_3^+ + HSO_4^-$

$H_2NO_3^+ \rightarrow H_2O + NO_2^+$

$c.HNO_3 + c.H_2SO_4 \rightarrow HSO_4^- + H_2O + NO_2^+$ *(overall equation)*

Bromination

Bromination is when a bromine atom replaces a hydrogen atom of a benzene ring. This halogenation reaction does not take place at room temperature unlike the reaction of an alkene with bromine water (B3.9e). For the reaction to take place between bromine and benzene, a **halogen carrier** needs to be present, *e.g.* anhydrous aluminium bromide ($AlBr_3$).

Question 22.1

1. Name the arenes **A** and **B** and explain which one is a substituted phenol and how they are related to each other.

CH₃, OH — A

CH₂OH — B

B3.10 (b) Electrophilic substitution of benzene

The delocalised π-system (A1.2d) in a benzene ring results in a decreased reactivity towards electrophiles (A3.1h) compared with the reactivity of π-bonds in alkenes. The aromatic stability (B3.10a) of the benzene ring is maintained by substitution reactions rather than addition reactions. The hydrogen atom(s) in a benzene ring can be swapped for other atoms or groups in electrophilic substitution reactions. Examples of atoms and groups which can take the place of a hydrogen atom in benzene include: a nitro group (NO_2), a bromine atom (Br), an alkyl group (CH_3, C_2H_5) or an acyl group (CH_3CO). Pi bonds are weaker than sigma bonds (A1.3e) and it is the weakest bonds which break during the reaction of benzene with electrophiles. The vast majority of benzene's reactions are electrophilic substitutions.

Bromobenzene

The bromonium ion (Br^+) is generated by the reaction of bromine with the aluminium bromide. The dashed lines indicate longer and weaker than usual covalent bonds.

The reaction between benzene derivatives and chlorine also takes place by electrophilic substitution. This time the halogen carrier is aluminium chloride. In the reaction between methylbenzene (toluene) and chlorine two positional isomers (A3.10d) are formed in addition to hydrogen chloride gas.

Alkylation (Friedel-Crafts)

The reaction between benzene derivatives and halogenoalkanes in the presence of a halogen carrier also takes place by electrophilic substitution. In **Friedel-Crafts alkylations** a hydrogen atom on the arene ring is swapped for an alkyl group, *e.g.* CH_3, C_2H_5, C_3H_7. Friedel-Crafts alkylation like other carbon-carbon bond forming reactions is very important synthetically as it increases the size of a carbon skeleton. In Friedel-Crafts alkylations, the electrophile is a **carbocation** (B3.9f). An example of carbocation (B3.9f) formation is when chloroethane reacts with aluminium chloride to form the aluminium tetrachloride anion and the ethyl cation. The positively charge ethyl group can attack the benzene ring and electrophilic substitution occurs. Aluminium chloride is a Lewis acid (B1.5b) and is an electron pair acceptor.

The overall equation for the generation of the ethyl cation can be written as: $CH_3CH_2Cl + AlCl_3 \rightarrow [AlCl_4]^- + CH_3CH_2^+$

Benzene

Ethylbenzene

Questions 22.2

1. Cumene is a very important industrial chemical used in the manufacture of phenol and propanone. Complete the equation (suggesting a halogen carrier) and name this type of reaction.

Benzene   Cumene

2. Trinitrotoluene (TNT) is a very useful explosive which is an active ingredient of dynamite. Describe how TNT can be made from benzene.

3. Suggest how the monomer styrene (phenylethene) might be prepared from benzene.

Acylation (Friedel-Crafts)

The reaction between benzene derivatives and acyl chlorides (B3.7a) in the presence of a halogen carrier also takes place by electrophilic substitution. In **Friedel-Crafts acylations** a hydrogen atom on the arene ring is swapped for an acyl group, *e.g.* ethanoyl (CH_3CO) or propanoyl (CH_3CH_2CO). Friedel-Crafts acylations, like alkylations, are important reactions because they form carbon-carbon bonds, increasing the size of a carbon skeleton. In Friedel-Crafts acylations the electrophile is a carbocation (B3.9f). An example is the reaction between ethanoyl chloride and benzene with either aluminium chloride or iron(III) chloride as the Lewis acid catalyst.

Benzene

Phenylethanone
(acetophenone)

Question 22.3

1. The non-steroidal anti-inflammatory drug (NSAID) Fenbufen can be synthesized by reaction of biphenyl (C_6H_5-C_6H_5) and succinic anhydride (dihydro-2,5-furandione).

Biphenyl   Succinic anhydride

?

Fenbufen

(a) Suggest a suitable Lewis acid catalyst for this reaction.

(b) Give the name of this type of reaction.

(c) What type of mechanism is operating?

(d) Identify the functional groups in Fenbufen.

(e) What is the molecular formula of Fenbufen?

B3.10 (c) Benzene rings and the Inductive Effect

Electron donating groups activate the benzene ring and include: alkyl (R), hydroxyl (OH), alkoxy (OR) and amino (NH_2) groups directly attached to the arene ring. These groups activate the benzene ring because they increase its electron density. This means that molecules such as methylbenzene, phenol, methoxybenzene and aminobenzene are more reactive toward electrophiles than benzene.

Alkyl groups activate the benzene ring because of a positive (+I) inductive effect (B3.11c). The simplest alkyl group methyl (CH_3) pushes electrons towards the arene ring which has the effect of increasing the electron density. This leads to an increased rate of reaction with electrophiles such as the nitronium ion (NO_2^+). Methylbenzene can be nitrated at room temperature whereas benzene requires a higher temperature. The mono-nitrated product is a mixture of two regioisomers (positional isomers); 2-nitrotoluene and 4-nitrotoluene.

Electron withdrawing groups deactivate the benzene ring and include: carbonyl (C=O) and nitro (NO_2) groups directly attached to the arene ring. These groups deactivate the benzene ring because they decrease the electron density in it. This means that molecules such as acetophenone and nitrobenzene are less reactive toward electrophiles than benzene.

Chlorine deactivates the benzene ring because of a negative (–I) inductive effect (B3.11c). It withdraws electron density from the arene ring which has the effect of decreasing the electron density and hence the decreased rate of reactions with electrophiles such as the nitronium ion (NO_2^+). Chlorobenzene can be nitrated by heating under reflux with a boiling mixture of concentrated nitric and sulfuric acids. The mono-nitrated product is a mixture of the 1,2- (ortho) and 1,4 (para) regioisomers.

The group (**Z**) attached to an aromatic ring controls two factors:

- the rate of electrophilic substitution (compared to benzene)

- and the position a new substituent (group) will add.

For monosubstituted benzenes (C_6H_5Z) there are three possible isomers: *ortho* (1,2-substitution), *meta* (1,3-substitution) and *para* (1,4-substitution). A statistical distribution of products; *ortho*: *meta*: *para* in a ratio of 2:2:1 (based on the number of each type of site) is not observed.

Electron withdrawing groups lead to a decrease in reactivity whereas electron releasing groups lead to an increase in reactivity. This can be thought of in terms of the attractiveness of the π-system to an electrophile which is governed by the electron density. The group attached to an aromatic ring (**Z**) can also affect the position where a new substituent (group) will add. Despite the fact there remain five carbons in a monosubtituted benzene the introduction of a second group only results in three isomeric disubstituted benzenes. A new group added in the C-2 or C-6 positions is referred to as *ortho*, a new group added in the C-3 or C-5 positions is called *meta*, and a new group added in the C-4 position is called *para*.

The table summarises the position of substitution and whether the group activates or deactivates the arene ring.

Group (Z)	(+I)	Activating	(−I)	Deactivating	ortho / para directing	meta directing
OH		√			√	
OR		√			√	
NH$_2$		√			√	
CH$_3$		√			√	
Cl				√	√	
CO$_2$H				√		√
COR				√		√
CO$_2$R				√		√
SO$_3$H				√		√
NO$_2$				√		√

The nitro group is *meta* directing because although it decreases reactivity, this decrease in electron density occurs least at the *meta-* position. The amine group is *ortho/para* directing because although it increases reactivity, this increase in electron density occurs most at the *ortho/para* positions. Studies have shown that both the deshielding and shielding effect (B4.6a) are in the same order, *i.e. ortho* > *para* > *meta* This idea of differences in electron densities at different positions in monosubstituted benzenes can be illustrated by looking at the relative partial charges present in nitrobenzene and aniline. In nitrobenzene there is a decreased electron density where the partial charge is shown as $\delta+$. In aniline there is an increased electron density where the partial charge is shown as $\delta-$.

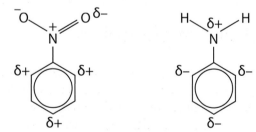

Evidence for this difference in electron density at the various carbon positions in a benzene ring comes from carbon-13 nmr spectroscopy (A4.5), proton nmr spectroscopy (B4.6) and electron density maps.

The equivalent hydrogen atoms in benzene all have a proton nmr resonance at a chemical shift (A4.5) of 7.26 ppm. Chemical shift values for protons >7.26 ppm indicate a decrease in electron density and values <7.26 ppm indicate an increase in electron density. Comparison of values for the *ortho*, *meta* and *para* positions indicate the most likely position(s) for electrophilic substitution.

Monosubstituted benzene + Y → ortho / meta / para

Table showing variation in electron densities in terms of ^1H nmr resonances (ppm)

Arene	X	ortho	meta	para
benzene	H	7.26	7.26	7.26
toluene	CH_3	7.06	7.14	7.04
phenol	OH	6.70	7.14	6.81
phenylamine	NH_2	6.51	7.01	6.61
nitrobenzene	NO_2	8.19	7.52	7.65
methylbenzoate	CO_2CH_3	8.03	7.38	7.47
benzaldehyde	CHO	7.87	7.56	7.64
chlorobenzene	Cl	7.30	7.19	7.29

Questions 22.4

1. Explain the difference between activating and deactivating groups on a benzene ring and their relative rates of electrophilic substitution.

2. Alkyl groups activate benzene rings in the *ortho / para* positions. What is the expected ratio? Explain why the *ortho / para* ratio for the nitration of methylbenzene is 1.6:1 and ethylbenzene is smaller at 0.9:1.

3. Predict how the reactivity of trifluoromethylbenzene ($C_6H_5CF_3$) with electrophiles might compare with the reactivity of methylbenzene ($C_6H_5CH_3$)?

Reactions of phenol

Phenol (C_6H_5OH) was discovered in coal tar after investigations by Joseph Lister. He worked out why amputee sailors who had their arm stumps treated with molten tar to cauterise the wounds were less likely to go gangrenous. The antiseptic properties of phenol led to it being used to sterilise wounds and surgical instruments. Two of the most famous phenol derivatives are trichlorophenol (TCP) and (dettol).

Phenol   2,4,6-trichlorophenol   4-chloro-3,5-dimethylphenol
(TCP)   (Dettol)

Phenol used to be known as carbolic acid and was a key ingredient in carbolic soap. Phenol is a toxic solid which is soluble in water at room temperature. It is corrosive because it is acidic (B3.11a). The test for phenol, and its derivatives, is the addition of neutral iron(III) chloride ($FeCl_3$) which gives a purple complex $Fe^{3+}(C_6H_5O^-)_3$.

Phenol is produced in the **Dow Process** in which chlorobenzene is treated with sodium hydroxide at high temperature and pressure. Phenol itself has a smell which is sometimes described as a 'hospital smell'.

The electron withdrawing effect of the chlorine atom (–I effect) makes chlorobenzene susceptible to attack by hydroxide (OH^-) in the 1-position. There is no change in functional group level (A3.2) at the 1-position, so this reaction is essentially a hydrolysis (A3.1h).

Phenol is very reactive compared with benzene and will react rapidly with bromine water at room temperature without the need for a Lewis acid catalyst.

Phenol   2,4,6-tribromophenol

The white solid product 2,4,6-tribromophenol has a familiar antiseptic smell. The formation of the white precipitate with bromine water can also be used as a test for phenol.

The arene ring is activated in phenol because of overlap between the lone pair of electrons in the 2p orbital of oxygen and the $2p_z$-orbitals in the benzene ring. Evidence for this overlap comes from the O-H bond length (0.136 nm) in phenol which is shorter than the O-H bond length (0.143 nm) in methanol. Overlap of oxygen's 2p orbital with the aromatic π-system in the arene ring is more significant because of the electron withdrawing effect (-I) of the highly electronegative (E_{neg} 3.5) oxygen atom. In phenol it is the 2-, 4-, and 6- positions which are activated.

Diagram to show the overlap of oxygen's lone pair with the π-system in phenol.

Aniline

2,4,6-tribromoaniline

Aniline is more reactive towards electrophiles than phenol. This can be explained by considering the electronegativities (A1.2i) of oxygen (E_{neg} = 3.5) and nitrogen (E_{neg} = 3.0). Nitrogen is less electronegative than oxygen so the lone pair on the nitrogen (aniline) is higher in energy than the lone pair on the oxygen (phenol). This results in nitrogen's lone pair being more available for overlap with the π-system. Evidence for the increased electron density at the *ortho-para* positions in aniline compared with phenol is in the form of hydrogen atom resonances for aniline and phenol in their proton-nmr spectra (B4.6c)

Question 22.5

1. Give an example of an electron withdrawing substituent that is *ortho / para* directing. Explain briefly why this happens.

Questions 22.6

1. Which option shows the correct number of positional isomers for disubstituted benzene derivatives?

   A   1

   B   4

   C   3

   D   5

Reactions of nitrobenzene

When the temperature of the nitrating mixture (c.HNO_3/c. H_2SO_4) is elevated to 110°C, pale yellow crystals of the disubstituted 1,3-dinitrobenzene are produced. The desired product can be isolated by pouring the reaction mixture into a beaker containing iced-water and filtering the yellow solid using a Buchner filter funnel.

Nitrobenzene   1,3-dinitrobenzene

Forcing conditions are needed because the nitro group is deactivating. The major product in the nitration of nitrobenzene is 1,3-dinitrobenzene because the nitro group is *meta*-directing.

Reactions of phenylamine

Phenylamine (aniline) reacts vigorously at room temperature with bromine water. The reaction is so rapid that it is not possible to isolate any monobrominated or dibrominated isomers and the organic product is exclusively 2,4,6-tribromoaniline. The amine group (NH_2) in aniline is activating because the lone pair on the nitrogen can overlap with the π-system.

2. Which option shows the correct number of equivalent carbon atoms for these disubstituted benzene derivatives? [Hint: consider the symmetry of these molecules].

	Cl (ortho)	Cl (meta)	Cl (para)
A	4	4	4
B	3	4	1
C	3	4	2
D	2	2	1

3. Which option shows two groups *meta* to each other?

A

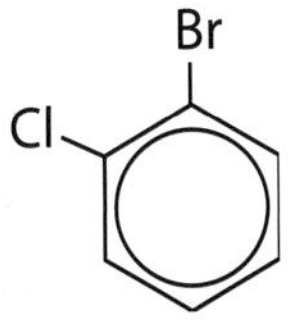

B

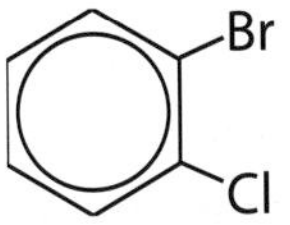

C

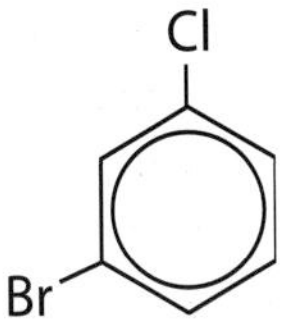

D

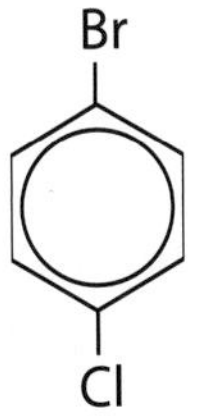

4. Mononitration of 1,4-dichlorobenzene will result in how many isomers?

A   4

B   2

C   1

D   3

5. Nitration of 1,3-dinitrobenzene will result in which isomer as the major product?

A   1,2,5-trinitrobenzene

B   1,3,4-trinitrobenzene

C   1,2,3-trinitrobenzene

D   1,3,5-trinitrobenzene

6. Draw skeletal formula for benzene, phenol, chlorobenzene and aniline and put these arenes in decreasing order of reactivity with electrophiles.

B3.10 (d)
Aryl amines from nitro arenes

Aryl amines are benzene derivatives, *e.g.* phenylamine ($C_6H_5NH_2$), also called aniline, which is prepared by reduction of nitrobenzene. This is an important transformation as there are many useful molecules which are aryl amines. Aryl amines are often carcinogenic and it is best to steer clear of them in a school laboratory. The reduction of nitrobenzene is achieved by heating it under reflux with metallic tin and concentrated hydrochloric acid. The reducing agent is believed to be a hydrogen radical (H·).

$$Sn\ (s) + 2\ HCl\ (aq) \rightarrow SnCl_2\ (aq) + 2\ H·$$

$$C_6H_5NO_2 + 6\ [H] \rightarrow C_6H_5NH_2 + 2\ H_2O$$

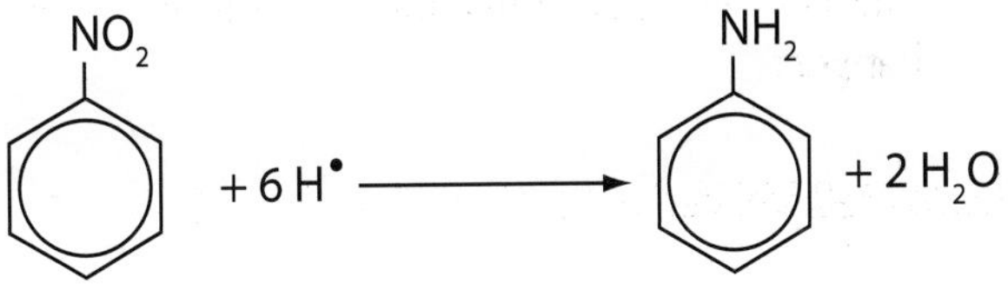

Aniline

A major use of aniline is in the formation of **azo dyes**. The indicator methyl orange used in acid-base titrations (B1.5g) is an example of an azo (RN=NR) compound.

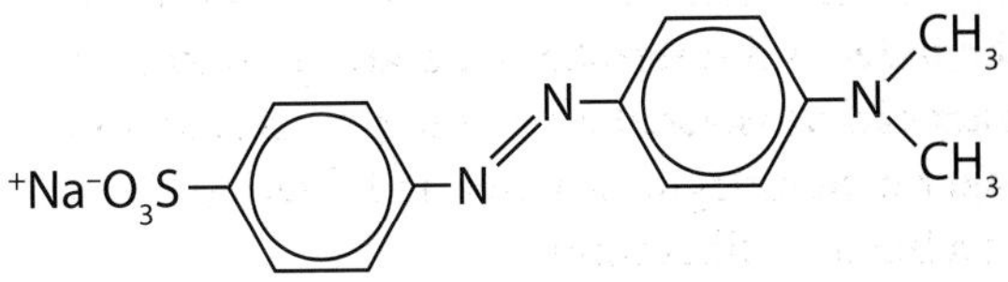

Methyl orange

William Perkin used aniline in the manufacture of the first industrially produced synthetic dye mauveine. This dye has the colour mauve which is a purple colour much enjoyed by Queen Victoria and used on early stamps. Today mauveine can be prepared by dissolving 1:2:2 mixtures of aniline and *ortho*-methylaniline (*o*-toluidine) and *para*-methylaniline (*p*-toluidine) in concentrated sulfuric acid, then water, followed by the addition of potassium dichromate(VI). By looking closely at the structure of mauveine A, it is possible to see how several aromatic amines have reacted to form this dye.

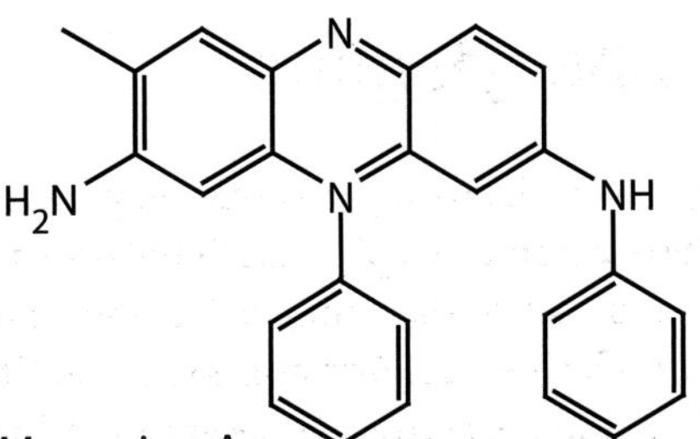

Mauveine A

Mauve coloured stamp

Aromatic amines are useful intermediates in the manufacture of plastics. Examples of aromatic amines are methylene dianiline (MDA) which is a curing agent for some epoxy-resins and methylene bisorthochloroaniline (MbOCA) which is used to make polyurethanes.

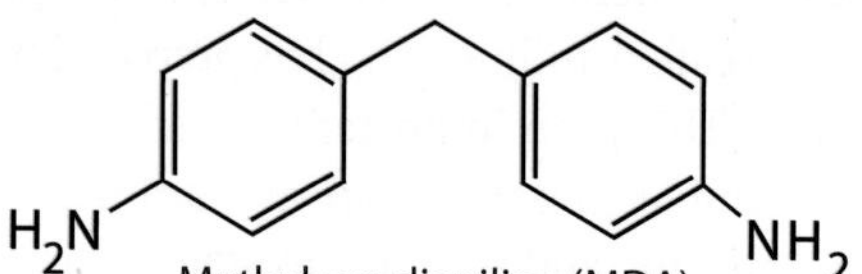

Methylene dianiline (MDA)

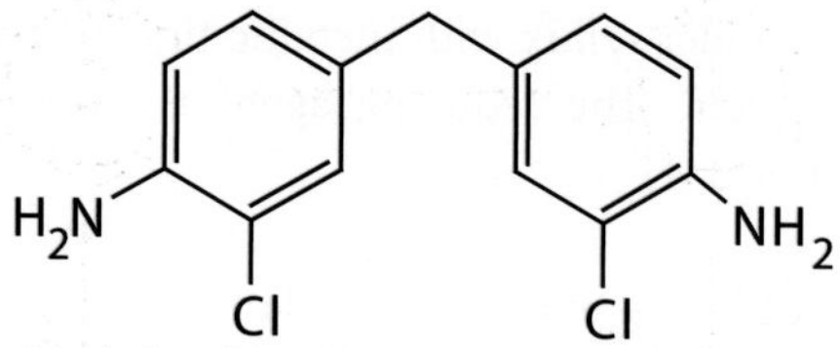

Methylenebisorthochloroaniline (MbOCA)

Questions 22.7

1. Which option shows the correct reduction products for 3-nitroacetophenone?

	Product 1	Product 2
A	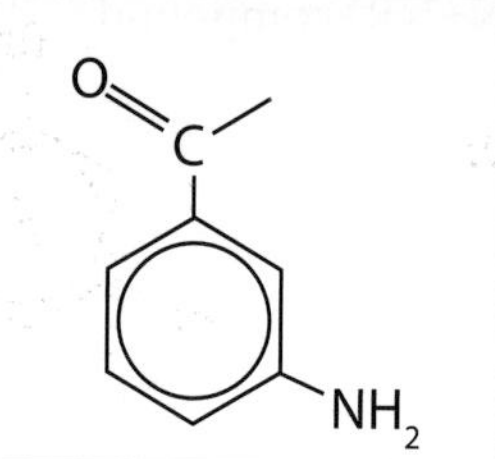	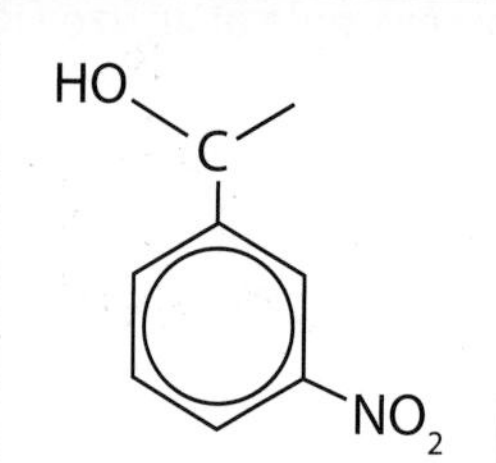
B	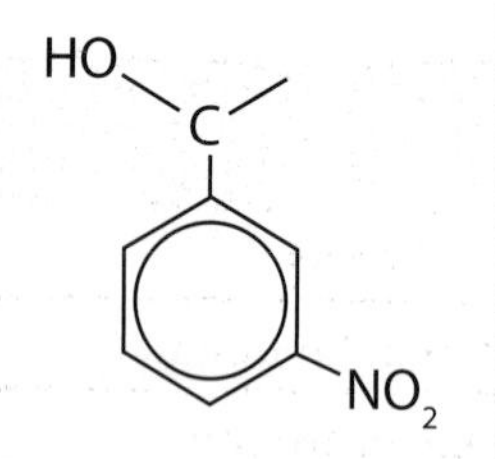	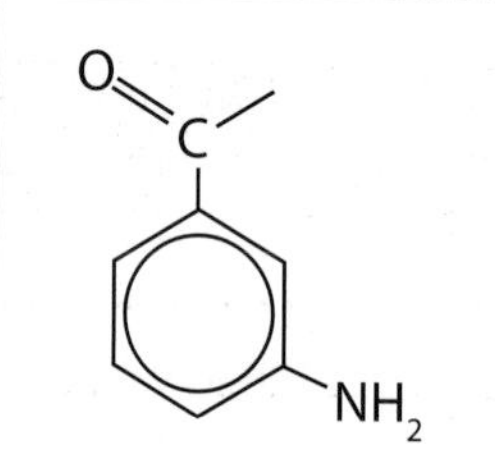
C	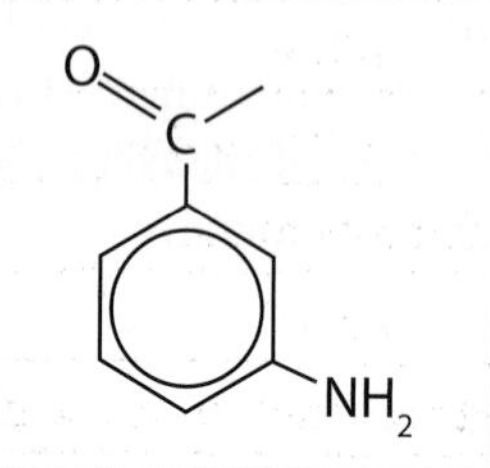	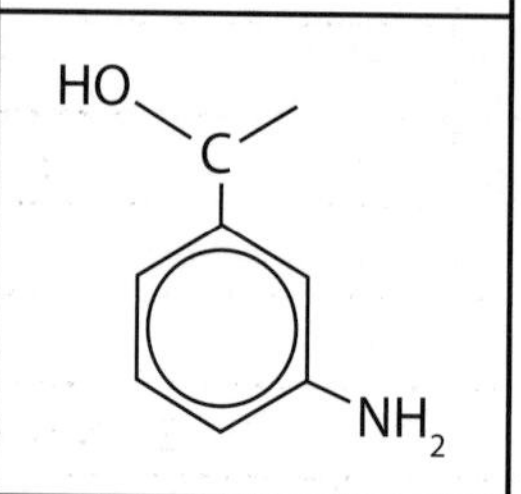
D	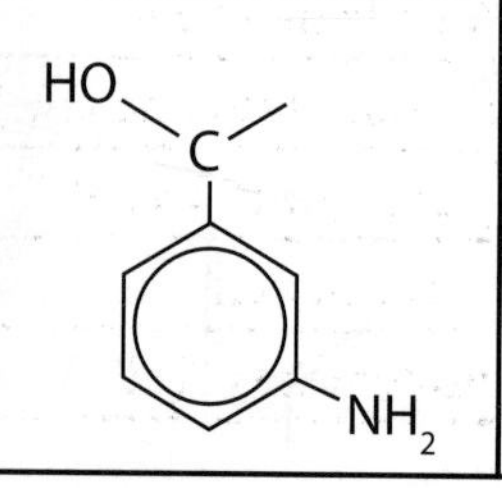	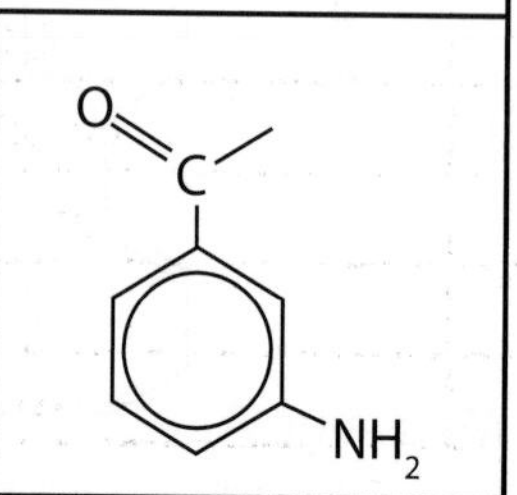

2. How would you prepare phenylamine from benzene in two steps? In the reaction scheme, give the name of each type of reaction.

3. Name and classify by type all the possible amines which contain a benzene ring with molecular formula C_7H_9N.

Polyaromatics

Naphthalene, which has two fused rings, can undergo the same electrophilic substitution reactions as benzene. Naphthalene is more reactive than benzene because aromaticity is retained in the non-reacting ring. Interestingly, substitution of the naphthalene ring is favoured at the C-1 position. If reaction mixtures are left, then it has been found that there is an increase in proportion of substitution at the C-2 position.

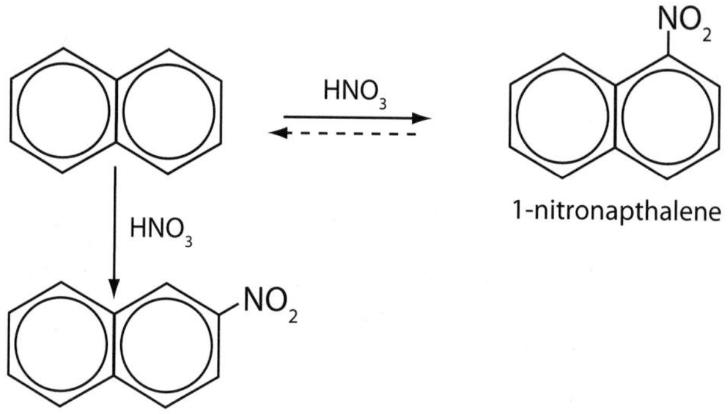

1-nitronapthalene

2-nitronapthalene

The initial product is under kinetic control and the rearranged product is under thermodynamic control (B1.4). The order in which these products are formed gives evidence for differences in activation energy and relative stabilities of the isomeric nitronapthalenes.

The spider diagram shows aromatic interconversions of benzene and its derivatives.

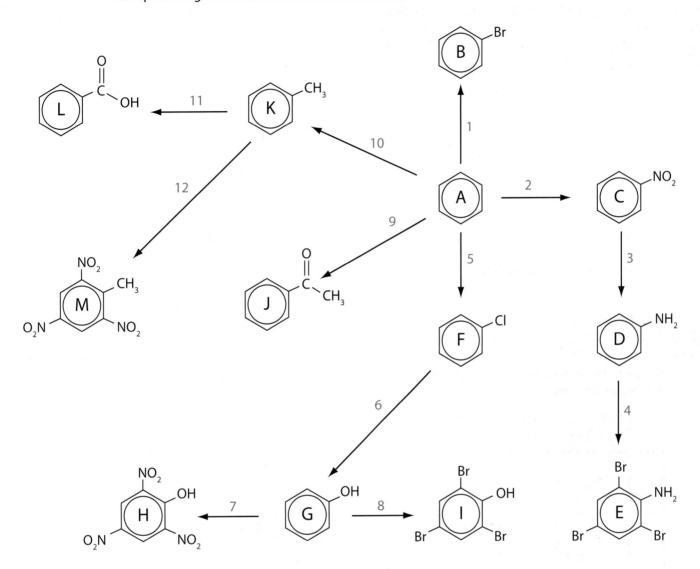

#	Type of reaction	Compound	Name
		A	benzene
1	bromination	B	bromobenzene
2	nitration	C	nitrobenzene
3	reduction	D	aniline
4	bromination	E	2,4,6-tribromoaniline
5	chlorination	F	chlorobenzene
6	hydrolysis	G	phenol
7	nitration	H	2,4,6-trinitrophenol (picric acid)
8	bromination	I	2,4,6-tribromophenol
9	Friedel-Crafts acylation	J	phenylethanone (acetophenone)
10	Friedel-Crafts alkylation	K	methylbenzene (toluene)
11	oxidation	L	benzoic acid
12	nitration	M	trinitrotoluene (TNT)

23

Acidity & Basicity

Contents

There are two particularly useful acid-base definitions (B1.5b) which are that acids are proton donors and bases are proton acceptors (**Brønsted-Lowry Theory**) and that acids are lone pair acceptors and bases are lone pair donors (**Lewis Theory**). The extent of ionisation of weak acids accounts for the concentration of hydrogen ions and is dealt with in terms of acid dissociation constants K_a (B1.5d) and pK_a values (B1.5f). This chapter takes a look at how the acidity of phenol and carboxylic acids changes with substituents and how the basicity of amines is affected by degree of substitution of hydrogen atoms. The pH scale gives a qualitative measure of relative acidity and basicity with the colour chart.

pH

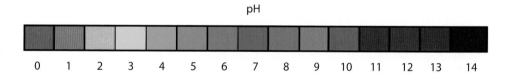

0   1   2   3   4   5   6   7   8   9   10   11   12   13   14

Substances which cover the entire pH range include pH 0 (car battery acid), pH 1 (stomach acid), pH 2 (vinegar), pH 3 (orange juice), pH 4 (tomato juice), pH 5 (black coffee), pH 6 (milk), pH 7 (pure water), pH 8 (sea water), pH 9 (toothpaste), pH 10 (milk of magnesia), pH 11 (household ammonia), pH 12 (soapy water), pH 13 (bleach) and pH 14 (caustic soda).

B3.11 (a) Relative acidities of water, alcohols and phenols

Water H-OH, alcohols R-OH and phenol(s) C_6H_5-OH all possess an OH group. Despite this similarity they all react quite differently with sodium. Sodium is stored under oil because of its high reactivity with water. Sodium is often used to dry solvents such as methylbenzene (toluene) and ethers (*e.g.* diethyl ether) when anhydrous reaction conditions are needed. Sodium reacts with cold water to produce a strongly alkaline solution of sodium hydroxide and hydrogen gas.

$$H_2O \text{ (l)} + Na \text{ (s)} \rightarrow NaOH \text{ (aq)} + \tfrac{1}{2} H_2 \text{ (g)}$$

The reaction is so exothermic that the sodium often melts into a ball as it whizzes around on the surface of the water. Sometimes orange sparks are seen and the indicator phenolphthalein can be used to show the presence of the alkali as a purple trail that follows the path of the sodium. When carrying out this reaction, teachers will limit themselves to pieces of sodium ~4 mm³. If a few drops of a detergent (washing-up liquid) is put into the water before the addition of the sodium it reduces the chance of explosion and pieces of sodium spitting out of the water trough towards the end of the chemical reaction.

When a small pellet of sodium is carefully added to ethanol (50 cm³) it reacts less vigorously than it does with water.

Sodium in ethanol

The sodium sinks at first and then floats on a raft of hydrogen bubbles. The alkaline sodium ethoxide (C_2H_5ONa) can be detected with phenolphthalein which slowly turns pink.

$$C_2H_5OH \text{ (l)} + Na \text{ (s)} \rightarrow C_2H_5ONa \text{ (ethanol)} + \frac{1}{2} H_2 \text{ (g)}$$

The hydrogen gas evolved can be tested for cautiously with a lit splint. It is important to keep the splint well away from the flammable alcohol.

Sodium will react directly with molten phenol to make sodium phenoxide and hydrogen gas.

$$C_6H_5OH \text{ (l)} + Na \text{ (s)} \rightarrow C_6H_5ONa \text{ (s)} + \frac{1}{2} H_2 \text{ (g)}$$

The fact that phenol is more acidic than alcohols is shown by its reaction with aqueous sodium hydroxide which results in the formation of a salt (sodium phenoxide) and water.

$$C_6H_5OH \text{ (l)} + NaOH \text{ (aq)} \rightarrow C_6H_5ONa \text{ (aq)} + H_2O \text{ (l)}$$

Alcohols do not give a reaction with aqueous solutions of sodium hydroxide.

The relative acidity for alcohols and phenols is shown by the data which includes K_a & pK_a values. The larger K_a, the stronger the acid and the smaller the pK_a value, the stronger the acid.

Name	Formula	K_a (mol dm⁻³)	pK_a
Picric acid	(structure)	1×10^{-1}	1.0
Ethanoic acid	CH_3COOH	1.7×10^{-5}	4.8
Phenol	(structure)	1.3×10^{-10}	9.9
Water	H_2O	$1 \times 10^{-14} (K_w)$	14
Ethanol	CH_3CH_2OH	1×10^{-16}	16

Simple aliphatic alcohols such as ethanol show few of the properties associated with acids which is unsurprising considering how small are their K_a values. Alcohols do not turn blue litmus paper red. Phenol is more acidic than alcohols because the arene ring is activated by the overlap between the lone pair of electrons in the 2p orbital of oxygen and the $2p_z$-orbitals in the benzene ring (B3.10c). The phenoxide ion produced in aqueous solution is also partially stabilised by delocalisation of the negative charge with the π-system of the arene ring. The O-H bond in phenol is weakened (compared to ethanol) by the lone pair delocalisation with the π-system of the benzene ring.

Phenoxide ion

2,4,6-trinitrophenol, trivially known as picric acid, is a much stronger acid than phenol. The three nitro groups (–I) on the benzene ring withdraw electrons, further weakening its O-H bond making this phenol derivative more acidic than phenol. Picric acid is so acidic compared with phenol that it will liberate carbon dioxide gas from aqueous solutions of sodium carbonate.

Questions 23.1

1. Why is phenol a stronger acid than ethanol?

2. Put ethanol, phenol and water in order of increasing acidity.

3. Which option shows the correct colour on addition of blue litmus paper.

	Water	Picric acid	Ethanol
A	blue	red	blue
B	green	blue	red
C	blue	red	red
D	green	red	blue

B3.11 (b) Relative basicities of ammonia, aliphatic and aromatic amines

Amines can be synthesized from halogenoalkanes using ethanolic ammonia (A3.3b). It is helpful to think of amines in terms of them being a substituted ammonia molecule where one or more of the hydrogen atoms of ammonia have been replaced by one, two or three alkyl and or aryl groups. Like alcohols, amines can also be classified as 1°, 2° or 3°, and in all cases the central nitrogen atom is saturated and trivalent.

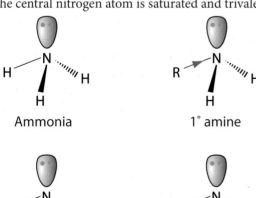

Ammonia and types of amines (aliphatic)

The chemistry of amines is dominated by the lone pair of electrons on the nitrogen atom. Like ammonia, which is a weak base, amines can also accept a proton using the lone pair of electrons on the nitrogen atom. Excess ammonia reacts with hydrogen bromide to form ammonium bromide. Methylamine (CH_3NH_2) reacts with hydrogen chloride to form the salt methylammonium chloride.

$$NH_3 + HBr \rightarrow NH_4Br$$

$$CH_3NH_2 + HCl \rightarrow CH_3NH_3^+Cl^-$$

Aliphatic amines (where R = alkyl) are stronger bases than ammonia because their alkyl groups push electrons away from themselves towards the nitrogen lone pair and are described as having a positive inductive effect (+I). Groups with a positive inductive effect (B3.10c) are electron releasing with respect to hydrogen. There will be an increased electron charge density on the nitrogen atom for aliphatic amines. The greater the electron density on the nitrogen, the more likely it is to act as a base (electron pair donor).

L = nucleophile for H

The order of the base strength of amines is due to the inductive effect. There will be a decreased electron charge density on the nitrogen atom for aromatic amines. Phenylamine (aniline) $C_6H_5NH_2$ is the simplest aromatic amine and is a weaker base than ammonia. It is a weaker base because the lone pair of electrons on the nitrogen atom becomes part of the delocalised π-system of the benzene ring (B3.10c). The amine group activates the arene ring (B3.10c) and makes the arene ring more reactive than benzene.

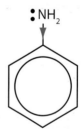

Phenylamine (aniline)

Phenylamine will dissolve in excess hydrochloric acid due to the formation of the water soluble ionic salt (phenylammonium chloride). The free amine can be recovered by the addition of sodium hydroxide to a solution of the ammonium salt.

$$C_6H_5NH_2 + HCl \rightarrow C_6H_5NH_3Cl$$

The base strength of amines is compared with ammonia from which they are derived. Amines with +I group(s) are more basic than ammonia. Amines with −I group(s) are less basic than ammonia, *e.g.* ethylamine > ammonia > phenylamine.

When a weak base such as ammonia accepts a proton from water it forms an alkaline solution,

$$\textit{e.g. } NH_3 + H_2O \rightleftharpoons NH_4^+ + OH^-$$

The base dissociation constant K_b is: $K_b = \dfrac{[NH_4^+][OH^-]}{[NH_3]}$

For ammonia $K_b = 1.74 \times 10^{-5}$ moldm^{-3}. K_b is a measure of relative basicity and the larger its value the stronger the base.

The pH of a base can be calculated from $K_b \approx \dfrac{[OH^-]^2}{[base]}$

$$[OH^-] \approx \sqrt{[base]K_b} \quad \dfrac{K_w}{[H^+]} \approx \sqrt{[base]K_b}$$

$$\log K_w - \log[H^+] \approx \tfrac{1}{2}(\log[base] + \log K_b)$$

$$-pK_w + pH \approx \tfrac{1}{2}(\log[base] - pK_b)$$

$$pH \approx pK_w - 0.5pK_b + 0.5\log[base] \text{ for weak, monobasic bases.}$$

$$(pH = pK_w + \log[base] \text{ for strong, monobasic bases})$$

Since: $K_w = 1 \times 10^{-14}$ mol^{2}dm^{-6} (B1.5d),

$$pK_w = -\log_{10}K_w, \ pK_b = -\log_{10}K_b,$$

If we use a concentration of 0.01 mol dm^{-3} for ammonia, this gives a pH of 10.6.

The order of basicity for alkyl amines might reasonably be expected to be 3° > 2° > 1° > NH$_3$, but this is not always the case as shown by the table of data for the selected amines. The larger K_b and the smaller pK_b the stronger is the base.

Name	Formula	Type of amine	K_b (mol dm^{-3})	pK_b
ammonia	NH_3	n/a	1.74×10^{-5}	4.76
methylamine	CH_3NH_2	1°	4.37×10^{-4}	3.36
ethylamine	$CH_3CH_2NH_2$	1°	5.25×10^{-4}	3.28
propylamine	$CH_3CH_2CH_2NH_2$	1°	5.89×10^{-4}	3.23
dimethylamine	$(CH_3)_2NH$	2°	5.89×10^{-4}	3.23
diethylamine	$(CH_3CH_2)_2NH$	2°	9.55×10^{-4}	3.02
trimethylamine	$(CH_3)_3N$	3°	6.31×10^{-5}	4.20
triethylamine	$(CH_3CH_2)_3N$	3°	4.37×10^{-4}	3.36
4-methylphenylamine	$H_3CC_6H_4NH_2$	aryl	1.20×10^{-9}	8.92
4-nitrophenylamine	$O_2NC_6H_4NH_2$	aryl	1.0×10^{-13}	13.0

The order of basicity for the three aryl amines fits the inductive effect argument. The methyl group (+I effect) releases electrons and increases the basicity relative to aniline and the nitro group (-I effect) withdraws electrons and decreases the basicity relative to aniline.

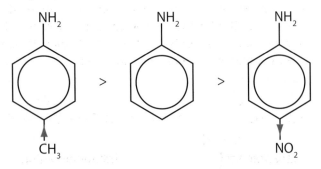

What might come as a surprise is that sometimes trialkylamines are weaker bases than dialkylamines in aqueous solution, e.g. the order of basicity order is:

dimethylamine > methylamine > trimethylamine

When trialkylamines react as bases they form R$_3$N$^+$H and when dialkylamines react as bases they form R$_2$N$^+$H$_2$. One fewer H on R$_3$N$^+$H compared with R$_2$N$^+$H$_2$ means it forms less hydrogen bonds to water and is less soluble. This reduced solubility counteracts the increased availablility of the lone pair in the trialkylamine.

Questions 23.2

1. Write balanced formula equations for the following reactions.

   i. Methylamine with hydrochloric acid.

   ii. Phenylamine with hydrobromic acid.

   iii. Benzylamine with hydrochloric acid.

2. Explain why phenylamine is a weaker base than benzylamine

3. Classify the following amines; triethylamine, ethylphenylamine, phenylamine, diethylamine, ethylmethylphenylamine, and ethylamine as 1°, 2°, 3°, aliphatic or aromatic.

4. Write a balanced formula equation to illustrate that ethylamine is a base and water is an acid.

5. Which one of the following statements about amines is incorrect?

   A The stronger the base, the greater its tendency to remove H⁺ ions from water.

   B The weaker the base, the stronger the conjugate acid.

   C The weaker the base, the larger the K_b value.

   D The stronger the base the smaller the pK_b value.

B3.11 (c)
Acidity of substituted carboxylic acids

When comparing the relative strength of carboxylic acids (B3.7), it is important to use acids having the same concentration (mol dm⁻³) to make it a fair test. The stronger the acid, the greater the extent to which it will have ionised to release protons (H⁺) and the greater will be its electrical conductivity and the lower its pH. Stronger acids will have larger acid dissociation constants K_a (B1.5d) and smaller pK_a values (B1.5f). Carboxylic acids are weak acids which partly ionise in solution which can be illustrated by two equally valid equations.

$$CH_3COOH \rightleftharpoons CH_3COO^- + H^+$$

$$CH_3COOH + H_2O \rightleftharpoons CH_3COO^- + H_3O^+$$

Methanoic acid is a stronger acid than ethanoic acid. The next three members of the homologous series (ethanoic, propanoic and butanoic acid) have only small differences in their acidity (acid strength) as measured under standard conditions.

Carboxylic acid	K_a / mol dm⁻³	$pK_a = -\log_{10}K_a$
HCOOH	1.7×10^{-4}	3.8
CH₃COOH	1.5×10^{-5}	4.8
CH₃CH₂COOH	1.3×10^{-5}	4.9
CH₃CH₂CH₂COOH	1.5×10^{-5}	4.8

The difference in acidity between methanoic acid and other simple carboxylic acids can be explained in terms of the inductive effect. Alkyl groups push electrons away from themselves towards the carboxyl group and have a positive inductive effect (+I). Alkyl groups, with their positive inductive effect (B3.10c), are electron releasing with respect to the hydrogen found in methanoic acid. The methyl group in ethanoic acid pushes electrons towards the carboxyl group. This increases the size of the negative charge density on the ethanoate ion (compared with methanoate), thereby increasing the chance that it will recombine with a proton forming a molecule of ethanoic acid. This is why ethanoic acid is a weaker acid than methanoic acid. Only 0.3% of 0.1 mol dm⁻³ ethanoic acid is ionised and the rest exists in molecular form.

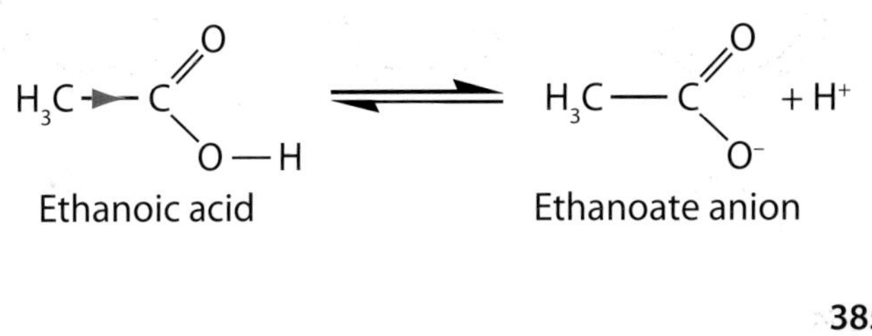

Ethanoic acid ⇌ Ethanoate anion + H⁺

Groups with a +I effect reduce the acidity of the carboxylic acid because they increase the electron density in the O-H bond of the carboxyl group which increases the O-H bond strength which, in turn, reduces the extent of the dissociation.

Atoms or groups with a negative inductive effect (B3.10c) are electron withdrawing with respect to hydrogen. These –I groups include electronegative elements such as chlorine. They increase the acidity of the carboxylic acid because they decrease electron density in the O-H bond of the carboxyl group which decreases the O-H bond strength which, in turn, increases the extent of the dissociation. As an increasing number of hydrogen atoms are substituted for chlorine atoms it decreases the size of the negative charge density on the substituted ethanoate ion thereby decreasing the chance that it will recombine with a proton forming a molecule of chlorinated ethanoic acid.

Chloroethanoic acid   Chloroethanoate anion

As the number of chlorine atoms increase from one, to two to three, the acid strength increases as seen by the considerable decrease in pK_a.

The order of acidity is ethanoic < chloroethanoic < dichloroethanoic < trichloroethanoic acid.

Carboxylic acid name	Structural formula	pK_a
Ethanoic acid	CH_3COOH	4.76
Chloroethanoic acid	$CH_2ClCOOH$	2.86
Dichloroethanoic acid	$CHCl_2COOH$	1.29
Trichloroethanoic acid	CCl_3COOH	0.65

Questions 23.3

1. Which option explains why ethanoic acid is a weak acid?

    A   It forms hydrogen bonds to water.

    B   It forms intramolecular hydrogen bonds.

    C   It only forms a few H^+ ions in solution.

    D   It is not very soluble in water.

2. Which option shows the correct order for the decreasing acidity of the chlorinated ethanoic acid derivatives and ethanoic acid?

    A $CH_3COOH > ClCH_2COOH > ...$
    $... > Cl_2CHCOOH > Cl_3CCOOH$

    B $Cl_3CCOOH > Cl_2CHCOOH > ...$
    $... > ClCH_2COOH > CH_3COOH$

    C $Cl_3CCOOH < Cl_2CHCOOH < ...$
    $... < ClCH_2COOH < CH_3COOH$

    D $CH_3COOH > Cl_3CCOOH > ...$
    $... > Cl_2CHCOOH > ClCH_2COOH$

3. Using displayed formulae, explain how the chlorine atoms of dichloroethanoic acid affect its acidity compared to ethanoic acid.

4. Which option shows the correct order for the +I effect for these simple alkyl groups?

    A $(CH_3)_2CH$ > $(CH_3)_3C$ > CH_3 > C_2H_5
    B $(CH_3)_3C$ > $(CH_3)_2CH$ > C_2H_5 > CH_3
    C $(CH_3)_3C$ < $(CH_3)_2CH$ < C_2H_5 < CH_3
    D $(CH_3)_2CH$ > $(CH_3)_3C$ > C_2H_5 > CH_3

5. K_a for benzoic acid is 6.3×10^{-5} mol dm^{-3} and K_a for ethanoic acid is 1.7×10^{-5} mol dm^{-3}. What information and conclusions can be drawn from their acid dissociation constants?

6. Describe a simple experiment that produces hydrogen gas to show that methanoic acid is a stronger acid than ethanoic acid.

7. What is the effect on acidity of replacing a single hydrogen atom by a different halogen atom in ethanoic acid?

Formula	pK_a
CH_2ICO_2H	3.2
CH_2FCO_2H	2.6
CH_2ClCO_2H	2.86
CH_2BrCO_2H	2.9

8. What is the effect of replacing a single hydrogen atom by a chlorine atom on different carbon atoms in propanoic acid?

Formula	pK_a
$CH_2ClCH_2CO_2H$	4.1
$CH_3CHClCO_2H$	2.8

B3.11 (d) Reaction of α-amino acids with acids and alkalis

Alpha-amino acids have a carboxylic acid group (CO_2H), an amine group (NH_2), a side chain (R) and a hydrogen atom (H) attached to a single tetrahedral carbon atom. The general formula for α-amino acids is $RCHNH_2COOH$. The chemistry of amino acids is interesting because they possess a basic group (amine) as well as an acidic group (carboxylic acid) so they are examples of amphoteric organic molecules. It has been shown using x-ray crystallography that solid amino acids form internal ionic salts (zwitterions) by the donation of a proton from the carboxyl group to the amine group.

Formation of the doubly charged but electrically neutral zwitterion

Amino acids are solids under standard conditions because of the strong ionic bonds formed between zwitterions. For many years, German was the main language of chemists and the word zwitterion comes from the German *zwei* meaning two. Amino acids also exist as zwitterions in solution and the presence of these ionic groups helps increase the water solubility. A zwitterion is an electrically neutral ion with both a negative and a positive charge and is formed at a pH called the **isoelectric point**.

There are twenty common and naturally occurring amino acids and each one is given a unique three letter symbol. This simplifies the drawing of polypeptides and proteins (B3.7c). The table shows R for the α-amino acids which fit the general formula $RCH(NH_2)(CO_2H)$.

Name	Symbol	R group
Glycine	Gly	H
Alanine	Ala	CH_3
Valine	Val	$CH(CH_3)_2$
Leucine	Leu	$CH_2CH(CH_3)_2$
Isoleucine	Ile	$CH(CH_3)C_2H_5$
Tryptophan	Trp	
Methionine	Met	$CH_2CH_2SCH_3$
Phenylalanine	Phe	$CH_2C_6H_5$
Serine	Ser	CH_2OH
Proline	Pro	(whole molecule)
Threonine	Thr	$CHOHCH_3$
Cysteine	Cys	CH_2SH
Asparagine	Asn	CH_2CONH_2
Glutamine	Gln	$CH_2CH_2CONH_2$
Tyrosine	Tyr	
Histidine	His	
Arginine	Arg	
Lysine	Lys	$CH_2CH_2CH_2CH_2NH_2$
Aspartic acid	Asp	CH_2CO_2H
Glutamic acid	Glu	$CH_2CH_2CO_2H$

In solution, amino acids act as acids and on addition of alkali (OH^-) they react by donating a proton to the hydroxide to form water. The result is that amino acids exist as anions in strongly alkaline solutions.

$$H_3N^+CHRCOO^- + OH^- \rightarrow H_2NCHRCOO^- + H_2O$$

In solution, amino acids act as bases and on addition of acid (H^+) they react by accepting a proton on the carboxylate anion to form the carboxylic acid group. The result is that amino acids exist as cations in strongly acidic solutions.

$$H_3N^+CHRCOO^- + H^+ \rightarrow H_3N^+CHRCOOH$$

The simplest α-amino acid, glycine, can react with water as an acid and as a base. In its reaction as an acid with water it donates a proton to form hydroxonium.

$$H_3N^+CH_2CO_2^- + H_2O \rightleftharpoons H_2NCH_2CO_2^- + H_3O^+$$

In its reaction as a base with water, glycine accepts a proton from water to leave behind hydroxide.

$$H_3N^+CH_2CO_2^- + H_2O \rightleftharpoons H_3N^+CH_2CO_2H + OH^-$$

The different amino acids have a unique pH at which they are electrically neutral. This difference in the isoelectric point is exploited during electrophoresis, which is how amino acids are sometimes separated in the laboratory.

2. Using the general formula for α-amino acids ($RCHNH_2COOH$), explain how they can act as buffers.

3. Draw structures for the zwitterions of these α-amino acids ($RCHNH_2COOH$).

   a. glycine (R = H)

   b. alanine (R = CH_3)

   c. aspartic acid (R = CH_2COOH)

   d. serine (R = CH_2OH)

   e. cysteine (R = CH_2SH)

4. Which option shows the most likely ions found in aqueous solutions of amino acids?

	Low pH	Medium pH (isoelectric point)	High pH
A	anion	cation	zwitterion
B	anion	zwitterion	cation
C	cation	anion	zwitterion
D	cation	zwitterion	anion

Questions 23.4

1. Use the structural formula $H_2N(CH_2)_4CH(NH_2)COOH$ for the α-amino acid lysine to answer the following questions.

   a. What is the IUPAC name of lysine?

   b. What is lysine's molecular formula?

   c. What is the abbreviation used for this amino acid?

   d. Which ionic species will be present in;

      i. strongly acidic solution?

      ii. neutral solution?

      iii. strongly alkaline solution?

24 Stereochemistry

Contents

Stereochemistry is the chemistry of stereoisomers, which are substances with identical molecular formulae but which are only different in the 3D arrangement (configuration) of their atoms/groups. Examples of the different types of stereoisomers are geometric isomers (A3.1d) and optical isomers (A3.1e). In this chapter we will first look at molecules with one chiral centre and then molecules with two chiral centres (B3.12d). Viktor Meyer introduced the term 'stereochemistry' in 1878 whilst giving university lectures on the concept of the tetrahedral atom.

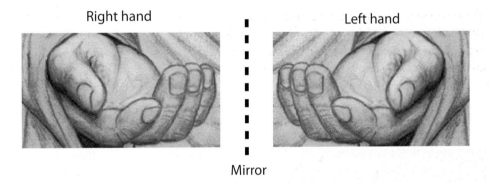

Our hands are non-superimposable mirror images, as everyone discovers when they accidentally try to put one of their hands into the wrong glove. Like hands, stereoisomers have the same atoms with the same bond order but a different spatial arrangement of atoms. In the diagram of the two hands, imagine you are facing someone who has both their hands turned up. Now you can see why the right hand is shown on the left hand side of the diagram.

The Greek for hand is *cheir* from which we get the term **chiral** which is used to describe a molecule as 'left' or 'right' handed. A carbon atom has asymmetry (unsymmetrical) if it has four different atoms or groups directly attached to it. To identify a carbon which is a chiral centre, it is often marked with an asterisk. The two optical isomers of alanine are shown.

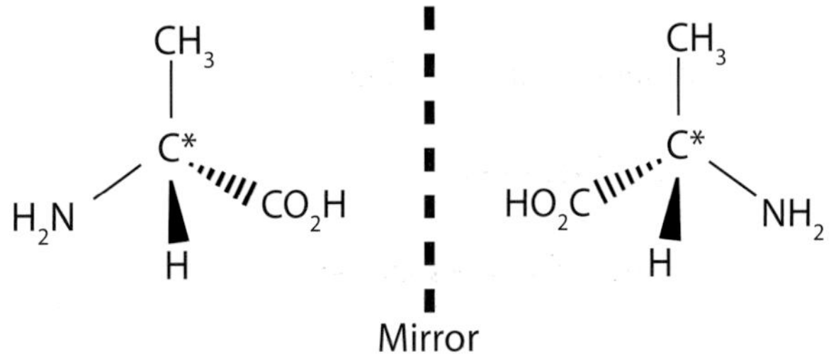

When drawing a 3D structure (A3.1f), it is important to show realistic tetrahedral angles (A3.1a). Some students find it helpful to think of stereoisomers as space isomers. Since optical isomers have a different arrangement in space they show a marked difference in their physiological activity. This important lesson was tragically learned in the 1960s when the morning sickness drug thalidomide was prescribed to pregnant women and resulted in miscarriages and birth defects. It is now clear that even if the optical isomer without teratogenic[1] side effects had been prescribed, the thalidomide molecule racemises (B3.9c) under physiological conditions. Interestingly, the harmful side effect of this drug is helping thalidomide to find use in the treatment of leprosy, a disease which was more prevalent in the past.

(−)-*S*-thalidomide   (+)-*R*-thalidomide

Mirror plane

The symbols (S) and (R) are explained in the next section (B3.12a) and the signs (+) and (−) are explained in section B3.12b. It is important to realise early on that there is no connection between the sign and the letter (B3.12c) assigned to any optically active molecule.

B3.12 (a) Cahn-Ingold-Prelog priority rules

In 1956 the British chemists Robert Cahn (Westminster School) and Christopher Ingold (Southampton University) in collaboration with Vladimir Prelog (Nobel Prize, 1975) proposed the Cahn-Ingold-Prelog priority rules. Their C-I-P rules are still used to assign the stereochemistry at chiral carbon atoms. Chemists rapidly adopted their rules because, for the first time, they allowed chemists to give unambiguous absolute configurations for optical isomers (steroisomers).

X-ray crystallography (B2.5) is used to determine absolute configurations in organic molecules which then allow chemists to accurately draw 3D molecules for the correct optical isomer that matches its optical rotation (B3.12b). There are two ways to arrange four different groups around a carbon atom in three dimensions. The two different versions (enantiomers) are known as **R** from the latin word *rectus* (right) and **S** from the latin word *sinister* (left). The two enantiomers are non-superimposable mirror images.

Cahn-Ingold-Prelog priority rules

These C-I-P rules have been devised to distinguish pairs of enantiomers using the letters *R* & *S*. These rules are applied in descending order, starting with rule number 1. Once the rules have been applied, each unique atom or group attached to the chiral carbon is given a priority number 1, 2, 3 and 4. The atom with the highest priority has the number 1 and the atom with the lowest priority has the number 4. The use of molecular model kits, where available, will greatly assist in the understanding of the C-I-P rules.

Rules

The atom with the highest atomic number directly attached to the chiral carbon atom takes precedence and is given number 1 priority ($_9F > _8O > _7N > _6C$).

1. If two atoms adjacent to the chiral carbon are identical, then we assign priority by looking at the next atoms attached to these identical atoms ($-CH_2OH > -CH_3$).

2. If two atoms adjacent to the chiral carbon are isotopes, then we assign priority by looking at their atomic masses ($^3H > ^2H > ^1H$).

3. Once all four priorities (1-4) have been established, at the chiral carbon atom, the molecule is turned (oriented) so that the atom with lowest priority number 4 is furthest away (dashed wedge).

4. When viewing the molecule from the chiral carbon atom down, its bond to the atom or group with priority number 4 (C–4 bond) is labelled *R* when the numbers (1, 2, 3) are arranged clockwise and *S* when the numbers (1, 2, 3) are anticlockwise.

---

1   Teratogen: an agent that causes birth defects.

Example 24.1 (Alanine)

Using the C-I-P rules, label the enantiomer for the amino acid alanine as *R* or *S*.

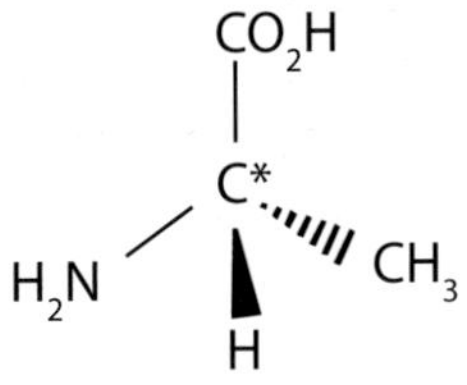

$$CO_2H$$
$$H_2N \quad C^* \quad CH_3$$
$$H$$

Alanine

In alanine, the four groups or atoms directly attached to the chiral carbon atom are the amine (NH_2), carboxylic acid (COOH), methyl (CH_3) and hydrogen (H). The NH_2 group is given priority number 1 as nitrogen has the highest atomic number ($_7N$) of the directly attached atoms. The carboxylic acid group is given priority number 2 over the methyl group which is given priority number 3. This is because although both groups are joined *via* a carbon atom ($_6C$), looking at the next atoms attached to these two carbon atoms, oxygen ($_8O$) in CO_2H has a higher atomic number than hydrogen ($_1H$) in CH_3. The lowest priority number 4 is given to the hydrogen atom with the lowest atomic number of the atoms directly attached to the chiral carbon atom. Turning the molecule so that the atom with lowest priority number 4 is furthest away, *i.e.* looking down the C-H bond, the numbers 1 to 2 to 3 go in an anticlockwise direction so the molecule is *S*-alanine.

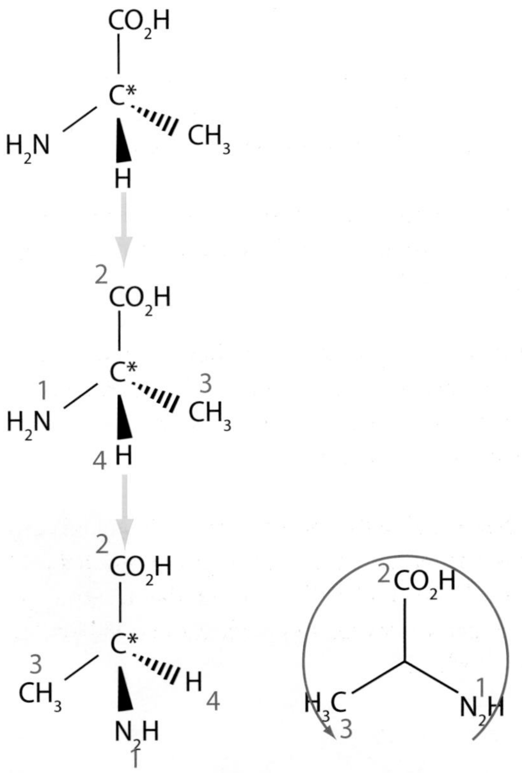

Example 24.2 (Lactic acid)

Using the C-I-P rules, label the enantiomer for lactic acid as *R* or *S*.

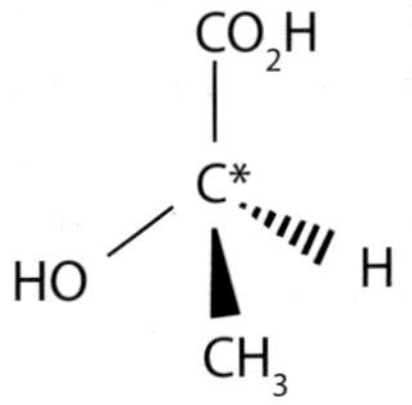

$$CO_2H$$
$$HO \quad C^* \quad H$$
$$CH_3$$

Lactic acid

In lactic acid the four groups in order of priority starting with 1 are: hydroxyl (OH) > carboxylic acid (CO_2H) > methyl (CH_3) > hydrogen (H).

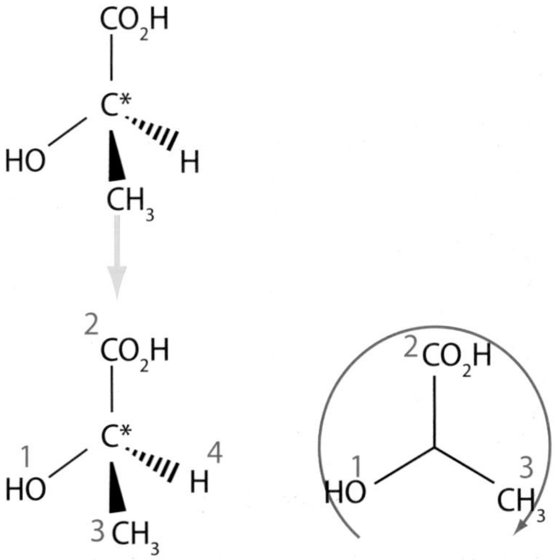

Turning the molecule so that the atom with lowest priority number 4 is furthest away, *i.e.* looking down the C-H bond, the numbers go in a clockwise direction from 1 to 2 to 3 so the molecule is *R*-lactic acid.

Questions 24.1

1. What are the Cahn-Ingold-Prelog priority rules?

2. When will a molecule with a central tetrahedral carbon have asymmetry? How many possible isomers are formed and how are they identified?

3. L-adrenaline was the first hormone which could be crystallized. Use the CIP rules to determine the stereochemistry (*R* or *S*) at the chiral carbon indicated with the asterisk (*).

L-adrenaline

4. Name the following molecules and determine their absolute configuration (*R* or *S*).

	3D formula	Name
W	H | C* H₃C ⁄ ▲ ''''' OH CH₂CH₃	
X	H | C HOH₂C ⁄ ▲ ''''' H CH₃	
Y	Cl | C* F ⁄ ▲ ''''' Br H	

5. Chiral amino acids are all found in the *S*-configuration, in natural proteins, except for cysteine. Draw and label the optical isomers for cysteine. Explain why this amino acid has the opposite configuration from the other amino acids.

Cysteine

B3.12 (b)
Rotating polarised light

Chiral molecules which are optically active rotate polarised light. Molecules which rotate polarised light in a clockwise direction have a positive optical rotation (+°). Conversely molecules which rotate polarised light in an anticlockwise direction have a negative optical rotation (–°). Pioneering work on optical rotations was carried out in 1832 by Jean-Baptiste Biot who discovered the optical rotation of tartaric acid (B3.12d).

The wave-particle duality of light has its place in physics as well as chemistry. At times it is helpful to think of light as being a particle, called a photon (A4.3b), and at other times to consider light to be an electromagnetic wave (A4.3a). Electromagnetic waves of light are thought to vibrate (transversely) in all directions at 90° to the direction of travel. In light, the electric field is at 90° to the magnetic field.

Electromagnetic wave

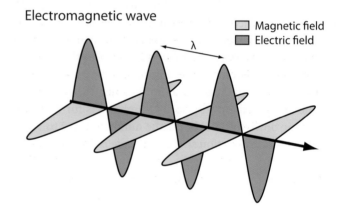

To observe optical rotation in a chiral molecule it is first necessary to make plane polarised light in an instrument called a **polarimeter**. This is achieved by passing yellow monochromatic light, supplied by a sodium lamp, through a polarising (**nicol**) prism. **Plane polarised light** is light which vibrates in one plane only. Plane polarised light is rotated when it passes through certain pure substances such as crystals and also when in solution. Inorganic substances which are optically active include crystals of sodium iodate ($NaIO_3$) and potassium thiocyanate (KSCN).

A polarimeter

There are lots of organic molecules which can rotate the plane of polarisation of light. This property of optical activity is therefore a consequence of the arrangement of atoms at a chiral carbon atom. Enantiomers, which are non-superimposable mirror images, rotate plane polarised light in equal but opposite directions. Optical rotation can only be determined by experimentation. The size of optical rotations measured can be used to follow biochemical reactions and to assess the purity of samples.

The specific rotation (α) of plane polarised light depends upon concentration of the substance (mol dm^{-3}), path length, and the substance itself. Values for specific rotation are quoted at 20°C using light from sodium at wavelength = 589.3 nm to allow meaningful comparisons to be made. The observed rotation of a sample is:

$$[\alpha] = \pm \frac{100\,\alpha}{c \times l}$$

where c = concentration (g per 100 ml) and l = path length of the cell in decimetres (dm).

Biologists tend to use L (**laevorotatory**) for $-°$ rotations and D (**dextrorotatory**) for $+°$ rotations. A biochemical reaction which can easily be followed using a polarimeter is the acid hydrolysis of sucrose. The disaccharide sucrose is hydrolysed to give the monosaccharides glucose and fructose. Experimentally you could dissolve sucrose (100 g) in hot water (40 cm^3). The optical rotation of the sucrose solution is recorded in a polarimeter. Concentrated hydrochloric acid (5 cm^3) is then added to the sucrose solution and its optical rotation is recorded every 5 minutes until it remains constant.

Question 24.2

1. Methylphenidate (Ritalin) is a stimulant used in the treatment of narcolepsy and attention deficit disorder and prescribed as the dextro version. From its skeletal formula, identify the chiral centre with an asterisk, its functional groups and its molecular formula.

Methylphenidate

B3.12 (c)
R/S and +/− assignments

There is no connection between the R/S and +/− assignments. The R/S assignment gives the absolute configuration found at a chiral carbon which is assigned using the C-I-P rules (B3.12a). The optical rotation (+/−) for a pure optical isomer is determined experimentally and cannot be predicted from looking at a molecule's structure. Some S-stereoisomers give a positive (+°) optical rotation whilst other S-steroisomers give a (−°) optical rotation.

Don't fall into the common mistake of thinking that there is a connection between the letter assigned to an enantiomer (R or S) and the direction of rotation of plane polarised light. The following examples illustrate there is no relationship or clear cut pattern between the two. The direction of rotation cannot be accurately predicted and needs to be determined experimentally. R-glyceraldehye rotates plane polarised light to the right +° but R-phenylsuccinic acid rotates plane polarised light −°. The structural formula for phenylsuccinic acid is $C_6H_5CH(COOH)CH_2COOH$

The distinctive smell of caraway seeds is due to the high concentration of S-carvone, a member of a family of compounds called **terpenoids**. The non-superimposable mirror image R-carvone smells like spearmint. The structure and optical rotations for the enantiomer (B3.12d) S-carvone is shown. This difference in smell between these stereoisomers suggests the presence of chiral groups in the olfactory receptors.

(+)-S-carvone

Nicotine is an alkaloid which is found in the leaves of the tobacco plant (*Nicotiana tabacum*). An alkaloid is a nitrogen containing natural product. In plants, nicotine acts as a natural insecticide, but in humans it acts as a stimulant. This effect is one of the reasons why nicotine is so addictive. It has been shown that each cigarette contains about 1 mg of nicotine. The isomer found in plants is (−)-S-nicotine which has the IUPAC name of (S)-3-(1-Methyl-2-pyrrolidinyl)pyridine.

(–)-S-nicotine

Adrenaline is a fight or flight hormone released from the adrenal glands when there is a threat of danger or excitement. It acts by boosting the supply of fuels (glucose and oxygen) to the brain and muscles, whilst also suppressing bodily procedures like digestion. The isomer found in the body is (–) R-adrenaline. Adrenaline is used to treat patients who have had a heart attack.

(–)-R-adrenaline

Glyceraldehyde is a simple triose monosaccharide that is an intermediate in carbohydrate metabolism. It is a sweet crystalline solid that has a specific optical rotation of +9.4° in the R-form.

(+)-R-glyceraldehyde

Questions 24.3

1. R-glyceraldehyde has an optical rotation of +9.4°. What would be the optical rotation of the S-form of glyceraldehyde and the optical rotation of a racemic mixture of glyceraldehyde?

2. How are the absolute configurations at chiral centres determined and how do they relate to the optical rotation?

3. The essential amino acid S-valine (2-amino-3-methylbutanoic acid) has a specific optical rotation of +27.5°. Draw this isomer and its optical isomer R-valine including its optical rotation.

B3.12 (d) Molecules with two chiral centres

Pairs of optical isomers which have non-superimposable mirror images are called enantiomers, e.g. R-phenylethylamine and S-phenylethylamine. Pairs of enantiomers have identical physical properties, e.g. melting point, boiling point, solubility, and density. Enantiomers also have identical spectroscopic data, e.g. carbon-13 nmr, proton nmr spectra, and infra-red spectra. Enantiomers also have identical chemical properties as they possess the same functional groups adjacent to identical groups with the same inductive effects. It is sometimes possible to separate enantiomers by crystallisation and also by chromatography using a chiral stationary phase. Enantiomers also have identical chemical properties but only one will be the key that fits into the active site of an enzyme. Enantiomers can be distinguished experimentally because of their differences in the direction that they rotate plane polarised light. Enantiomers rotate light in equal and opposite directions (B3.12c) one clockwise (+°) and the other anticlockwise (–°).

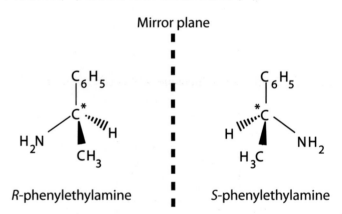

R-phenylethylamine   S-phenylethylamine

Racemic mixtures, which are also known as racemates are equimolar mixtures of enantiomers. Solutions of racemic mixtures do not rotate plane polarised light. An example of a racemic mixture is one that contains 50% R-alanine and 50% S-alanine. Chemists can calculate the relative proportions of mixtures of enantiomers (enantiomeric excess) by measuring the optical rotation of a mixture and comparing it to the pure enantiomers. If a mixture contained 95% R-alanine and 5% S-alanine it would have an optical rotation, near to, but lower than that for pure R-alanine. The size of the optical rotation would depend on the enatiomeric excess which can be calculated as follows:

enantiomeric excess = (% enantiomer A – % enantiomer B)

= 95% – 5%

= 90%.

Diastereoisomers are pairs of stereoiosomers with at least two chiral centres which are not related to each other as mirror images. Diastereoisomers differ in one or more of their stereocentres. Pairs of diastereoisomers have different physical and chemical properties. It is found that inverting one chiral centre leads to a structure which is not a mirror image of the other. In a molecule with two non-identical chiral centres, the following pairs of stereoisomers are related to each other as diastereoisomers; SR & SS, RR & RS, SR & RR and RS & SS. Examples of diastereoisomers are (2R, 3R)-2-chloro-3-iodobutane & (2R, 3S)-2-chloro-3-iodobutane.

(2R, 3R)-2-chloro-3-iodobutane

(2R, 3S)-2-chloro-3-iodobutane

(2R, 3R)-2-chloro-3-iodobutane is labelled as follows:

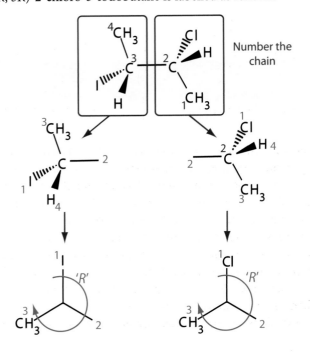

and (2R, 3S)-2-chloro-3-iodobutane is labelled as follows:

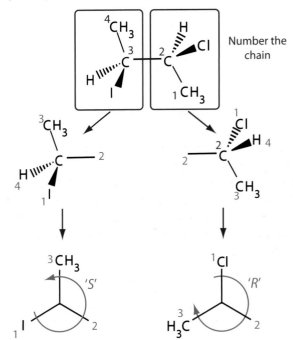

When a molecule has two chiral centres, the enantiomers are recognised as pairs of stereoisomers where both chiral centres have opposite configuration, e.g. (2S,3R)-2-chloro-3-iodobutane & (2R,3S)-2-chloro-3-iodobutane. When a molecule has two chiral centres, the diastereoisomers are recognised as pairs of stereoisomers where one of the chiral centres has an opposite configuration, e.g. (2S,3R)-2-chloro-3-iodobutane & (2R,3R)-2-chloro-3-iodobutane.

The diagram shows which pairs of stereoisomers are enantiomers and which pairs are diastereoisomers for molecules which have two non-identical chiral centres.

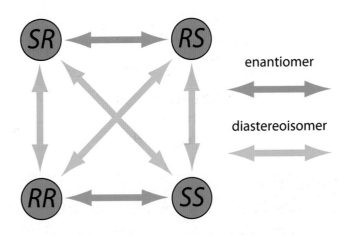

Louis Pasteur was the first chemist to separate a mixture of enantiomers when he was growing crystalline derivatives of tartaric acid, an organic acid found in the sediments of fermenting wine. He was observant enough to spot that there were two types of crystals present in samples of sodium ammonium tartrate that he had prepared. He separated the two types of crystals by hand and found that their solutions had opposite optical rotations. Students at Winchester College have grown crystals of tartaric acid which are mirror images of one another (enantiomorphs).

Tartaric acid (2,3-dihydroxybutanedioic acid) is a molecule with two adjacent chiral centres which are identical. Each chiral carbon has attached a carboxylic acid (CO_2H), a hydrogen atom (H), a hydroxyl group (OH) and $CH(OH)$ CO_2H. A molecule of tartaric acid is shown below, without showing the 3D arrangement around the chiral centres.

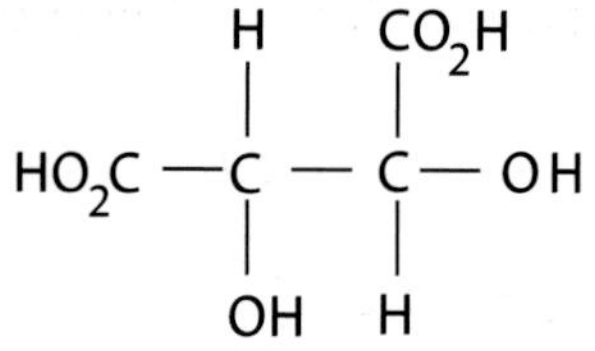

Tartaric acid

The simple formula to work out the number of possible stereoisomers is 2^n where n = number of chiral centres. This formula holds true when there is an absence of symmetry between chiral centres. Tartaric acid would be expected to have four stereoisomers since $n = 2$. Tartaric acid has only three stereoisomers as two of them are equivalent and only two of the stereoisomers are optically active. The *meso* form is inactive through internal compensation. This reduction in the number of stereoisomers for tartaric acid is due to the molecule having a plane of symmetry.

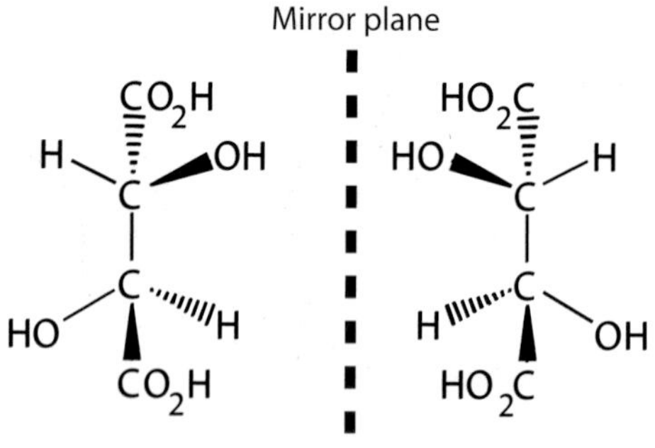

Mirror plane

(+) tartaric acid   (−) tartaric acid

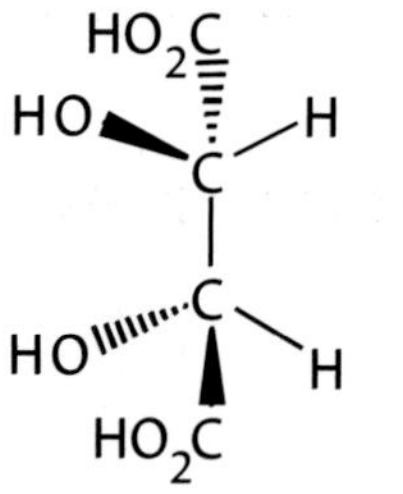

meso tartaric acid

The molecular models below show the pair of optically active enantiomers, namely (+) R,R-tartaric acid and (-) S,S-tartaric acid.

The molecular models show the optically inactive meso tartaric acid enantiomers, namely R,S-tartaric acid. This is identical to S,R-tartaric acid and is why there are only three stereoisomers for tartaric acid.

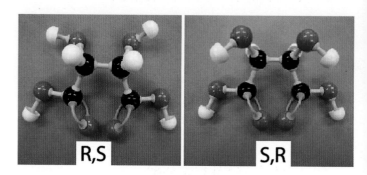

For tartaric acid, *R,R* and *S,S* are a pair of enantiomers which are both diastereoisomers to meso tartaric acid. Today, tartaric acid has found use as an antioxidant (E334) and as a mild laxative as Rochelle salt, which is potassium sodium tartrate.

Questions 24.4

1. What is the simple formula used to calculate the number of possible stereoisomers for molecules containing one or more chiral carbons? How many stereoisomers will a molecule with four chircal centres have and how many pairs of enantiomers?

2. What would be the enantiomeric excess for a racemic mixture?

3. Complete the table to show which pairs of stereoisomers are enantiomers and which pairs of stereoisomers are diastereoisomers.

	SR	RS	RR	SS
SR				
RS				
RR				
SS				

4. Which of the following statements are TRUE and which statements are FALSE.

i. Enantiomers have identical solubilities.

ii. One enantiomer is (+) and the other enantiomer is (−).

iii. Molecules with one chiral centre can form diastereoisomers.

iv. *RR* & *SS* are enantiomers.

v. *RR* & *SR* are enantiomers.

vi. *SS* & *RS* are diastereoisomers.

vii. Diastereoisomers have identical melting points.

5. Describe the stereoisomers for 2,3-dibromobutane and the relationship between them.

6. Natural (−) menthol occurs in peppermint oil and has the interesting property of making you feel cool as it triggers cold receptors in the skin. Identify the absolute configurations at its three chiral centres in the cyclohexane at the 1, 2 and 5 positions. How many possible stereoisomers are there for menthol including the isomer (−) menthol?

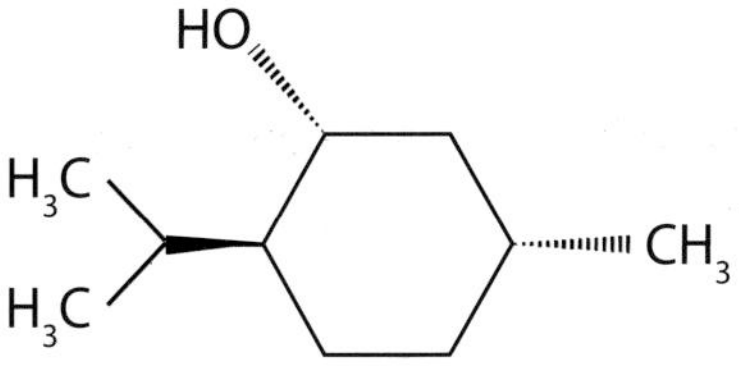

(−) menthol

7. What is the theoretical number of stereoisomers for a protein with one hundred amino acid residues. Why is only one version of the molecule found in nature?

8. Chloramphenicol is an antibiotic which is used for bacterial conjunctivitis and for the treatment of cholera and typhoid. Give the absolute configurations for the chiral centres in chloramphenicol using C-I-P priority rules.

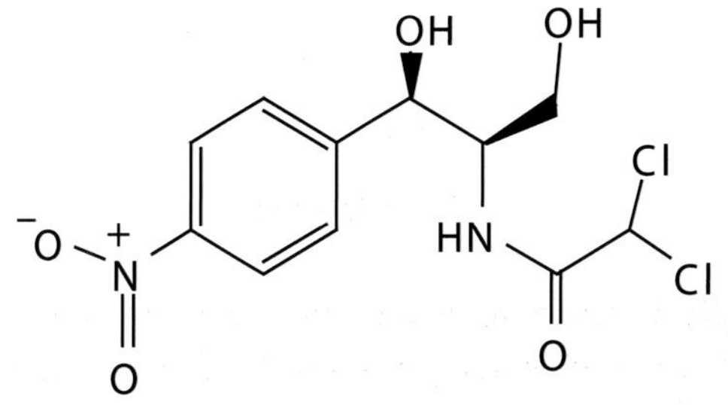

chloramphenicol

9. Citalopram is an antidepressant used to treat mood disorders. Identify any chiral centres (*) in this selective serotonin reuptake inhibitor and suggest why it is prescribed as a racemic mixture.

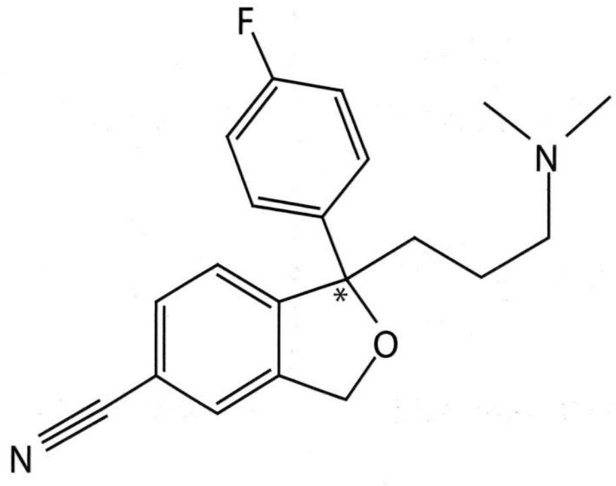

citalopram

25

Qualitative & Quantitative Analysis

Contents

A colleague, whilst walking on a Down[1] in Hampshire, found what he thought might be a meteorite which later turned out to be a lump of non-magnetic haematite. It was only through qualitative analysis and ion tests that this material could be identified with authority. It is often useful to be able to test for the presence of an ion in an unknown substance or for a gas that is formed in a chemical reaction. Chemistry as a subject has developed from experiments carried out by thousands of scientists over millennia. It is easy to forget the hard work that has gone into developing tests which reveal the contents of a test tube by a simple colour change. It is just a few who annually receive the highest accolade, namely the Nobel Prize in Chemistry, and we should also remember their colleagues who worked hard and with great attention to detail whilst in their laboratories around the world. One should also keep in mind that if you lift the veil from any chemical reaction, the beauty of the mathematics which truly underpins the subject will be revealed. This section on quantitative analysis will show how important the scientific method is to chemistry. As Einstein said, "imagination is more important than knowledge." But without knowledge little will be imagined.

A4.1 (a) Qualitative analysis

Qualitative analysis is finding out what elements are present in a substance.

Gas tests

The gases which can be tested for include: NH_3 (ammonia), CO_2 (carbon dioxide), H_2 (hydrogen), Cl_2 (chlorine), SO_2 (sulfur dioxide), O_2 (oxygen), HCl (hydrogen chloride). At one time chemists used to have to identify chemicals by smell and even taste. Extreme caution is recommended when smelling even the smallest quantities of the pungent gases.

---

1   In England, a 'Down' is a hill, not a valley. If you are wondering why it is not called an 'Up', this is because the word comes from the same Old English root word for 'Dune' (as in 'sand dune').

Gas or vapour	Colour & odour	Test	Positive test result
NH_3	Colourless & pungent rather unpleasant smell.	Moist (red) litmus paper.	Turns litmus paper blue.
CO_2	Colourless & sweet.	Bubble through limewater $Ca(OH)_2(aq)$.	From colourless to a milky (cloudy) suspension. This precipitate eventually becomes colourless with prolonged exposure to excess carbon dioxide.
H_2	Colourless & odourless.	Lit splint.	Squeaky pop & mildly explosive.
Cl_2	Greenish yellow with a choking odour.	Moist (blue) litmus paper or bubble through Br_2 (aq).	Turns litmus paper quickly red and then it bleaches the paper. Turns orange $Br_2(aq)$ colourless.
SO_2	Colourless with a choking odour.	Bubble through $Cr_2O_7^{2-}/H^+$.	Turns the solution from orange to green without a precipitate being formed.
O_2	Colourless & odourless.	Glowing splint.	Splint relights or glows brighter.
HCl	Colourless & pungent.	Moist (blue) litmus paper **or** contact with drop of c.NH_3 on a glass rod.	Turns litmus paper red **or** smoky white fumes of NH_4Cl.

Preparation of gases

Many chemical reactions will generate a gas. Always remember that if there is a rapid build up of pressure it might lead to an explosion unless the gas is vented. When collecting a gas it is important to consider its physical properties of density compared with air and its solubility in water.

Gas	Density (> air)	Soluble in water (>1g per 100cm³)
NH_3	×	√
CO_2	√	×
H_2	×	×
Cl_2	√	√
SO_2	√	√
O_2	√	×
HCl	√	√

Collection of gases

Hydrogen is insoluble in water so can be collected by displacing water in an inverted test tube which is full of water.

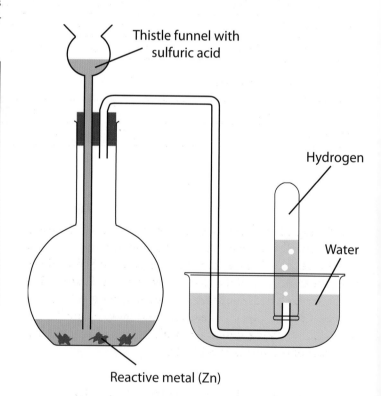

Thistle funnel with sulfuric acid

Hydrogen

Water

Reactive metal (Zn)

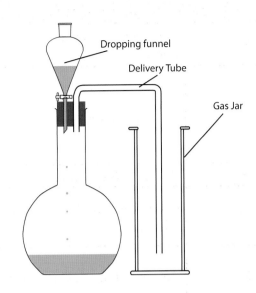

Gases more dense than air can be collected in a gas jar where they will displace the air.

Once the gas jar is full, the top needs to be covered with a lid.

Organic tests

The different functional groups have different chemistry so it should come as no surprise that some have their own tests. The organic groups which can be tested for include: unsaturation in alkenes using Br_2 (aq), alcohol using Na (s) or $Cr_2O_7^{2-}$ (aq) / H^+ (aq), distinguishing between 1°, 2°, 3° alcohols using **Lucas' Reagent** (Zn / c.HCl), carboxylic acid, aldehyde in glucose using Na_2CO_3 (aq) **Brady's reagent** and **Tollens' reagent**.

Substance	Test	Observation
Alkene ($R_2C=CR_2$)	Bromine water Br_2 (aq)	Bromine water decolourises (orange to colourless)
Alcohol (ROH)	Na (s) plus phenolphthalein	H_2 (g) bubbles seen and indicator turns pink (alkali)
1° or 2° alcohol (ROH or R_2CHOH)	$Cr_2O_7^{2-}$ (aq) / H^+ (aq)	Colour change from orange to blue-green
Alcohol (ROH)	Warm with RCO_2H / H^+ (aq)	Volatile, fruity smelling ester
1° Alcohols (RCH_2OH)	Lucas' reagent (Zn / c.HCl)	No cloudiness (turbidity)
2° Alcohols (R_2CHOH)	Lucas' reagent (Zn / c.HCl)	Slow Cloudiness (turbidity)
3° Alcohols (R_3COH)	Lucas' reagent (Zn / c.HCl)	Rapid Cloudiness (turbidity)
Carboxylic acid (RCO_2H)	Na_2CO_3 (aq)	Bubbles (effervescence) of gas which can be tested with limewater to confirm as CO_2
Aldehyde (RCHO)	Brady's reagent (2,4-DNPH)	Yellow/orange/red precipitate
Aldehyde (RCHO)	Tollens' reagent	Silver mirror formed (or black silver(I) oxide formed)

Lucas' Reagent provides an environment that favours the S_N1 mechanism, the presence of zinc chloride. It is made *in situ* from the reaction between zinc and concentrated hydrochloric acid. The OH group of the alcohol swaps with a Cl atom. The rate of reaction is different with the three types (1°, 2°, 3°) of alcohol. Cloudiness in the reaction mixture is caused by the alkyl chloride being immiscible with the aqueous solutions. The order of reaction is 3° > 2° > 1°.

$$ROH + HCl \xrightarrow{ZnCl_2 / \Delta} RCl + H_2O$$

Cation tests

There are a number of positive ions (metals and ammonium) which are known as **cations** that can be tested for with aqueous solutions of sodium hydroxide and also with ammonia solution. A lot of metal hydroxides are insoluble and the colour of the precipitate (abbrev.: ppt) can be a useful tool for identifying the metal ion. The list of cations is by no means exhaustive, but does include all the ions for the Pre-U chemistry course;

- NH_4^+ is tested with only aqueous NaOH.

- Al^{3+}, Ba^{2+}, Ca^{2+}, Cr^{3+}, Cu^{2+}, Fe^{2+}, Fe^{3+}, Pb^{2+}, Mg^{2+}, Mn^{2+}, Zn^{2+} are tested for with NaOH & NH_3.

Ammonia solutions often give the same result as addition of sodium hydroxide because the ammonia is a weak base (proton acceptor) that reacts with the water (proton donor) producing an equilibrium mixture that contains hydroxide ions

$$NH_3\ (aq) + H_2O\ (l) \rightleftharpoons NH_4^+\ (aq) + OH^-\ (aq)$$

Flame tests are also a useful way to identify the presence of some metal cations.

Substance	Test with NaOH	Test with NH$_3$	Observation
Al^{3+}	√		White precipitate of Al(OH)$_3$ which dissolves in excess NaOH.
Al^{3+}		√	White ppt of Al(OH)$_3$ which insoluble in excess NH$_4$OH.
NH$_4^+$	√		There is a pungent smell of ammonia which can be detected using moist red litmus paper which turns blue.
Ba^{2+}	√		No precipitate if reagents are pure (otherwise milky white Ba(OH)$_2$ is observed).
Ba^{2+}		√	No precipitate (negative test).
Ca^{2+}	√		White precipitate of Ca(OH)$_2$ with high [Ca^{2+}] which is insoluble in excess NaOH.
Ca^{2+}		√	Sometimes a very faint white precipitate of Ca(OH)$_2$.
Cr^{3+}	√		Initially a grey-green precipitate forms which dissolves in excess NaOH to form dark green chromite.
Cr^{3+}		√	Grey green gelatinous precipitate of Cr(OH)$_3$.
Cu^{2+}	√		Pale blue precipitate of Cu(OH)$_2$ forms which does not dissolve in excess NaOH.
Cu^{2+}		√	Initially a pale blue precipitate of Cu(OH)$_2$ forms which dissolves in excess NH$_3$ to form a deep blue solution of [Cu(NH$_3$)$_4$(H$_2$O)$_2$]$^{2+}$.
Fe^{2+}	√		Green gelatinous precipitate of Fe(OH)$_2$ which is insoluble in excess NaOH and which quickly turns orange-brown at the air/solution interface.
Fe^{2+}		√	Green gelatinous precipitate of Fe(OH)$_2$.
Fe^{3+}	√		Orange-brown gelatinous precipitate of Fe(OH)$_3$.
Fe^{3+}		√	Orange-brown gelatinous precipitate of Fe(OH)$_3$.
Pb^{2+}	√		White precipitate of Pb(OH)$_2$ soluble in excess NaOH.
Pb^{2+}		√	White precipitate of Pb(OH)$_2$ insoluble in excess NH$_3$.
Mg^{2+}	√		White precipitate of Mg(OH)$_2$ insoluble in excess NaOH.
Mg^{2+}		√	Slight (faint) precipitate of Mg(OH)$_2$ insoluble in excess NH$_3$.
Mn^{2+}	√		Cream gelatinous precipitate of Mn(OH)$_2$.
Mn^{2+}		√	Cream gelatinous precipitate of Mn(OH)$_2$.
Zn^{2+}	√		A white precipitate of Zn(OH)$_2$ forms with a few drops of NaOH. The precipitate dissolves in excess NaOH.
Zn^{2+}		√	A white precipitate of Zn(OH)$_2$ forms which dissolves in excess NH$_3$.

The ionic equations

Al³⁺, Zn²⁺ & Pb²⁺. A white precipitate forms in the presence of NaOH. In the case of Al³⁺:

$$Al^{3+} (aq) + 3\ OH^- (aq) \rightarrow Al(OH)_3 (s)$$

The white precipitate dissolves in excess sodium hydroxide as a further reaction occurs as an additional hydroxide joins forming soluble tetrahydroxoaluminate ions

$$Al(OH)_3 (s) + OH^- (aq) \rightarrow Al(OH)_4^- (aq)$$

Similarly:

$$Zn^{2+} (aq) + 2\ OH^- (aq) \rightarrow Zn(OH)_2 (s)$$

$$Zn(OH)_2 (s) + 2\ OH^- (aq) \rightarrow Zn(OH)_4^{2-} (aq)$$

and

$$Pb^{2+} (aq) + 2\ OH^- (aq) \rightarrow Pb(OH)_2 (s)$$

$$Pb(OH)_2 (s) + 2\ OH^- (aq) \rightarrow Pb(OH)_4^{2-} (aq)$$

One way to remember which of these white hydroxide precipitates dissolves is **ZAP**. Where $\mathbf{Z} = Zn(OH)_2$, $\mathbf{A} = Al(OH)_3$ and $\mathbf{P} = Pb(OH)_2$. These three hydroxides are amphoteric (can react as an acid or a base depending upon other reactants).

NH₄⁺. Ammonia is an alkaline gas because it is (readily) soluble in water and turns moist red litmus paper blue. The reaction works for solid ammonium compounds as well as for aqueous solutions.

$$NH_4^+ (aq) + OH^- (aq) \rightarrow NH_3 (g) + H_2O (l)$$

Impure Ba²⁺. $Ba^{2+} (aq) + 2\ OH^- (aq) \rightarrow Ba(OH)_2 (s)$

The white precipitate is very water soluble.

Ca²⁺. $Ca^{2+} (aq) + 2\ OH^- (aq) \rightarrow Ca(OH)_2 (s)$

Cr³⁺. $Cr^{3+} (aq) + 3\ OH^- (aq) \rightarrow Cr(OH)_3 (s)$

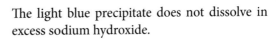

Grey-green precipitate of chromium(III) hydroxide.

Cu²⁺. $Cu^{2+} (aq) + 2\ OH^- (aq) \rightarrow Cu(OH)_2 (s)$

The light blue precipitate does not dissolve in excess sodium hydroxide.

A pale blue precipitate of copper(II) hydroxide also forms when ammonia solution is added to copper(II) ions, as ammonia reacts with water to produce hydroxide ions according to the equation:

$$NH_3 (aq) + H_2O (l) \rightarrow NH_4^+ (aq) + OH^- (aq)$$

The pale blue $Cu(OH)_2$ dissolves in excess ammonia to produce a dark blue soluble complex of $[Cu(NH_3)_4(H_2O)_2]^{2+}$

Fe²⁺. The gelatinous green precipitate which forms does not dissolve in excess sodium hydroxide. The precipitate darkens on exposure to the air after several minutes as the iron(II) hydroxide is oxidised to the orange-brown iron(III) hydroxide. The iron(II) hydroxide floats whereas the iron(III) hydroxide sinks.

$$Fe^{2+} (aq) + 2\ OH^- (aq) \rightarrow Fe(OH)_2 (s)$$

Fe³⁺. Precipitate which forms does not dissolve in excess sodium hydroxide.

The iron(III) hydroxide sinks.

$$Fe^{3+} (aq) + 3\ OH^- (aq) \rightarrow Fe(OH)_3 (s)$$

Pb^{2+}. Pb^{2+} (aq) + 2 OH$^-$ (aq) → $Pb(OH)_2$ (s)

The white precipitate which forms dissolves in excess sodium hydroxide.

$Pb(OH)_2$ (s) + 2OH$^-$ (aq) → $Pb(OH)_4^{2-}$ (aq)

Mg^{2+}. Mg^{2+} (aq) + 2 OH$^-$ (aq) → $Mg(OH)_2$ (s)

The white precipitate which forms does not dissolve in excess sodium hydroxide. Take care when writing manganese and magnesium as it is very easy to unintentionally write down the wrong name or symbol.

Mn^{2+}. Mn^{2+} (aq) + 2 OH$^-$ (aq) → $Mn(OH)_2$ (s)

The cream precipitate which forms does not dissolve in excess sodium hydroxide. It quickly turns brown on exposure to air.

Anion tests

There are a number of negative ions (non-metallic ions) which are known as **anions** that can also be tested for and which include:

- Carbonate, chromate(VI), sulfite and nitrite tested with dilute acids, H$^+$ (aq).

- Chromate(VI), sulfate and sulfite tested with Ba^{2+} (aq) and Pb^{2+} (aq).

- Chloride, bromide and iodide all tested with Ag$^+$ (aq) and Pb^{2+} (aq).

- Heating nitrate and nitrite with OH$^-$ (aq) and Al foil.

Substance	Test	Observation
Carbonate	Dilute acids, H$^+$ (aq)	Effervescence (bubbles)
Chromate(VI)	Dilute acids, H$^+$ (aq)	Yellow to orange
Sulfite	Warm with dil. acids, H$^+$ (aq) (test gas with acidified $K_2Cr_2O_7$ paper	SO$_2$ gas is evolved that turns dichromate paper from orange to green
Nitrite	dilute acids, H$^+$ (aq)	Instant effervescence, pale blue solution and red-brown NO$_2$ gas is evolved

Substance	Test	Observation
Chromate(VI)	Ba^{2+} (aq)	Yellow precipitate
Chromate(VI)	Pb^{2+} (aq)	Yellow precipitate
Sulfate	Ba^{2+} (aq)	Fine white powdery precipitate
Sulfate	Pb^{2+} (aq)	White precipitate
Sulfite	Ba^{2+} (aq)	White precipitate
Sulfite	Pb^{2+} (aq)	White precipitate
Chloride	Ag$^+$ (aq) and Pb^{2+} (aq)	A curdy white precipitate
Bromide	Ag$^+$ (aq) and Pb^{2+} (aq)	Pale cream precipitate
Iodide	Ag$^+$ (aq) and Pb^{2+} (aq)	Yellow precipitate
Nitrate	Heat with OH$^-$ (aq) with Al foil or Devarda's alloy	Pungent NH$_3$ gas evolved
Nitrite	Heat with OH$^-$ (aq) with Al foil	NH$_3$ gas evolved on heating. Colourless gas NO liberated by dilute acids, which turns pale brown (NO$_2$) in air

The ionic equations

Carbonate. On addition of acid bubbles evolve.

$$CO_3^{2-} (aq) + 2 H^+ (aq) → CO_2 (g) + H_2O (l)$$

Chromate(VI) is yellow in alkaline conditions and becomes orange in acidic conditions as it 'dimerises' without change in oxidation state (number).

$$2 CrO_4^{2-} (aq) + 2H^+ (aq) \rightleftharpoons Cr_2O_7^{2-} (aq) + H_2O (l)$$
yellow   *orange*

Nitrate. To a nitrate solution (2 cm^3) add dil. NaOH (3 cm^3), then approximately half a spatula of Devarda's alloy. Gently warm the mixture noting the smell of ammonia.

Devarda's alloy (Al 45%, Cu 50% and Zn 5%) is a reducing agent.

$$3NO_3^- (aq) + 8Al (s) + 5OH^- (aq) + 18H_2O (l)$$
$$\rightarrow 3NH_3 (g) + 8[Al(OH)_4]^- (aq)$$

A **sulfate** (SO_4^{2-}) will produce a white precipitate of barium sulfate when reacted with a soluble barium salt such as $BaCl_2$ or $Ba(NO_3)_2$. Barium sulfate is one of the most insoluble of all substances and has been known to precipitate out onto the drill bits on oil rigs. A sulfate will also produce a white precipitate of lead(II) sulfate.

$$Ba^{2+} (aq) + SO_4^{2-} (aq) \rightarrow BaSO_4 (s)$$

$$Pb^{2+} (aq) + SO_4^{2-} (aq) \rightarrow PbSO_4 (s)$$

A **sulfite** (SO_3^{2-}) has one less oxygen than the more familiar sulfate ion and it has the same 2– charge which means the sulfur is in a different oxidation state. A sulfite (SO_3^{2-}) will produce a white precipitate with barium and lead(II) solutions.

$$Ba^{2+} (aq) + SO_3^{2-} (aq) \rightarrow BaSO_3 (s)$$

$$Pb^{2+} (aq) + SO_3^{2-} (aq) \rightarrow PbSO_3 (s)$$

It is possible to further distinguish between sulfates and sulfites by the solubility of their precipitates in hot dilute hydrochloric acid. Barium sulfite is soluble (see equation below) whereas barium sulfate is insoluble in hot dil. HCl (aq). Sulfur dioxide is so soluble in water that it is unlikely that bubbles will be observed.

$$BaSO_3 (s) + 2H^+ (aq) \rightarrow Ba^{2+} (aq) + H_2O (l) + SO_2 (g)$$

Halide salts

The unknown substance is usually dissolved in nitric acid as all nitrate salts are soluble. On addition of silver nitrate a precipitate will immediately form if a halide ion is present.

$$Ag^+ (aq) + Cl^- (aq) \rightarrow AgCl (s)$$
white

$$Ag^+ (aq) + Br^- (aq) \rightarrow AgBr (s)$$
cream

$$Ag^+ (aq) + I^- (aq) \rightarrow AgI (s)$$
yellow

It can sometimes be quite difficult to distinguish between the silver salt of the halides, especially silver bromide which is part way between white and yellow in colour. The final confirmation test for the silver halides is their relative solubilities in dilute and concentrated ammonia solutions.

Silver Halide	Soluble in dil. NH_3	Soluble in c. NH_3
AgCl	√	√
AgBr	×	√
AgI	×	×

Miscellaneous tests

There are a number of additional tests that are needed.

- Insolubility of lead(II) chloride in water and silver iodide in NH_3 (aq).

- Solubility of silver chloride, silver bromide and silver iodide in dil. NH_3 (aq) & c.NH_3 (aq).

- Solubility of barium sulphate and barium sulfite in excess dilute strong acids.

- Starch test for iodine.

- Indicators to test for alkalinity / acidity to include; phenolphthalein, methyl orange, screened methyl orange, bromophenol blue, red and blue litmus.

Question 25.1

1. Which carbonyl compounds react with both ammoniacal silver nitrate (Tollens' reagent) and the reducing agent sodium borohydride ($NaBH_4$)?

   A   Only ketones.

   B   Neither ketones or aldehydes.

   C   Aldehydes and ketones.

   D   Only aldehydes.

A4.1 (b) Empirical and molecular formulae

Once the elements present in a substance have been identified by **qualitative analysis**, the amounts of each element can be determined by **quantitative analysis**. The use of these tests along with the different spectroscopies (A4.2-A4.5, B4.6) and crystallography (B2.5) allow new substances that have been isolated from organisms or synthesized in a laboratory to be determined. The first formulae to be determined are the empirical and molecular formulae followed by the structural formulae.

Organic molecules are the most numerous of all the known compounds. The amounts of carbon and hydrogen present can be detected by heating a little of the compound with an excess of copper(II) oxide. Any carbon will be oxidised into carbon dioxide which turns limewater milky. Carbon dioxide can be absorbed onto solid sodium hydroxide held in gauze and from the mass increase, the percentage of carbon can be calculated. Any hydrogen present will be oxidised to water which turns anhydrous copper(II) sulfate blue. Water can be absorbed onto solid anhydrous magnesium perchlorate, $Mg(ClO_4)_2$, and, from the mass increase, the percentage of hydrogen can be calculated. Once all the elements have been quantified it is possible to calculate the empirical formula from the percentage of each element.

Empirical formula

This is the simplest whole number ratio of elements in a compound. Empirical formulae can be calculated from percentage composition. Benzene has the molecular formula C_6H_6. Dividing the molecular formula by six gives the simplest whole number ratio, *i.e.* its empirical formula is CH. This tells us that there is one hydrogen atom for every carbon atom in benzene.

Empirical formula from % by mass

If the percentage by mass of hydrogen in a substance was 14.2% then it is like saying if there was 100 g of substance then there would be 14.2 g of hydrogen atoms. The percentage by mass of an element can be turned into an amount (moles) by dividing the % by mass by its relative atomic mass (A_r). This leads to a molar ratio of elements. Each element's molar ratio is then divided by the smallest molar ratio, which often gives the empirical formula. If the answer is within ±0.05 of a whole number they can be rounded as these small errors are due to experimental error in the quantitative analysis. If a whole number is not obtained then each ratio is multiplied by 2 or 3 *etc.* until a whole number is obtained, which is the empirical formula. It is often the case that the % by mass of one

element such as oxygen is not given. It can often be calculated by subtracting all the other values from 100%. When doing calculations it is always worth checking that the % by mass totals 100% and to work to at least two decimal places.

Example 25.1

A substance contains 10.9% H, 13.9% N, 59.4% C and 15.8% O by mass. Calculate its empirical formula.

Solution:

	H	N	C	O
%	10.9	13.9	59.4	15.8
A_r	1	14	12	16
% / A_r	10.9	0.993	4.95	0.988
/ smallest (0.988)	11.03	1.01	5.01	1
whole number	11	1	5	1
Empirical formula	$C_5H_{11}NO$			

Example 25.2

A substance contains 10.34% H, 62.07% C and 27.59% O by mass. Calculate its empirical formula.

Solution:

	H	C	O
%	10.34	62.07	27.59
A_r	1	12	16
% / A_r	10.34	5.17	1.72
/ smallest (1.72)	6.01	3.01	1
whole number	6	3	1
Empirical formula	C_3H_6O		

Questions 25.2

1. A substance contains 11.10% H, 35.56% O and 53.34% C by mass. Calculate its empirical formula.

2. Three iron compounds have the following % by mass. Calculate their empirical formulae.

(a) 77.7% Fe & 22.3% O

(b) 72.4% Fe & 27.6% O

(c) 70.0% Fe & 30.0% O

3. Which pair of compounds do not have the same empirical formulae?

A CH_3COOH & CH_3CH_2COOH

B C_6H_6 & C_2H_2

C CH_3CH_2CHO & CH_3COCH_3

D C_2H_5OH & CH_3OCH_3

4. Which compound has the same empirical formula as glucose?

A CH_3CH_2OH

B $CH_3CH_2CH_2OH$

C CH_3COOH

D $HCOOH$

5. Calculate the empirical formula for a hydrocarbon containing 18.2% hydrogen. Suggest its identity.

6. An organic compound only contains C (40.0%), H (6.67%) and O. Calculate its empirical formula and suggest its identity.

Molecular formula

A molecular formula gives the actual numbers of atoms present in a molecule. A molecular formula groups the atoms by type and number. It is very useful to know the molecular formula as it is needed for calculating relative molecular mass (M_r). The molecular formula of ethanol is not C_2H_5OH but is, in fact, C_2H_6O. A substance's molecular formula can be identical to its empirical formula, e.g. methane CH_4 and methanal CH_2O. A molecular formula is always a simple multiple of the empirical formula. The molecular formula for ethanoic acid (CH_3COOH) is $C_2H_4O_2$ and its empirical formula is CH_2O. This makes the molecular formula of ethanoic acid twice its empirical formula.

The positional isomers but-1-ene $CH_2=CHCH_2CH_3$ and but-2-ene $CH_3CH=CHCH_3$ both have the same molecular formula C_4H_8. It is helpful to realise that functional group isomers (A3.1d) e.g. aldehydes and ketones also have the same molecular formula. Propanal CH_3CH_2CHO has a molecular formula of C_3H_6O and propanone CH_3COCH_3 also has a molecular formula of C_3H_6O.

Combustion analysis can be used to determine a substance's empirical formula. This can be used in conjunction with a mass spectrum to solve the molecular formula.

Example 25.3

Combustion analysis showed that a dicarboxylic acid contained 40.68% of carbon, 54.24% of oxygen and 5.08% of hydrogen. The mass spectrum of this organic compound reveals it to have a molecular ion at 118. Calculate the empirical and molecular formulae and suggest the identity of the dicarboxylic acid.

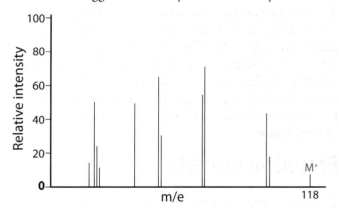

Solution:

Empirical formula

Carbon $\frac{40.68}{12} = 3.39$

Oxygen $= \frac{54.24}{16} = 3.39$

Hydrogen $= \frac{5.08}{1} = 5.08$

So that:

Carbon $= \frac{3.39}{3.39} = 1$

Oxygen $= \frac{3.39}{3.39} = 1$

Hydrogen $= \frac{5.08}{3.39} = 1.5$

and:

Carbon $= 1 \times 2 = 2$

Oxygen = $1 \times 2 = 2$

Hydrogen = $1.5 \times 2 = 3$

Empirical formula = $C_2H_3O_2$

Using the empirical formula:

$2C + 3H + 2O = 2(12) + 3(1) + 2(16) = 59$

Molecular formula

The molecular ion has mass 118.

To work out the ratio of the two formulae is $\frac{118}{59} = 2$.

Therefore the empirical formula is half the molecular formula which is: $C_4H_6O_4$

The dicarboxylic acid could be $COOH(CH_2)_2COOH$ butane-1,4-dicarboxylic acid which is known trivially as succinic acid. Or it could be an isomer such as 2-methylpropane-1,3-dicarboxylic acid $COOH(CH(CH_3))COOH$, known trivially as methylmalonic acid.

Question 25.3

1. Name the alcohol with the same molecular formula as methoxymethane.

A4.1 (c) Volumetric analysis

Volumetric methods of analysis are quantitative and include techniques that are based on volumes of liquids such as **titrations**. The purpose of a titration is to calculate the unknown concentration of one substance by reaction with another substance that has a known concentration. The different types of reaction that are suitable for titration are acid-base reactions (B1.5g) and redox reactions (B1.5j & B2.4i). In a **redox titration** the reductant is titrated against a standard solution of oxidant. During a titration the reaction can be followed until it has gone to completion by several different methods. It is possible to find the equivalence point from changes in temperature (**thermometric titration**), changes in conductivity (**potentiometric titration**) and using indicators (B1.5g). The equivalence point is the stage in a titration when the reactants and products are all present in the equivalent amounts that match the stoichiometric ratio in the balanced formula equation. When a large number of titrations

of the same type are needed, *e.g.* testing for the use of banned substances in the blood or urine of athletes, the titrations can be automated and carried out by machines. The advantage of titrations is that they can be carried out very quickly without the need for high cost machines such as the various types of spectrometer. Titrations can also be used to monitor the rates of reactions (B1.6i) when a catalyst can be removed or the reaction quenched by cooling.

Titration

In order to carry out a titration you need to know the equation for the reaction, the concentration of one reactant and the volumes of both reactants. The reactant whose concentration is not known is usually placed in the burette. The substance of known concentration is pipetted into a conical flask which is placed on top of a white tile. During the titration, small amounts of liquid are added from the burette into the conical flask. It takes practice to be able to add one drop at a time from the burette. The reactants can be mixed efficiently by carefully swirling the contents of the flask. The alternative method for mixing the reactants is to add a magnetic 'flea' to the conical flask and to stir the contents using a magnetic stirrer.

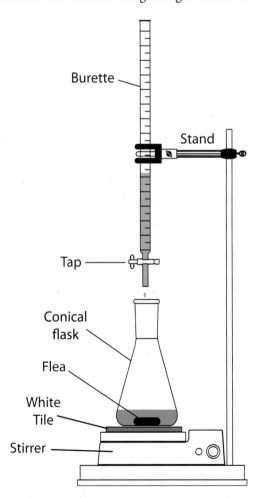

Useful practical tips include: ensure no air bubbles are trapped below the burette's tap, the burette is vertical, the burette does not leak at the tap, the funnel is not left in the burette during the titration, only 2-3 drops of indicator are added to the conical flask. Once at least two titrations have been carried out where the volume added (**titre**) is within ± 0.1 cm³, a good level of accuracy and repeatability has been achieved. The meniscus is the curve on the surface of the liquid and it needs to be read at the same point, *e.g.* bottom of the meniscus to avoid errors due to **parallax**. It is possible to read a burette to the nearest ± 0.05 cm³. As the volume of liquid added from the burette is calculated by difference it is a waste of time to attempt to start each titration with the initial burette reading at exactly 0.00 cm³.

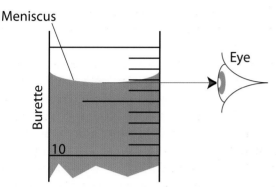

When doing a titration, it is important to record results in a logical manner in order to assist you with the subsequent calculation. The suggested table of results (below) allows for rapid calculation of the volume added from the burette. Remember to only take the average of results that are within the acceptable margin of error, *i.e.* ± 0.1 cm³. Rough titrations tend to overshoot the actual end point and are not included in the average titre calculation.

Burette readings	Rough	1st	2nd	Average
Final / cm³	17.70	35.20	52.70	
Initial / cm³	0.00	17.70	35.20	
Titre / cm³	17.70	17.50	17.50	**17.50**

When doing calculations for titrations it can be useful to use a calculation triangle.

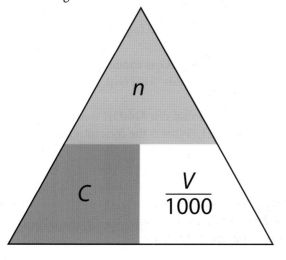

n = amount (mol), c = concentration (mol dm⁻³) and v = volume in cm³. The volume is divided by 1000 to convert the units of volume from cm³ to dm³.

The three equations from this triangle are:

$$n = c \times \frac{v}{1000} \qquad c = \frac{n}{\frac{v}{1000}} \qquad \& \qquad \frac{v}{1000} = \frac{n}{c}$$

Example 25.4

Calculate the concentration in mol dm⁻³ of 8.55g of barium hydroxide dissolved in 1 dm³ (1000 cm³) of deionised water. [A_r: Ba (137), O (16), H (1)]

Solution:

Barium hydroxide has the formula $Ba(OH)_2$

Relative formula mass (M_r) for $Ba(OH)_2$ = 137 + 2(16 + 1) = 171 g mol⁻¹

Amount of $Ba(OH)_2$ $n = \frac{m}{M_r} = \frac{8.55}{171} = 0.05$ mol

As the volume is 1 dm³ the concentration $\frac{n}{V} = \frac{0.05}{1} = 0.05$ mol dm⁻³

Example 25.5

20 cm³ of a 1 mol dm⁻³ solution of NaOH (aq) was neutralised by 25 cm³ of hydrochloric acid. What is the concentration of the hydrochloric acid [HCl (aq)]?

Solution:

There are two approaches (methods) when the stoichiometric ratio is a simple 1:1 as it is with this alkali and this acid to solve the concentration of the unknown. In both cases it is always wise to write the balanced formula equation.

NaOH (aq) + HCl (aq) → NaCl (aq) + H₂O (l)

Method 1

$C_1V_1 = C_2V_2$ [where C = concentration and V = volume, **1** refers to NaOH & **2** refers to HCl]

$1 \times \frac{20}{1000} = C_2 \times \frac{25}{1000}$

$0.02 = C_2 \times 0.025$

$$C_2 = \frac{0.02}{0.025}$$

$[HCl] = 0.8 \text{ mol dm}^{-3}$

Method 2

$$n(NaOH) = c \times \frac{v}{1000}$$

$$n(NaOH) = 1 \times \frac{20}{1000}$$

$$n(NaOH) = 0.02 \text{ mol}$$

1 mole NaOH : 1 mole HCl

Therefore $n(HCl) = 0.02 \text{ mol}$

$$[HCl] = \frac{n}{\frac{v}{1000}} = \frac{0.02}{\frac{25}{1000}} = 0.8 \text{ mol dm}^{-3}$$

Example 25.6

What is the concentration of sodium hydroxide when 25 cm³ is neutralised by 12.5 cm³ of sulphuric acid of concentration 0.15 mol dm⁻³?

Solution:

Step 1: Write the balanced equation for the reaction

$$2\,NaOH + H_2SO_4 \rightarrow Na_2SO_4 + 2\,H_2O$$

Step 2: Consider the relevant stoichiometries needed in the calculation

$2\,NaOH : 1\,H_2SO_4$

There are twice as many moles of alkali than acid.

Step 3: Mole calculations where n = amount (mol)

$$n(H_2SO_4) = c \times \frac{V}{1000} = 0.15 \times \frac{12.5}{1000} = 1.875 \times 10^{-3} \text{ mol}$$

$$n(NaOH) = 2 \times n(H_2SO_4) = 2 \times 1.875 \times 10^{-3} = 3.75 \times 10^{-3} \text{ mol}$$

$$[NaOH] = \frac{n}{\frac{V}{1000}} = \frac{3.75 \times 10^{-3} \text{ mol}}{\frac{25}{1000}} = 0.15 \text{ mol dm}^{-3}.$$

Questions 25.4

1. Calculate the concentration in mol dm⁻³ of the following;

   a) H^+ ions in 1 dm³ of a solution containing 7.3 g of hydrogen chloride.

   b) H^+ ions in 250 cm³ of a solution containing 29.2 g of hydrogen chloride.

   c) OH^- ions in 500 cm³ of a solution containing 56 g of potassium hydroxide.

   d) Cu^{2+} ions in 1 dm³ of a solution containing 24.95 g of hydrated copper(II) sulfate.

2. What volume of 0.25 moldm⁻³ hydrobromic acid (HBr) is needed to neutralise 150 cm³ of 0.12 moldm⁻³ barium hydroxide solution?

   A   72 cm³

   B   144 cm³

   C   216 cm³

   D   288 cm³

3. For each part, is the statement true or is it false?

   a) 200 g NaOH is enough to neutralise 1 dm³ of 2 mol dm⁻³ HCl (aq)

   b) 200 g NaOH is enough to neutralise ½ dm³ of 4 mol dm⁻³ H_2SO_4 (aq)

   c) 200 g NaOH is enough to neutralise 300 cm³ of 20 mol dm⁻³ HCl (aq)

   d) 76 g Na_2CO_3 is enough to neutralise 490 cm³ of 1 mol dm⁻³ HCl (aq)

   e) 0.76 g Na_2CO_3 is enough to neutralise 250 cm³ of 0.25 mol dm⁻³ HCl (aq)

4. 30 cm³ of 0.1 mol dm⁻³ NaOH were netralised by 28.2 cm³ of H_2SO_4. What is the concentration of the acid?

5. 20 cm³ of 0.05 mol dm⁻³ $Ca(OH)_2$ were neutralised by 27 cm³ of HCl. What is the concentration of the acid?

Primary standards

Primary volumetric standards are solutions made from high purity compounds made up to precise concentrations. Primary standards are used to standardise all other solutions whose concentrations are not known. Primary standards are prepared by dissolving a known mass of solid in a known volume of distilled water in a volumetric flask. The substance used as a primary standard needs to be 100% pure, *i.e.* **analar quality**. Sodium hydroxide cannot be used as a primary standard as it is hygroscopic (it absorbs moisture from the air). Different primary standards are used in the different types of titration.

Name	Formula	Titration
Anhydrous sodium carbonate	Na_2CO_3	Acid-base
Potassium dichromate(VI)	$K_2Cr_2O_7$	Redox
Potassium manganate(VII)	$KMnO_4$	Redox
Sodium thiosulfate	$Na_2S_2O_3$	Redox
Silver nitrate	$AgNO_3$	Precipitation

Picture of volumetric flasks

Example 25.7

Calculate the mass of substance needed to prepare 1 dm³ of 0.1 mol dm⁻³ sodium hydroxide.

[A_r: Na (23), O (16), H (1)]

Step 1: write the correct formula

NaOH

Step 2: calculate the relative formula mass (M_r)

M_r (NaOH) = 23 + 16 + 1 = 40 g mol⁻¹

Step 3: calculate amount n (mol)

$n = c \times v$ [no need to divide volume by 1000 if it is already in dm³]

$n = 0.1 \times 1 = 0.1$ mol

Step 4: calculate the mass (g)

$$n = \frac{m}{M_r}$$

therefore $m = n \times M_r$

m (NaOH) = 0.1 × 40 = 4 g

Question 25.5

1. Calculate the mass needed to prepare the following substances:[A_r: Ba (137), Cl (35.5), K (39.1), Cr (52.0), O (16.0), Fe (55.8), S (32.1), Mn (54.9)]

Substance	Conc. (mol dm⁻³)	Volume (cm³)	M_r (g mol⁻¹)	Mass (g)
$BaCl_2$	0.1	500		
$K_2Cr_2O_7$	0.2	250		
$FeSO_4$	0.3	750		
$KMnO_4$	0.1	500		

Example 25.8

Find the concentration of acidified iron(II) sulfate given that 25.0 cm³ needed 19.8 cm³ of 0.0200 mol dm⁻³ potassium manganate(VII) to complete the reaction.

Equation: MnO_4^- (aq) + 5 Fe^{2+} (aq) + 8 H^+ (aq) → Mn^{2+} (aq) + 5 Fe^{3+} (aq) + 4 H_2O (l)

Amount of MnO_4^- (aq) = $0.0200 \times \frac{19.8}{1000} = 3.96 \times 10^{-4}$ mol

Amount of Fe^{2+} (aq) = $5 \times n$ (MnO_4^-)

$= 5 \times 3.96 \times 10^{-4} = 1.98 \times 10^{-3}$ mol

$[Fe^{2+}] = \dfrac{n}{\frac{v}{1000}} = \dfrac{1.98 \times 10^{-3}}{\frac{25.0}{1000}} = 0.0792$ mol dm⁻³

Questions 25.6

1. 25.0 cm^3 of 0.2 mol dm^{-3} aqueous iodine solution is reduced by what volume of thiosulfate of concentration 0.36 mol dm^{-3}?

$$2 S_2O_3^{2-} \text{ (aq)} + I_2 \text{ (aq)} \rightarrow S_4O_6^{2-} \text{ (aq)} + 2 I^- \text{ (aq)}$$

2. 1.185 g of $K_2Cr_2O_7$ was dissolved in distilled water and made up to 250 cm^3 in a volumetric flask. 25.0 cm^3 of $K_2Cr_2O_7$ (aq) was pipetted into a conical flask and acidified with H_2SO_4. To this acidified dichromate solution was added an excess of potassium iodide to liberate the iodine.

$$Cr_2O_7^{2-} \text{ (aq)} + 6 I^- \text{ (aq)} + 14 H^+ \text{ (aq)}$$
$$\rightarrow 3 I_2 \text{ (aq)} + 2 Cr^{3+} \text{ (aq)} + 7 H_2O \text{ (l)}$$

The liberated iodine was titrated against a solution of sodium thiosulfate of unknown concentration. Use an average titre of 17.5 cm^3 to calculate the concentration of $Na_2S_2O_3$. What indicator could be used to sharpen the end-point and what colour changes would be observed?

Finding the equivalence point

Acid-base reactions are usually exothermic and it is possible to find the equivalence point by carrying out a **thermometric titration**. The reaction is carried out in a polystyrene cup and the thermometer has the dual purpose of recording the reaction mixture's temperature and being used as a stirrer. A known volume and concentration of sodium hydroxide (50.0 cm^3, $1.000 \text{ mol dm}^{-3}$) is pipetted into the polystyrene cup. An acid such as hydrochloric acid is added in 5.0 cm^3 portions from a burette. The temperature is recorded until a total of 50.0 cm^3 of acid is added. It is important to complete the reaction quickly to prevent errors due to cooling. A graph of temperature ($°C$) on the y-axis $vs.$ volume of acid (cm^3) on the x-axis is plotted. A typical set of results is shown. Two lines of best fit are drawn on the graph. Where the two lines cross corresponds to the volume of acid which is needed to neutralise the alkali. It is possible to calculate the acid's concentration from this value.

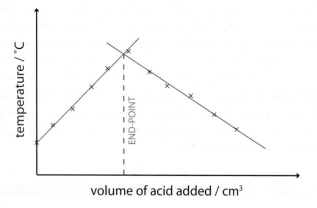

The reaction between sodium hydroxide and hydrochloric acid can also be monitored by using a conductivity meter in a **potentiometric titration**. The conductivity measures the degree of ionisation which, in this example, reaches a minimum at the equivalence point. The graph plotted is the meter reading on the y-axis $vs.$ the volume of reagent added on the x-axis.

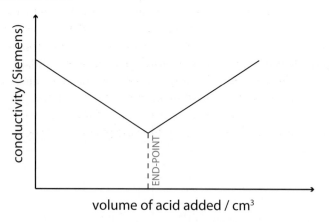

The shape of the titration curves depends on the strength of the acid and or base in an acid-base neutralisation. In a redox reaction such as the reaction between iron(II) and cerium(IV) the curve looks more like a titration curve where volume of titrant added from the burette (Ce^{4+}) is plotted against emf (V). The end point is taken as the almost vertical part of the curve.

$$Fe^{2+} \text{ (aq)} + Ce^{4+} \text{ (aq)} \rightleftharpoons Fe^{3+} \text{ (aq)} + Ce^{3+} \text{ (aq)}$$

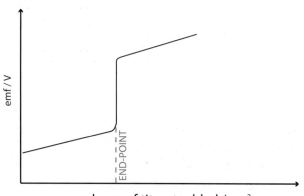

A4.1 (d)
Gravimetric analysis

There are two types of gravimetric analyses; thermal **decomposition reactions** and **precipitation reactions**. In both examples an accurate mass of a single product is obtained. These techniques were vital in the historical development of chemistry as a subject. A multitude of modern spectroscopic techniques are now available which have largely superseded the gravimetric tests. But a good chemist will gain a lot by carrying out gravimetric analyses and their supporting mole calculations on the quantitative data. These gravimetric techniques can be used to determine the purity of substances.

Thermal decompositions

Heating solid substances can sometimes bring about chemical changes rather than the physical process of melting. The decompositions we will consider are losing water from hydrated salts, *e.g.* hydrated copper(II) sulfate, and the decomposition of carbonates such as calcium carbonate.

Water of crystallisation

The water combined with some salts is known as **water of crystallisation**. Salts containing water are described as being **hydrated**. The water in hydrated salts is included as part of their formula, *e.g.* $CuSO_4.5H_2O$ which is hydrated copper(II) sulfate. It can also be thought of as a pentahydrate from its formula. Some crystals will release their water of crystallisation as water vapour when heated. This water is most often associated with the compound within the crystal's lattice structure. The following table gives examples of the most commonly met hydrated crystalline salts.

Formula	Common name	Type of hydrate	Trivial name
$Na_2CO_3.10H_2O$	Sodium carbonate	Decahydrate	Washing soda
$Na_2SO_4.10H_2O$	Sodium sulfate	Decahydrate	Glauber's salt
$CuSO_4.5H_2O$	Copper(II) sulfate	Pentahydrate	Blue vitriol
$FeSO_4.7H_2O$	Iron(II) sulfate	Heptahydrate	Green vitriol
$MgSO_4.7H_2O$	Magnesium sulfate	Heptahydrate	Epsom salt
$CaCl_2.6H_2O$	Calcium chloride	Hexahydrate	
$CaSO_4.2H_2O$	Calcium sulfate	Dihydrate	Gypsum
$CoCl_2.6H_2O$	Cobalt(II) chloride	Hexahydrate	

A simple experiment to demonstrate that a salt is a hydrate is to heat a small sample in a test tube. A piece of cobalt chloride paper is placed at the open mouth of the dry test tube. When water vapour is released it will come in contact with the blue cobalt chloride paper turning it pink. This results in the water vapour reacting with anhydrous cobalt(II) chloride to form hydrated cobalt(II) chloride ($CoCl_2.6H_2O$).

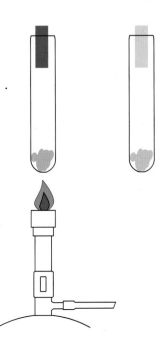

In order to work out the numbers of moles of water in a hydrate, a known mass of salt needs to be heated until no more mass is lost with additional heating. This is the point at which all the water has been driven off and the anhydrous salt remains. Temperature control is very important in these experiments as decompositions occur within certain temperature ranges. A particularly interesting example is the thermal decomposition of calcium ethanedioate monohydrate. It is also known as calcium oxalate monohydrate, a salt which is found, rather unpleasantly, in kidney stones. Three different products can result depending on the temperature chosen for the decomposition. The factors affecting the heat getting to a substance are: rate of heating, container's composition, and the purity of the test sample.

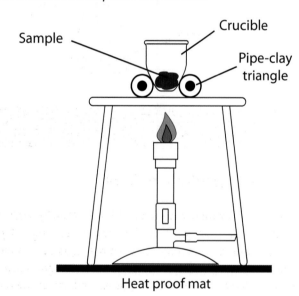

$$CH_3 \text{(structure)} \xrightarrow{100\text{-}226\,°C} \text{(structure)}$$

$$\xrightarrow{398\text{-}660\,°C} CaCO_3$$

$$\xrightarrow{660\text{-}840\,°C} CaO$$

Determining water of crystallisation

To calculate the water of crystallisation, heat a known mass of sample in an oven dried crucible. Heat the solid gently at first and then more strongly. Heat until a constant mass is achieved allowing the crucible to cool in a dessicator between heating. This prevents moisture from the air adding to the mass of the dehydrated salt. An example of how to calculate the number of moles of water of crystallisation for magnesium sulfate follows. This salt was historically used as a laxative.

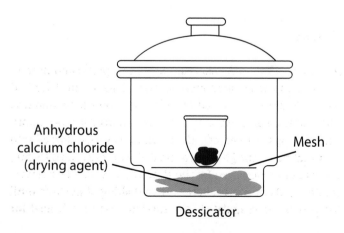

Example 25.9

A sample of hydrated magnesium sulfate was heated to determine its formula with the following results:

Mass of Crucible = 35.98 g

Mass of crucible + $MgSO_4$ crystals = 41.30 g

After heating:

Heating time (mins)	Mass of crucible + $MgSO_4$ crystals
10	39.06 g
15	38.62 g
20	38.59 g
25	38.59 g

Calculation:

Mass of hydrated $MgSO_4$

$\quad$ = crucible + $MgSO_4$ crystals – crucible

$\quad$ = 41.30 g – 35.98 g = 5.32 g

Mass of anhydrous $MgSO_4$

$\quad$ = crucible + $MgSO_4$ crystals (25 mins) – mass of crucible

$\quad$ = 38.59 g – 35.98 g = 2.61 g

Mass of water = hydrated $MgSO_4$ – anhydrous $MgSO_4$

$\quad$ = 5.32 g – 2.61 g = 2.71 g

Molar mass of $MgSO_4$ = 120.5 g mol^{-1} and molar mass of H_2O = 18 g mol^{-1}

Number of moles of $MgSO_4 = \dfrac{2.61}{120.5} = 0.0217$ mol

Number of moles of $H_2O = \dfrac{2.71}{18} = 0.151$ mol

Moles of water of crystallisation $= \dfrac{\text{moles water}}{\text{moles of } MgSO_4}$

$\qquad = \dfrac{0.151}{0.0217}$

$\qquad = 6.96$ mol

Formula is **$MgSO_4.7H_2O$** (to the nearest whole number)

Other thermal decompositions

Anhydrous substances do not contain water of crystallisation. Examples include magnesium carbonate ($MgCO_3$), calcium carbonate ($CaCO_3$), sodium hydrogen carbonate ($NaHCO_3$) and potassium chlorate ($KClO_3$). When heated, these substances decompose, releasing gases. When heating the first three substances, 2 g of material is sufficient to give reasonable results. It is advised that no more than 1g of potassium chlorate be used in experiments and that these be performed by the teacher, because of the risk of explosion.

$$MgCO_3\,(s) \xrightarrow{\text{heat}} MgO\,(s) + CO_2\,(g) \qquad (>800°C)$$

$$CaCO_3\,(s) \xrightarrow{\text{heat}} CaO\,(s) + CO_2\,(g) \qquad (>840°C)$$

$$2\,NaHCO_3\,(s) \xrightarrow{\text{heat}} Na_2CO_3\,(s) + H_2O\,(l) + CO_2\,(g)$$
$$(>60\text{-}950°C)$$

[At about 1000°C, Na_2CO_3 will decompose further into sodium oxide (Na_2O) and carbon dioxide.

$$Na_2CO_3\,(s) \xrightarrow{\text{heat}} Na_2O\,(s) + CO_2\,(g)\,]$$

$$2\,KClO_3\,(s) \xrightarrow{\text{heat}} 2\,KCl\,(s) + 3\,O_2\,(g) \qquad (>300°C)$$

Precipitation reactions

Precipitation reactions happen when two solutes in solution react to form one insoluble product and one soluble product. If the solid forms very quickly there is insufficient time for a lattice to grow and instead tiny particles called a **precipitate** will form in the liquid. The precipitate, if left for several minutes, will eventually settle to the bottom of the test tube. The formation of a precipitate is governed by the solubility product (K_{sp}) which is dealt with elsewhere in this book.

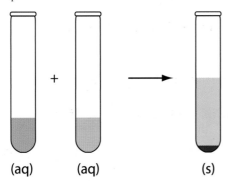

(aq)　　(aq)　　(s)

Insoluble salts which form as precipitates are used as both anion and cation tests in the section on qualitative analysis. Always remember to add state symbols when writing the balanced formula equation for a precipitation reacton; (s) = solid & (aq) = aqueous (dissolved in water).

Examples of precipitation reactions

$$AgNO_3\,(aq) + KCl\,(aq) \rightarrow AgCl\,(s) + KNO_3\,(aq)$$

$$AgNO_3\,(aq) + HCl\,(aq) \rightarrow AgCl\,(s) + HNO_3\,(aq)$$

$$Pb(NO_3)_2\,(aq) + 2\,KI\,(aq) \rightarrow PbI_2\,(s) + 2\,KNO_3\,(aq)$$

$$BaCl_2\,(aq) + H_2SO_4\,(aq) \rightarrow BaSO_4\,(s) + 2\,HCl\,(aq)$$

Many silver and lead(II) salts are prepared in precipitation reactions. Once a precipitate forms, it needs to be filtered, washed and then dried in an oven or a dessicator. The soluble salt is found in the filtrate and the precipitate is collected in the filter paper.

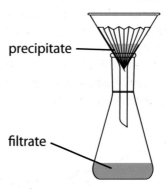

precipitate

filtrate

Example 25.10

Determining purity of rock salt

Rock salt is primarily sodium chloride (NaCl) with other impurities such as sand (SiO_2). There are large deposits underground in the county of Cheshire (England) as well as in Ireland and elsewhere on Earth. Rock salt is a good source of sodium chloride which is an important industrial chemical as well as finding use in keeping roads ice free in winter.

Results

A sample of rock salt was crushed using a pestle and mortar. 0.9945 g of the crushed material was dissolved in deionised water (20 cm³) and heated to its boiling point for 5 minutes. The next stage of the experiment was carried out in a laboratory with the lights turned off. The solution was then filtered into a conical flask. The filtrate was treated with nitric acid (5 cm³, 2.0 mol dm⁻³) followed by the slow addition of silver nitrate solution (30 cm³, 0.6 mol dm⁻³) with shaking of the flask until the precipitate coagulated. The mixture was then heated for

2 minutes. The precipitate (AgCl) was then rapidly collected by vacuum filtration and washed with HCl (0.001 mol dm^{-3}) until the unwanted filtrate tested negative for chloride ions. The precipitate was oven dried to a constant mass which was found to be 2.158 g. Calculate the percentage of sodium chloride (NaCl) in the original rock salt.

[Molar mass NaCl = 58.5 g mol^{-1}, AgCl = 143.5 g mol^{-1}].

Explanation

The sodium chloride dissolves readily in hot deionised water. Any insoluble substances would be removed by the first filtration. The amount of light getting to the silver chloride precipitate was minimised as it decomposes in sunlight (which is the basis of photography). All nitrates are soluble so the addition of nitric acid to the sodium chloride solution ensures no precipitates form as the first filtrate cools. Silver nitrate is slowly added with shaking to reduce the possibility of super saturation of the solution or a colloid forming. The second heating ensures all the silver chloride is precipitated. The second filtrate was periodically tested with AgNO$_3$ to check when the chloride from the HCl was removed from the precipitate. The desired reaction is shown by the following equation.

NaCl (aq) + AgNO$_3$ (aq) → AgCl (s) + NaNO$_3$ (aq)

Calculation

Assuming the rock salt was 100% NaCl.

Number of moles of NaCl $= \dfrac{0.9945 \text{ g}}{58.5 \text{ g mol}^{-1}} = 0.0170$ mol

The stoichiometric ratio for NaCl : AgNO$_3$ is 1:1 from the balanced equation

Therefore the moles AgCl precipitated assuming 100% completion is 0.0170 mol.

The mass of AgCl = number moles AgCl × molar mass of AgCl

Mass of AgCl = 0.0170 mol × 143.5 g mol^{-1} = 2.440 g

Therefore the percentage of NaCl $= \dfrac{2.158 \text{ g}}{2.440 \text{ g}} \times 100\% = 88.4$ %.

Questions 25.7

1.   Which of the following is **not** a precipitation reaction?

A $Mg^{2+} + SO_4^{2-} \rightarrow MgSO_4$

B $Ba^{2+} + SO_4^{2-} \rightarrow BaSO_4$

C $Ag^+ + Cl^- \rightarrow AgCl$

D $Pb^{2+} + 2\,Cl^- \rightarrow PbCl_2$

2.   What mass of water would be lost if 17.22 g of gypsum ($CaSO_4.2H_2O$) was fully dehydrated?

A   1.8 g

B   3.6 g

C   0.18 g

D   0.36 g

3.   When collecting a precipitate of AgCl (s) in a gravimetric analysis, how is it treated?

A   Evaporate, wash with water and dry to constant mass.

B   Filter, wash with dilute HNO$_3$ and dry to constant mass.

C   Filter, wash with dilute HCl and dry to constant mass.

D   Filter and dry to constant mass.

4.   Precipitation is the reverse process to?

A   evaporation

B   crystallisation

C   sublimation

D   dissolving

Another precipitation reaction

Nickel ions precipitate from solution using an alkaline solution of dimethylglyoxine. The precipitate is colored scarlet (red) and is an insoluble nickel dimethylglyoxine complex. The complex can be prepared using the following method. Transfer a small amount of nickel salt (50 mg = 0.05 g) to a 500 ml beaker and dissolve it in deionised water. Add dilute hydrochloric acid (10 ml, 2 moldm^{-3}) and make the volume up to 200 ml with deionised water. Heat the solution to 80°C and then quickly add a slight excess of 1% dimethylglyoxine in ethanol (25 ml). Immediately add dilute ammonia solution dropwise with constant stirring until the solution is alkaline as indicated by litmus paper. Cover the beaker with a watch glass and leave it for 30 minutes. The cold solution is then filtered, ideally using a sintered-glass crucible, and washed with cold water until the filtrate is free of chloride ions as tested with aqueous silver nitrate. The red precipitate is dried to constant mass. Drying at 100°C for 60 minutes should suffice.

red precipitate

This reaction is particularly useful in testing the skills of a chemist in a laboratory. A pure nickel salt can be mixed with known masses of other salts which do not form a precipitate with dimethylglyoxine. Metals salts which are unreactive with dimethylglyoxine include: cobalt, iron, aluminium, chromium, copper, zinc and manganese.

Question 25.8

1. Barium chloride dihydrate is one substance which can be subjected to three sets of gravimetric analyses. Describe three separate experiments to test for the purity of a 15 g sample of this salt. Remember to write full, balanced or ionic, equations for the key reactions that take place in your chosen methods. Give reasons for any safety precautions that might be necessary when carrying out these reactions.

A4.1 (e) Gas volumes

It was back in 1811 that Avogadro developed his Principle which stated that equal volumes of different gases contain the same number of molecules. This led to the finding that a mole of any gases occupies approximately 24 dm^3 at room temperature (298 K) and pressure (100 kPa ≈ 1 atmosphere). The molar volume is the volume per mole of any gas. The ideal gas equation (B1.6b) can be used to calculate the volume of a gas for any stated pressure and temperature. The reason a mole of any gas occupies the same volume is because most of a gas is empty space and the molecules themselves take up less than one thousandth of the total volume.

The large glass jar in the picture holds 24 dm^3 and contains one mole of air.

At a lower temperature a mole of gas would be expected to have a smaller volume. The particles would on average have a lower kinetic energy at the lower temperature and therefore will be colliding with the container with a smaller force. The contraction in volume is necessary in order for the pressure to remain at 1 atmosphere.

The ideal gas equation (equation 6) states that $PV = nRT$.

Rearranging the equation the volume $V = \dfrac{nRT}{P}$.

If the temperature is 273 K, the volume of a mole of gas will be;

$$V = \frac{1 \times 8.31 \times 273}{1.00 \times 10^5} = 0.0227 \text{ m}^3 = 22.7 \text{ dm}^3.$$

Another useful equation is; amount of a gas in moles = gas volume (dm^3) / molar volume (dm^3)

Expressed in terms of symbols; $n = \dfrac{V}{24}$, therefore $V = 24 \times n$.

Questions 25.9

1. Using equation 6 (ideal gas equation) what will be the volume of 1.37 moles of gas at 296 K and 1 atmosphere (~100 kPa) of pressure?

2. What is the equation $pV = nRT$?

   A   Avogadro's Law.

   B   Charles's Law.

   C   Boyle's Law.

   D   Ideal Gas equation.

3. Which of the following masses of gas does not occupy about 4 dm³ at 25°C and 1 atmosphere?

   [1 mole ~24 dm³ at RTP, C = 12, H = 1, Cl = 35.5, O = 16]

   A   0.333 g of H_2

   B   7.333 g of CO

   C   6.083 g of HCl

   D   11.83 g of Cl_2

Example 25.11

The decomposition of hydrogen peroxide (A2.2f) generated 1000 cm³ of oxygen gas with a mass of 1.317 g. [A_r of O = 16]. Calculate the volume of one mole of oxygen gas (dm³).

The equation to use is $n = \dfrac{m}{M}$

where n = amount, m = mass in grams, and M = relative molar mass.

The relative molecular mass of $O_2 = 2 \times 16 = 32$ g mol⁻¹

The amount of oxygen in 1 dm³ = $\dfrac{1.317}{32} = 0.04116$ mol dm⁻³

Therefore the volume of one mole of oxygen is the reciprocal,

i.e. $\dfrac{1}{0.04116} = 24.3$ dm³

Questions 25.10

1. Calculate the molar volume of the three gases using the tabulated results.

Gas	Mass (g) of 1 dm³	M_r of gas	Molar volume / dm³
Nitrogen	1.152	28	
Carbon monoxide	1.150	28	
Carbon dioxide	1.810	44	

2. At 1 atmosphere pressure and 273K a gas occupies a volume of 450 cm³. What volume in cm³ will the gas occupy at 0.92 atmospheres and 318 K?

   A $\dfrac{450 \times 0.92}{1 \times \left(\frac{273}{318}\right)}$

   B $\dfrac{450 \times 0.92}{1 \times \left(\frac{318}{273}\right)}$

   C $\dfrac{450 \times 1}{0.92 \times \left(\frac{273}{318}\right)}$

   D $\dfrac{450 \times 1}{0.92 \times \left(\frac{318}{273}\right)}$

3. What volume would a mole of gas occupy at the surface of the planet Venus which has a pressure of 92 atmospheres and a temperature of 735K? [Molar volume = 24 dm³ at 298K].

4. What volume of hydrogen gas (cm³) will be produced at 298 K and 1 atmosphere when 8.6 g of pure iron is reacted with excess sulfuric acid?

   [A_r of iron is 55.8 gmol⁻¹].

   $Fe (s) + H_2SO_4 (aq) \rightarrow FeSO_4 (aq) + H_2 (g)$

5. What is the molar volume of hydrogen which has a density of 0.089 g dm⁻³?

26

Mass Spectrometry

Contents

Mass spectrometry is a very important technique which is routinely used by organic chemists. Mass spectrometry is colloquially referred to as 'mass. spec.' It provides invaluable information about the presence of isotopes (A1.0g), relative molecular mass (M_r) of molecules and how atoms are arranged in molecules, from fragmentation patterns (A4.2b). It is a destructive method (unlike IR spectroscopy (A4.4) and nmr spectroscopy (A4.5, B4.6)) where the sample under investigation is obliterated inside the machinery. It is fortunate that only a very small amount of sample is needed, hence its use by forensic scientists. Modern mass spectrometers can detect samples as small as a nanogram.

Forensic Scientist

Questions 26.1

1. Which option correctly shows the only information that is uniquely provided by mass spectrometry?

   A   Relative molecular mass.

   B   Number of protons.

   C   Number of carbons.

   D   Functional groups.

2. Which spectroscopic technique does not involve the absorption of electromagnetic radiation?

A   Infra-red spectroscopy.

B   Mass spectrometry.

C   Carbon-13 nmr spectroscopy.

D   Proton nmr spectroscopy.

A4.2 (a) Time of flight mass spectrometry

Mass spectrometry was developed by Francis Aston in 1919. He used this analytical tool in the discovery of the isotopes of chlorine (A4.2b), bromine (A4.2b) and krypton. There have been many different types of mass spectrometry developed since these early experiments. Traditional A-level courses covered electron impact mass spectrometry where ions of different sizes are separated by their different deflections in a magnetic field. At universities in the 21st century it is 'time of flight' mass spectrometry (TOF-MS) which is routinely performed. TOF-MS measures how long it takes for different sized ions to fly undeflected along a set path inside the mass spectrometer. Heavier ions move more slowly than less massive ions. When faced with large polar molecules such as peptides, mild ionising techniques are needed such as Fast Atom Bombardment Mass Spectrometry (FAB-MS).

F.W. Aston

A Time of Flight Mass Spectrometer (Warwick University, UK)

By linking mass spectrometers to separation techniques such as GC (Gas Chromatography) and HPLC (High-Performance Liquid Chromatography) reactions can be followed very closely.

Physical processes

Once the sample has been vaporised on the end of a piece of kit called a 'probe', there are four basic steps. These four steps are the physical processes involved in TOF-MS. The order of events is firstly **ionisation**, followed by **acceleration** of the ions, then **separation** of the ions and finally **detection** of the ions. One way to remember the order is **I**gloos **A**re **S**now **D**omes = **I**onisation **A**cceleration **S**eparation **D**etection.

Question 26.2

1. Which option gives the correct sequential order for the physical processes involved in time of flight mass spectrometry?

A   ionisation, separation, acceleration, detection.

B   acceleration, ionisation, deflection, detection.

C   ionisation, acceleration, separation, detection.

D   ionisation, acceleration, deflection, detection.

Ionisation (removing an electron or adding an ion)
Electron impact

Highly energetic electrons with a high speeds are emitted from a filament and these collide with the sample being tested (the **analyte**). The result of these collisions is to cause ejection of one or more electrons from the molecule (M). When one electron is removed from a molecule, by repulsion, it results in a positively charged parent ion, M^+. It is possible to remove two electrons to give doubly charged ions M^{2+} but these ions won't make it as far as the detector. So, essentially, a molecule (M) has an electron removed when impacted by a high energy electron inside the mass spectrometer. This method of ionisation is known as **electron impact ionisation**. As one electron collides with the molecule, a cation is formed and two electrons are shown in the diagram moving away. It is a common misconception to expect the electrons to hit the sample and to 'stick', thereby making a negatively charged anion M^-. It is helpful to think of the impact in terms of what is happening to the electrons, *i.e.* one in and two out. To avoid unwanted reactions taking place in a mass spectrometer the whole process is carried out under high vacuum conditions (10^{-6} torr).

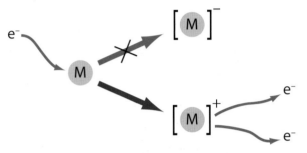

Diagram of electron impact ionisation

Chemical ionisation

Some compounds fragment after electron impact ionisation without giving a molecular ion (M^+). The preferred method of ionisation for particularly unstable or labile molecules is **chemical ionisation**. Instead of colliding molecules with high speed electrons they collide instead with positively charged molecules such as ammonia (NH_3). The ammonia is ionised by high speed electrons and this leads to the primary ion $[NH_3]^+$. Some primary ions can in turn collide with neutral ammonia molecule to make the secondary ion $[NH_4]^+$.

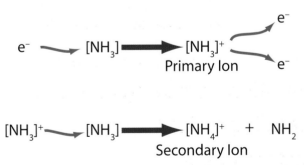

This chemical ionisation, using a charged molecule such as ammonia, is a milder technique than ionisation by electron impact. This is because the ions produced in a mass spectrometer by chemical reaction do not have the excess energy of high speed electrons that leads to the fragmentation observed using the electron impact method. Interestingly, with this ionisation method, in addition to the molecular ion, M^+,

the following peaks are observed in a mass spectrum; $[M+H]^+$ and $[M+NH_4]^+$.

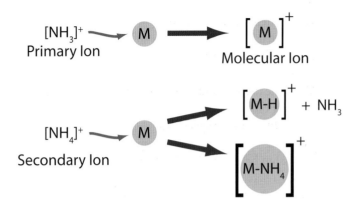

Acceleration (repulsion from a plate)

Sample ions M^+ are accelerated by an electric field. This is possible by repelling positive ions from a positive plate or attraction by a negative plate.

Separation of ions (lighter move faster)

Time of Flight Mass Spectrometry (TOF-MS) is the technique that has been commercially available since the late 1950s and is now routinely run in universities and industry. The technique gives very fast analyses with an almost unlimited mass range. Ions of the same mass to charge ratio (m/z) arrive at the detector at the same time. It is possible to get spectra on very small sample sizes even down to 10^{-18} mole. This TOF-MS is particularly useful for forensic scientists when analysing biological samples. A small molecule of 26 amu (atomic mass units) would travel this distance in about 6×10^{-6} seconds. The resolution is 2×10^{-9} seconds.

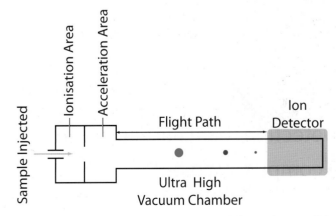

It is assumed that all 1+ ions (unipositive) leave the tip of the MS probe at the same time with the same Kinetic Energy (KE) when subjected to acceleration by the same potential difference.

All ions go the same distance in the mass spectrometer which is the distance of flight path which, in small mass spectrometers, is typically about 60 cm. The difference for the different sized ions generated in a TOF-MS will be the acceleration of these particles. Smaller particles are less massive so will have a shorter time-of-flight over the set distance. The ions are analysed using the time it takes for them to arrive at the detector. In the diagram the smaller green particle arrives first and the larger blue particle arrives last.

By rearranging some simple equations it is possible to show the relationship between the mass of ions and their velocities and also to relate the mass of ions to their time of flight. Equation 1 is the standard equation for kinetic energy (KE), where m = mass of ion & v = velocity of ion.

Equation 1: $KE = \frac{1}{2}\, m\, v^2$

Rearranging *equation 1* gives:

$$\frac{KE}{\frac{1}{2}\, m} = v^2 \rightarrow \frac{2\, KE}{m} = v^2 \rightarrow v = \sqrt{\frac{2\, KE}{m}}$$

Equation 2 is the standard equation for final speed (s), distance of path (d) and time of flight (t) when a particle moves from rest under constant acceleration. The average speed is half this figure.

Equation 2: $s = \frac{2d}{t}$

Rearranging *equation 2* gives:

$$t = \frac{2d}{\text{speed} \equiv \text{velocity as the path direction is known}}$$

Substituting v for s in *equation 2* gives:

$$t = \frac{2d}{\sqrt{\frac{2\, KE}{m}}}$$

Rearranging gives:

Equation 3: $t = 2d \times \sqrt{\frac{m}{2\, KE}}$

So the time of flight (t) is proportional to the square root of the mass (m) of the ion

$t \propto \sqrt{m}$ because the final velocity depends on the mass of the ion.

Detection (bar chart appears on a computer screen)

Early mass spectrometry detection methods involved the use of photographic plates. Today the electrical signal from 'flying' ions colliding with the negatively charged conducting surface (Cu-Be alloy) of the detector triggers the release of electrons.

This signal is amplified and the data are processed to produce charts of abundance or relative intensity *versus* mass to charge ratio (A4.2b). The signal generated in the detector depends on the number of ions of particular mass arriving at the detector.

Questions 26.3

1. In the mass spectrum of molecule M, to what does the highest mass correspond?

    A M^+

    B M^-

    C M^{2+}

    D M^{2-}

2. When would ionisation by electron impact not give a peak for its molecular ion (M^+) in a mass spectrum? What alternative ionisation method could be used to generate a peak for M^+?

A4.2 (b) Interpreting spectra (molecular ions and fragments)

Mass spectrum

A mass spectrum is a bar chart. Each bar will be referred to as a 'peak'. On the y-axis, relative intensity is expressed as a percentage (%). The x-axis is the mass to charge ratio, which has the usual symbols m/z. Sometimes the mass:charge ratio is shown as m/e. As only one electron is lost in the process, *i.e.* the charge $z = 1$, the x-axis is taken as essentially being the mass. In most mass spectra, the peak furthest to the right hand side is the molecular ion (M^+), which is sometimes called the **parent ion**. In a mass spectrum of a pure compound, the highest mass corresponds to the singly charged molecular ion. Mass spectra are often complicated because, as well as an electron being knocked off molecules to form M^+, it is possible for the high speed electrons to break bonds during collisions inside the mass spectrometer. The weaker bonds are more likely to break and smaller molecules called **fragments** which retain a positive charge will also be detected in the mass spectrometer. The most intense signals in a mass spectrum are due to the weakest bonds in a molecule breaking most readily. The most intense (largest) peak is called the **base peak** and this is assigned a value of 100% in order to compare other peak intensities. It is worth remembering that a fragment is often the base peak rather than that corresponding to the molecular ion. By their very nature, fragments have smaller masses than the molecular ion. Fragments are found to the left of M⁺ in a mass spectrum. The size of the signal generated at the detector for the various fragments depends on their relative proportions. Some information about structure can be gleaned from fragments in a mass spectrum, but more often than not, comparing fragments to a genuine sample will suggest authenticity. The mass spectrum of ethanoic acid illustrates the relative positions of the molecular ions, base peak and fragments.

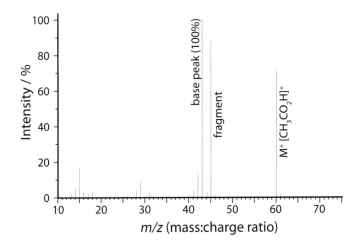

Mass spectrum of ethanoic acid CH_3CO_2H

The table of fragments shows typical mass losses from the molecular ion that correspond to groups or fragments breaking free from the original molecule in the mass spectrometer.

Ion	Fragments / Groups
$[M-1]^+$	H
$[M-15]^+$	CH_3
$[M-16]^+$	O or NH_2
$[M-17]^+$	OH
$[M-18]^+$	H_2O
$[M-19]^+$	F
$[M-28]^+$	CO or C_2H_4
$[M-29]^+$	CHO or C_2H_5
$[M-31]^+$	OCH_3
$[M-42]^+$	CH_2CO or C_3H_6
$[M-44]^+$	CO_2 or C_3H_8
$[M-45]^+$	CO_2H or OC_2H_5
$[M-46]^+$	NO_2
$[M-76]^+$	C_6H_4
$[M-77]^+$	C_6H_5

Nitrogen Rule

When the ionisation method is electron impact, a molecular mass with an **odd** number is a good clue that the molecule might contain an odd number (1, 3, 5 *etc*) of nitrogen atoms. Molecules without nitrogen atoms 'usually' have **even** relative molecular masses.

The diagram below shows some possible outcomes for the high speed collision between an electron and a molecule of methanol. The simplest thing to happen is the removal of a single electron to form the molecular ion. If sufficient energy is present from the collision between the methanol and an electron, any one of the five covalent bonds in the molecule might break. This would result in three possible fragments. If the O-H bond broke, the fragment would be $[CH_3O]^+$. If the C-O bond broke, the fragment would be $[CH_3]^+$. If one of the three C-H bonds broke, the fragment would be $[CH_2OH]^+$.

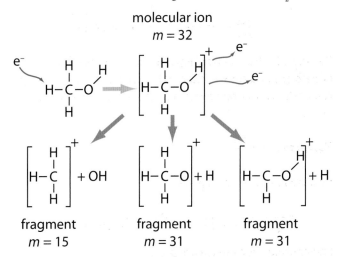

Ionisation and fragmentation of methanol in a mass spectrometer

The mass spectrum for ethanenitrile (CH_3CN) shows how high speed collision between an electron and the molecule leads to M⁺ and the various fragments. Note how the very strong triple bond (C≡N) is not affected.

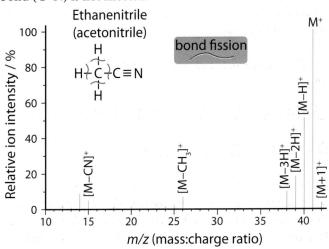

The mass spectrum for benzoic acid ($C_6H_5CO_2H$) shows M^+ and the suggested identity of two major fragments.

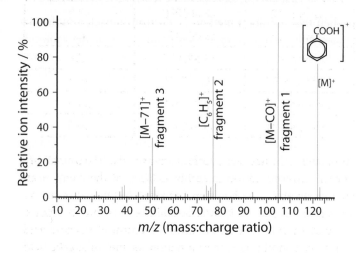

Mass spectrum of benzoic acid C_6H_5COOH

Fragmentation patterns can be characteristic of a particular isomer, *e.g.* look at the differences between the mass spectra of propan-1-ol and propan-2-ol. In the case of propan-1-ol the base peak is at 31 and for propan-2-ol the base peak is at 45. There is an obvious $[M-1]^+$ peak at 59 for propan-1-ol but this is not detected for propan-2-ol.

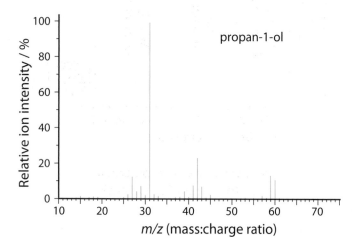

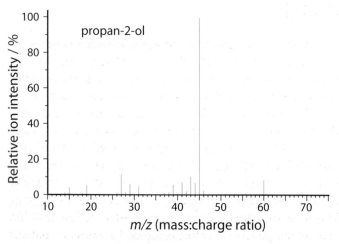

Questions 26.4

1. Why does fragmentation occur in mass spectrometry? What is the charge on the fragments?

2. Which option shows all the carbon isotopes which can be observed in a mass spectrometer?

	carbon-12	carbon-13	carbon-14
A	√	√	
B	√		√
C		√	√
D	√	√	√

3. Which option correctly shows the base peak and the molecular ion in the mass spectrum?

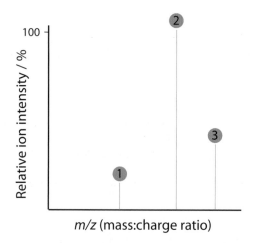

	Base peak	Molecular ion
A	1	3
B	3	2
C	2	3
D	3	1

4. Furan is an interesting aromatic heterocyclic molecule which, when hydrogenated, makes the versatile solvent tetrahydrofuran (THF). In the mass spectrum of furan, to what do the peaks at 68 and 69 correspond?

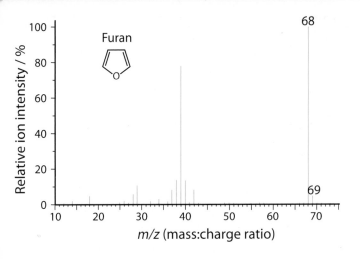

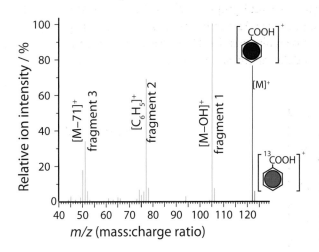

5. Label the mass spectrum for 4-hydroxybenzaldehyde assigning the peaks at 93, 105, 121, 122 and 123.

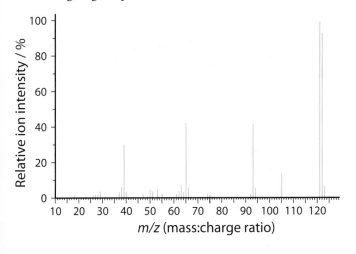

A4.2 (c) Isotopes and mass spectrometry

One of the main advantages of mass spectrometry as a technique is that it does allow for the detection of molecules containing different isotopes. A good example is the detection of carbon's two most abundant isotopes: carbon-12 (98.9%) and carbon-13 (1.1%). It is not possible to detect the trace amounts of the radioactive carbon-14 isotope. Mass spectrometry is very good at detecting the halogens chlorine-35 (~75%) & chlorine-37 (~25%) and bromine-79 (~50%) & bromine-81 (~50%). The more accurate masses and percentages, which are essential for high resolution mass spectrometry, for the commonly met isotopes, are listed in the table.

Isotope	Atomic Weight	Natural Abundance (%)
Carbon-12	12.000000	98.9
Carbon-13	13.003354	1.1
Chlorine-35	34.968855	75.8
Chlorine-37	36.965896	24.2
Bromine-79	78.918348	50.5
Bromine -81	80.916344	49.5

As benzoic acid has seven carbon atoms and as the probability of each carbon atom being carbon-13 is 1.1% there will be an approximately $7 \times 1.1\% = 7.7\%$ chance that at least one carbon atom in any benzoic acid molecule will be a carbon-13 isotope. For convenience sake in the mass spectrum of benzoic acid it has been shown as the carbon atom of the carboxylic acid functional group. The red peak corresponding to M+1 is approximately thirteen times (100/7.7) smaller than the blue peak for the molecular ion M^+ where all seven carbon atoms are the carbon-12 isotope.

Mass spectrum of benzoic acid to show the carbon-13 M+1 peak

Halogens

It is essential to be able to recognise the isotope patterns for organic compounds containing one chlorine atom or one bromine atom. Functional groups fitting this criterion include; chloroalkanes, bromoalkanes, chloroarenes, bromoarenes and acid chlorides. A molecule containing **one** chlorine atom will show a molecular ion with two peaks separated by 2 mass units in ~3:1 ratio. The peak at higher mass will have the lower intensity because the ratio of isotopes is ~3:1 for ^{35}Cl and ^{37}Cl. A molecule containing **one** bromine atom will show a molecular ion with two peaks separated by 2 mass units in a ~1:1 ratio. This is because the ratio of isotopes is ~1:1 for ^{79}Br and ^{81}Br. The isotopic patterns are more complex if a molecule contains more than one halogen, *e.g.* dichloromethane (CH_2Cl_2), or if there are two different types of halogen present, *e.g.* 1-bromo-2-chloroethane (CH_2BrCH_2Cl). The diagram shows some isotopic patterns for various combinations of halogens in organic molecules. It is an interesting exercise but one which is beyond the scope of college level mass spectrometry.

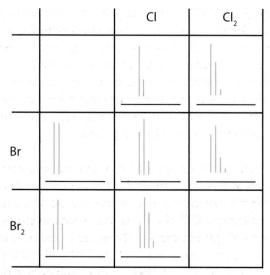

Ethanoyl chloride has the formula CH_3COCl. Its relative molecular mass is 78.5. The ratio of chlorine isotopes is 3:1 for chlorine-35 and chlorine-37. As the molecule contains one chlorine atom, this ratio of 3:1 is apparent in the molecular ions in the mass spectrum for $CH_3CO^{35}Cl$ at 78 amu and $CH_3CO^{35}Cl$ at 80 amu.

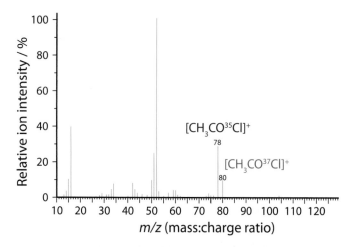

Mass spectrum of ethanoyl chloride

Bromoethane has the formula C_2H_5Br. Its relative molecular mass is 108.9. The ratio of bromine isotopes is approximately 1:1 for bromine-79 and bromine-81. As the molecule contains one bromine atom this ratio of 1:1 is apparent in the molecular ions in the mass spectrum for $C_2H_5^{79}Br$ at 108 amu and $C_2H_5^{81}Br$ at 110 amu.

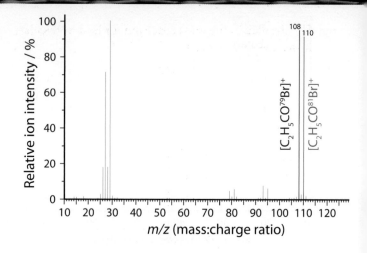

Mass spectrum of bromoethane

Questions 26.5

1. Which option correctly shows the probability of at least one atom being carbon-13 for buckminsterfullerene C_{60}?

   A   34.4%

   B   6.6%

   C   48.5%

   D   66.0%

2. Urea was first discovered and extracted from urine in 1773. Label the peaks at 17, 44, 60 and 61 in the mass spectrum for this metabolite.

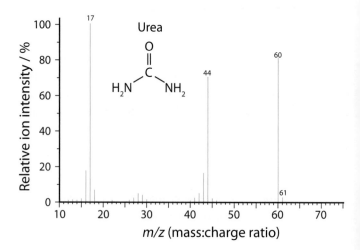

3. Use the data in the mass spectrum for lead to calculate its relative atomic mass.

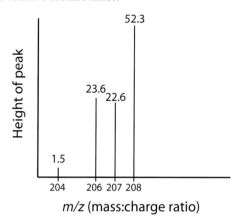

Mass spectrum of lead

4. The mass spectrum is for which element? How do you account for the two molecular ions?

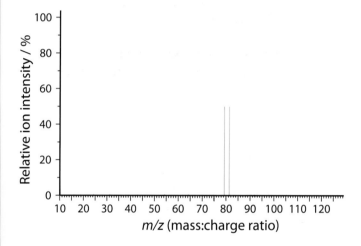

Additional uses of mass spectrometry

Water companies use mass spectrometry to monitor levels of pollutants in water. Certain substances such as dioxins are extremely toxic to humans and must not be present in potable (drinking) water. Pollutants are first separated by GC or HPLC before being sent into a mass spectrometer. As each molecule has a unique fragmentation pattern, it is possible to identify unknown substances by comparison with data in databanks. With the advent of supercomputers this job is now very fast where once it would have taken many laboratory hours to solve the identity of an unknown pollutant.

High resolution mass spectrometry can measure masses up to five decimal places. This level of accuracy allows molecules with relative molecular masses to the nearest whole number to be distinguished. It also alerts mass spectrometrists to the identity of illegal substances. The accurate masses for some commonly met elements are; ^{12}C (12.00000), ^{1}H (1.00782), ^{14}N (14.00307) & ^{16}O = (15.99492). Two examples of molecular formulae with approximate masses of 123 are $C_6H_5NO_2$ and $C_7H_7O_2$. Clearly they have very different structures and in one case the nitrogen rule applies. Their accurate masses are quite different; $C_6H_5NO_2$ (123.0320) and $C_7H_7O_2$ (123.0446).

27 Electronic Spectroscopy

Contents

I n the 19th century, spectroscopy played a very important part in the discovery of new elements. The historical timeline below gives a brief summary of the main scientists and their contributions to this area of chemistry which is inextricably linked to the development of photography. The advantage of photography is that it allows for the spectra to be studied beyond the visible range. Astronomers use spectra to analyse the atmosphere of other heavenly bodies (stars, asteroids and planets).

- 1817: Joseph von Fraunhofer observed dark spectral lines when sunlight had been passed through a prism.

- 1840: William Herschel photographed spectra.

- 1848: Balfour Stewart investigated the ability of materials to absorb and emit heat radiation at various wavelengths (λ).

- 1858: Gustav Kirchoff identified nine elements present on the sun's surface.

- 1859: Robert Bunsen & Kirchoff made the first spectroscope.

- 1861: Bunsen & Kirchoff discovered caesium (Cs) (from its blue spectral lines) and rubidium (Rb).

- 1861: William Crookes discovered thallium from its green spectral line.

- 1868: Joseph Lockyer discovered helium in the sun.

- 1869: Anders Ångström expressed his wavelengths in units of 10^{-10}m.

- 1885: Johann Balmer discovered his spectral series (visible) for hydrogen.

- 1888: George Stoney suggested that spectra have an electrical origin.

- 1897: Pieter Zeeman discovered that spectral lines can be split in a magnetic field.

- 1913: Niels Bohr interpreted the hydrogen spectrum using Quantum Theory.

- 1936: Gerhard Herzberg wrote *Atomic Spectra & Atomic Structure*.

A4.3 (a) Atomic absorption and emission

White light contains all visible wavelengths and the symbol for wavelength is lambda (λ). When white light is passed through a substance, black lines appear in the spectrum where light of particular wavelengths has been absorbed by the substance. Spectrometers are instruments used for viewing these absorption spectra.

Robert Bunsen and Gustav Kirchoff discovered caesium (blue flame) and rubidium (red flame) using the burner Bunsen developed and a spectroscope like the one shown below.

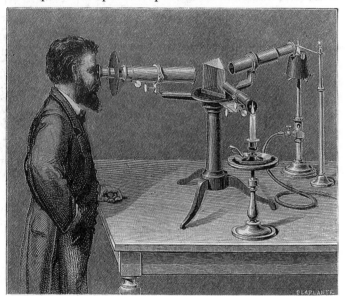

The absorption spectrum of hydrogen

Absorption Spectroscopy works because light is absorbed when an electron in an atom is excited to a higher energy level from a lower energy level. In the spectrum above, you can observe black lines which corresponded to the frequencies that are absorbed as incident radiation passes through the sample. Each element has a unique absorption spectrum and the lines can be used to identify the elements present in a substance.

According to the **Aufbau principle** (A1.1f), electrons in atoms are usually found in their ground state (A1.1g). When atoms absorb extra energy (electromagnetic radiation) their electron(s) can be promoted to higher energy levels. When this happens we say the atom is 'excited'. **Excitation** is achieved by heating substances in a Bunsen burner or by passing an

electric discharge through a vapour or by using a light source (laser). This is how a red neon advertising sign and a yellow sodium street lamp work.

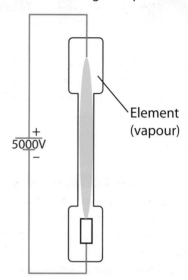

Discharge lamp

When the excited electrons fall back from the higher to lower energy levels, the excess energy is emitted as photons and an emission spectrum can be observed. Like an absorption spectrum, an emission spectrum also has a unique set of lines with set frequencies. These emission spectra can be thought of as the element's bar code. This time there are a series of coloured lines on a dark background. The (atomic) emission spectrum of hydrogen is also known as a **line spectrum**.

The emission spectrum of hydrogen

Each element gives a unique line spectrum because of differences in energy levels and their unique number of electrons. Lines can also occur outside the visible region (UV and IR). Eventually it was realised that spectra provide evidence for discrete energy levels in the atoms of all elements. Don't make the mistake of many students by thinking that the line spectrum is the energy level diagram 'turned on its side'. The emission spectra of helium and sodium are shown.

The emission spectrum of helium

The emission spectrum of sodium

If you get the opportunity to look at a yellow street lamp with a hand held spectroscope you will observe the emission spectrum for sodium. Sodium has a characteristic yellow colour due to a D-line at ~589 nm.

Flame tests

Flame tests can be used to identify the presence of different elements in a substance. This is achieved practically by dipping a nichrome wire with a loop on the end into concentrated hydrochloric acid and then using this moisture to get a small amount of the substance to stick to the wire. Heating a metal salt on a loop of nichrome wire in a blue Bunsen flame provides enough energy to excite electrons within the atoms. Photons, released as electrons falling from higher to lower energy levels, can be seen as colours of characteristic frequencies in the visible part of the electromagnetic spectrum. There are characteristic flame colours for some Group 1 & 2 metals and some transition elements (B2.4g).

Metal	Flame colour
Li	red
Na	yellow (orange)
K	lilac
Cs	blue
Ca	(brick) red
Sr	(crimson) red
Ba	(apple) green
Cu	blue green
Pb	(pale) blue

The flames can be analysed with a spectrometer. Each element's unique spectrum will contain many lines each of which corresponds to a particular electron transition.

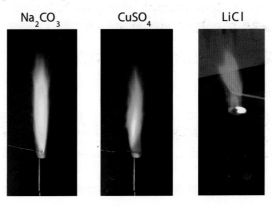

Na_2CO_3 $CuSO_4$ LiCl

For those students not studying Physics it is worth having a 'feel' for where the colours of visible light appear in terms of wavelengths (nm).

Red	Orange Yellow	Green	Blue	Violet

700nm 600nm 580nm   500nm   450nm   400nm

The frequency of light is related to its wavelength by the equation $v = f\lambda$.

where v = speed of light (3.00×10^8 ms^{-1}), f = frequency of light (s^{-1}) and λ = wavelength (m).

Everyone around the world seems to enjoy the spectacle of fireworks. The colours of fireworks are the result of emissions of light (photons) by energetically excited atoms. The gunpowder used in fireworks heats and excites the electrons in metal ions, raising their electrons to higher energy levels. Fractions of a second later these excited electrons return to their normal (ground state) energy levels and the energy is given out as light. Fireworks containing Cu^{2+} appear blue-green as red light is absorbed (B2.4g).

Notice how the subshells of a hydrogen atom within a quantum shell ($n = 2, 3$ etc.) have the same energy due to the absence of any shielding.

A4.3 (b)
Plank's Equation $E = hf$

Planck's equation relates the frequency (f) of light to its energy E (in Joules). Planck's equation is $E = hf$. Energy and frequency are directly proportional. As the energy of the light increases, so does its frequency. The proportionality constant is called Planck's constant (h) and has the value 6.63×10^{-34} Js. This equates to a value of 4×10^{-13} kJ mol^{-1} s which is calculated by $h \times L$ where L = Avogadro's constant 6.02×10^{23} mol^{-1}.

When electrons in excited atoms (A4.3a) lose the absorbed energy they fall back to a lower energy level closer to the nucleus. The energy of the light (photons) emitted is the same as the energy difference (ΔE) between the two orbits (shells). To calculate ΔE for any electronic transition, Planck's equation and the equation relating the speed of light to its frequency and wavelength ($v = f\lambda$) both need to be utilised.

Example 27.1

The characteristic yellow D-line of sodium is at 589 nm. Calculate the energy of a photon of light resulting in this line in sodium's emission spectrum [$c = 3.00 \times 10^8$ ms^{-1} and $h = 6.63 \times 10^{-34}$ Js].

$v = f\lambda$ and rearranging gives $f = \dfrac{v}{\lambda}$.

$E = hf$ and substituting in $\dfrac{v}{\lambda}$ for f gives $E = \dfrac{h\,v}{\lambda}$.

$E = \dfrac{6.63 \times 10^{-34} \times 3.00 \times 10^8}{589 \times 10^{-9}}$

[remember to convert the wavelength to metres]

$E = 3.38 \times 10^{-19}$ J.

In elements' emission spectra their lines converge as the frequency increases. This means that each successive line is closer to the previous one until they finally meet. Frequency and wavelength are related by the equation $v = f\lambda$ and because the speed of light is a constant, it follows that lines in spectra converge as wavelength decreases. Always check carefully which scale (f or λ) is being used when looking at line spectra. Three of the series in the line spectrum of hydrogen are shown, and the convergence limit for each series is shown as a dashed line.

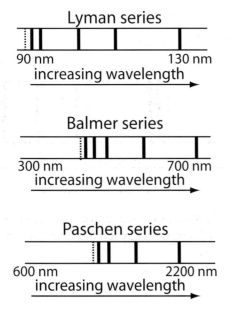

The convergence limit for the Lyman series is the point at which electrons responsible for the spectral line have been excited into an orbit ($n \to$ infinity) of such high energy that they have escaped the attractive force of the nuclear charge. Therefore the ionisation energy (A1.1i) for any element can be calculated from the convergence limit for the line at highest frequency (lowest wavelength). Examiners sometimes give questions using different units for the various quantities as illustrated by worked examples 27.2 & 27.3. It is also possible to calculate the value of ΔH_{i1} graphically by plotting frequency (y-axis) *versus* change in frequency (Δf) between adjacent lines (x-axis). The continuum begins at the point extrapolated on the graph where $\Delta f = 0$ and it is this value which is substituted into the equation (9) $E = hf$.

Example 27.2

Write an equation for the first ionisation energy of hydrogen and calculate its value from the convergence limit frequency $f = 32.7 \times 10^{14}$ Hz, [$h = 4 \times 10^{-13}$ kJ mol^{-1}].

ΔH_{i1} (hydrogen) = H(g) → H$^+$ (g) + e$^-$.

Equation 9: $E = h \times f,$

$\qquad\qquad = 4 \times 10^{-13} \times 32.7 \times 10^{14}$

$\qquad\qquad = 1308$ kJ mol^{-1}.

Example 27.3

In the Lyman series for hydrogen's line spectrum, the frequency of the line at the convergence limit was found to be 3.27×10^{15} s^{-1}. Calculate the first ionisation energy of hydrogen using equation 9 [$E = h \times f$], $h = 6.63 \times 10^{-34}$ Js, $L = 6.02 \times 10^{23}$ mol^{-1}.

$E = h \times f$

$\qquad = 6.63 \times 10^{-34} \times 3.27 \times 10^{15}$

$\qquad = 2.17 \times 10^{-18}$ J (photon energy).

1 mole = $E \times L$

$E = 2.17 \times 10^{-18} \times 6.02 \times 10^{23}$

$\qquad = 1306340$ J mol^{-1} = 1306 kJ mol^{-1}

[divide by 1000 to convert to kJ mol^{-1}]

Questions 27.1

1. Calculate the frequency of the line at the convergence limit for sodium given that its first ionisation energy is $\Delta H_{i1} = 496$ kJ mol^{-1}

[Planck's constant, $h = 4 \times 10^{-13}$ kJ mol^{-1}].

2. The visible part of the line spectrum for hydrogen is the Balmer series. For each of the lines in the series calculate the wavelength (nm) given that the speed of light in a vacuum is 3.00×10^8 ms^{-1}. Suggest colours for each line in this series.

Line number	Frequency / 10^{14} s^{-1}
1	4.568
2	6.167
3	6.907
4	7.309
5	7.551

3. Calculate the energy of a single photon of red light with a wavelength of 700.0 nm. [Speed of light in a vacuum is 3.00×10^8 ms^{-1} and $h = 6.63 \times 10^{-34}$ Js]

A4.3 (c) Line spectrum of hydrogen (qualitative)

It was in 1913 that Bohr interpreted the hydrogen spectrum helping to explain why hydrogen only emitted energy at a limited number of measurable frequencies. Bohr used the idea of **quantisation of energy** which states that electrons can only possess certain quantities of energy called **quanta**. A single electron can only exist in certain specific energy levels. These are often thought of as being rungs on a ladder. A photon of light is absorbed when an electron moves to a higher energy level and a photon of light is emitted when it moves to a lower energy level. The energy of a photon is the difference in energy (ΔE) between the energy levels ($\Delta E = hf_1 - hf_2$).

The **Bohr model of the atom** shows that electrons only exist in certain energy states (quantum states). The different allowable electronic transitions give rise to five series. These five series are named after their discoverers and are called the Lyman, Balmer, Paschen, Brackett and Pfund series. Each series gives rise to a set of lines in the line spectrum of hydrogen which converge at the high frequency end. It is the Balmer series that is observed in the visible region. The numbers in the Bohr model of the atom are the numbers of the energy levels (**Principal quantum number**). The lowest energy level, *i.e.* the ground state, $n = 1$, is the 1s orbital sometimes referred to as the K shell.

Bohr's circular orbits & hydrogen electronic transitions

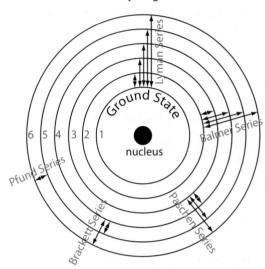

Each spectral line is caused by electrons losing the energy gained by heating as light energy. The greater the difference in energies between levels (ΔE) the higher the frequency of the line and therefore the smaller its wavelength. Part of the **Line Spectrum of Hydrogen** is shown. An animation which illustrates the hydrogen spectrum is found online at *http://www.btinternet.com/~chemistry.diagrams/Hspec_animation2.swf*

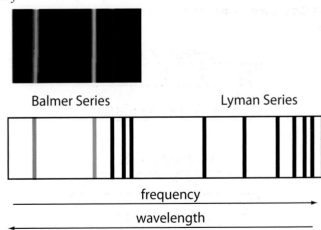

The allowable transitions for a hydrogen atom are shown following on a familiar energy level diagram (A1.1d).

Hydrogen Atom (Energy States)

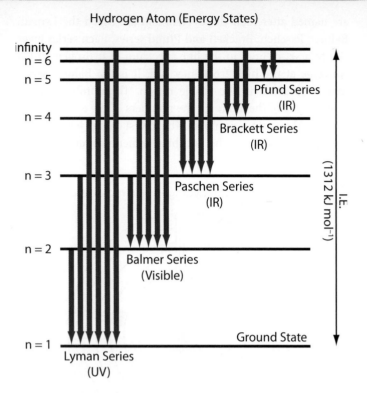

Radiation	Infrared	Visible	Ultraviolet	X-rays
Wavelength / nm	>750	750-400	400-10	< 10 nm

The point at which an electron is removed from the atom is the **ionisation energy** and has been calculated to have the value of 1312 kJ mol^{-1} for hydrogen. The Lyman series arises when electrons fall from higher energy levels to $n = 1$. The following table summarises the energy changes that give rise to the other series in the line spectrum of hydrogen.

Electromagnetic Spectrum	Series	n	m
UV	Lyman	1	2, 3, 4 *etc*
visible	Balmer	2	3, 4, 5 *etc*
IR	Paschen	3	4, 5, 6 *etc*
IR	Brackett	4	5, 6, 7 *etc*
IR	Pfund	5	6, 7, 8 *etc*

The position of any line in the hydrogen emission spectrum is given by the formula:

$$\frac{1}{\lambda} = R_H \left(\frac{1}{n^2} - \frac{1}{m^2} \right)$$

(R_H = Rydberg constant, n and m = integers (whole numbers).

This equation will be met at university and is not an examinable part of the Pre-U course.

Approximate wavelengths of different types of radiation: 1 nanometre (1 nm) = 1×10^{-9} m.

Questions 27.2

1. How can the line spectrum of hydrogen be used to find the ionisation energy of hydrogen?

2. Which option is **incorrect** for the atomic emission spectrum of hydrogen?

   A It shows the frequencies of radiation emitted by excited atoms.

   B It consists of lines in series which converge to a limit at the low frequency end.

   C It consists of lines in series which converge to a limit as wavelength decreases.

   D It provides information for measuring ionisation energy for the hydrogen atom.

3. Which series in the hydrogen spectrum is in the visible region?

   A Paschen

   B Lyman

   C Brackett

   D Balmer

4. Which one of the following electronic transitions in the hydrogen atom produces the third line of the second series in the hydrogen spectrum?

    A $n_2 = 5$ to $n_1 = 1$

    B $n_2 = 5$ to $n_1 = 2$

    C $n_2 = 4$ to $n_1 = 2$

    D $n_2 = 4$ to $n_1 = 1$

5. The Balmer series is the set of lines in the visible region of the hydrogen line spectrum. Draw the energy transition level diagram to show how these lines are formed up to $n = 6$.

6. Which diagram shows a similar pattern to the emission spectrum of the hydrogen atom in the visible region?

increasing wavelength

28

Infra-red Spectroscopy

Contents

Humans can detect only a small range of wavelengths in the visible spectrum (from 300 nm to 800 nm). The infra-red part of the electromagnetic spectrum is at longer wavelength than visible light. Infra-red spectroscopy is a particularly important technique routinely used by organic chemists to confirm the presence of functional groups. Infra-red spectroscopy is colloquially referred to as IR. It provides structural information about the presence or absence of particular functional groups as well as providing evidence for both intermolecular and intramolecular hydrogen bonding. It is a non-destructive method (unlike mass spectrometry A4.2) where the sample under investigation is exposed to infra-red radiation which causes bonds to vibrate (resonate) at particular frequencies.

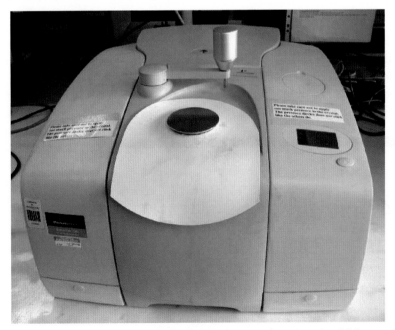

Picture of Infra-red spectrometer (Warwick University, UK)

Samples prepared for infra-red spectroscopy can be prepared in several ways. They can be dissolved in solvents, *e.g.* chloroform ($CHCl_3$), carbon tetrachloride (CCl_4), carbon disulfide (CS_2).

Alternatively, they can be made into a KBr disc or they can have a drop of the liquid hydrocarbon nujol added. Nujol has a characteristic C-H stretch at 2924 cm^{-1} and other identifiable and sharp troughs at 1603 cm^{-1}, 1028 cm^{-1} and 906 cm^{-1}.

Questions 28.1

1. Which option correctly shows the only information that is uniquely provided by infra-red spectroscopy?

     A   Relative molecular mass.

     B   Number of protons.

     C   Number of carbons.

     D   Functional groups.

2. Which of these spectroscopic techniques involves the absorption of the longest wavelength electromagnetic radiation?

     A   Infra-red spectroscopy.

     B   X-ray diffraction.

     C   X-ray crystallography.

     D   Ultra-violet spectroscopy.

3. Explain which of the following analytical techniques is the odd one out: infra-red spectroscopy, mass spectrometry, nmr spectroscopy and electronic spectroscopy.

A4.4 (a)
Resonant bond vibrations

Even at absolute zero (0K), atoms in molecules which are joined by covalent bonds are continually vibrating. This is because covalent bonds are not rigid and they can stretch and bend. To picture what is happening at the molecular level it can be quite useful to think of atoms as being like small spheres held together by springs which represent the bonds. Atoms and groups of atoms have increased vibrations called **resonant bond vibrations** when infra-red radiation is absorbed at certain frequencies in the electromagnetic spectrum. The frequency of the vibration depends on the nature of the bonding atoms. It has been shown that the greater the mass of the atoms the slower the vibration (A4.4b). Each type of bond

(hence functional group) vibrates at its own characteristic frequency. This is why infra-red spectroscopy is routinely used to give information about molecular structure and the presence of functional groups. The major types of molecular vibrations are **stretching** and **bending** and these are shown (in the following diagram) for carbon dioxide. Carbon atoms are black whilst oxygen atoms are red. Motion is shown as yellow coloured arrows adjacent to the oxygen atoms. When infra-red radiation is absorbed at certain frequencies the associated energy is converted into bending and stretching bond vibrations. The symmetric stretching of carbon dioxide is the only vibration that does not lead to a change in dipole moment and is therefore not detected in the infra-red spectrum.

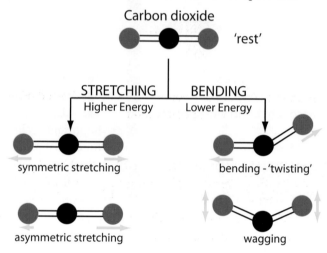

Infra-red molecular vibrations of CO_2

Not all vibrations of molecules will absorb infra-red radiation. It has been found that only modes of vibration that produce a net change in the dipole moment (A3.2a) of a molecule result in IR activity. Chlorine, nitrogen and hydrogen have no dipole so they will not absorb infra-red radiation. Carbon monoxide and hydrogen fluoride are gases with a dipole so these molecules do absorb infra-red radiation.

The source of the infra-red radiation is an electrically heated filament. In infra-red spectroscopy a compound is exposed to infra-red radiation from 400 cm⁻¹ to 4000 cm⁻¹. The units of frequency have historically been given as **wavenumber** (cm⁻¹) which is the reciprocal of the infra-red radiation wavelength in centimetres (cm). Modern infra-red spectra are obtained using **Fourier Transform Infra-red (FTIR) spectrometers**. An infra-red beam is shone through the sample under investigation and this is compared with an infra-red reference beam. All the wavelengths that correspond to frequencies in the range 400 cm⁻¹ to 4000 cm⁻¹ are shone through the sample. The infra-red spectrum (A4.4c) is produced by a computer after analysis of the differences between the two beams.

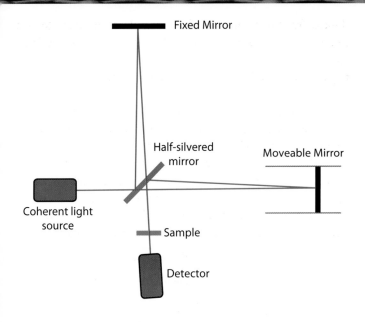

Schematic diagram of a Fourier Transform Infra-red (FTIR) spectrometer

Questions 28.2

1. Will sulfur dioxide absorb infra-red radiation when its bonds stretch and/or bend?

2. Which option best describes infra-red spectroscopy?

	Process	Principle
A	non-destructive	bond fission
B	destructive	bond vibrations
C	non-destructive	bond vibrations
D	destructive	bond fission

3. Which of the following options cannot be considered an absorption spectroscopy?

A   Mass spectrometry.

B   Nuclear magnetic resonance spectroscopy.

C   Infra-red spectroscopy.

D   Ultra-violet spectroscopy.

4. Which region of the electromagnetic spectrum corresponds to the energy of most molecular vibrations?

A   Radiowaves

B   Ultra-violet

C   Visible

D   Infra-red

5. Complete the table by placing a tick ($\checkmark$) in each box where infra-red radiation is absorbed by the named vibration.

Carbon dioxide	Vibration	IR absorbed?
CO_2	asymmetrical stretching	
CO_2	bending	
CO_2	symmetrical stretching	

A4.4 (b)
Stretching frequencies (bond strength and atomic masses)

The energy involved in any bond vibration depends on variables such as bond length, bond strength and the mass of the atoms at either end of the bond. This means that each different bond will vibrate in a different way, involving different amounts of energy. The IR stretching frequency increases in the order: single bonds (except those to hydrogen), double bonds, triple bonds, single bonds to hydrogen. Stronger bonds need more energy to make them vibrate, so consequently they absorb a higher frequency of infra-red radiation (higher wavenumber).

Infra-red spectrum

In an infra-red spectrum such as the one shown for ethanal (CH_3CHO), **transmittance** (%) or **absorbance** (%) is on the *y*-axis and the frequency expressed as wavenumber (cm^{-1}) is on the *x-axis*. The horizontal scale reads from right to left like chemical shift in nmr (A4.5). An individual absorption in an infra-red spectrum will be referred to as a trough (coloured blue to make it easier to spot on first meeting) which rather confusingly in many textbooks is still referred to as a 'peak'. When the transmittance is over 90%, little or no energy is absorbed at this frequency. Troughs in the graph show where energy is absorbed. In the specific case of ethanal there is a very large trough (dip in the graph) at about 1720 cm^{-1}. It is important to realise that the scale on the *x*-axis is not linear and the change in scale occurs at 2000 cm^{-1}. This means that there is more detail in this lower frequency region.

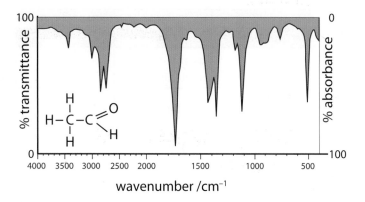

IR spectrum of ethanal (CH_3CHO)

An infra-red spectrum can be sub-divided into two regions; the band region 1500-4000 cm^{-1} where functional groups are found and the **'fingerprint region'** where the frequency is less than 1500 cm^{-1}. The fingerprint region is to the right-hand side of an IR spectrum (from about 1500 cm^{-1} to 400 cm^{-1}). It usually contains a very complicated series of absorptions. These are mainly due to all manner of bending vibrations within the molecule. The importance of the fingerprint region is that each compound produces a different pattern of troughs in this part of the spectrum.

Fingerprints are sometimes used by airlines to identify passengers before boarding

A detailed look at the infra-red spectrum of ethanal shows a C-H stretch at 2900 cm^{-1} and a strong C=O (carbonyl) stretch at 1720 cm^{-1}. These troughs, shaded green, in the fingerprint region, are characteristic of ethanal.

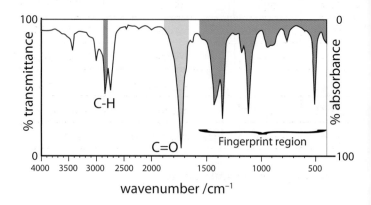

In an infra-red spectrum there are four regions to look at in turn:

- 1000 cm^{-1} to 1500 cm^{-1} (single bonds; C-O, C-Cl),

- 1500 cm^{-1} to 2000 cm^{-1} (double bonds; C=O, C=C),

- 2000 cm^{-1} to 3000 cm^{-1} (triple bonds; C≡N, C≡C), and

- 3000 cm^{-1} to 4000 cm^{-1} (single bonds to hydrogen; C-H, N-H & O-H).

As the frequency increases (cm^{-1}) so does the energy being supplied to vibrate the bonds since both quantities are proportional according to the equation $E = hf$ (A4.3b) which is equation 9 in the data booklet. As the bond order (A1.2f) increases, so does the frequency at which resonant vibrations occur because multiple bonds are 'stiffer' than single bonds. Shorter, and therefore stronger, bonds vibrate faster. The relationship between the frequency of the bond vibration, atomic mass and bond enthalpy (A1.3d) is similar to **Hooke's Law** for a simple harmonic oscillator. Without going into the details, frequency is proportional to the square root of bond strength and inversely proportional to the square root of the atomic mass.

Table to show characteristic absorbance frequencies for covalent bonds

Bond	Type	Functional group	Frequency / cm^{-1}
C-O	single	Alcohol /ether	1000-1300
C=O	double	Aldehydes / ketones / carboxylic acids / esters	1680-1750

Bond	Type	Functional group	Frequency / cm^{-1}
C≡N	triple	nitrile	2220-2260
C-H	single	alkane	2850-2960
=C-H	single	alkene	3075-3095
≡C-H	single	alkyne	2100-2260
O-H	single	carboxylic acids*	2500-3300
N-H	single	amine	3300-3500
O-H	single	alcohols* / phenols*	3590-3650

broad troughs due to hydrogen bonding.

It is possible to use infra-red spectroscopy to distinguish between intermolecular hydrogen bonding (A1.2k) and intramolecular hydrogen bonding. This is because, at increased concentrations, troughs for intermolecular hydrogen bonds increase in intensity but those troughs arising from intramolecular hydrogen bonds do not increase.

The greater the mass (A_r) of the atoms in a covalent bond the slower will be the vibration. Comparison of the frequencies for a carbon covalently bonded to hydrogen and deuterium illustrates this idea. The C-H stretch is at 3000 cm^{-1} compared with the C-D stretch which occurs at 2200 cm^{-1}. The heavier deuterium isotope (^2H) resonates at a lower frequency than the much lighter ^1H isotope.

Questions 28.3

1. Which option gives the correct order of frequency of vibration in ascending order for the H-Cl bond and the two most abundant isotopes for hydrogen and carbon?

    A $^1H\text{-}^{35}Cl < {}^2H\text{-}^{35}Cl < {}^1H\text{-}^{37}Cl < {}^2H\text{-}^{37}Cl$

    B $^1H\text{-}^{35}Cl > {}^2H\text{-}^{35}Cl > {}^1H\text{-}^{37}Cl > {}^2H\text{-}^{37}Cl$

    C $^2H\text{-}^{37}Cl > {}^1H\text{-}^{37}Cl > {}^2H\text{-}^{35}Cl > {}^1H\text{-}^{35}Cl$

    D $^1H\text{-}^{35}Cl > {}^1H\text{-}^{37}Cl > {}^2H\text{-}^{35}Cl > {}^2H\text{-}^{37}Cl$

2. What is an infra-red spectrum?

3. What is wavenumber and what is its unit?

4. Calculate the frequency in cm^{-1} for infra-red light of wavelengths; i) 15×10^{-6} m, ii) 26×10^{-6} m.

5. Calculate the wavelengths of electromagnetic radiation having wavenumbers;

    i)   1020 cm^{-1}

    ii)   1748 cm^{-1}

    iii) 2300 cm^{-1}

    iv)   3420 cm^{-1}

    and suggest which bonds might resonate at these frequencies.

6. What is the relationship between bond order and infra-red frequency for carbon-oxygen bonds?

    C≡O (2143 cm^{-1}), C=O (1715 cm^{-1}) & C-O (1100 cm^{-1}).

A4.4 (c) Stretching frequencies (bonds to H)

As infra-red frequency data are not given in exams, it is important to be able to recall the approximate stretching frequencies observed in IR spectra. The more infra-red spectra you assign, the easier it will become to recognise the frequencies characteristic of particular functional groups.

Order	bonds to H	triple bonds	double bonds	single bonds (except to H)
Frequencies / cm^{-1}	3700-2500	2300-1900	1900-1500	< 1500
Examples	O-H N-H C-H	C≡C C≡N	C=C C=O	C-O C-N

The order in terms of decreasing frequency is: bonds to H, triple bonds, double bonds, single bonds (except to H). Learning this pattern will make assigning infra-red spectra more straightforward.

In addition to considering the mass of atoms, one also needs to consider the strength of bonds. The three adjacent Period 2 elements in Groups 14-16 have similar masses, *i.e.* ^{12}C, ^{14}N & ^{16}O. A look at their frequencies of vibration when joined by a single covalent bond to a hydrogen atom shows how the bond enthalpy is the deciding factor on infra-red frequency of vibration. The relationship is 'the stronger the bond the higher the frequency'.

Substance	Bond	Bond enthalpy / kJ mol^{-1}	IR frequency / cm^{-1}
methane	C-H	440	2900-3200
ammonia	N-H	450	3300-3400
water	O-H	464	3500-3600

Interestingly the aromatic amine, aniline ($C_6H_5NH_2$) has two NH stretches, a symmetric N-H stretch (lower frequency) and an asymmetric N-H stretch (higher frequency).

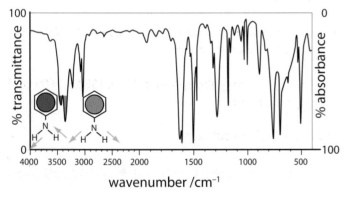

The infra-red spectrum of aniline ($C_6H_5NH_2$)

The importance of differences in the fingerprint region of an infra-red spectrum is highlighted by comparing the infra-red spectra of the structural isomers propan-2-ol and propan-1-ol. Both isomers have the characteristically broad and strong trough at ~3500 cm^{-1} for their hydrogen bonded alcohol functional group (O-H).

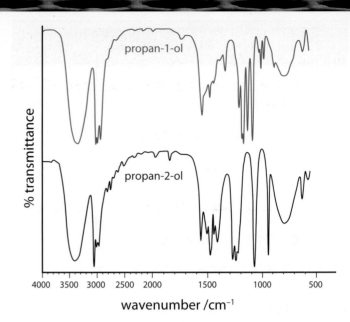

The three important bonds in ethanol are seen in its infra-red spectrum:

- 3200-3500 cm^{-1} broad trough for hydrogen bonded O-H

- sharp trough at ~3000 cm^{-1} for C-H

- and at 1030 cm^{-1} there is a large trough (low % transmittance) which is the C-O stretching vibration.

O-H is at higher frequency than C-H as the bond is more polarised and therefore stronger and more resistant to vibration.

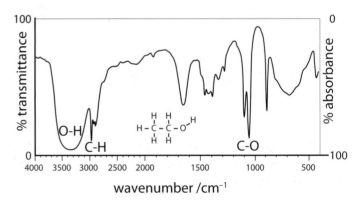

The infra-red spectrum of ethanol

Question 28.4

1. Which option gives the usual range for an infra-red spectrum?

A   625 cm⁻¹ to 4000 cm⁻¹

B   400 cm⁻¹ to 625 cm⁻¹

C   625 nm to 4000 nm

D   625 nm to 400 nm

A4.4 (d)
Interpreting simple spectra (alcohols & carboxylic acids)

If tables of data are not provided in your chemistry examinations, it becomes really important to have a handle on the figures for the main groups and to go through a series of logical steps in order to 'solve' infra-red spectra successfully. Other analytical data will usually be available to help solve structures. It should be remembered that as an analytical technique it is only an infra-red spectrum which will always positively identify the functional group. One method for interpreting an infra-red spectrum is a logical stepwise approach which involves asking a series of key questions.

Step 1:

Is there a strong carbonyl (C=O) absorbance at around 1700 cm⁻¹? If YES go to STEP 2 if NO go to STEP 3.

Step 2:

It could be **aldehyde, ketone, carboxylic acid** or an **ester.** Identifying the presence of the other bonds present will confirm the identity of the FG

wavenumber / cm⁻¹	C=O	O-H	C-O	C-H
Carboxylic acid	~1700-1725	~2500-3300	~1100-1300	
Ester	~1715-1750		~1050-1300	
Aldehyde	~1720-1740			~2750 & 2850
ketone	~1705-1720			

Step 3:

Is there a broad OH band ~3300-3600 cm⁻¹ and C-O band ~1000-1300 cm⁻¹? If YES it is an **alcohol** if NO go to STEP 4.

Step 4:

If there is a weak absorbance at 1650 cm⁻¹ it is due to C=C of an **alkene**. If there are strong absorptions at 1450-1650 cm⁻¹ it is **aromatic**. If there is a C-H stretch ~3000 cm⁻¹ and a band near 1450 cm⁻¹ it is an **alkane**. If it is a simple spectrum with an absorption <667 cm⁻¹ it might be a **halogenoalkane**.

Example 28.1 (Phenol)

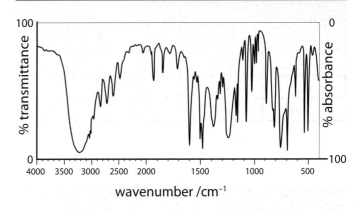

The infra-red spectrum of phenol (C₆H₅OH)

There is a broad trough at 3250 cm⁻¹ corresponding to the O-H stretch.

There is a sharp moderate sized trough at 2750 cm⁻¹ corresponding to a C-H stretch.

There are three strong absorptions at 1470, 1500 & 1600 cm⁻¹ showing it is aromatic.

The C-O stretch is ~1050 cm⁻¹.

Example 28.2 (Ethanoic acid)

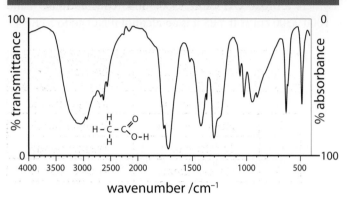

The infra-red spectrum of ethanoic acid

There is a very broad trough from 2500 cm^{-1} to 3300 cm^{-1} corresponding to the O-H stretch.

There is a moderate sized trough at 2700 cm^{-1} corresponding to a C-H stretch.

There is a strong absorption at 1710 cm^{-1} showing it contains a carbonyl C=O group.

The C-O stretch is the one at ~1300 cm^{-1}.

Questions 28.5

1. Identify the major absorbances in the infra-red spectrum of benzaldeyde.

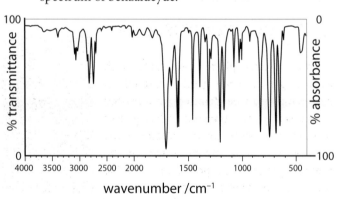

The infra-red spectrum of benzaldeyde (C_6H_5CHO)

2. Identify the major absorbances in the infra-red spectrum of ethyl ethanoate.

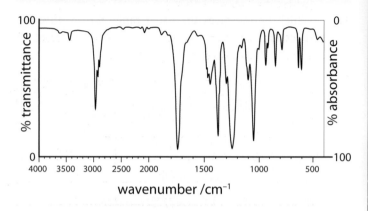

The infra-red spectrum of ethyl ethanoate

3. Identify the major absorbances in the infra-red spectrum of chlorobenzene.

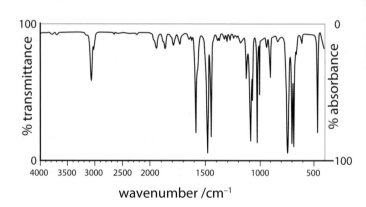

The infra-red spectrum of chlorobenzene

4. Identify the major absorbances in the infra-red spectrum of acetonitrile (ethanenitrile).

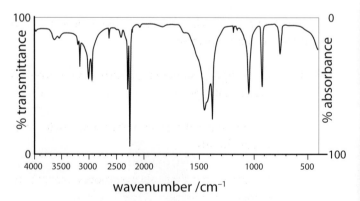

The infra-red spectrum of acetonitrile

5. What is the wavenumber for a trough in an infra-red spectrum for a frequency that absorbs at 2.3×10^{13} Hz? [where $c = 3.00 \times 10^8$ m s^{-1}]

6. Use the table of data to help explain the different IR absorptions for three hydrogen halides.

Hydrogen halide	Bond enthalpy / kJ mol^{-1}	Infra-red absorption / cm^{-1}
HCl	432	2886
HBr	366	2559
HI	298	2230

7. From the infra-red spectrum of propanone what structural information can be determined?

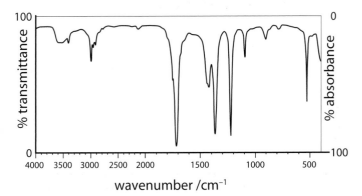

8. Explain why two different carboxylic acid derivatives have quite different infra-red stretching of their carbonyls (C=O). For example acid chlorides (1815 cm^{-1}) and esters (1745 cm^{-1}).

9. Which of the following statements about absorption in infra-red spectra is **false**?

A Large dipole moments give stronger absorptions than small dipoles.

B Strong bonds absorb at higher frequencies than weaker bonds.

C Hydrogen bonding always moves troughs to higher frequencies.

D Bonds joining light atoms absorb at high frequency than bonds joining heavier atoms.

10. Which option gives the correct relationships between the effect of the relative mass of atoms and their bond strengths on frequencies of infra-red vibrations?

	Low frequency	High frequency
A	Lighter atoms	Stronger bonds
B	Heavier atoms	Stronger bonds
C	Lighter atoms	Weaker bonds
D	Heavier atoms	Weaker bonds

11. Which option gives the correct order for descending wavenumber (cm^{-1}) for infra-red absorptions?

A N-H > C≡N > C-H > C=O

B C-H > C=O > C≡C > C-O

C N-H > C≡N > C-O > C=O

D O-H > C≡C > C=O > C-O

12. Calculate the stretching frequency of the C-H bond in wavenumbers which is 9.3×10^{13} Hz.

Additional uses of infra-red spectroscopy

Levels of atmospheric pollutants such as nitrogen dioxide (NO_2) formed in car engines can be detected by infra-red spectroscopy. The brewing industry uses infra-red spectroscopy to determine the alcohol content at various stages of the brewing process. The police use roadside infra-red spectrometers (intoximeters - pictured) to determine the concentration of alcohol in a breath which is proportional to the blood alcohol concentration.

Customs and excise can quickly identify smuggled drugs from the infra-red spectra by comparison with known samples held in databases.

29

Carbon-13 NMR Spectroscopy

Contents

Introduction

The part of the electromagnetic spectrum needed for Nuclear Magnetic Resonance (NMR) Spectroscopy is radiowaves. These radiowaves are used to detect changes in the alignment of nuclear magnetic dipoles (B4.6a) in strong magnetic fields for atoms of carbon-13. Nuclear Magnetic Resonance Spectroscopy is a particularly important technique and used specifically by organic chemists to identify the number and type of carbon environment present in organic molecules. Carbon-13 NMR spectroscopy gives useful information about individual atoms in molecules where infra-red spectroscopy (A4.4) only provides information about groups of atoms (functional groups). Other spin-½ nuclei (B4.6c), *e.g.* ^1H, ^{15}N, ^{19}F and ^{31}P can also be identified by NMR spectroscopy because their nuclei also absorb this type of electromagnetic radiation. This chapter will look at how to interpret carbon-13 NMR spectra. It is a non-destructive method where the sample under investigation is exposed to radiowaves which cause changes in the magnetic dipoles of nuclei (B4.6a).

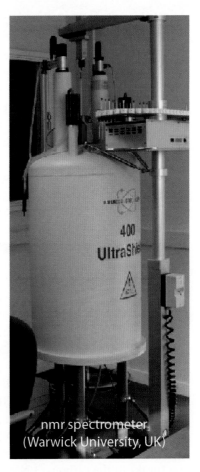

nmr spectrometer
(Warwick University, UK)

The natural abundance of the carbon-13 isotope is only 1.1% (A4.2c) and, because its nucleus also has a relatively low sensitivity, the sample size needed for carbon-13 NMR spectroscopy is about ten times that needed for proton NMR spectroscopy (B4.6c). Samples prepared for NMR spectroscopy are generally dissolved in deutero-solvents which contain no hydrogen atoms, *e.g.* d_1-chloroform ($CDCl_3$), deuterium oxide (D_2O), d_6-benzene (C_6D_6), d_4-methanol (CD_3OD), d_6-acetone (CD_3COCD_3) & d_6-dimethylsulfoxide (CD_3SOCD_3). Solvents without hydrogen atoms such as carbon disulfide (CS_2) and carbon tetrachloride (CCl_4) are also used. These solvents are chosen because the proton (^1H) NMR spectra (A4.6c) are also needed. It is important to select a solvent that the compound is soluble in and does not have a signal that masks a peak in the sample being analysed.

Solvent	Formula	Chemical shifts for ^{13}C atoms / ppm
d_4-methanol	CD_3OD	49.2
d_2-dichloromethane	CD_2Cl_2	54.0
d_1-chloroform	$CDCl_3$	77.2
d_6-acetone	$(CD_3)_2CO$	29.9 & 207.7
d_6-dimethylsulfoxide	$(CD_3)_2SO$	39.5
d_6-benzene	C_6D_6	128.4
d_3-acetonitrile	CD_3CN	1.4 & 118.7

Carbon-13 NMR spectra are comparatively simple to interpret because the hydrogen atoms (protons) are irradiated at the same time that the spectrum is recorded. This means that any ^{13}C-^1H coupling is removed and the result is a spectrum that is described as decoupled carbon-13 NMR spectrum. In each of these carbon-13 NMR spectra each individual line (singlet) shows the presence of a unique carbon atom in the molecule. Fortunately peaks for carbon atoms seldom overlap. It is worth noting that, unlike proton NMR spectroscopy (B4.6d), the sizes of the peaks (intensity) for carbon-13 NMR are not proportional to the number of nuclei in a given environment. This means that carbon-13 NMR spectroscopy is a simple way for a scientist to count the number of different types of carbon nuclei within an organic molecule.

Molecules with one peak

Each unique carbon gives a single peak in a carbon-13 decoupled NMR spectrum. Therefore simple molecules with only one carbon atom will only have one peak in their carbon-13 NMR spectrum. A look at where the peaks come for different carbon environments is considered later (A4.5b).

Question 29.1

1. Which spectroscopy involves electromagnetic radiation having the longest wavelength?

    A   Infra-red spectroscopy.

    B   Ultra-violet spectroscopy.

    C   Nuclear Magnetic Resonance Spectroscopy.

    D   Atomic emission spectroscopy.

Example 29.1 (Methanol)

There is a single peak at 50 ppm which corresponds to the one carbon atom (C-O).

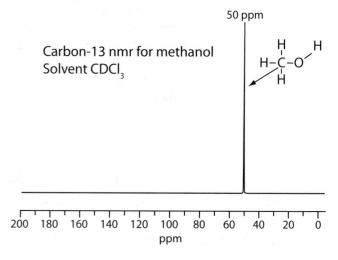

Carbon-13 nmr for methanol
Solvent $CDCl_3$

A4.5 (a) Number of peaks in a carbon-13 NMR spectrum

On the x-axis of a carbon-13 NMR spectrum the scale is chemical shift (B4.5b) which has the symbol delta (δ) and is in the range 0-230 ppm. The scale is calibrated to an internal standard; the symmetrical **tetra**methyl**silane** (TMS) $(CH_3)_4Si$. All four carbon atoms in TMS are equivalent and its single line (peak) in the carbon-13 NMR spectrum has been given a value of 0 ppm which is a frequency much lower than the carbon atoms found in most organic molecules.

Tetramethylsilane

Example 29.2 (Methanal)

There is a single peak at 166 ppm which corresponds to the one carbon atom (C=O).

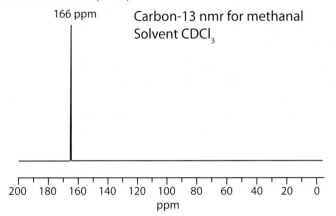

When a molecule possesses symmetry it will reduce the number of unique carbon environments. So instead of two peaks for methoxymethane, (CH_3OCH_3) with its two carbon atoms, there is only one peak as both carbon atoms are equivalent.

Molecules with two peaks

Molecules with two carbon atoms which are not symmetrical will have two peaks in their carbon-13 NMR spectrum, *e.g.* ethanal, ethanol, ethanoic acid and methyl methanoate. When a molecule possesses symmetry the number of peaks in its carbon-13 NMR spectrum will be reduced. Molecules with three carbon atoms with two peaks in their carbon-13 NMR spectra include propan-2-ol and propanone. The peak at 0 ppm is for the internal reference standard, TMS.

Example 29.3 (Ethanal)

There are two peaks (31ppm and 200 ppm) for ethanal for its two distinct carbon atoms.

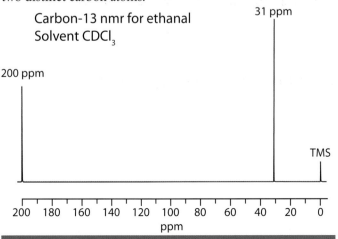

Questions 29.2

1. Which option gives a carbon-13 NMR spectrum with more than one peak?

   A   Methanoic acid.

   B   Cyclohexane.

   C   Ethoxymethane.

   D   Benzene.

2. Which option shows the correct number of peaks (lines) in the carbon-13 NMR spectrum for the deuterated solvent d_6-propanone?

   A   6

   B   2

   C   3

   D   1

3. Which option shows the correct number of peaks in the carbon-13 NMR spectrum for the isomers having molecular formula C_3H_8O?

	propan-1-ol	propan-2-ol	ethoxy-methane
A	3	3	3
B	3	3	2
C	2	2	3
D	3	2	3

4. Explain how many peaks there are in the decoupled carbon-13 NMR spectrum for benzoic acid.

5. For each isomer of dichlorocyclobutane indicate using skeletal formulae how many peaks there will be in their decoupled carbon-13 NMR spectra.

A4.5 (b) Chemical shift values

Chemical shift is frequency with units in parts per million (ppm). It is found on the *x*-axis of a carbon-13 NMR spectrum. The carbon atoms in most organic molecules are to be found within the range 0 ppm to 200 ppm. Four major types of bonds to carbon fall into convenient divisions of approximately 50 ppm batches. Single bonds to carbon are found between 0 ppm and 100 ppm, *e.g.* C-C bonds (0-50 ppm) and C-O bonds (50-100 ppm). Double bonds to carbon are found between 100 ppm and 200 ppm, *e.g.* C=C bonds (100-150 ppm) and C=O bonds (150-200 ppm). Chemical shift is the difference in frequency between carbon atoms and the four equivalent carbon atoms of TMS at 0 ppm. Mathematically, chemical shift can be expressed as:

$$\delta = \frac{[\text{Frequency of resonance (Hz)} - \text{Frequency of TMS (Hz)}]}{[\text{Frequency of TMS (MHz)}]}$$

It is helpful to learn the diagram which shows the approximate carbon-13 NMR chemical shift ranges for saturated and unsaturated carbon atoms connected directly to a carbon atom or to an oxygen atom.

Table to show characteristic chemical shifts
(bonds to carbon)

Bond	Type	Functional group	Chemical shift δ /ppm
C-C	single	Alkane	0-50
C-X	single	Halogenoalkane	0-80
C-N	single	Amine	20-60
C-O	single	Ether, alcohol, ester	50-100
C=C	double	Alkene	100-150
C=C	'double'	Aromatic	~140
C=O	double	Aldehyde, ketone, acid, ester, amide	150-200
C=N	double	Imine	~160
C=O	double	Carboxylic acids, esters, amides	< 180
C=O	double	Aldehydes, ketones	> 180

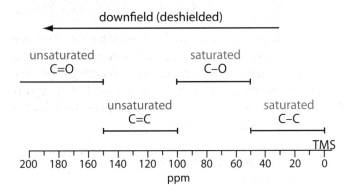

The chemical shift of any carbon atom depends on its environment, *i.e.* the inductive effect (B3.11c) of its substituents, which is determined by their electronegativity (A1.2i). The less the shielding (A1.1d) experienced by a carbon atom the higher (numerically) the chemical shift. In the case of single and double bonds from carbon to the highly electronegative oxygen they have a higher ppm compared with that of the less electronegative carbon atom. Values at higher ppm are often described as being 'downfield'. The effect of electronegative elements on chemical shift is also apparent when comparing the carbon resonances for $(CH_3)_4Si$ (0 ppm), CH_3OH (50 ppm) and CH_3F (75 ppm).

A4.5 (c) Interpreting decoupled carbon-13 NMR spectra

When interpreting a carbon-13 NMR spectrum it is often easier to read from right to left, *i.e.* to read in the same direction as the languages of the Middle East. This way you are less likely to misread the scale and make mistakes in assigning the exact chemical shift for a peak.

On the *y*-axis of an NMR spectrum is intensity, and unlike ^{1}H NMR, the peak areas (intensities) are not proportional to the number of carbon atoms of this type and in this environment.

Once again it is worth emphasizing that if tables of data are not provided in chemistry exams it becomes really important to be able to recall chemical shifts for the main bonds to carbon. Single bonds are to be found from 0-100 ppm (upfield) and double bonds are found at higher field (downfield) from 100-200 ppm. ^{13}C NMR spectra are easier to solve (interpret) than ^{1}H NMR because the peaks are not split by spin-spin coupling (B4.6c).

When the structure of a molecule is provided, or its name given, you need to take the following simple steps to assign its carbon-13 NMR spectrum:

Step 1: Count the number of different types of carbon atom.

Step 2: Look at the individual atoms bonded to each carbon atom.

Step 3: Saturated bonds are C-C (0-50 ppm) and C-O (50-100 ppm).

Step 4: Unsaturated bonds are C=C (100-150 ppm) and C=O (150-200 ppm).

It is important to remember that the number of carbon atoms does not necessarily match the types of different carbon atoms. This is because some molecules have symmetry which leads to equivalent carbon atoms either side of the line of symmetry. When faced with isomers, the type of carbon atoms is often the quickest route to solving the spectrum, *e.g.* propan-1-ol and propan-2-ol.

The following table illustrates what types of bonds to a carbon atom will be present for various simple molecules containing only one functional group. Ignore C-H bonds when interpreting the carbon-13 NMR spectra of molecules.

Functional groups	C-C	C-O	C=C	C=O
Alkane	√			
Ether	√	√		
Ethene			√	
Alkene	√		√	
Methanal				√
Aldehyde or ketone	√			√
Methanoic acid		√		√
Carboxylic acid	√	√		√
Ester	√	√		√

Example 29.4 (Ethanal)

There are two peaks because there are two types of carbon environment. The peak at 31 ppm corresponds to C-C of the CH_3 (methyl group) as C-C (0-50 ppm). The peak at 200 ppm corresponds to C=O of the CHO (aldehyde group) as C=O (150-200 ppm).

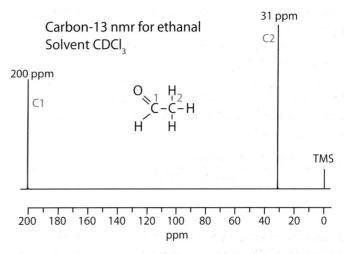

Example 29.5 (Propanone)

There are three carbon atoms in propanone but there are only two different types of carbon environment because the molecule is symmetrical (through the carbonyl group). The peak at 31 ppm corresponds to C-C of the two CH_3 groups as C-C (0-50 ppm). The peak at 207 ppm corresponds to C=O of the ketone group as C=O (150-200 ppm).

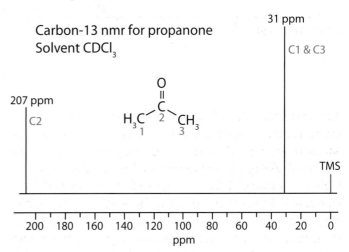

Example 29.6 (Propanal)

There are three peaks in propanal because there are three types of carbon environment. The peak at 6 ppm corresponds to C-C of the CH$_3$ (methyl group) as C-C (0-50 ppm). The peak at 37 ppm corresponds to C-C of the CH$_2$ (methylene group) as C-C (0-50 ppm) and it is further downfield than CH$_3$ as it is adjacent to the carbonyl. The peak at 203 ppm corresponds to C=O of the CHO (aldehyde group) as C=O (150-200 ppm).

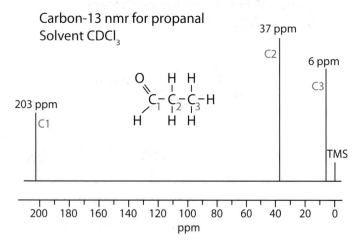

Carbon-13 nmr for propanal
Solvent CDCl$_3$

Example 29.7 (butan-2-one)

There are four peaks because there are four unique types of carbon environment. The peak at 8 ppm corresponds to C4 of the CH$_3$ (methyl group) adjacent to the methylene. The peak at 30 ppm corresponds to C1 of the CH$_3$ (methyl group) adjacent to the carbonyl. The peak at 37 ppm corresponds to C3 of the CH$_2$ (methylene group). The peak at 209 ppm corresponds to C2 of the R$_2$CO (ketone group).

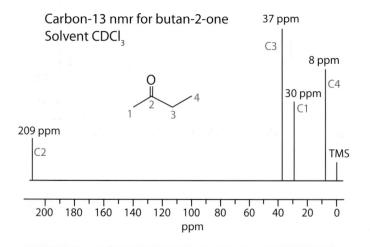

Carbon-13 nmr for butan-2-one
Solvent CDCl$_3$

Questions 29.3

1. Identify the peaks in the carbon-13 NMR spectrum of ethanol.

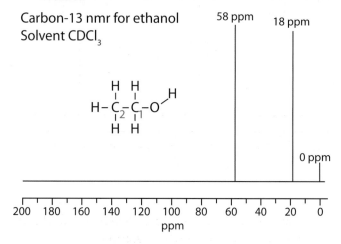

Carbon-13 nmr for ethanol
Solvent CDCl$_3$

2. Identify the peaks in the carbon-13 NMR spectrum of propan-1-ol. What is the symbol and unit of chemical shift on the x-axis?

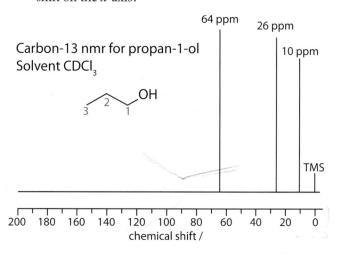

Carbon-13 nmr for propan-1-ol
Solvent CDCl$_3$

3. Identify the peaks in the carbon-13 NMR spectrum of propan-2-ol. How does this carbon-13 NMR spectrum differ from that for its isomer having the same functional group?

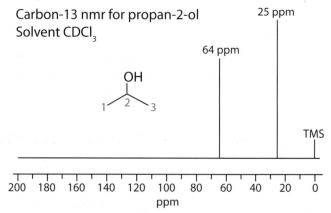

Carbon-13 nmr for propan-2-ol
Solvent CDCl$_3$

4. Identify the peaks in the carbon-13 NMR spectrum of cyclohexanol.

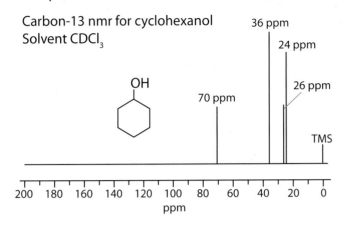

Carbon-13 nmr for cyclohexanol
Solvent CDCl₃

5. Draw a skeletal formula for cyclohexene and label the peaks in its carbon-13 NMR spectrum.

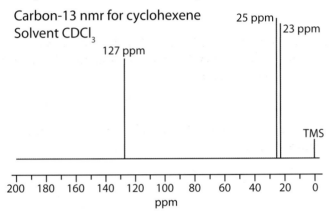

Carbon-13 nmr for cyclohexene
Solvent CDCl₃

6. Label the peaks in the carbon-13 NMR spectrum of ethanoic acid.

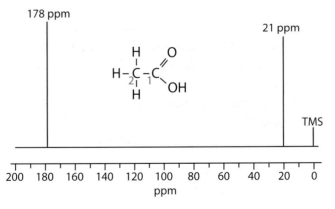

Carbon-13 nmr for ethanoic acid
Solvent CDCl₃

Example 29.8

Ethanoic acid and methyl methanoate have the same molecular formula ($C_2H_4O_2$) but they have quite different structures. In methyl methanoate, C2 has both a C-O and a C=O bond. In examples such as this where more than one type of bond occurs at the same carbon atom, the resonance will be in the region of the one furthest downfield, *i.e.* largest chemical shift.

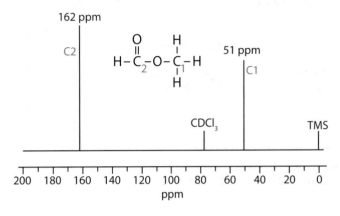

Carbon-13 nmr for methyl methanoate
Solvent CDCl₃

Questions 29.4

1. Label the peaks in the carbon-13 NMR spectrum of ethyl ethanoate.

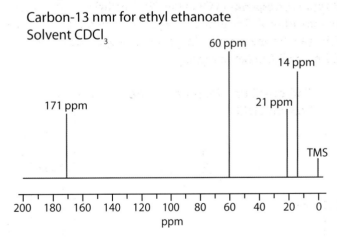

Carbon-13 nmr for ethyl ethanoate
Solvent CDCl₃

453

2. Label the peaks in the carbon-13 NMR spectrum of propane-1,2,3-triol (glycerol).

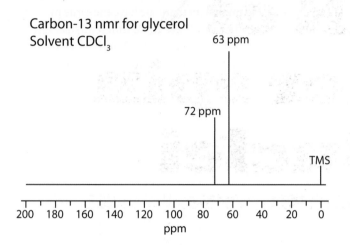

Carbon-13 nmr for glycerol
Solvent $CDCl_3$

63 ppm

72 ppm

TMS

200 180 160 140 120 100 80 60 40 20 0
ppm

3. Maleic acid was dissolved in the versatile solvent dimethylsulfoxide (DMSO) and its ^{13}C NMR spectrum was obtained. Maleic acid has the molecular formula $C_4H_4O_4$. Solve its structure from the ^{13}C NMR spectrum given. [Hint: consider symmetry].

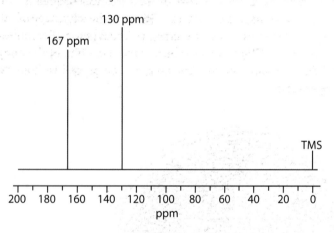

Carbon-13 nmr for maleic acid
Solvent $CDCl_3$

130 ppm

167 ppm

TMS

200 180 160 140 120 100 80 60 40 20 0
ppm

4. How many peaks will the following have in their carbon-13 NMR spectra?

	Substance	# peaks
(a)	Maleic anhydride	
(b)	Lactic acid (2-hydroxypropanoic acid)	
(c)	1,4-Dioxane	
(d)	Ethylene glycol (1,2-dihydroxyethane)	
(e)	Butane-1,3-diol	
(f)	Butane-2,3-diol	

Summary

You can imagine how complex it becomes for researchers trying to solve the structure of novel natural products. Carbon-13 NMR spectroscopy is one of a number of analytical techniques that helps in structural elucidation.

Carbon-13 NMR has proved useful in stereochemical analyses. Differences can be observed in the carbon-13 NMR spectra for geometric isomers (A3.1d), *e.g.* mesaconic acid which is derived from citric acid. You get lower frequency shifts for the carbon of the CH_3 group in the *trans*-isomer. The differences in frequencies are due to van der Waals contact with the substituents.

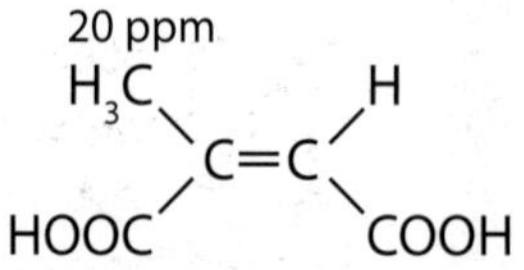

20 ppm

H_3C H
C=C
HOOC   COOH

cis-mesaconic acid

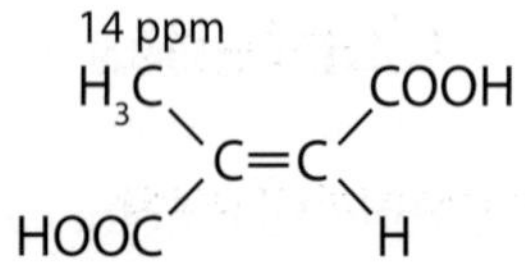

14 ppm

H_3C COOH
C=C
HOOC   H

trans-mesaconic acid

It is also possible to do spectrum editing such as **DEPT-135 (Distortion Enhancement by Polarization Transfer)** where, in the carbon-13 NMR spectrum, the quaternary carbon signals disappear, the methine (CH) and methyl (CH_3) point upwards and the methylene (CH_2) point downwards.

30

NMR of other spin ½ Nuclei

Contents

Nuclear magnetic resonance is a spectroscopic technique used to determine molecular structure. It gives useful information about the arrangement of atoms in molecules. In addition to information about ^{13}C atoms (A4.5a), it can be used for other atoms such as ^1H, ^{15}N, ^{19}F and ^{31}P. Only a few milligrams of sample is needed to acquire the most commonly met ^1H nmr spectrum which can be obtained in minutes using a modern fourier transform nmr spectrometer.

Magnetic resonance imaging (MRI) is a familiar version of nmr used in hospitals to identify injuries and diseases by doctors as part of their medical diagnoses. The patient has to lie inside a very large magnet during an MRI scan. The advantage of this technique is that, unlike x-rays, it causes no tissue damage as it makes use of 'harmless' radio frequencies. Hydrogen atoms (^1H) in water, which makes up ~70% of the body, give different signals in different tissues which allow organs to be probed without the need for an exploratory operation.

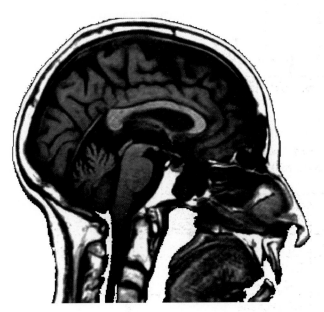

MRI scan of a healthy brain (Lahey Clinic, Burlington, USA)

Active areas of the brain with detectable electrical signals are fuelled by the molecule **a**denosine **tri**phosphate (ATP). MRI can give a 3D picture of the brain by detecting the ^{31}P in ATP.

B4.6 (a) The NMR Process

NMR is concerned with the interaction of nuclei with radiowaves, typically of frequency 100-1000 MHz. BBC radio 4 is 92-95 MHz. Nuclei of atoms with an odd mass number possess the property of spin, which has already been described for electrons (A1.1e). Examples of isotopes with spin-½ nuclei commonly explored using nmr include; ^{1}H, ^{13}C, ^{15}N, ^{19}F and ^{31}P. These spin-½ nuclei resonate at different radio frequencies and not all of them are the major isotope for the element. If a nucleus has an even number of protons and neutrons (^{12}C) their magnetic fields cancel out and these isotopes are nmr inactive.

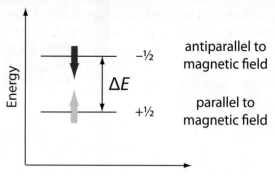

Alignment of spin ½ nuclei in a magnetic field

Field strength of 11.74 Tesla			
Nucleus	Spin	Natural abundance %	Resonant frequency MHz
^{1}H	½	99.98	500.00
^{13}C	½	1.11	125.72
^{15}N	½	0.37	50.66
^{19}F	½	100	470.39
^{31}P	½	100	202.4

Other examples of isotopes of elements having spin–½ nuclei include; ^{29}Si, ^{57}Fe, ^{77}Se, ^{103}Rh, ^{113}Cd, ^{119}Sn, ^{133}Cs, ^{187}Os, ^{195}Pt, ^{199}Hg and ^{207}Pb. As with carbon-13 nmr spectroscopy, samples are usually examined as pure liquids or dissolved in proton-free solvents where the hydrogen atoms have been replaced by deuterium (A4.5). In solution, a signal can be detected for each nmr active atom with a spin–½ nucleus contained within a molecule.

The physical process of nmr spectroscopy is essentially magnetic dipoles interacting with an external magnetic field. Nuclei behave as if they are tiny bar magnets. If these nuclei are placed in a magnetic field, the nuclei (bar magnets) can adopt two positions. They are either aligned with the magnetic field, which is the low energy position (spin +½), or in the high energy position (spin –½) which is aligned against the magnetic field.

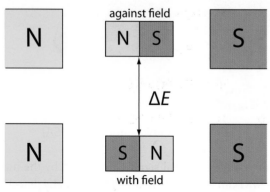

Nuclei bar magnets in a magnetic field

At room temperature, the majority of nuclei are aligned with the external magnetic field in the low energy state. It is possible to get a small percentage of the nuclei to 'flip' to the higher energy state so that their nuclei are aligned against the external magnetic field. The nucleus spin flip happens when the sample is subjected to radiowaves of a frequency that exactly matches the energy difference (ΔE) between the two spin states. Samples are given pulses of radio frequencies and a detector records the differences in the signal that it receives compared with the original signal. The differences are caused by absorption of the energy equal to ΔE when nuclei reverse their magnetic dipoles. In order to produce an nmr spectrum, the applied magnetic field is varied. The quanta of energy absorbed that change the direction of the magnetic dipoles for spin–½ nuclei depends on their different environments (B4.6b). The absorption of energy that makes the spin of the nucleus flip is called **nuclear magnetic resonance**. The energy of the radiowaves is approximately 10^{-25} J.

Nuclei are shielded from external magnetic fields by their electrons. The greater the number of electrons or the higher electron density around a nucleus, the more shielded (A1.1d) it is compared with a nucleus with fewer electrons or lower electron density. Protons (^{1}H) will be used to illustrate the effect of shielding on nuclear magnetic resonance. As the electron density increases around a hydrogen atom it has increased shielding. One consequence of increased shielding is that a larger magnetic field, or a smaller radio frequency, will be needed to cause the nuclei to flip. Spectra with different peaks are obtained when molecules contain protons with different degrees of shielding (B4.6b). The electron density around protons is low when they are attached to highly electronegative (A1.2i) atoms such as oxygen, *e.g.* the hydroxyl group (O-H) in alcohols.

Coupling of protons is a phenomenon which occurs between non-equivalent protons on neighbouring carbon atoms. These carbon atoms which are next to each other are often described as 'adjacent' to each other. Neighbouring protons with nuclei aligned with the external magnetic field will have a slight deshielding effect because their field will add to the applied field. Neighbouring protons with nuclei aligned against the external magnetic field will have a slight shielding effect because their field will reduce the applied field. Protons on neighbouring carbon atoms are said to be 'coupled' as their magnetic fields caused by their spin-½ nuclei are close enough to interact. This spin-spin coupling leads to splitting of peaks in nmr spectra and is covered in detail elsewhere (B4.6c & B4.6d).

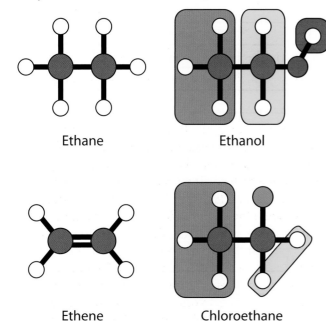

Ethane   Ethanol

Ethene   Chloroethane

Diagram to show what is meant by 'non-equivalent' protons on adjacent carbon atoms

- All six protons are equivalent in ethane as they are in the same environment so there will be no coupling.

- There are three types of proton in ethanol which are the methyl (CH_3 - blue box), the methylene (CH_2 - yellow box) on adjacent carbon atoms and the hydroxyl (OH - red box). There will be coupling between the methyl and methylene protons as they are in different environments and on adjacent carbon atoms.

- All four protons are equivalent in ethene as they are in the same environment so there will be no coupling.

- There are two types of proton environments in chloroethane which will couple as they are on adjacent carbon atoms.

Chemists routinely examine ^1H and ^{13}C atoms in molecules using nmr spectroscopy as these atoms are both found in the vast majority of the millions of organic compounds.

Questions 30.1

1. What is being probed during nmr spectroscopy?

   A   Nuclei

   B   Electrons

   C   Ions

   D   Bonds

2. Which option is a correct description for nuclei aligned against the magnetic field?

   A   Spin+½ & low energy

   B   Spin–½ & high energy

   C   Spin+½ & high energy

   D   Spin–½ & low energy

3. Which nucleus is invisible in nmr spectroscopy?

   A ^{15}N

   B ^{13}C

   C ^{16}O

   D ^{19}F

4. Which option shows the correct order of descending resonant frequencies for spin–½ nuclei?

   A $^1H > {}^{13}C > {}^{19}F > {}^{31}P$

   B $^{13}C > {}^{19}F > {}^{31}P > {}^1H$

   C $^{31}P > {}^{19}F > {}^{13}C > {}^1H$

   D $^1H > {}^{19}F > {}^{31}P > {}^{13}C$

5. Complete the sentences by filling in the gaps.

"Hydrogen nuclei are shielded from the external magnetic field by their **(a)**_____."

"The **(b)**_____ the electron density around the hydrogen atom then the greater will be the magnetic field that is going to cause their nuclei to **(c)**_____."

B4.6 (b) Origin of the chemical shift scale (δ)

The magnetic environment of spin–½ nuclei such as protons can be measured as their chemical shift (A4.5b). Chemical shift has the symbol δ (delta) with units of parts per million (ppm). The internal reference standard TMS which is often added to samples for calibration has a resonance at $\delta = 0$ ppm. The extent to which other protons resonate compared with TMS is called the chemical shift. The majority of observed chemical shifts for protons are positive and generally have values from 0-10 ppm. The chemical shifts observed for protons in a particular environment do not depend on the operating frequency of the nmr spectrometer. Chemical shift for a peak in an nmr spectrum can be worked out by reference to the scale. It is important to remember that the scales for spectra, for historical reasons, read from right to left. The equation for chemical shift is:

$$\delta = \frac{\text{observed frequency (Hz)} - \text{frequency of TMS (Hz)}}{\text{spectrometer frequency (Hz)}} \times 10^6 \text{ ppm}$$

There is no need to learn values for chemical shifts as chemists will interpret spectra using chemical shift tables such as those shown below for different types of proton environments. A nucleus in a particular environment is characterised by a chemical shift. An aliphatic methyl group has a chemical shift of 0.9 ppm compared with a methyl ketone, which has a chemical shift of 2.1 ppm. After assigning a number of spectra, most students will soon begin to recognise which protons appear at particular chemical shifts.

Typical proton chemical shifts δ / ppm

Group	Name of group	chemical shift / ppm
R-CH$_3$	methyl	0.9
RCH$_2$R	methylene	1.3
R$_2$CHR	methine	2.0
ROCOCH$_3$	ester	2.0
RCOCH$_3$	ketone	2.1
C$_6$H$_5$CH$_3$	methyl (aromatic)	2.3
R-C≡C-H	alkyne	2.6
RCH$_2$X	halogenoalkane	3.2
ROCH$_3$	ether	3.8
R-OH	alcohol (aliphatic)	4.5
RCH=CH$_2$	alkene	4.9
RCH=CH$_2$	alkene	5.9
C$_6$H$_5$OH	alcohol (aromatic)	7.0
C$_6$H$_5$H	aromatic	7.3
RCHO	aldehyde	9.7
RCOOH	carboxylic acid	11.5

Another way of representing the different chemical shifts for the main functional groups is included as some students and teachers might find it easier to use the information in this visual format.

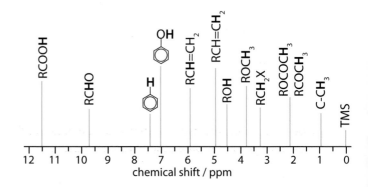

Chemical shifts of some common functional groups

Chemical shifts result from differences in the electron distribution around different hydrogen atoms. The inductive effect (B3.11c) is a major factor affecting chemical shift. The larger the chemical shift, the less shielding there is around the nucleus and the higher frequency needed for it to resonate. This finding is illustrated by looking at the δ values for methyl groups attached to carbon ($E_{neg} = 2.5$), nitrogen ($E_{neg} = 3.0$) and oxygen ($E_{neg} = 3.5$).

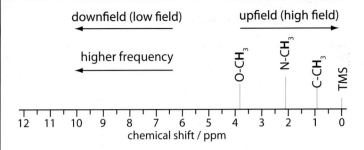

The more electronegative the atom that a methyl group is attached to, the further **downfield** (higher ppm) its chemical shift. This is because it is **deshielded** (electron density is withdrawn). It is helpful to remember that **deshielding** moves signals **downfield** and so the numerical value of chemical shift increases.

Questions 30.2

1. Where would the chemical shifts be expected for the protons of ethanoic acid?

2. Which option shows the usual range for chemical shifts of protons in a ^1H nmr spectrum?

    A   400-4000 ppm

    B   0-100 ppm

    C   0-200 ppm

    D   0-10 ppm

3. How can you distinguish between aliphatic and aromatic hydroxyl groups in a ^1H nmr spectrum?

4. Which option shows the correct effect of +I and –I groups on the chemical shift of protons on adjacent carbon atoms?

	+I	–I
A	No effect	No effect
B	No effect	Shift downfield
C	Shift upfield	Shift downfield
D	Shift downfield	Shift upfield

B4.6 (c) Interpreting spin-½ NMR spectra

The rules for interpreting nmr spectra are independent of the particular spin–½ nucleus. It is easiest to introduce spin–½ nmr spectroscopy with proton nmr spectroscopy as there are many more examples of these spectra that have been produced and analysed. Every peak in a low resolution nmr spectrum corresponds to atom(s) in different environments. The chemical shift will help to identify the type of proton in that environment. The relative numbers of protons can be calculated from the integrated trace. The splitting of the peaks in a high resolution nmr spectrum will provide information about its nearest neighbours (B4.6d).

When analysing an nmr spectrum the symmetry of molecules needs careful consideration. Symmetrical molecules have much less complex nmr spectra as symmetry reduces the number of unique proton environments. 1,2-dichloroethane has four protons but only one signal in its nmr spectrum at δ 3.7 ppm as all its protons are identical. The symmetry line is shown for this halogenoalkane (A3.3b).

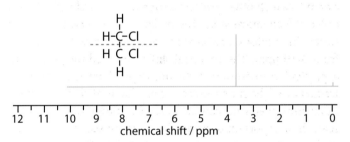

^1H nmr spectrum of 1,2-dichloroethane
in $CDCl_3$ at 300 MHz

Proton nmr spectra

Chemical shift is on the *x*-axis and absorption is on the *y*-axis of a proton nmr spectrum. The usual range is 0-10 ppm. Any resonances greater than 10 ppm are often included in the main spectra in a separate box described as **off-set** as it is 'off scale'. All twelve hydrogen atoms in tetramethylsilane (TMS) are equivalent, giving a single line (peak) at a chemical shift of 0 ppm which is a frequency much lower than the hydrogen atoms found in most organic molecules. Using just the data for chemical shifts (B4.6b), it is possible to assign the proton nmr spectra for simple molecules.

Example 30.1 (ethanal)

Ethanal has the structural formula CH₃CHO. It has two hydrogen environments so there are two peaks in its low resolution ¹H nmr spectrum. The peak at 2.2 ppm corresponds to the methyl protons (CH₃) and the peak at 9.8 ppm corresponds to the aldehyde protons (CHO).

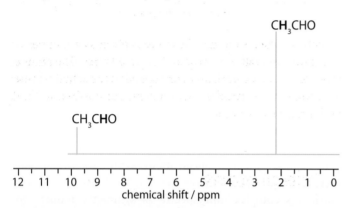

Example 30.2 (methanal)

Methanal has the structural formula HCHO. It has one hydrogen environment because of its symmetry, so there is only one peak in its low resolution ¹H nmr spectrum at 9.60 ppm which corresponds to the aldehyde protons (**HCHO**).

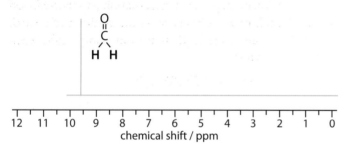

Example 30.3 (propanone)

Propanone has the structural formula CH₃(CO)CH₃. It has one hydrogen environment because of its symmetry so there is only one peak in its low resolution ¹H nmr spectrum at 2.16 ppm.

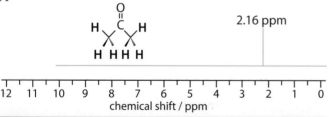

Spin-spin coupling

In a low resolution nmr spectrum, each environment results in a single peak in the nmr spectrum. In a high resolution spectrum, the peaks can be split according to the number of protons on adjacent carbon atoms. The extent of splitting can be worked out using the '*n*+1 rule' where *n* = number of protons on adjacent carbon atoms. Hydrogen atoms on the same carbon atom are considered equivalent (identical) and there is no interaction (coupling) between them. A single peak is known as a **singlet** (s), a peak split into two is called a **doublet** (d), a peak split into three is called a **triplet** (t), and a peak split into four is called a **quartet** (q) or sometimes a **quadruplet**. Spin-spin coupling which leads to peak splitting is only over one C-C bond. A more detailed explanation of splitting is found in section B4.6d.

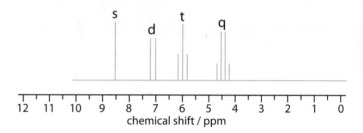

The number of peaks from splitting provides chemists with useful information about the number of protons on adjacent carbon atoms. Nmr is one of a combination of techniques which also includes mass spectrometry (A4.2), qualitative analysis (A4.1), infra-red spectroscopy (A4.4) and x-ray crystallography (B2.5) which might be needed in the identification of compounds.

Example 30.4 (ethanol)

Ethanol has the structural formula CH₃CH₂OH. It has three hydrogen environments and there will be splitting of the methyl and methylene protons as they are adjacent to each other. In the high resolution ¹H nmr spectrum the methyl group (**CH₃**CH₂OH) is a triplet at 1.2 ppm and the methylene group (CH₃**CH₂**OH) is a quartet at 3.7 ppm . The alcohol group (CH₃CH₂**OH**) is a broad singlet at 2.6 ppm.

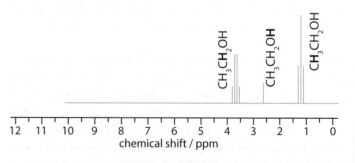

Example 30.5 (propan-1-ol)

Propanol has the structural formula $CH_3CH_2CH_2OH$. It has four hydrogen environments and there will be splitting of the methyl group and both sets of methylene protons. In the high resolution ^1H nmr spectrum the methyl group ($\mathbf{CH_3}CH_2CH_2OH$) is a triplet at 0.95 ppm and the alcohol group ($CH_3CH_2CH_2\mathbf{OH}$) is a broad singlet at 2.3 ppm. Of the two methylene groups, the one next to the highly electronegative oxygen atom of the OH is most downfield at 3.6 ppm. This methylene ($CH_3CH_2\mathbf{CH_2}OH$) is split into a triplet. The methylene group adjacent to the methyl group appears as a 'sextet' which might be explained in terms of $n = 5$. Peaks beyond quartets will not be examined at Pre-U level as non-equivalent protons lead to more complex splitting which is best left until university.

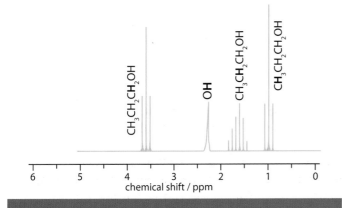

Signal integrations

Nmr spectrometers can automatically calculate the areas under peaks. This information is displayed as lines which look like steps by the peaks in an nmr spectrum. These steps are either called 'integrated traces' or 'integrated curves'. The height of the step is proportional to the area under the peak and this is proportional to the relative number of protons generating that peak. The height of the peak does not provide information about the number of protons, which can only be obtained from the integrated trace. When measuring integrated traces, you usually find that you are given convenient numbers to allow the ratio to be easily solved. If you should end up with more difficult numbers for the integrated traces, treat the problem in the same way that you would with empirical formulae (A4.1b) and divide by the smallest number for an integrated trace.

The proton nmr spectrum of methyl ethanoate showing the integrated traces (red steps) by both peaks follows. The height of the integrated trace steps are identical, which shows that the ratio of protons in each environment is 1:1. This is what you would expect for methyl ethanoate CH_3OCOCH_3. There are six protons with three protons in the two environments. A ratio of 3:3 cancels down to 1:1.

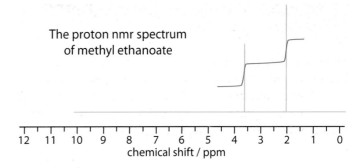

The proton nmr spectrum of methyl ethanoate

Sometimes the area under the curve is given as a number on top of the peak rather than as an integrated trace. The number given on top of the peak may correspond to the actual number of protons in a particular environment, but it is best to think of this number as a ratio.

Labile protons

The hydroxyl proton of ethanol ($CH_3CH_2\mathbf{OH}$) gives a single peak (singlet) in its high resolution proton nmr spectrum, despite its neighbouring carbon atom having two protons attached. The reason a triplet is not observed is that this hydroxyl proton exchanges very rapidly with other protons in the water that will be present in the solvent in trace amounts. This hydroxyl proton is described as **labile**. This ability to exchange with hydrogen atoms in water has been exploited by a technique called a '$\mathbf{D_2O}$ shake'. Chemists discovered that the peak in a proton nmr spectrum corresponding to the hydroxyl proton of alcohols will disappear on the addition of a small drop of deuterium oxide (D_2O) to the nmr sample tube when the spectrum is re-run.

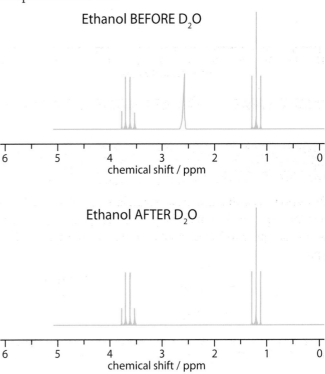

461

The reaction between ethanol and deuterium oxide is a rapidly reached dynamic equilibrium (B1.5a). Deuterium does not absorb in the same region as protons (0-10 ppm), so the peak for OH essentially disappears.

$$CH_3CH_2OH + D_2O \rightleftharpoons CH_3CH_2OD + HOD$$

The protons of carboxylic acids (A3.2d) and amines (A3.2g) are also labile and will exchange with a deuterium atom from deuterium oxide. The 'D$_2$O shake' is very useful for the identification of labile protons and on the occasions where peaks overlap.

Fluorine-19 nmr spectra

Familiar fluorine containing compounds are the chlorofluorocarbons (CFC) such as dichlorodifluoromethane (CF$_2$Cl$_2$). These compounds were extensively used as propellants and refrigerants before it was discovered that they were leading to damage to the earth's protective ozone layer. Compared with the total number of organic compounds, there are very few compounds which contain fluorine. The chemical shift is somewhat different since fluorine is the most electronegative element. In the ^{19}F nmr of 2,5-difluoroaniline, there are two peaks as there are two different environments for the fluorine atoms. The fluorine atom in the 2-position on the arene ring (B3.9a) is more downfield than the fluorine atom in the 5-position because its adjacent carbon atom is bonded to the highly electronegative nitrogen atom of the amine group. The position of fluorine atom(s) follows the same rules as described for the proton nmr spectra.

The ^{19}F nmr of 2,5-difluoroaniline

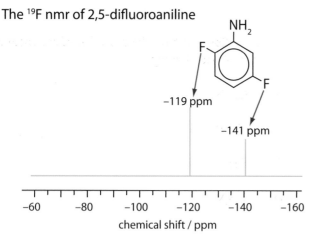

Often the ^{19}F nmr spectra are decoupled (A4.5a) because most fluorinated compounds contain hydrogen that couples with the fluorine nuclei. It is possible to make fluorinated alcohols where all the hydrogen atoms joined to carbon atoms are replaced by fluorine atoms. These substances are known as **perfluorinated alcohols** and have found use as solvents and as building blocks in the pharmaceutical and agrochemical industries. The perfluorinated analogue of ethanol is

1,1,2,2,2-pentafluoroethanol (CF$_3$CF$_2$OH) and it shows the same splitting patterns as ethanol but obviously with very different chemical shifts. The $n+1$ rule applies to compounds containing fluorine atoms where n = number of fluorine atoms on adjacent carbon atoms.

Perfluoroethanol (^{19}F nmr)		
alcohol	CF$_3$CF$_2$OH	CF$_3$CF$_2$OH
multiplet	triplet	quartet

Ethanol (^{1}H nmr)		
alcohol	CH$_3$CH$_2$OH	CH$_3$CH$_2$OH
multiplet	triplet	quartet

Phosphorus-31 nmr spectra

Nature makes use of phosphorus to provide a means of storing and utilising energy in living systems in the form of ATP. Huge molecules of **d**eoxyribo**n**ucleic **a**cid (DNA) are made water soluble by the phosphate groups which make up part of the backbone of the double helix. Many organic compounds contain phosphorus, so the running of ^{31}P nmr spectrum is quite routine in research. ^{31}P nuclei are much less sensitive than ^{1}H nuclei but more sensitive than ^{13}C nuclei. Most ^{31}P nmr spectra are decoupled (A4.5a) because the majority of phosphorus containing compounds contain hydrogen that couples with the phosphorus nuclei. This decoupling makes the interpretation of ^{31}P nmr spectra comparatively simple as each type of phosphorus will resonate at a different chemical shift. There is only one type of phosphorus environment in triphenylphosphine (TTP) and its ^{31}P nmr has a single resonance at -6 ppm.

TTP and its ^{31}P nmr spectrum

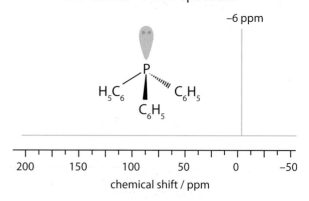

Questions 30.3

1. Identify the peaks in the low resolution proton nmr spectrum of ethanoic acid.

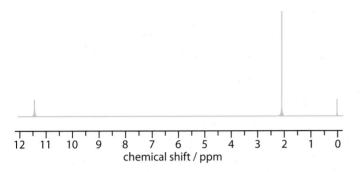

2. Identify the peaks in the low resolution proton nmr spectrum of methyl methanoate.

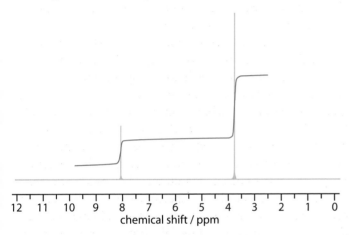

3. Identify the peaks in the low resolution proton nmr spectrum of methyl ethanoate.

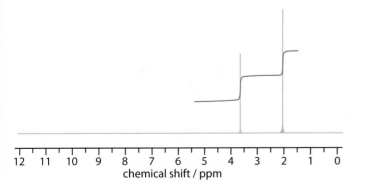

4. The high resolution proton nmr spectrum of propan-1-ol has been assigned.

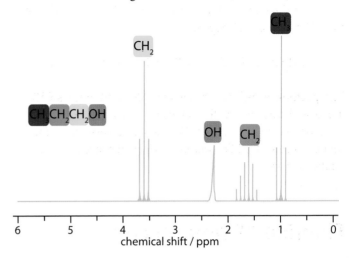

Explain why there are two triplets at different chemical shifts in this spectrum.

5. Which option does not give a single peak in its proton nmr spectrum?

A   Methoxymethane

B   Benzene

C   Phenol

D   Methanal

6. Which option will have the most downfield chemical shift for its methyl group?

A CH_3Br

B CH_3H

C CH_3F

D CH_3I

7. What would the proton nmr spectrum look like for propan-2-ol using $CDCl_3$ as the solvent? How would it change if a few drops of D_2O were added to the nmr tube and the proton nmr spectrum run again?

8. Symmetry of a molecule is an important consideration when assigning nmr spectra. Write out all the letters of the UPPER CASE alphabet and underline all those that possess rotation and/or reflection symmetry.

9. Which option correctly describes the ^{1}H nmr of TMS?

	Number of protons	Number of environments
A	12	4
B	12	1
C	9	1
D	9	4

10. How many peaks are there in the ^{1}H nmr spectrum of 1,4-dimethylbenzene?

A 4

B 3

C 1

D 2

11. What are integrated traces and what information do they provide?

12. Which option will not have a peak which disappears from its ^{1}H nmr spectrum on addition of D_2O?

A CH_3CO_2H

B CH_3CHO

C CH_3OH

D CH_3NH_2

13. What would the decoupled ^{19}F nmr spectra look like for the following fluorinated compounds?

a. CF_3CO_2H

b. CHF_2CHFOH

c. $(CF_3)_2CO$

d. CHF_2COF

14. In its ^{31}P nmr spectrum, triphenylphosphine $P(C_6H_5)_3$ gives a singlet with a chemical shift of –6 ppm. Explain how the chemical shift of triphenylphosphine oxide $(C_6H_5)_3PO$ will compare to triphenylphosphine.

B4.6 (d) Pascal's triangle and the $n+1$ rule

In a high resolution proton nmr spectrum, the peaks split according to the $n+1$ rule (B4.6c). When there are no hydrogen atoms on adjacent carbon atoms, there will be a singlet in the nmr spectrum since there is no coupling. A doublet means there is coupling to one equivalent nucleus on an adjacent carbon atom. A triplet means that there is coupling to two equivalent nuclei on adjacent carbon atom(s). A quartet means that there is coupling to three equivalent nuclei on adjacent carbon atom(s).

So why does coupling to n equivalent nuclei give $n+1$ peaks? This is because the magnetic field experienced by a proton is very slightly altered due to the orientations of the coupled spins in the nuclei of protons on adjacent carbon atoms. This can be thought of in terms of vectors which will either add to, or subtract from, the magnetic field experienced by the nuclei, thereby altering their chemical shifts. The nuclei can align with the applied magnetic field, which is shown as a green upward arrow. Otherwise, it is aligned against the applied magnetic field, shown as a yellow downward arrow. If the value of $n = 1$ the coupled nuclei can adopt two arrangements so the peak is split into two (doublet).

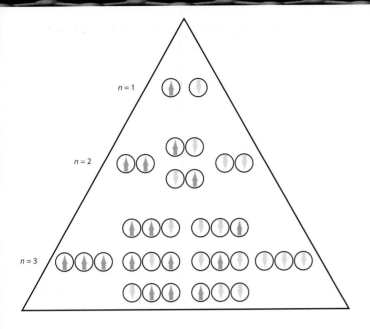

Spin of adjacent protons for values n = 1, 2 and 3

If the value of $n = 2$, there are four possible arrangements for this pair of coupled nuclei and two of them are equivalent. Therefore when $n = 2$ a triplet is obtained. How would you describe the types and number of arrangements when there are coupled nuclei ($n = 3$)? The different combinations of nuclear spins might well look familiar as they are in fact a form of Pascal's triangle.

```
            1
          1   1
        1   2   1
      1   3   3   1
    1   4   6   4   1
  1   5  10  10   5   1
```

Pascal's triangle (first six rows)

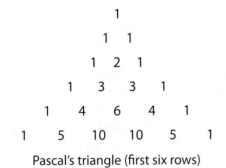

Pascal's triangle (multiplet intensities)

In Pascal's triangle, the number **1** is found along the diagonal edges of the triangle at the edge of each row and the top (apex) of the triangle. All other numbers in a row are arrived at by adding together the numbers directly above and to the left in the triangle and directly above and to the right in the triangle. Pascal's triangle

is used to predict the intensities of the lines in multiplets in nmr spectroscopy.

Number of adjacent protons (n)	Splitting ($n+1$)	Multiplet (symbol)	Relative intensities
0	1	singlet (s)*	1
1	2	doublet (d)	1:1
2	3	triplet (t)	1:2:1
3	4	quartet (q)	1:3:3:1

*not a multiplet as $n=0$

Another version of Pascal's triangle, which can be used to predict the intensities of the lines in multiplets in nmr spectroscopy, is given where the heights of the peaks match the relevant numbers in Pascal's triangle.

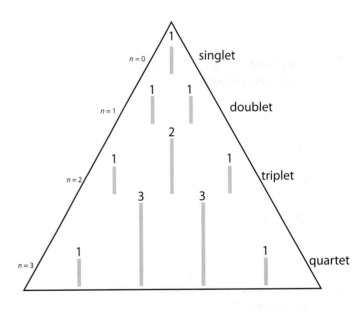

When $n = 1$ there are two possibilities, the adjacent nucleus has spin up or spin down. The chance of these different orientations is 1:1 so the spin-spin coupling for $n = 1$ results in a doublet with lines of equal intensity (1:1). When $n = 2$, there are three possibilities for the spin of the two adjacent nuclei. These are: both up, one up and one down or both down. There are two possibilities for the one up and one down orientation of the nuclei spins. Therefore, the spin coupling for $n = 2$ results in a triplet where the middle line is twice the area of the outer two lines, *i.e.* the relative intensities are 1:2:1. Using the same approach for $n = 3$, a quartet is the result with relative intensities of 1:3:3:1.

Questions 30.4

1. Complete the table using the *n*+1 rule for spin-spin coupling.

n	*n*+1	Name	Abbreviation
0			
1			
2			
3			

2. Work out which hydroxybenzaldehyde has the low resolution proton nmr spectrum shown. The peak at 10.6 ppm 'disappears' on the addition of D_2O.

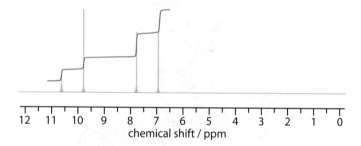

3. How will the high resolution proton nmr spectra of the isomers 1,1,1-trichloroethane and 1,1,2-trichloroethane differ?

4. Complete the table to show what the high resolution proton nmr spectrum looks like for butanone $CH_3CH_2COCH_3$.

Formula	CH_3	CH_2	CO	CH_3
chemical shift				
multiplicity				
integral ratio				

5. How will the high resolution proton nmr spectra of the isomers ethyl ethanoate and methyl propanoate be similar? Why are they not identical?

6. Which isomer having molecular formula C_3H_7Cl will give a proton nmr spectrum having two signals with integral ratios of 6:1?

Index

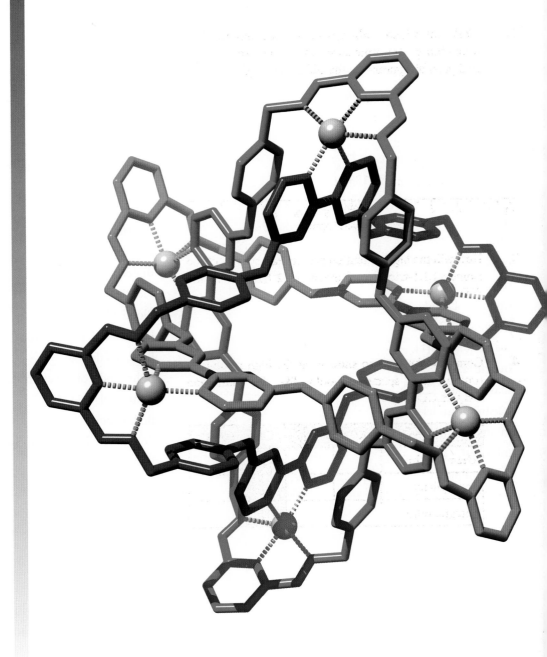

Index

Cysteine 387